The WISH
— AND —
The WATERFALL

K.B. BACHELDER

LUMINARE PRESS

WWW.LUMINAREPRESS.COM

The Wish and the Waterfall
© 2015 Ken Bachelder

Printed in the United States of America

Cover image and cabin: Kellie Weathers

Luminare Press
467 W 17th Ave
Eugene, OR 97401
www.luminarepress.com

LCCN: 2015959434
ISBN: 978-1-937303-65-5

ACKNOWLEDGEMENTS

THERE WAS A TIME WHEN I DIDN'T HAVE ENOUGH FAITH IN MYSELF that I could get this done but owing to a large support system it all came to fruition. To all of those who helped me move this project along…I don't know if I can tell you how much it meant to me.

My wife Tammie…Whose constant admonishments to Get It Done were a driving factor in the completion of Book One. Did I mention constant? Without her help and encouragement I couldn't have accomplished this.

To Mark Sizemore and Lori Olson…You two were the first and it wasn't by accident that I chose you. Your feedback was critical in my going forward.

To Patricia Marshall, Donna Reynolds, Claire Flint and everyone at Luminaire Press…Your professionalism coupled with a personal touch made this process so much easier.

To my family…My daughter Jennifer and Son-In-Law Andy, whose above and beyond contribution made this possible. To my sons Chris, Jesse and Brad, Grandchildren Jenna, Parker, Chase, Claudia, Katlyn, Aubrey, Carson and Van. Thank You all.

To Kellie Weathers. Your own considerable talent was an inspiration to me.

And to all of the rest of my family and friends for being who you are.

INTRODUCTION

THANK YOU FOR TAKING THE TIME TO READ *THE WISH AND THE WATERFALL*. This is Book One of a three-part series.

This story has been floating around my head since the late 80s. I think I first began to write it out by hand until I came upon an actual word processer that I was able to procure. Man, oh man! I had really taken a step up in the world! I wrote originally about 300 or more pages of manuscript, printed them out single-spaced, even took the time to turn the paper over and print on the backside. I really thought I knew what I was doing. But the story faltered and as I took one step forward and two steps back in my personal life, the manuscript gathered dust and the word processor went to the old word processor graveyard.

I revisited the story several times during the next two decades. I changed the initial setting of the story to rural Oregon instead of Vermont (don't ask me why I chose that locale to begin with) and changed the characters somewhat, though Willoughby and Jake have been there from the start. But it wasn't until about two years ago, when my wife bought me a laptop, that I really started to believe I could finish this thing. And finish this I will. If I have to publish it myself and just give it to grandkids and friends that will be okay—the tale will be told.

The Wish and the Waterfall is a coming-of-age story about troubled fourteen-year-old Willoughby Baxter. Struggling in the shadow of his deceased father, a larger-than-life sports hero, Willoughby moves with his mother and sister to his father's hometown of Spirit Falls, Oregon, a small logging community nestled in the foothills of the Cascades. There he finds nothing but more disappointment and emotional strife as he fails to live up to anyone's expectations, including his own. Bullied, misunderstood, and unable to escape the specter of his father's untimely death in what is whispered to have been a pill and alcohol fueled suicide, he turns to the one person who seems to understand what he is going through—a formidable and towering presence in Jake Thompson. A Klamath Indian and recovering alcoholic, it is Jake's tales of his ancestors' sacred and spiritual ties to the land around the Baxter dairy farm that spur Willoughby to visit the waterfall for which the town is named and ultimately change his destiny.

This is a tale of adventure and fantasy where Willoughby finds himself in a harsh, alternate reality where nothing is as it should be. A battle between good and evil woven around the elements of power, greed, betrayal, and swords and sorcery awaits and I hope you will come along for the ride.

Once again, thank you for taking the time to read this. Hopefully it will leave you wanting to continue the journey.

—KB Bachelder

CHAPTER ONE

WILLOUGHBY BAXTER WAS HOT. NOT A sweat-stain-under-your-armpit, give-me-a-glass-of-water type hot, the kind you would expect on a TV game show set with its bright lights. No, this was a Michael Jordan-fifty-point-night hot. This was rolling-downhill-picking-up-speed-with-nothin'-in-his-way-to-stop-him hot. He was kickin' ass and not stopping to take names.

In the past three days of competition, the young teen had scorched his opponents mercilessly and the media had picked up on the phenomenon and rolled with it. The fact that a teenager was competing against some of the smartest adult minds in the country was news enough in itself, but what had caught America's, and the world's attention was the way he had done it. After winning the teen version of the game show without even being remotely challenged, he had broached the idea to the game show's producers.

"Let me go against the adults," he had pleaded. "It will make the ratings go off the charts." And it certainly had. "Teen Genius," and "Fourteen-Year-Old Einstein" read the headlines. Every media outlet in the country and plenty from abroad were at the show's final night to get a shot at the amazing teen's story. People in the know had also predicted just what Willoughby had promised—the ratings had skyrocketed.

The set of Jeopardy was on a break. Alex Trebek, the game show's popular host, was getting a once-over from the make-up girl, but he managed to slip Willoughby a quick wink as he got his hair primped into place.

Careful, Alex, Willoughby thought to himself as he glanced quickly from side to side, checking to see if the other two Jeopardy contestants may have caught the graying host's surreptitious display. *Don't want to seem like you're showing any kind of favoritism here.*

The contestant on Willoughby's right hadn't seemed to notice anything; he had been too busy wiping the sweat from his shiny bald head. A professor in advanced mathematics at Stanford, the man had burned up the competition on previous Jeopardy shows. So much for past history. Against this amazing young talent he looked completely out of his league. Willoughby couldn't help but chuckle to himself. He wasn't being rude or smart; he just thought the guy looked like a big fat bug about to be squashed.

The young woman on his left gave him a forced half-smile as he looked her way. Armed with a Harvard law degree, she was a pretty thirty-something, wearing a stylish pantsuit with her brunette hair trimmed short. She looked every bit the high achieving corporate lawyer she was. She too had come into this Jeopardy Tournament of Champions with impressive credentials, but just like her counterpart from Stanford, had wilted under the teenager's amazing onslaught.

Amazing wasn't quite the right word for it. The monikers used to describe the young teenager's blazing assault of prime time television's most popular game show didn't come close to doing him justice. "Willoughby mania," as it was now called, had washed over the country. Day and night time talk shows were all vying to outbid one another for the youngster's appearance and every newspaper, gossip rag, and magazine were all clamoring for interviews. The world was watching and tonight would be the culmination of events that would seal Willoughby's future as the new superstar of pop culture. In just a few minutes, he would win the Jeopardy Championship and all the fame and money that came with it.

The money. Willoughby suppressed a grin of confidence as he thought about the huge payoff that came with winning the championship and all the money he would reap in the future from his post-game stardom. His mom's, his sister's, and his grandma's futures depended upon this and there was no way he was going to let them down. Envisioning the looks of sheer joy and gratitude on their faces, he could almost hear their tear-filled apologies as they begged his forgiveness for doubting him.

Willoughby could not lose. His opponents were so far behind him in the earnings column that only by wagering the whole amount on the final Jeopardy question, and then getting it wrong, could he possibly squander away his opportunity. The strategy was simple—bet conservatively, and then if he slipped, he would still walk away the winner.

No fucking way, Willoughby hissed under his breath as he thought about the consequences of his wager. He was going all in. They had announced the final jeopardy subject just before they went on break, Ancient Greek History. A tough category, but he had not come all this way and worked so hard to play the game like a pussy. His family needed the money to save the dairy farm in Oregon and Willoughby would be satisfied with nothing less than winning it all. The final tournament victory check, paid appearances on the big talk shows—he already had some whopper offers, but if he won this thing, he had a notion to hold out for more. He would show them. All the countless people who had doubted him. His family, the people in his hometown who had compared him to his father, they were all wrong. He would lay it all on the line.

"Quiet on the set," came the producer's warning. "On in five … four … three … two … one."

Final Jeopardy. It was time. The tension in the studio was palpable. The audience noise shut off as if someone had flipped a switch. Willoughby took a deep breath—he was ready. In front of tens of millions of TV viewers around the world, the young teenager from tiny Spirit Falls, Oregon, population 2,307, was calm, cool, and focused.

C'mon Alex, let's get this over with, he fumed under his breath.

"So would you please answer the question, Mr. Baxter? We are waiting."

"What?" Willoughby wondered aloud. That was wrong. Somehow the game show host had screwed up. The answer came first and then the contestants framed their response in the form of a question. What the hell was Trebek up to?

"Willoughby Baxter. I am tired of playing games with you. Do you have an answer or not?"

He was confused. The voice didn't even sound like Alex Trebek's anymore. What was going on? It sounded an awful lot like...

"Wake up dumb ass," someone behind him sneered in a low voice.

Willoughby could hear the snickers coming from the rest of the class. He knew where he was now, painfully so. Miss Bertha Havercroft, Spirit Falls High School's spinster English teacher was standing at the front of the classroom next to her desk and she was not happy. Sixty-six years old, standing four feet eight inches tall and probably not hitting the ninety pound mark soaking wet with all of her clothes on, she was nonetheless a fearsome entity and the scourge of miscreant teenage boys from the freshman class to the senior. "Bertha the Bitch" is what they called her and she lived up to the name. Quick with a biting tongue and quicker yet with detention slips, it had been Willoughby's misfortune to find out the hard way about her temperament. It appeared he was about to get his ass bitten again.

"Mr. Baxter." She glared at Willoughby hard, tapping her three-foot pointer into the palm of her hand for emphasis like a tough cop with a billy club. "Do we have a problem here?"

She had his complete attention now. More snickers and giggles came from behind him.

"No, Miss Havercro..."

"Quiet!" The pointer smacked onto the top of her desk as she cut him off, scattering a stack of ungraded English test papers into the air. The snickers and giggles disappeared, leaving just the fluttering sound of paper falling to the floor. Evidently she hadn't really wanted an answer to her question.

Willoughby was starting to get sick. He hadn't been in this school for even a month and things had gone steadily to hell. Miss

Havercroft had already laid all of her cards on the table for him.

"I do not coddle to young men who daydream in class, wasting my and the other students' time by not paying attention," she warned.

But Willoughby was struggling, and not just in Miss Havercroft's class, though his other three teachers seemed to have a little more patience with him. Bottom line was he hadn't fit in at his new school and what made matters worse—he didn't want to fit in. This small hick town with its hick high school had been his mom and sister's choice—not his. But he remembered his mother's plea.

"Please, Willoughby," she had sobbed through tears after an intense argument in his grandma's living room just two weeks ago. "Please don't screw this up for the rest of us. I can't handle any more of this."

Through his own tears, he had promised. That was part of why he was starting to get sick to his stomach—his promises didn't go very far anymore.

Having finally gotten Willoughby and the rest of the class's undivided attention, Miss Havercroft returned to her desk, grabbed a pad from the top drawer, and began writing.

"Did we not come to an understanding after your last episode that not paying attention in my class would not be tolerated?" she asked without looking up.

Willoughby slouched farther down in his seat, trying to make himself as small as possible. He didn't respond. It was another one of those questions you really weren't supposed to answer. Knowing the rest of the class had their attention focused solely on him, he stared intently at his hands on the desk in front of him. His stomach churned furiously. Miss Havercroft finished writing and slapped her pen down on the desk. She held out the bright pink detention slip.

"Please gather your things and leave my classroom Will-ough-by."

The emphasis she placed on the syllables of his first name did not escape him, nor did it the rest of the class. Whether she had done it deliberately mattered not, it had the same humiliating effect. He flinched at the cheap shot as the rest of the class resumed their snickering. It was as if they all knew how much he hated his name. As he felt tears starting to form, he grabbed his backpack from beneath his desk and crammed his English books in on top of his others. Time was critical now. If he let his emotions get the best of him, it would be committing social suicide. He could not let them see him cry.

Willoughby swung the heavy backpack over his shoulder by one strap and approached Miss Havercroft's desk, focusing on the ugly pinkness of the detention slip dangling from her wrinkled hand. Just as he reached for it, she snatched it away from his grasp. She wasn't done with him yet.

"I am not sure where your belligerence has come from Mr. Baxter. Your father sat in this same classroom and was nothing but an exemplary student who had not only a respect for knowledge, but for those who endeavor to teach it. I am quite sure if he were alive today he would highly disapprove of your attitude."

It was about as vicious of a kick to his emotional crotch as anyone could have given him, though whether she had intentionally meant for it to be so hurtful could have been debated. But in the overall scheme of things, it probably wouldn't have changed what happened in her fifth period English class that day. Willoughby Baxter had a Mount St. Helens-sized volcano churning furiously in his stomach. The two tacos and milk he had for lunch roiled and swirled in bitter bile. Things had nearly reached critical mass.

But Miss Havercroft had delivered her last shot; she was done. She pushed the detention slip back into his hand. The volcanic activity in Willoughby's stomach abated just a touch. He had the slip and now all he had to do was make the twenty feet to the door and then it would be out into the relative sanctuary of the deserted hallway.

It should have been easy. Out the door, into the hallway, and then down to Principal Hurd's office. Oh, it still would have been a tough day. The principal wasn't going to be too thrilled given Willoughby's brief, but tumultuous history at Spirit Falls High. And his mother. That was going to be really ugly. But shit just seemed to happen to Willoughby, and today, shit was piled six feet two inches high and sitting in the front of the row nearest the door. Willoughby had to walk right by him to exit the class.

Eddie Dean Anderson. Spirit Fall's freshman football sensation. One of those rare kids who had full growth by the sixth grade and the hair on his balls to go with it. Eddie was a stud. None too bright but a stud nonetheless, and the worst thing was—he knew it. Packing two hundred thirty pounds on that six two frame, there was still plenty of room to put on more muscle and he was a beast in the weight room doing just that. Add the killer instinct so rare in athletes his age and you had the total package, and the folks in Spirit Falls loved it.

The people in this small Oregon town were fanatics about their high school sports, both girls and boys, and their teams were always in the top tier. The town ate it up, there was really nothing else, and this year they were already talking about taking the Class 3A football championship with Eddie playing a major role. Not since the days of one of the greatest athletes in Oregon high school sports history, James William Baxter, had the town been this excited.

James William Baxter, Spirit Falls High's sports legend, was Willoughby's father. Six feet four, two hundred forty-five pounds of muscle, speed, and attitude. Everything his son wasn't. He played fullback and linebacker for the Spartan's only back-to-back 3A football championships and quite possibly there could have been three in a row had not a sprained ankle derailed Baxter in his sophomore year. But football had been only part of his athletic prowess. Basketball, track and field—he did it all. He still held Oregon high school state records for both javelin and discus—for all levels. He was one of only three Spartans to ever play for an NCAA Division 1 school and most importantly, the only Spirit Falls athlete to play professional sports. Opting for a full ride to San Diego State instead of accepting offers to play at either of the two big Oregon universities, Oregon and Oregon State, he had disappointed all of his local fans. He had made a recruiting visit and had fallen in love with the climate in San Diego, but the Spirit Falls locals loved him nonetheless and followed every second of his great career. Winning the WAC conference Player of the Year during both his junior and senior seasons, he was drafted by the San Diego Chargers in the first round of the NFL draft. Experiencing three great years in the NFL until two severe knee injuries cut short his career, he was still revered by the people in the small backwoods town. His tragic death in a horrific traffic accident had been a shock to everyone but now the people here could get excited again. It was time to embrace a new sports legend and Spirit Falls was rockin'.

But Eddie Anderson, if you looked beyond his obvious athletic talent, had one serious flaw—he was a fucking jerk. Mean Eddie Dean was a name he had earned not only by his exploits on the football field, but more so because he was, simply put—a bully. One who had made Willoughby Baxter his target of choice since Willoughby's first day at Spirit Falls High, not more than a month ago. Maybe because Willoughby's dad was a sports legend, or maybe because assholes like Eddie felt the need to torment out of place and timid kids like Willoughby, whatever the reason, he wasn't about to let an opportunity pass him by.

Willoughby kept his eyes to the floor as he took the pink detention slip out of Miss Havercroft's bony hand. Only twenty feet to the door, but directly in front of his nemesis. There was a reason Eddie had to sit in the front. After all, he was a troublemaker and often disrupted class when allowed to sit in the back with his entourage. But Miss Havercroft tolerated none of that. Football star or not she had brought Eddie up short and placed him in the front where she could keep an eye on him. No one would say Eddie's bulb burned very bright but he was smart enough to know that running afoul of teachers like Miss Havercroft could cut short his football ambitions. But even tough as she was, she could not avert the collision that loomed ahead, a perfect storm of a troubled and embarrassed new kid and an oversized bully who fed off tormenting such weaker prey.

Willoughby kept his head down as he rounded the corner in front of Eddie's desk, avoiding eye contact. Eight feet now to the door and at least this piece of a very bad day would be over—or so he thought.

"Will-ough-by go bye-bye?"

For a large, quasi-mature male, Eddie's high falsetto baby talk was pretty damn good and the reaction was all he could have hoped for. The class erupted in riotous laughter, followed immediately by Miss Havercroft's shouted attempts to quell the outburst. It gave Mean Eddie Dean all the cover he needed for his next shot.

"Dick suckin' little faggot," he hissed as Willoughby walked by.

Willoughby Baxter's chemistry was unbalanced. For him, the embarrassment and humiliation of being called to task in front of his peers had created instant and powerful nausea. The tacos and milk he had consumed for lunch mixed with the bile and acid in his stomach like oil did with water; his insides churned and burned, demanding release. But there was something else hidden under Willoughby's delicate façade that had also reached critical mass. A steam boiler of emotion that had reached its ultimate pressure point, demanding a release, and Mean Eddie Dean had just provided it. Those four whispered words, sharp and cruel, acted like a needle popping a ripe pimple.

Jackie Chan couldn't have choreographed the next sequence of events any smoother than they transpired. In one seamless motion, the strap of the book-filled backpack slipped off Willoughby's right shoulder into his right hand. As it did, his arm extended fully, adding serious momentum to the 360-degree pivot he was now executing. Eddie was half-turned in his desk, watching Willoughby's departure, a huge victorious smile plastered on his face. The heavy backpack took Eddie flush on the left side of his stupid grin.

Five textbooks, each weighing maybe two pounds, a pair of gym tennis shoes, a three-quarters full water bottle and a few other sundry items normally found in a student backpack probably brought its weight to about twelve or thirteen pounds. Speed + Weight = Force of Impact. Whatever you called it, it added up to a perfect strike that crashed hard against Eddie Anderson's left temple.

Ironically, if forensic science could have broken the strike down, it would have shown that the book having the honor of leading the assault on the bully's head was none other than Miss Havercroft's English literature text. Eddie had been leaning slightly forward in his seat and the force of the blow propelled him straight to the floor, this time the right side of his head striking hard on the smooth linoleum. With either blow, or maybe a combination of the two, Willoughby Baxter had just accomplished what no muscle bound lineman had ever been able to do—Mean Eddie Dean was out cold.

It happened so fast that Willoughby was not even sure of what he had just done. One second he had been heading for the classroom door and the next Eddie was sprawled out cold at his feet. The room was stone silent; students who seconds ago had been laughing so heartily at Willoughby's misery now sat with their mouths hanging open in stunned disbelief. He stared stupidly at the pack still dangling from his hand and then towards an incredulous Miss Havercroft, momentarily frozen in a state of absolute shock.

But the state of suspended animation enveloping the entire classroom was short-lived, for the second part of the event that would become the most talked about in the history of Spirit Falls High School was about to unfold.

In that brief, frozen nanosecond of time, before Miss Havercroft or anyone else could react, Willoughby struck his second blow. It had happened before, in moments of great stress or anxiety, but never with such an impact. The strike lacked the force of the first blow but its effect was every bit as powerful—Willoughby puked.

Miss Havercroft had snapped out of her temporary trance and was starting to move towards the scene when Willoughby's stomach spewed its pungent brew into the chaos formerly known as Fifth Period Freshman English. A colorful stew of taco chunks, milk, and that morning's Fruit Loops shot out in a powerful stream, striking Kyra Becker (the unfortunate occupant of the desk right behind Eddie's) squarely between her ample boobs.

Kyra's blonde brain was struggling to register what had just happened to Eddie (still inert on the floor at her feet) when Willoughby deposited his breakfast-lunch combo onto her chest.

"Eeeuuuuuw!" she squealed as chunky barf dripped down the front of her. Pieces of yellow taco shell, slimy green strings of lettuce, and partially digested bits of hamburger and cheese covered her newest, lowcut sweater. A partially digested red Fruit Loop dangled from her chin.

Kyra jumped up out of her desk gagging and squealing at the same time, trying desperately to flip puke off the front of her sweater. As she did, she promptly tripped over Eddie's splayed legs. Fortunately, or unfortunately, she was able to get her hands out in front of her as she fell over Eddie's prone form. The fortunate part was that she broke the momentum of her fall and probably saved herself from a more serious injury. The unfortunate part was that it caused her short skirt to hike up over her hips, thereby answering a question that had been on the majority of the male students' minds (and probably some of the females') at one time or another. Oh yeah, Kyra did indeed wear thong panties when she wore her short skirts.

The class was now a tornado of movement. Those in the spray zone (wearing pieces of Willoughby's lunch) were scrambling desperately to get out of the way lest the volcano spew forth again. Others were trying just as desperately to move forward to get a better look at Kyra's red thong and butt crack. But it was Miss Havercroft who now showed the quickest footwork of them all. She had seen a lot in her four-and-a-half-decade tenure as a high school English teacher, and while this one pretty much topped the list as the strangest, she knew exactly what she needed to do. To her mind, there was only one person responsible for this unprecedented disruption and it was her job to take the perpetrator out. She headed directly for the still uncomprehending Willoughby.

His eyes and ears took in what his brain had yet come to grips with. For some strange reason, Eddie Anderson was sprawled unmoving at his feet. Kyra Becker was also on the floor, though now struggling to regain a sitting position. She had a horrified look on her pale face as she was looking down, pulling her sweater out in front of her and making odd gurgling noises. Still not comprehending the scope of the situation, he scanned the rest of the faces in the classroom. Some of the kids seemed extremely delighted while others seemed to be under severe duress.

In an instant it came rushing back to Willoughby like a wave crashing on the beach. He knew why Eddie was prone on the floor. He knew why Kyra was decorated with Fruit Loops and tortilla chips, and just as quick as the realization swept over him the smell did, too. The unmistakable odor of puke wafted through the classroom in a pungent and palpable cloud. No wonder some of the students had such a distressed look about them—the domino effect of puke was taking over.

Bertha Havercroft was eight diminutive steps away from apprehending the source of this absolute mayhem. At five steps, Kyra's internal plumbing reached maximum overload. Though she hadn't eaten much lunch (she thought she was getting fat) the apple, low-fat vanilla yogurt, and Diet Pepsi she had consumed didn't appreciate the intrusion of Willoughby's taco and milk full meal deal. From her sitting position on the floor, Kyra spewed.

The unintentional recipient of her low calorie stew was Tyler Bowman-Smith. Tyler—a nondescript student whose only claims to fame were (1): he could maintain a four-point average in his sleep, and (2): he had the only hyphenated name in the whole school—was trying to be a gentleman. When he saw Kyra trip over the inert Eddie, his first instinct had been to jump out of his seat and try to help her. But he had been inflicted with a temporary state of paralytic shock by the sudden and very clear view of her butt (he would spend many nights replaying this brief mental video clip of paradise in the sanctity of his bedroom). Only after Kyra rolled to a sitting position, thus removing the source of Tyler's paralysis, was he was able to come to his senses and reach out to help her. But timing is everything and for Tyler, the timing was very bad. As Miss Havercroft was hitting step three, he bent over and reached his hand out to Kyra. Their eyes met and locked on to each other. Tyler had always had a crush on her and now he was coming to her rescue. A fantasy come true. She opened her mouth—was she going to tell him how she had always felt? Was she about to whisper the words he dreamed of hearing?

Not quite. Instead, she spewed a powerful stream of vomit that took poor Tyler right between his eyes, not only catching him square in the face but also catching his mouth partway open. Chivalry died an inglorious death as his own gag reflexes kicked in, sending Kyra's vomit right back at her along with some of Tyler's own lunch. While he had fantasized about exchanging bodily fluids with Kyra, this manifestation wasn't quite what he had in mind. But in a sense it was, and maybe in his late-night solitary love sessions he could mentally make the substitution. And certainly Tyler had fulfilled part of his fantasy—he could truly brag that he had deposited a load on Kyra's boobs.

Absolute chaos now reigned supreme in Miss Havercroft's fifth period freshman English class. The crowd that had sought to get a view of Kyra's rear end was now getting more than they bargained for as the hot, nasty smell of more fresh puke assailed them. Grossed out kids screamed and scrambled to reverse direction and get to the windows.

Willoughby was still recovering from shock as the realization of what he had done became clear, but he had run out of time to figure out his next move. Bertha Havercroft had taught in rural high schools her entire career and had seen her share of scrapes between sons (and some daughters) of farmers, loggers, and mill workers. But never had she let her diminutive stature keep her from what she felt was one of the most sacred trusts bestowed on a teacher—to never allow fighting on school grounds. She had waded in amongst the biggest of them to restore order and now the advantage was entirely hers as she caught Willoughby still in a state of confused paralysis. In a flash, she slammed the miscreant against the wall, trussed up in a perfect half nelson with the arm still holding the pack locked securely behind him in a painful arm bar.

"All of you—settle down now!" she screamed at the class, trying to regain some semblance of order. But as for Willoughby, she seemed to sense she had a major emotional breakdown on her hands, and not just a minor classroom altercation.

"Please Willoughby," she whispered close in his ear. "No more. It's all over."

He didn't try to resist. The frustration, anger, and uncontrolled outburst of energy that had exploded—transforming a hulking bully into an unconscious heap—was gone, leaving him drained emotionally and physically.

As she felt him relax, Miss Havercroft eased her grip on him. Control of the classroom was again hers as she started directing students to helping Eddie, now starting to show signs of life, and Kyra, still dry heaving. Gently but firmly she eased a compliant Willoughby out into the hall and towards Principal Hurd's office.

The event was over. Elements of the story would get changed, truth blurred into fiction. The part where Eddie Anderson wet his pants as he lay unconscious was truth; the part where some of the boys swore they were able to see Kyra Becker's sweet spot was not. Fact or fiction, Willoughby Baxter had, for all the wrong reasons, carved himself out a permanent place in the history of Spirit Falls High School.

CHAPTER TWO

THE TICKING OF THE BIG CLOCK MOUNTED ON the wall of the school office complex was driving Willoughby nuts. He wasn't sure how long he had sat there before becoming aware of the damn thing but since he had, it seemed to have gotten progressively louder and intensely more irritating. Forty minutes it had been since he had arrived at Principal Hurd's office. Forty minutes since Miss Havercroft had trussed him up, steered him out of her class, and down the hall. Forty long minutes since she had deposited him in the chair with a warning not to move while she caught Mr. Hurd up on the situation that had just occurred in her fifth period English class. Willoughby wasn't quite sure exactly what had happened, remembering only bits and pieces of it. He was still slightly nauseous and he could still smell some of the puke. Fortunately for him, not so much for Kyra Becker, he had managed to avoid getting too much on himself. What he did know was that he was in trouble—big trouble.

After Miss Havercroft had returned to her class, the clock ticked aggravatingly on. It was all a conspiracy to torment him, of that he was sure—the clock and Miss Torpedo Tits. She was Mr. Hurd's personal secretary, whose name was actually Terri Lanz. She was a former cheerleader and graduate of Spirit Falls High who had gone on to junior college and several different jobs before landing back at her alma mater. That she had been hired by Theodore Hurd to be his secretary raised plenty of eyebrows in the small town, since it had been rumored she had an affair with her then math teacher during her senior year.

But it was a small town and rumors were just that. It hadn't seemed to bother Mrs. Hurd too much about whether her husband might or might not be banging his secretary, but that might have been because it was rumored she spent most of her time (and Mr. Hurd's paychecks) playing video poker in the local bars or down in the valley at one of the Indian casinos.

Terri, aka Torpedo Tits, kept glancing up from her computer screen towards the miscreant Willoughby as if he might be contemplating making a run for it. For a moment he wondered what she would actually do if he did get up and walk out the door. But he was in enough trouble as it was, so he just filed it away in the "Things I Wish I Had Done" category.

He watched the principal through the big plate glass window that separated them. Every now and then the man would turn from his phone conversation to shoot Willoughby a dire glare. Theodore Hurd III, or Mr. Hurd The Third Turd, as he was called by the majority of the SFHS student body, was a slightly built man in his early fifties. Bald, except for a fringe of graying hair, he wore out-of-style black rimmed glasses and an omnipresent rumpled white shirt and tie. The man was anything but what you would call handsome.

"He's got Little Man's Syndrome" was what Jennifer Baxter, Willoughby's mom, said about him. He reminded her of Wally, the short little character in the comic strip *Dilbert*. She had even let it slip during dinner one evening that he had made a pass at her when she was getting Willoughby and Kendall enrolled for school. Grandma Rose added her two cents' worth when she said that it was rumored that Mr. Hurd was only small in stature, not where it counted most.

"Gotta be something there that Lanz girl can sink her teeth into," she said. The joke was an instant gross-out for both his mom and his sister but it had taken Willoughby several moments to catch on to what was being hinted at.

But as he sat there, he couldn't help but wonder if the rumor was true. Even though she wore bras that made her look like the lead actress in a bad fifties B-movie, Terri Lanz wasn't bad looking. It might have been the boredom from the wait, or maybe he was just trying to keep from thinking about the impending confrontation with Mr. Hurd, but Willoughby's mind kept trying to visualize her naked. He squirmed in his chair as an unwanted physical reaction started to manifest itself. As if she could read his mind, she looked up from her computer screen and glared at him. Willoughby's arousal was short-lived.

"You may send the young man in, Miss Lanz," the telephone intercom crackled to Willoughby's rescue.

"You heard him," Torpedo Tits responded testily as Willoughby made no effort to move. When he did walk by her desk, he was thankful he hadn't been any more aroused, because she glowered at the front of his jeans, as if expecting to catch him in such a noticeable state.

Mr. Hurd's office was nondescript as far as offices went. A few pictures taken in various settings around the school and a few plaques honoring him for achievement in various academic endeavors adorned the walls. Beyond the computer screen and telephone, his desktop was uncluttered except for a large calendar pad and picture of his wife, a rather dour and frumpy-looking woman. Willoughby couldn't help but wonder what Torpedo Tits thought about that omnipresent reminder of the marital status of her boss.

"Have a seat, young man." Mr. Hurd stood up and motioned towards the huge leather swivel chair positioned directly in front of his desk. When Willoughby sat down, the thing almost swallowed him it was so big.

"I hope you find the chair comfortable. I make it a point to ensure that students are relaxed when they come to me with their problems. It helps ease the tension, don't you think?"

It made Willoughby feel small, that's what he thought. "Yes sir," was what he said.

"Good," Mr. Hurd replied as he sat down. "You do seem to have some problems, don't you young man?" The chair gulped and swallowed. Willoughby slid a little further into the abyss.

"I guess," Willoughby shrugged. He had meant to keep his

answers short, not wanting to expound on anything that might incriminate him, but the instant he said it, he was sorry. With all that he had been through over the years, he had encountered adults like Mr. Hurd before and had learned that they didn't like it when they deemed young people, especially troubled ones like Willoughby, gave them answers that they thought seemed flippant.

"You guess?" Mr. Hurd's terse tone told Willoughby that it had indeed been the wrong thing to say. "You get dismissed from your classroom once again for not paying attention, then assault another student on the way out, and all you can say is 'I guess'? I would dare to state, young man, that you do not fully comprehend the serious nature of your actions."

Willoughby squirmed as the seat swallowed him a little more. This was going to be as bad as he had feared.

Mr. Hurd proceeded to read the statement Miss Havercroft had given him describing the incident. When it came to the part about walloping Eddie Anderson on the side of his head with his backpack and the ensuing chaos in the classroom, Willoughby slid further into the maw of the kid-eating chair.

"I have been on the phone with both Police Chief Dent and Eddie's mother," Mr. Hurd continued. "That is why I kept you waiting so long, Willoughby. Do you know there could be an assault charge filed against you?"

Assault! That was something he hadn't considered. Willoughby knew he was in as much trouble as he had ever been, but assault charges? That was some serious shit there.

"I think I have convinced Eddie's mother that such a course would be unnecessary and that this incident can be handled appropriately by the school, but it does lead to the question of why, Willoughby. Why did you strike Eddie Anderson? Don't you know you could have seriously injured or perhaps even killed him if you had hit him in the right spot?"

Mr. Hurd reached down beside his desk and brought up the offending backpack. "This thing is heavy. It is a weapon, young man. A weapon."

The backpack wasn't the only heavy thing. Reality was starting to put a lot of weight on Willoughby now. It had all happened so fast he could hardly remember doing it. His stomach was churning furiously again, the nausea reasserting itself. His mom was going to come unglued over this one; that was his greatest fear now. For two years he had been screwing up, causing her more grief each time—and now this. Yep. This was going to be friggin' bad.

"Is Eddie all right?" he finally managed to ask.

Mr. Hurd put the pack back down on the floor. "Fortunately, yes. He was checked out by Mr. Iverly, the football trainer. There are no signs of a concussion but they have to keep an eye on him for the next couple of hours. Do you know it puts him in jeopardy of not being able to play in the game against Creswell tonight?"

Willoughby didn't even remember there was a football game, which was pretty hard to do in a town that lived for Friday nights. For the most part, he didn't care one iota about any kind of sport. He went to his sister's volleyball games only because his mom and grandma pestered him to. The fact that Kendall was one of the best players in the state was just something else he had to deal with. She had been the one who had inherited their dad's athletic prowess and his mother's good looks. Standing six feet tall, exceptionally attractive with a friendly and outgoing personality, she had been extremely popular from the moment she arrived in town. People had raved about the upcoming volleyball and basketball seasons when they got wind of how talented James Baxter's daughter was.

State championships. That's what got people in this town excited. With Eddie Anderson and the football team looking to be one of the best teams in the 3A division, and now with the athletically gifted daughter of Spirit Falls' most celebrated athlete enrolled in school, the town was stoked. They talked sports in the aisles and checkout lines at Ray's Supermarket. At any one of the town's four eateries you were apt to get an injury update as quickly as you were a cup of coffee. Over your Budweiser or Pabst down at The Landing or The Alibi, the town's two bars, if you weren't discussing this year's talent pool, you were talking about the good old days and great

Spartan teams of the past. This town lived and breathed high school athletics. For the son of the town's greatest athlete, it was just plain unnatural not to be interested in sports.

But that's what Willoughby was—not interested. He hated walking past the school's trophy case in the main hall; his dad's picture was everywhere. He could be seen in championship team photos, in individual shots of his great plays, or accepting awards like State 3A Athlete of the Year (twice). There was a huge picture of his dad in his Charger uniform; the very same uniform and an autographed helmet also resided in the display case. You couldn't get away from James Baxter's influence on Spirit Falls' athletics, and it haunted Willoughby everywhere he went.

Mr. Hurd continued, "Let's hope Eddie gets to play tonight. It would be a shame to lose an important game because you lost your temper and took out your anger on our best player."

"He called me a dick sucking little faggot," Willoughby angrily blurted, loud enough it caused Miss Lanz to look up from her computer screen. "He said that to me as I was walking out of class and I just lost control. I didn't mean for it to happen." Tears welled in his eyes as his fragile emotions started to slip over the edge once again.

To his credit, Theodore Hurd was not a total jerk. He could sense the turmoil in his young student.

"Okay, Willoughby. Settle yourself down. I did not know Eddie said that to you. Did Miss Havercroft or anyone else hear him call you that?"

Willoughby shook his head, he was pretty sure no one had. "He whispered it as I walked by his desk but I heard it."

"Regardless, Willoughby," Mr. Hurd continued, "while it was a crude thing to say and he should be brought to task for it, you know full well Eddie will deny it. His reputation for being a bully and a loudmouth has not escaped my attention, but even if he did say it, there was still no excuse to strike him."

Willoughby buried his head in his hands, not so much to keep Mr. Hurd from viewing his tears, but his head was starting to hurt. His emotional outburst often triggered severe headaches. There was an extremely nasty one wreaking havoc in his head right at the moment.

"I have gone over your records, Willoughby," Mr. Hurd said, softening his tone considerably. "I know you have been having behavioral problems since the tragic death of your father. I also know it was one of the reasons your mother chose to relocate here to Spirit Falls. She told me she thought it would be a good change for you."

A good change for you. Willoughby had heard that enough lately. It was his mother's favorite excuse but for him, the only change that could make things any better would be for that day two years ago to have never happened. They were right. He hadn't been the same since his dad was killed in a traffic accident—one everyone said was caused by him speeding on a busy San Diego street in the middle of the day—a horrific event that also took the life of a young mother and her six-year-old daughter. What kid could be the same after that? Willoughby's life had been turned upside down and stomped on. Mr. Hurd was just saying the same thing the others who tried to figure him out had said.

"I think we need to get you some more counseling, beyond what is available here at school. We don't have anyone here in Spirit Falls who is qualified but Salem is only an hour away. I can talk to your mother and see if we can get that arranged. We are happy to have you and your family here, Willoughby, and we want this to be a better place for all of you, but you have to try and make this work."

"I have had counseling, Mr. Hurd. Three counselors in San Diego to be exact, and here I am—still a loser." The bitterness and anger spilled from Willoughby's mouth like rock from a dump truck. "I don't fit in here. People wonder why I'm not like my dad. I don't know why I'm not like him. I'm God's idea of a joke, I guess. Here people look at me and can't believe that I'm the great James Baxter's kid." He looked squarely at the principal, who was somewhat taken aback by the sudden outburst. "I wish I was in another world or something. Anyplace but here. Everywhere I go in this town there's a reminder of my dad. People want me to be him and they're disappointed when they find out I'm not. I can't get away from it. At least in San Diego I could hide from all of that. Do you know what that's like for me?"

"No son, I don't," Mr. Hurd answered softly after an uncomfortable pause. "I knew your dad very well, Willoughby. I taught him math all four of his high school years. But he was the kind of kid who comes along rarely; no one can expect you to be like him. The comparison is natural because that is what people do, one of the follies of human nature, I guess. Maybe your mother didn't think about that kind of thing when she chose to move you and your sister here, but don't you think that maybe they needed this change as much as she thought you did?"

The statement struck a raw nerve. Willoughby *had* thought about it. San Diego was as hard for his mother as this town was for him. She had never called his demands to return to California selfish, but in his heart he knew it was true. His mother and sister were comfortable here, even with the memories of his father everywhere you looked. Living at Grandma Rose's farm was good for them and his sister was going to be everything he wasn't.

"I suppose they did. Her and my sister like it here and I know my grandma is happy that we came to live with her. But it still don't fix me. I don't know where I belong," Willoughby said, the depression in his voice speaking volumes. "I meant what I said Mr. Hurd; I wish I could just wake up and find myself in another world. Here I'm just a loser. I don't have any friends, I'm not any good at anything."

Theodore Hurd was no psychiatrist by any means, but he knew trouble in a young teenager's mind when he heard it. Sitting in front of him was a very troubled young man. "You are not a loser, Willoughby. Please do not call yourself that. We can find a way to get you out of this but first we have to deal with the situation in Miss Havercroft's class today. Regardless of everything else, we cannot ignore that."

Their conversation had gotten away from the main reason he was sitting here in Mr. Hurd's office. "Am I going to go to jail?"

"No son, you are not going to jail. But there are going to be consequences, Willoughby. I am bound to follow the school's guidelines when it comes to fighting on the school grounds. The fact that it wasn't just a fistfight and that you used your backpack as a weapon complicates matters. I am going to call your mother and arrange a meeting here in my office Monday morning. We will discuss what steps need to be taken to try and prevent anything like this from happening again. As for you, there will be a mandatory two-week suspension from school."

A two-week suspension. Willoughby's heart sank. He knew it was going to be bad but that was more than he had anticipated. The shit was going to hit the fan when he got home. "Two weeks?" he asked.

Mr. Hurd nodded. "I am afraid so. It would have been three days for a fistfight, three days for both offending parties, regardless. But you used a weapon. I know, it was just a backpack, but Chief Dent agreed, and we can't really hold Eddie responsible for any kind of compliance in the matter, even if he did say something nasty. He was sitting down at his desk and made no threatening overtures towards you, did he?"

"No sir." Willoughby's answer was barely audible.

"Very well. I am going to let you spend the rest of the day in the library. I will call your mother this afternoon. Normally I would have her come and get you but I know she is working at City Hall and I won't trouble her by dragging her down here today. You had better get your books from your locker and take them home with you."

He handed the backpack across the desk to Willoughby, testing its weight once more as he did so. "Feels like most of them are already in here. Two weeks is a long time to be absent, and we can't have you falling any further behind in your studies."

He pulled a pad from his desk and scribbled a note on it. "Your locker and then the library. Nowhere else. Give this to Mrs. Haney once you get there."

Willoughby took the note and started for the door.

"Willoughby." Mr. Hurd stopped him. "I know this is hard on you. You have been through a lot and I am sorry you lost your dad.

No young man should have to go through that. But please, give this town a chance. We can help you if you let us."

Willoughby didn't say anything. He just nodded and headed for the door.

When the bell marking the end of the school day finally rang, it caught Willoughby napping. The events of the day had totally exhausted him. Mrs. Haney had guided him to a corner of the library that was unoccupied; Willoughby was sure it was to keep him away from any of the other students. There was still plenty of finger-pointing and whispering regardless. The story of him taking out Eddie had spread like a wildfire in dry slash.

As he left the library and entered the crowded hall, he had to walk directly past the trophy case—his dad's face looked out from behind the glass. He had seen that face a thousand times in the last two years; the same photo was on the wall in his grandma's house. But today Willoughby was sure he detected disappointment in his dad's eyes. He turned away.

"Hey bro," a familiar voice hailed from behind. A lanky, tanned arm wrapped around his shoulders and gave him a squeeze as Kendall caught up with him in the hallway.

"Hey," he greeted. His sister was already a head taller than he was. Wearing a green and white SFHS Spartan sweatshirt (it was game day) and jeans, with her shoulder length auburn hair tied up in a ponytail, she was casual beauty defined. Willoughby was, in fact, very proud of his sister, and the two were very close.

As the two siblings jostled their way through the crowded hall, several students called out greetings to Kendall and to the surprise of both of them a shy and pretty freshman named Katelyn gave Willoughby a smile and a "hi" as she passed. Knots of students were talking and looking in their direction as the pair made their way to the big double doors at the end of the hall.

A blast of cool fall air enveloped them as they exited and started down the concrete steps taking them to the sidewalk in front of the school where the big yellow kid taxis were lined up and ingesting their charges. The bigleaf maples in the island that separated the school from the street were starting to put on their fall colors, splashing their brilliant yellows against the constant green of the Douglas firs. The air had a clean, fresh smell to it. Willoughby's desire to go back to San Diego certainly had nothing to do with the beauty of Western Oregon. Spirit Falls was nestled in a little valley in the Cascade foothills, an island surrounded by a sea of trees. He had always been amazed at how green this place was with forest everywhere you looked. Patchworks of clearcut acreage could be seen dotting the landscape, but even those greened up quickly, adding a lighter shade of emerald to the deeper hues of the older conifer stands. The air had just a bit of a bite to it, hinting of the possibility of the first frost coming soon. Another thing Willoughby had always found that he liked on the family's visits to Oregon—there were actually changes of seasons here. Spring, summer, fall, winter; in San Diego the seasons for the most part just blended together.

As they waited to board the bus, Willoughby was glad he had worn his sweatshirt, though the faint smell of vomit still clung to it. But unlike his sister, he hadn't even thought about it being game day and wearing his school colors—just more evidence that he hadn't gotten into the spirit of this small town yet. The lightning yellow of his Chargers sweatshirt stood out like the maple leaves against the firs as most of the students sported the Trojan green and white.

Willoughby and Kendall found an unoccupied seat towards the center of the bus. "I guess you heard?" he asked as he took the inside and she slid in next to him.

"Oh yeah," Kendall replied. "You know this is going to upset Mom." Willoughby knew too well.

"What did The Third Turd have to say?" Kendall asked as they waited for the bus to fill.

"Suspension. Two weeks. He even had to talk to the Chief of Police 'cause they said they were thinkin' about an assault charge."

"Jeez, Will." She was the only one who ever called him that. "You hit him with your backpack? What brought that on? Not that the big ass wipe doesn't deserve it, but that isn't like you."

"I don't know what it was, Kendall," Willoughby answered as

the buses pulled away from the school and headed for their routes. "I got in trouble by Havercroft for not payin' attention. She kicked me out and as I was walking out of her class, Eddie called me a name and I just flipped. I just plain lost it. Mom is going to lose it too, ain't she?"

They both knew the answer.

"You promised after the last time, Will. You sat there and swore that you were going to try harder. That wasn't more than two weeks ago. Now here you are again, and this time it's really bad. How is she supposed to feel about it?"

They both sat there, absorbed in their own thoughts, for several minutes. The bus wound its way out onto Main Street and turned east, out of the city limits and past the mill where the bus encountered what passed as the tiny town's version of rush hour traffic—the town's biggest employer was changing shifts. Vehicles were lined up coming out of the main parking lot waiting to get out onto the street. Pickups for the most part and a few cars, but this was logging country and if you didn't have a pickup you were definitely in the minority.

Willoughby looked up at the big sign that hung across the main gate of the mill—"C.A. WOOD PRODUCTS INC." The C.A. stood for Carlton Anderson, Eddie Anderson's grandfather. The two Anderson boys, Charles and Curtis, now ran the company, which included many thousands of acres of timberland. Charles Anderson was Eddie's dad. The town was tied to the Andersons and had been fortunate that they were shrewd businessmen. The downturn in the U.S. economy and especially the housing crisis had hit the timber industry hard, but the Andersons had managed to keep the mill and the logging that supplied it afloat, saving hundreds of jobs and keeping the economic structure of the small town intact. There was hardly a business in Spirit Falls that didn't owe its existence to the Andersons, their mill, and their timberlands. When the bus was a mile past the mill it turned right onto Spirit Creek Road. Five miles down that county road was the Baxter farm.

"You know Mom probably isn't going to let you go to Seattle

tomorrow don't you, Will?" Kendall asked as the bus made its first stop.

"Shit!" Willoughby cursed. He had forgotten the family's planned trip north to watch the Chargers and the Seahawks play on Sunday. The Charger front office and many of the players stayed in contact with Jennifer Baxter and her family and had supplied them with free tickets before. Even though Willoughby didn't care about football, the prospect of taking a road trip and seeing the sights excited him. They had planned to leave early in the morning, get to Seattle by noon or so, check into their hotel, and spend the rest of the afternoon and evening hitting a couple of the hot spots like the Space Needle and the Pike Street Market. So much for great plans—his escapade with Eddie had taken care of that.

"Maybe I can talk her into letting you go," said Kendall, trying to brighten his spirit. "It won't be as fun without you."

Willoughby wasn't as optimistic as his sister was. "Thanks, but you know Mom. She's going to make a statement on this one, I'll just bet you on it. Like you said, after all of the promises I made last time. Shit. I'm such a fuckin' loser."

"Bullcrap, Will," Kendall shot back with irritation in her voice. "You aren't a loser, so don't talk like that. You also need to quit using that word. Someday you're going to say it in the wrong place. And you need to quit beating yourself up. We've all had a hard time since Dad died. It's just taking you a little longer to adjust, but that doesn't mean you won't. You need to give this place a chance."

Willoughby couldn't help but crack a slight smile when she said that. "Crap, Kendall. That's exactly what The Third Turd said."

"Well, he said it because it's true. You haven't really tried. Mom and I are both happier here, and you know how much Grandma likes the fact that we're around. It's been rough on her since Grandpa died and to have us in that big house tickles the heck out of her."

It was true and Willoughby knew it. The house in San Diego had felt cold and empty after his dad died. They had been on the verge of losing it anyway before the accident with his career-ending injuries, the drug and alcohol problems, and the fact that the money just wasn't there as it had been before. After the accident, the lawsuit was the final straw. The move to Oregon was not only necessitated by the need for a change emotionally, but financially it was about the only thing they could do. But Willoughby hadn't accepted any of the rational logic behind the decision and had been a pain in everyone's ass ever since.

"You're right as usual," he said, forcing a smile. "I don't know why I can't be happy here. It's just that I get the feeling everyone here is disappointed because I ain't a jock like Dad."

Kendall returned his smile. "You are who you are, Will. People will get used to it. Give 'em time. They'll find out what a great guy you are."

"Easy for you to say. You fit right in. No issues for Kendall Baxter. She swoops in and takes over as Miss Popularity."

Before Kendall had a chance to counter her little brother's sarcasm, the bus rolled to a halt in front of a long gravel lane. It was their stop. The two exited with a flurry of goodbyes and "see you at the game" directed at Kendall. As they stepped out the door and onto the gravel, someone shouted, "You rock, Willoughby!"

They both turned to see who it was but the doors shut and the long yellow bus pulled away leaving the two siblings standing alone.

"See?" Kendall punched Willoughby slightly on his shoulder as they watched the bus disappear around the corner. "You're starting to get more popular already. You don't think there aren't a lot of kids who wished they could have done the same thing to that jerk?"

Willoughby walked over to the oversized silver mailbox standing next to the driveway with the name "BAXTER" arrayed in big black letters across its side. Underneath the box hung a small sign—"Oregon Century Farm." Though significantly smaller than its original 360 acres, the family farm had been there for a long time. Bits and pieces had been sold off over the years to get the family through lean times but it still hung on as one of the few family dairy farms left in the business, mostly due to the hard work and stubbornness of Will and Rose Baxter, Willoughby's grandparents. But its financial situation was tenuous at best with Will Baxter having been gone now for four years. But Rose Baxter was a determined person and managed to hold on with the help of their only hired hand, a towering Klamath Indian by the name of Jake Thompson, also known as Tall Bear. Though the dairy herd had dwindled right along with the property, it still kept the bank at bay. Jennifer Baxter's job at City Hall was helping to ease the burden.

"Your new *Cosmo* is here." Willoughby waved the glossy magazine at Kendall as he groped in the big box for the rest of the mail.

"Cool," she replied, taking it out of his hands. "Anything else for me?" The two were shuffling through the wad of envelopes and junk mail when they heard the howling whine of tires on pavement. Both looked at the same time down the county road back towards town.

A jacked up, black Ford F-250 pickup roared into view around the corner, its oversized tires squalling in protest against the asphalt, joining the deep growl of headers and a custom exhaust as the driver took the corner at a high rate of speed. The tires squealed and smoked as the driver downshifted quickly.

"Fuck!" Willoughby cursed as he and Kendall jumped back out of the way just in time as the black pickup slid to a gravel-throwing, dust-raising stop in front of them. The passenger door flew open before the truck had even come to a complete stop. Eddie Anderson landed with both big feet on the gravel three feet in front of Willoughby and Kendall.

"Well now, if it ain't the very fuckin' person I'm looking for."

"What do you want, Eddie?" Kendall demanded as she stepped protectively in front of her little brother. "And what's up with drivin' like a damn idiot, Tristan?" She directed the second question at the driver as he came around the front of the pickup.

"Sorry, Kendall. Didn't mean to throw gravel," the teen apologized as he approached the other three. Tristan 'Carrot' Kemper was Eddie Anderson's toady. They made a strange pair. He wasn't much bigger than Willoughby and about as athletically inclined, his shock of red hair and the accompanying freckles earning him his nickname. But nonetheless he was part of Eddie's clique, earning the spot mainly because his dad was the owner of the log truck fleet that delivered logs from the woods to the mill for Eddie's dad. The other reason, and probably most important as far as Eddie was concerned, was that Carrot Kemper had the coolest pickup in town. The tricked out Ford had been his sixteenth birthday present and with an eight-inch lift kit and thirty-two-inch mud tires, it sat up almost as high as Al Kemper's log trucks did. The company's name, Big Log Trucking Inc., was emblazoned in big white letters on both doors of the black Ford. Eddie thought it was one badass truck and allowed Carrot the privilege of driving him around since he had no driver's license of his own yet.

"Get out of the way, Kendall," Eddie growled, his face flushed red with anger. There was a slight swelling on the left side of his head just in front of his ear, a visual reminder of the meeting with Willoughby's backpack. "Your punk brother took a cheap shot at me and that earns him the right to get his fuckin' ass kicked."

Willoughby's knees were turning to jelly. He had known that sooner or later Eddie was going to come after him for what had happened in Miss Havercroft's class. That Eddie sought revenge so quickly was something he hadn't counted on. But Eddie Anderson had also made a serious error in judgment, and it was standing between him and his intended target.

"You touch my brother and I swear to God you'll wish you hadn't," Kendall hissed as she took a step closer to the hulking Eddie. "Get back in the truck and get out of here *now*."

"C'mon Eddie," Tristan Kemper pleaded. It was obvious he had been bullied into bringing his friend out here and wanted no part of it. He also harbored a secret crush on Kendall Baxter and really didn't want to get on her bad side. "You'll get in trouble and get kicked off the football team."

"Fuck football and fuck you, Carrot," Eddie growled as he locked glares with Kendall. "What ya gonna do Will-ough-by? Hide behind your sister?"

A physical confrontation with Eddie was the last thing Willoughby wanted but he couldn't let his sister stand up for him. His legs were watery and his guts were tied up in knots but he had to do something. He stepped up beside his sister.

"I don't want to fight Eddie. I didn't really intend to hit you with my backpack. I'm offering you an apology."

Eddie clenched his meaty fists. "Say you're sorry all you want but it ain't gonna change nothin'. Nobody takes a cheap shot at me and gets away with it. Grow some fuckin' balls ya little pussy and tell your sister to get outta the way before she gets hurt, too."

"Only person gettin' hurt round here gonna be you if'n you don't haul your fat ass back in that truck and head for town, Anderson."

The heads of all four teenagers snapped around to look in the direction the voice had come from. A large clump of blackberries, the bane of every farmer and landowner in Western Oregon, grew along a portion of the fence line that marked the Baxter property. From behind this ten-foot-high tangled mass stepped the speaker.

Jake Thomson was an impressive sight. Six feet eight inches of lean and rock hard muscle. His shoulder length black hair, tied in twin braids, showed little hint of gray even though he was somewhere around sixty years old. No one knew for sure and Jake certainly wasn't telling anybody. A colorful beaded headband kept the hair in place. You could mistake Jake for nothing other than what he was, the high cheekbones, a protruding bony nose with a slight buffalo hump to it, dark eyes set under a proud forehead. The only thing marring his classic features was a four-inch-long scar running from just above his right eye and down across his cheek. Jake Thompson was about as native as a Native American could get.

The four teenagers stood silently as the big Indian walked up to the barbed wire fence, the machete he was carrying making a solid 'thwack' as he buried it deep into the top of the fencepost. Pushing the top strand of wire down with his hand, he easily stepped over the fence.

"Kendall, Willoughby," Jake acknowledged the siblings as he strode up to the group. He stopped next to Kendall, folded his muscled bare arms across his chest, and glared directly at Eddie. "What in the hell is goin' on here?"

"It's okay, Jake," Kendall answered. "There was a little bit of a disagreement but we have it taken care of. Eddie and Tristan were just leaving. Weren't you, guys?"

One look at the towering and intimidating countenance of Jake was all the convincing Tristan Kemper needed. "Yeah. We was just leavin'." He turned and headed for the other side of the pickup. "C'mon Eddie. I'm outta here."

"Well, Anderson?" Jake asked as Eddie pondered his next move. Eddie was young, hot-headed, and already bigger and stronger than a lot of grown men, but to his credit, wasn't totally stupid. The formidable presence standing less than an arm's length away made any kind of threat against Willoughby no longer an option and he knew it. But not being totally stupid still didn't keep Eddie from being bull-headed.

"This ain't done, Baxter." He glowered at Willoughby. "You can't have your bodyguard or your sister around to protect you all the time."

"This better be over, Eddie," Kendall countered. "My brother offered you an apology. Be man enough to take it."

Eddie and Willoughby locked eyes and the message he passed to the smaller teen was silent but clear. Between the two of them, it definitely wasn't over.

Eddie turned and walked towards the truck as Tristan keyed the beefed up engine to life. As he pulled himself into the passenger seat, he looked back towards Jake.

"You don't scare me old man," he yelled over the throaty roar of the Ford as Tristan revved the engine. "I think I'll tell my dad and my uncle how tough you think you are. See what they have to say about that."

Eddie slammed the door of the truck as Tristan popped the clutch and threw gravel. The rubber burned and the oversize tires screeched in protest as he spun the truck in a tight U-turn and accelerated towards town. Eddie waved his middle finger at them as the truck disappeared around the corner.

"Assholes," Kendall swore as gravel dust and acrid rubber smoke swirled around them.

"Mind tellin' me what that was all about?" asked Jake, looking at the two teens. Kendall filled in the details as best she knew with her brother adding small bits and pieces. Willoughby was content to let her do the talking. It had been a thoroughly challenging day that unfortunately wasn't finished yet. Knowing that a confrontation with his mother still lay ahead and combined with the embarrassment he was feeling about the whole situation didn't make him very talkative. Life was sure going to suck at home and school for a while.

"You hit 'im with your backpack?" a surprised Jake asked when Kendall finished the story.

Willoughby just shrugged. "It just happened. He said something to me I didn't like and the next thing I know he was on the floor out cold."

Jake grunted his amusement and gave Willoughby a big grin. "No wonder he was so pissed. Got his ass kicked in front of the class like that."

"Mom isn't going to think it's very funny," Kendall reminded. "Ten to one she isn't going to let Will go to Seattle tomorrow. We were probably lucky you came along when you did, Jake. Things might have gotten a little ugly."

The big Indian nodded towards the blackberry vines that had hid his presence. "Damn things are takin' over. Been meanin' to get out here and trim 'em back for quite a while. They'll pull down a wire fence if'n you let 'em."

"Do you think Eddie will tell his dad and his uncle like he said he would?" Willoughby asked. He didn't want any more trouble to come out of this mess than there already was. "They won't come after you, will they Jake?"

Jake let out a booming laugh. "Ol' Charlie and Curt Anderson already done tried that one time. I was down at The Landing tyin' one on one night and they jumped me out in the parkin' lot. They was flyin' pretty high and actin' tough. Guess they thought they could handle an old drunk like me. Turned out they guessed wrong."

"They ganged up on you?" Kendall asked. "They're pretty big guys."

Jake shrugged. "Nothin' but bullies, the whole bunch of 'em. Folks think the Andersons walk on water 'cause they keep people workin' but down inside they're all a bunch a friggin' jerks. Seems like Eddie gonna be just like 'em. Pickin' on folk 'cause they're smaller or don't have as much money. I worked for the old man Carlton a couple of times but he never did like me much either. The only reason the brothers took me on is they thought they had an advantage. Too chicken shit to try me one on one, but that's the Andersons. But in the end, they got me anyway. They told Barry Dent that I jumped them and I'll be damned if'n he didn't come out and arrest me the next day for assault. It was their word against mine and I ended up doin' thirty days workin' on the county jail road crew."

"Principal Hurd said that Eddie's mother wanted me arrested for assault," Willoughby added.

Jake laughed again. "There ya go. Kid is twice as big and everybody knows he's a bully but they blame it on you. Shows ya what money and power can do."

"Well thanks for your help, Jake," Kendall said as she started down the gravel lane. "We better get up to the house, Will. Mom is going to be home in a little while."

"Yeah, thanks," Willoughby added. "You probably kept me from getting my butt kicked pretty severely." He turned to follow his sister but was gently stopped by Jake's huge hand on his shoulder.

"Don't you worry 'bout what happened today, son," Jake said. "You done good and I'll bet a lotta kids are gonna look at you with new respect. You're gonna run into people like asshole Eddie all of your life and you gotta take a stand or they'll never let you be. Just 'tween you and me, I think big Eddie there will probably forget about you and look to pick on someone who don't fight back."

Willoughby looked up at the big Indian towering above him. In the first couple of months that Willoughby had lived on his grandma's farm, he and Jake had never spoken more than a few words to each other. Jake's towering size and fierce appearance had always made Willoughby somewhat leery. But he had grown quite a bit closer with the big Indian by default, filling the vacant spot as the boy's male role model, though role model would have been a moniker that Jake would have split a gut laughing at. But regardless, the two had formed a strange bond with Jake taking Willoughby under his wing and trying to teach him things he thought a boy Willoughby's age, living on an Oregon farm, should know. Jake Thompson was, for the most part, a loner—a lot like the young boy in front of him. Though they had arrived at their current lot in life by different paths, they had come together and found they shared common ground.

"Thanks," he told the big man. "But I don't think my mom is going to see things the same way as you do, Jake. I might have gotten some respect from some of the kids but my mom will see nothing good about what happened today. I haven't given her a lot to be happy about lately and I think this deal is going to really be hard for her to take."

"Women are that way, Will," Jake answered, shocking the boy with the use of the name that had belonged to his grandfather. His sister called him that but to everyone else he was Willoughby, a name he despised. It felt good to have Jake call him Will.

"I have a lot of respect for your mom," Jake continued. "Your whole family has been through a lot with first your grandpa dyin' and then the thing with your dad. Tough for folks to take on that much grief. I try to stay out of personal stuff but it's kinda hard when you're as close as I am. Your family has been good to me Will; they're the only ones who thought I was worth anything and for that I owe 'em a lot."

"Did you know my dad very well?" Willoughby asked. It felt strange to be having this kind of a conversation with Jake, but deep down he felt like maybe the big guy might have a better understanding of what he was going through than anyone else.

"I watched him as he was growin' up. Used to go to a lot of the games but I never worked for your family then. I didn't get this job 'til after your dad had gone off to college. But he was somethin' special, that's for sure."

"Yeah," Willoughby answered. "Special. Too bad I ain't special like him. I wouldn't be goin' through all this crap."

"Guys like your dad don't come 'round very often. I hear folks in town talkin' 'bout Anderson like he was some kinda special player. Shit. Your dad woulda chewed him up and spit him out. Bein' big and strong don't necessary make you somethin'. What made your dad special was his heart. He gave everything he had all of the time. Your grandpa was the same way. Didn't make no difference if'n it was sports or anythin' else, when they went about doin' something, they put all they had into it. A man gotta respect that."

"You ever play sports Jake?" Willoughby was curious.

"Me?" The big Indian's laugh boomed loud and strong. "Shit. I never liked doin' anything anybody told me to do. They tried. I had the size for a lot of stuff but I just didn't cotton to listenin' to what the coaches tried to tell me. You gotta have a certain 'mount a discipline for sports and discipline was somethin' I was allergic to. Side's that, I woulda had to go to school. Me'n school never got along much neither."

Willoughby smiled. For all the times he had avoided saying anything to the big Indian because he was intimidated, he was now truly sorry. The fact that Jake could talk to him about a pressing problem and actually make him feel better was something not a lot of people could do.

"Well, thanks again, Jake. I'd better get up to the house and let you get back to work. I'll see you later."

"No problem," Jake said as they walked down the lane to where he had buried the machete in the top of the fencepost by the blackberries. "Damn things have probably grown a foot since I stopped. One more thing afore you go. Ever you need to talk to somebody, you know, get a male point of view on things, you come by and see me, okay? Anytime."

"I'll do that," Willoughby said, smiling up at him.

"Good. You got some spunk, kid. Maybe you didn't inherit their size, but you got the spirit of your ancestors and that'll get you a long way. See ya later."

Willoughby began the walk down the gravel lane, a straight line between two fenced cow pastures with the big white, two-story farmhouse nestled at its end in a clump of bigleaf maples and white oaks. Jake had made him feel better about things but there was still major conflict yet to come. His mother would be home in about an hour and a half. The Third Turd would have spoken to her on the phone by now, ruining what could have been a pretty good day for her. But he had made up his mind about one thing. He was going to accept whatever punishment his mother dealt without an argument—he deserved it. He would take it like a man, tell her he was sorry, and promise to try and be better. Not that she would believe his promises—she had heard them countless times before and he hadn't followed through, so why should she think this time would be different? But Willoughby knew. There was something in his heart, something that told him things were going to change in a big way between him and his mother. He couldn't put a finger on it, but he sensed it. Things were going to be different.

CHAPTER THREE

B Y THE TIME WILLOUGHBY GOT TO THE HOUSE, Kendall was already on the telephone, one of her favorite pastimes. He could hear her in the den and it wasn't a surprise to hear his and Eddie's names being dropped. Besides the phone, a lot of texts, tweets, and emails would be passing the story of the bully's fifth period beat down by the hands of Willoughby Baxter; more than likely getting embellished and enhanced with every telling. The only silver lining of this thing so far was the two-week suspension; at least he wouldn't have to deal with things at school for a while.

He dropped his backpack in the hall and made his way to the kitchen. "Hey, Grandma," he greeted, heading straight to the cookie jar.

Rose Baxter was up to her elbows in chicken when Willoughby came in. Friday night meant fried chicken at the Baxters' and nobody could do it like his grandma. She raised her own fryers on the farm and they were plump and tender, but it was the herbs and spices she used to coat the bird pieces that made it special. Fried in a huge cast iron skillet on top of her one–hundred-and-twenty-year-old Majestic wood cook stove, Grandma's chicken was crisp, golden perfection on the outside and chin dribbling juicy on the inside. The Colonel had nothing on Grandma Rose.

"Hello, Willoughby," she responded warmly. Physically she was a diminutive woman, smaller than Willoughby, but that was as far as you could go in saying she was small. She had done nothing but work on farms and ranches her entire life and she could still buck hay bales, run farm equipment, and handle uncooperative milk cows as well as anyone. She bought her jeans and hickory shirts in the boys section of clothing stores and could probably count the times she had worn dresses on her two small, calloused hands. Even for church on Sunday she wore her working clothes, only bothering to change her cow-shit-covered boots for tennis shoes.

"God just wants you to be in church," she would state emphatically when anyone dared question her Sunday best. "He don't give a ding dang what you're wearing." When she was outside, she kept her short gray hair tucked under a worn baseball cap, and the only other piece of wardrobe she wore with any kind of regularity was her apron, because besides farming, the other thing Rose Baxter could do quite well was cook.

Rose Ellen Hayes, her maiden name, had been raised on a working ranch outside of Burns, Oregon, and had begun helping her mother feed farm hands since she had been old enough to handle eggs without breaking them. Other than the rare times an illness of some sort kept her down, she had gotten up at four o'clock in the morning nearly every day of her sixty-seven years. She was a rare throwback of a woman and it was one of the main reasons a burly young buck of a farmer named Will Baxter had been smitten with her.

They had met at a farm equipment auction in Bend; he, looking for a used but serviceable tractor and she, accompanying her dad as they sought to unload some surplus ranch equipment. She had tripped over Will's long legs as he lay under a John Deere checking for oil leaks. He bought her lunch to make amends for her skinned elbow and had managed to get her address before they parted. They began a courtship by mail and the two were married a year to the day they had met.

It had always been their intention to have a large family—if you were planning on running a farm to make a living it always helped to have plenty of live-in farm hands—but for Rose and Will Baxter, having children would prove to be a daunting, and for Rose, a nearly fatal challenge.

When she was seventeen, Rose had been thrown and stepped

on by a horse she had been trying to break. It certainly hadn't been the first time she had been tossed to the ground and she usually got up, dusted herself off, cursed the horse, and got right back on. But this time was different. This time the horse planted both his rear hooves on her stomach just below the buckle of her belt. The injury to her insides had been horrific, her spleen had ruptured and her lower intestines damaged so badly they had to remove a section. But the worst damage had been to her female plumbing. The doctors told her in the frankest of terms that chances of her ever having a child were slim to none.

Rose had been upfront about her situation with Will Baxter before they had become married, and though it was a hard pill for him to swallow, the only thing he wanted more than a big family was the spunky wisp of a cowgirl he had fallen in love with. Together they faced the stark reality that having the large family they both desired would never come to pass. But despite the doctor's warning, they persisted, only to meet with bitter heartbreak. Rose miscarried twice. They had come to accept the fact they would be childless and had considered adopting, but the couple had little time to pursue that option. Trying to keep the Baxter family farm afloat in Spirit Falls was a full-time challenge and family expansion was put on hold. But in one of those strange turns of fate, Rose Baxter became pregnant again, nearly fourteen years after their last tragic attempt. While they had braced for the distinct possibility of another miscarriage, the couple was finally blessed with a healthy baby boy. But Baxter men were wont to come into the world large and robust and the ordeal was nearly fatal for the diminutive Rose—there would be no more. James William Baxter, Willoughby's father, would be the couple's only child.

"How was school today, Willoughby?" his grandma asked as she wiped her floury hands on a towel and poured him a tall glass of fresh cold milk to go with his snack.

"S'okay," he mumbled through a mouthful of cookie.

"I'll bet you're excited about our trip to Seattle, aren't you?" she asked as she returned to her chicken.

42

"Mmmhm," he mumbled again. He was going to have to recount the details of his day all too soon when his mother got home. No sense in reliving it with his grandma and then turning around and having to do it again.

"I'm gonna watch a little TV, Grandma, unless you need some help," he told her as he grabbed a couple more cookies.

"Thanks, but I'm fine, Willoughby. Supper is in an hour so don't you load up on cookies and spoil your appetite."

"I'll never be too full not to eat your fried chicken, Grandma," Willoughby responded as he walked out of the kitchen with his milk and cookies. As he plopped on the sofa and started surfing through channels, he could hear Kendall still talking on the phone in the den, more than likely making entries on her Facebook page at the same time. He finally settled on an old *Little House on the Prairie* episode. The early ones where Laura and Mary were little were his favorites, but tonight even those held no interest for him. His mind drifted to thoughts of his mother and their upcoming discussion.

"Boy if you aren't the talk of the town," Kendall said, surprising him a bit later as she plopped herself into the easy chair next to the sofa with her own snack of milk and cookies. "I didn't realize you caused that big of a commotion. You puked on Kyra Becker?"

"Lousy lunch I guess." Willoughby wasn't really in the mood to talk about it but she didn't give him much of a chance not to.

"So what'cha gonna say to Mom?" she prodded.

"What am I supposed to say? Eddie called me something that pissed me off and I hit him with my friggin' backpack," he answered testily, immediately regretting his sharp tone.

"Look, Will, I'm just trying to help," she fired back. "This isn't just about today and what happened with Eddie and you know it. You're killin' Mom with the attitude. I know it's hard but it's the same for all of us and what you're doing is making it worse."

"I'm always makin' things worse, ain't I, Kendall?" he grumbled. "If what I do bugs you so much why don't ya just butt out and let me deal with it?"

It was another one of those things that shot out of his mouth without much thought behind it. She was just trying to help and he had given her a cheap shot for her effort. He was immediately regretful.

"I'm sorry, Kendall," he apologized as she angrily grabbed her glass and her cookies and started to leave. "Don't be mad at me," he pleaded. "I know you're tryin' to help but it's been a tough day."

Kendall replaced her frown with a half-smile. She knew her kid brother was on edge and while she usually never backed down from verbal combat with him, she decided to let his angry comment slide and accept his apology. She foresaw big trouble ahead with his 'me against the world' demeanor.

"I know it's been a tough day Will, but it's about to get tougher. Do yourself a favor and lose the attitude before you talk with Mom. I agree with what you said earlier—she's going to push it on this one and if you come on with the smart ass thing it's not going to be good. We don't need this, Will. Please, I know you don't mean to, but you gotta see what this is doing to us."

Willoughby sat there and stared blankly at the TV. He heard every word she said and he knew she was right. There were times when he wished he could just disappear and let his family get on with their lives. Kendall had it pegged. That's what he felt like—a chain around their necks that was dragging them under.

"Well, I gotta get ready to go to the game. Brit's picking me up right after supper. Try to think about what I said Will, okay?"

Willoughby looked up at her and gave her a half smile of his own. "I'll try and take your advice, Kendall. And thanks for bein' my big, protective sister."

She reached out and ruffled his hair. "Good enough. Love you, bro."

Willoughby sat there alone in the huge living room suddenly feeling very small. The house had always made him feel that way. Ironically, while it had been built and expanded over the years for a large family, it had never come to pass. Grandma Rose called it the Baxter curse. The largest contingent of the Baxter clan that had ever resided there at one time had been Grandpa's Will's family when he had been a young boy. He had a sister, Willoughby's great aunt, who now lived in Maine near her daughter and her family. There was also a brother Edward, who had been killed in a logging accident when he was just twenty-three. With Willoughby, his sister, and their mother now living with Grandma Rose, the house seemed a little fuller, but to him it was still too big, although its ten-foot-high ceilings made for a great tree at Christmas time.

Willoughby thought how lonely it must have been for his grandma and grandpa when his dad had left the house to go off to college. There had been just the two of them for so many years, all of those Thanksgiving and Christmas dinners without a family to fill the house. With a life wrapped around football, there had only been a couple of times when Willoughby's dad had been able to bring the family up to Oregon for the winter holidays. Then after Grandpa Will passed away four years ago, it was just Grandma Rose. She had tried to get Willoughby's dad to move back to Spirit Falls and help her run the farm, but he had wanted no part of it. James Baxter had been well down the path of alcohol and pain killer addiction by that time. But Grandma was happy now. It delighted her to be able to finally have her grandchildren and her daughter-in-law near and she needed them. But it was too bad one of them was being a real jerk and trying his best to make life miserable for everyone.

The local five o'clock news coming on the TV told him his mom would be home soon and he made the decision to go out onto the porch and wait for her. There was no need to get this thing started in the house where his grandma and his sister could hear.

The cool air that greeted him felt good as he nestled into one of the patio chairs. The house was big and old but always warm with the wood heat from the big wood stove in the living room and the wood cook stove in the kitchen. Grandma was happy with nothing else. His dad had offered to pay for the installation of an expensive heat pump system after he had signed his rookie contract for the Chargers, but Rose and Will had respectfully declined and settled for getting the house re-roofed instead.

"We live in the woods in the greatest tree-growing state in

America," Grandpa Will had said after James had tried to talk them into the heat pump. "Ain't nothin' feels better on a cold day than wood heat."

Grandma Rose loved her wood heat and cook stove as much as Grandpa did, but it was labor intensive. Jake kept the wood coming in—that was one of the many things he took care of—and there were plenty of good fir trees and hardwood on the place. Windfalls were common after winter storms and there were always dead ones that needed to be removed. Dragging them down to the woodshed next to the barn with the D-4 cat, he would fire up his Stihl chainsaw and cut them up, feeding the rounds through the hydraulic wood splitter. Once a mountain of stove-sized wood was built up, he would stack it into the woodshed to dry. It seemed to Willoughby that keeping the two stoves supplied with seasoned wood was a chore that never ended. There were plenty of jobs like that on the farm—tending the cows and chickens, weeding the garden, maintaining the wood supply, mending fences, and fighting back the brush and blackberries. There was always work to be done but Jake and Grandma never complained. "Idle hands get into trouble," was one of Grandma Rose's favorite sayings. She thought Willoughby's hands were too idle.

A breeze rustled its way through the big oaks and maples in the yard, sending a wave of dry leaves flittering to the ground in its wake, making Willoughby thankful that he had put his sweatshirt back on when he came outside. The big yellow maple leaves, some the size of dinner plates, bounced from branch to branch before gently rocking their way to earth, maneuvering past those brethren not quite ready to release their tenuous hold on the home tree. The brown oak leaves, smaller and lighter, seemed to pause for a moment at each obstacle, fighting their inevitable descent at every chance. It was a trickle now but Jake said that after the first frost, and when the rains and heavier winds set in, it would become a flood. It all smelled like work to Willoughby.

His contemplation of future events, centered on a leaf rake in his hands, was interrupted by his mom's silver Accord turning

46

onto the driveway. *No attitude,* was the mental reminder he gave himself as she eased by the front gate and turned into the covered carport. She would normally go into the house through the kitchen but Willoughby's presence on the porch had caught her attention.

"Hey, Mom," he greeted apprehensively as she came around the corner.

Smartly dressed in a black blazer over a white blouse with black slacks, Jennifer Baxter looked like a high rising female executive instead of a front desk receptionist at a small town city hall. She was nearly as tall as Kendall and had the same auburn hair, but had it cut stylishly short. With her San Diego tan and classy demeanor, she was a sharp contrast to Agatha Mason, the now retired former receptionist who had held sway in her matronly, overbearing manner for fifty years. It was said that foot traffic through the City Hall doors had increased dramatically since Jennifer Baxter had taken the receptionist seat, with most of the rise in volume coming from young and middle-aged males.

But on this Friday afternoon Jennifer Baxter just looked tired. She took a seat next to her son.

"Hey, Willoughby," she returned his greeting. Slipping her shoes off, she dropped her tired legs onto the footrest in front of her, tilted her head back, and closed her eyes. Willoughby let her rest quietly for a couple of minutes before he broke the ice.

"Pretty rough day, huh?"

"A very rough day made worse by the phone call from Mr. Hurd this afternoon, thank you very much." She leaned her head forward and gave him a glance to make sure he caught the sarcasm. When she was sure he had, she leaned her head back again and closed her eyes. "It seems people can't wait for the Tuesday night City Council sessions to air their complaints. They bring them to me and I have to document them and make sure they get passed along to the right department head. It wouldn't be so bad if they would just leave the nasty attitudes at home. I don't know why they think they have to get pissed at me. I'm just the dang receptionist."

It was the key that signaled the start of their conversation.

"Speaking of nasty attitudes, yours seems to be in prime form. You hit Eddie Anderson with your backpack?"

The backpack thing seemed to surprise everyone. Willoughby wondered if his grandma would ask the same question when she heard the story.

"I got in trouble with Miss Havercroft—not paying attention. When I was going out the door, Eddie called me a …, well he called me a name and I just lost control. I swung my backpack and the next thing I knew he was on the floor." It was short, no excuses, and, no attitude.

"From what I know of the Andersons I won't say that he didn't deserve to have the shit knocked out of him. But to do it like that, well, that's not you, Willoughby. This thing with you seems to be progressing, not getting better like you promised. The question is, how far is it going to go? How long until you lose your temper and really hurt someone, Willoughby?"

She was getting right to the point, something he had already thought about. Was he truly capable of hurting someone just because they pissed him off? Last year he would have said never, it was unthinkable. But now he truly didn't know. She kept going when he didn't answer the question.

"We can't keep doing this, son."

"I'm not gonna to lie to you Mom, I don't know what happened. I've never even been in a fight before except for that neighbor kid in the first grade. Dad took me out of Pop Warner 'cause I was afraid of getting hit. I don't even remember swingin' the stupid pack—it just happened."

What he told her next was frightening, for both of them, but he had thought about it and had vowed to be totally honest with her. "It was the backpack because that's what I had… If I would have had a gun, I think I would have used it." The tears were flowing now; he looked at her and could see the moisture in her eyes, too. "I think I'm goin' crazy, Mom. Something is wrong with me."

As angry with her son as she was, Jennifer Baxter let her motherly instincts take over. She reached out and pulled Willoughby into her arms and held him close. "You're not going crazy, Willoughby," she sobbed through her tears as both of them were now crying freely. "We'll get to the bottom of this and get you some help. We're not going to give up on you." They sat there in the twilight of the evening without speaking, holding tight to each other.

"Mom?" The light from the house spilled onto the porch as Kendall opened the front door and poked her head outside. "Is everything all right?" she asked pensively, the concern obvious in her voice.

Her mom looked up and smiled at her, still clutching tight to Willoughby. "We're fine Kendall. It's been a rough day, for both of us."

"Grandma says to tell you supper is ready." The heady smell of their grandma's fried chicken had followed Kendall out the door, adding an aromatic exclamation point to her announcement.

"Thanks, Kendall. We'll be right in," Jennifer Baxter acknowledged her daughter as she dabbed her eyes dry with a Kleenex. Willoughby dried his eyes on the sleeve of his sweatshirt. "We have to finish this before we go in, Willoughby," she said after Kendall had returned to the house. "Mr. Hurd said a two-week suspension. I tried to talk him out of it but he said his hands were tied—school policy."

She looked at her son. The raw emotional moment they had shared had averted any head-on confrontation but the issue still had not been resolved. Willoughby was still in trouble.

"It won't be two weeks of watching TV and playing video games, either. I'm going to make a list of things that need to be done every day, and you can't neglect your schoolwork. Mr. Hurd said he would get a list of assignments from your teachers and send them home with Kendall, so at least you won't fall behind any further." She paused for a moment. Willoughby waited…he knew what was coming next.

"I guess you know that going to Seattle tomorrow with the rest of us is out of the question."

It wasn't a surprise—his sister had warned him of the possibility of that happening. They had all been excitedly looking forward to the mini vacation. Shopping, the Space Needle, Pike Place Market—they had been talking about it since they had received the tickets three weeks ago. It was going to be a chance for them to relieve a lot of the pent-up stress they had all felt with the move and adjusting to their new life. While he had been prepared, it still hurt.

"I'm sorry son, but do you understand the seriousness of this thing?"

He did and wasn't going to argue. It was past time to accept the fact that he had been acting pretty selfishly lately, putting more stress on an already overloaded family. Most importantly, the temper thing with Eddie had scared him. He had blanked out and lost total control, and what he had told his mom was no bullshit—it could have been a baseball bat—it could have been a gun. As he looked at her, he was shocked to see what the last two years had done. Like muddy boot prints on a new carpet, stress and exhaustion were leaving their ugly tracks across her forehead and around her eyes, eyes that now looked tired and sad. Guilt stabbed his heart as he wondered why he hadn't been able to see what all of this had been doing to her. Reaching out, he took her hands in his.

"I figured as much Mom, and it's okay. I know you're tired of hearing my promises, but I'll try, for you, for Kendall, for Grandma. I'll try."

A hint of a smile forced its way onto her tired face. She squeezed his hands in return. "I hope so, son. I want to believe you."

The smile made him feel better. Missing the trip to Seattle was going to be hard but the bitter confrontation he feared had been avoided. All in all, it hadn't gone too badly. An idea came to him.

"Why don't you see if Brit can go with you guys? It would make Kendall happy to have someone along and you wouldn't have to waste the ticket."

"That's a great idea, Willoughby." The stress lines on her tired face softened and she flashed him a wide smile. "That'll make your sister very happy. Now let's go get some of your grandma's chicken."

Kendall and Rose were seated around the big dining room table when Willoughby finished washing up, and to his surprise, Jake had joined them for supper. Normally he was content taking care of his own meals in his trailer.

"Hey, Jake," Willoughby greeted as he pulled out a chair and sat down.

"Willoughby," the big Indian nodded in return. He had even managed to find a clean hickory shirt.

They all bowed their heads as Grandma Rose gave a quick blessing. Along with Friday night's main entrée of her kickass chicken was a heaping bowl of mashed potatoes with steaming chicken gravy to top it with, green beans, sliced tomatoes, a tossed green salad, and a huge platter of hot, flaky biscuits fresh from the oven. It had always amazed Willoughby that almost everything Grandma set down on the dinner table in front of them came off the farm.

It had taken some time for Kendall, Willoughby, and their mother to get used to the structured mealtimes at their grandma's. Sit-down meals together had been a rarity in San Diego, especially after their father had died and Jennifer Baxter had been forced to return to work. Take-out or something microwavable had been the norm, but that came to a screeching halt when they had moved to Oregon. There was no grabbing something quick and heading off to watch TV. Mealtimes were family time and an opportunity to catch up on what was going on, and you were expected to be at the table. Grandma Rose thought the loss of family time around the supper table was a big part of what was wrong with America. She made no bones about her opinion on the matter and would accept no compromise. Conversation went hand in hand with the food, and unfortunately, on this particular Friday night, when it started, it didn't take long for the specter of Willoughby's explosive adventure at school to raise its ugly head.

"So how are you two kids getting to the game tonight?" Grandma Rose asked as she started the food dishes around the table.

Kendall stole a quick glance at her mother before answering; Grandma was yet unaware of the circumstances.

"Brit is picking me up after supper. I don't think Willoughby wants to go."

"Why don't you want to go to the game, Willoughby?" his grandma asked as he plopped a big spoonful of creamy mashed potatoes onto his plate. "Even if you don't care that much for football, you ought to support your team. I'm sure your friends will all be there."

"Willoughby won't be going to any school functions for a while, Rose," Jennifer Baxter interjected as she passed the green beans on to Jake. "He got in a little altercation at school today and has been suspended."

"Suspended!" Grandma Rose paused in the middle of pouring gravy over her potatoes.

Great, Willoughby thought to himself as he poked around his plate. He didn't want the day's events to become the topic of suppertime conversation. An ugly confrontation with his mother had been avoided and he had hoped that would be the end of it, but since nobody had informed Grandma of what had happened, she couldn't be blamed for her reaction. The cat that had been stuffed into the bag had just clawed its way out.

"What in the heck is that all about and how come nobody told me?" Grandma didn't like surprises.

"I'm sorry, Rose," Jennifer apologized. "It happened just this afternoon and we really didn't have time to catch you up on things. Willoughby has been suspended for two weeks, which means no games and no functions, or anything having to do with school. Kendall will pick up his work so he can at least keep up with that."

Willoughby's hope that his mom's brief explanation might be the end of it was short-lived. He kept his head down, poking at his mashed potatoes. His appetite had gotten lost under the gravy somewhere.

"Well?" Grandma Rose demanded. She was, if anything, persistent and slightly irritated at being left out of the loop. "I'm sure there's a lot more to the story than that. What do you have to say, Willoughby?"

Willoughby simmered. Like a Paul Harvey program—Grandma

wanted to hear "the rest of the story." She deserved an explanation but the timing of her question couldn't have been worse; she had inadvertently stirred the shit pile and the resulting stench hit the table with a vengeance. It was the scenario that had played itself out in Miss Havercroft's fifth period all over again. Willoughby's penitent attitude and relief that the situation between him and his mother had seemingly reached a calm understanding was lost in an instant. He didn't understand why and it certainly wasn't his grandmother's fault, but common sense and logic flew out the window as quickly as the backpack had wiped the grin from Eddie's stupid face.

"Eddie Anderson called me a dick sucking faggot so I hit him with my backpack. I knocked the fucking asshole out."

Jake nearly spit his mouthful of mashed potatoes into his plate. He quickly grabbed his napkin and raised it to his mouth, covering what may have actually been a very inappropriate grin. Kendall's reaction was to roll her eyes and shoot her brother an OMG-that-was-so-stupid look. Grandma Rose sat there with dumbfounded shock on her face; the gravy she had been pouring was now spilling over the edge of her plate onto the tablecloth.

But for Jennifer Baxter, all the understanding that had been reached in the emotional scene on the front porch disappeared as quickly as her son's common sense had.

"Willoughby Baxter, how dare you utter that word at the dinner table! Take your plate and your filthy mouth up to your room and eat by yourself. There is no call for you to talk like that."

Plates and glasses rattled as Willoughby pushed himself forcefully away from the table. His emotional dam had been breached and the tears were flowing. "I ain't hungry," he shot back angrily as he ran out of the room.

None of the four at the table said a word as they listened to the sound of the distraught teen stomping his way up the stairs, followed by the resounding bang of his bedroom door being slammed shut. A tense and uncomfortable silence settled over the dining room table, but the outburst quickly claimed its second victim.

"I am so sorry," Jennifer apologized as she stood up, dabbing her napkin at her teary eyes. "I hope you all will excuse me." With that, she turned and left.

Grandma Rose started to say something to her daughter-in-law but was too late, as Jennifer exited almost as fast as Willoughby had. The door to her downstairs bedroom didn't slam as hard as her son's, but it came close.

"Well, that went well," a perplexed Grandma Rose offered after an uncomfortable period of silence. Troubled by the outburst, Kendall sat there in total shock at what had just taken place. Jake busied himself with a chicken thigh, keeping his tall head down as far as he could, trying hard, but not succeeding, to look small.

"Willoughby hit him with his backpack?" Grandma asked as she stirred her food absently. As far as mealtime conversation went, this one had been fairly unique. Not that arguments hadn't taken place around the big table before, but having the two antagonists both leave so abruptly was a first. It seemed Jake was the only one left with an appetite.

"Eddie Anderson has been picking on Willoughby for a long time, Grandma," Kendall finally spoke in her little brother's defense. "He had a bad day in Miss Havercroft's class and she kicked him out. The big jerk called him a name as he was leaving and Willoughby lost control and let him have it with his backpack. Knocked his fat butt out cold. I know it was wrong, but I think most everyone in the school was glad it happened. He didn't mean to blurt out the f-bomb Grandma. I thought he was okay but I guess talking about it set him off. Please forgive him."

Grandma Rose shook her head. "Well I wish someone had clued me in before I opened my big mouth. And it isn't like I haven't heard that word before, Kendall. Maybe not so much at my dinner table but farmers can be as colorful as loggers and sailors any day." She turned to Jake, who was still failing to look inconspicuous. "I suppose you knew about this?"

Jake grunted around a big mouthful of potatoes and gravy. "Only by accident, Rose," he pleaded his innocence after swallowing his food. "I was working on that big patch of blackberries by the main gate when the Anderson kid and Al Kemper's boy came haulin' ass up in that overgrown truck a his."

Kendall came to Jake's rescue. "He came after Willoughby, Grandma. It was a good thing Jake was there or things would have gotten ugly."

Grandma Rose shook her head. "Those Andersons have always thought they was better'n everybody else. Your Grandpa Will had his share of run-ins with Carlton. Tried to cheat us on some logs we sold him one time. Had his scalers trimming hundreds of board feet on each load. He was screwin' a whole bunch of people he was buying wood from. Asshole got in a lot of trouble over that one. Should've gone to jail, but his lawyers got him off."

"Everyone knows Eddie is a bully and deserved what he got," Kendall added. "But it was Willoughby's last straw as far as Mr. Hurd was concerned. He said he had no choice but to suspend him."

Grandma Rose pointed to the heaping platters on the table. "Well, it was a bad deal and I'm sorry it had to blow up at the supper table but you two need to get after all of this food."

"Hey," Jake held up a knife in one hand and fork in the other. "I never let an opportunity to set at your table go to waste, Rose. I'm doin' my best."

"Mom said Willoughby couldn't go with us to Seattle, Grandma," Kendall continued as she picked at her food; she still hadn't regained her appetite. "Do you think you could talk to her and see if she will let him go?"

Grandma Rose shook her head emphatically. "That I can't do, honey. I have to support your mom on this one. Even if Eddie Anderson did have it coming, you can't condone what your brother did. Looks like he'll just have to keep Jake company for the week-end."

"Thank you, Rose." The three sitting at the table snapped their heads around as a subdued Jennifer Baxter stepped back into the dining room. "I appreciate your backing me on this," she said as she sat back down at the table. "I'm sorry about the outburst. I just couldn't believe he said that word at your dinner table of all places.

But I still overreacted and I shouldn't have. It seems Willoughby isn't the only one in the family with a temper."

Grandma Rose gave her a smile and patted her hand. "Don't you fret none about it, honey. You just need to eat; it'll make you feel better." Food was Grandma Rose's answer for almost anything.

"I guess I need to thank you, Jake, for keeping that bully from hurting Willoughby." Jennifer smiled at the big Indian. "I heard Kendall say that you came to their rescue."

He returned her grin sheepishly. "I think Eddie might've bit off more'n he could chew. Might be I rescued Eddie 'cause I don't think he would have gotten past Kendall here." He pointed with his fork.

Jennifer gave him a weary smile. "Well, thanks anyway. What is done is done and we need to move on. But I'm thinking maybe we should cancel the trip to Seattle, Kendall. I don't want to impose on Jake."

Kendall started to protest but Jake laid his utensils on the table and held both his hands up. "Now just hold your horses, ladies. I don't mean ta horn in on family matters but I think ya all should just keep on with your plans. Me'n the boy'll be just fine. I aim on tacklin' that woodpile over the next couple of days and could use his help, truth be told."

"You sure about that, Jake?" Grandma Rose asked as she shot him a questioning glance. "Your salary don't include bein' a baby sitter."

"Sure it don't, Rose," he answered. "But I don't see no baby. I see a young kid what got some trouble on his mind. Sure won't hurt to get his hands dirty."

Jennifer looked pensive. "Well…I don't know. What do you two think?" she asked Kendall and Rose.

"Well, I wish Willoughby could go but I know that isn't going to happen," answered Kendall first. "But maybe it will do us some good if we do go ahead and go."

"Rose?"

"I guess it will be all right. Long as Jake doesn't teach him how to chew or something else just as nasty." That brought a much-needed laugh from everyone.

"Well, if Jake doesn't mind, then I guess it's okay," Jennifer continued. "We do have an extra ticket. Kendall, why don't you ask Brittany if she would like to go?"

Kendall's face lit up. "You mean it, Mom? Brit would die to go!"

Jennifer nodded. "You can give her a call. If she wants to go, have her pack her things and stay the night with us after the game. It'll make things easier if we don't have to run out to her place and pick her up in the morning. I'll talk to her mom if she needs me to."

An excited Kendall jumped up from the table. "Can I be excused? I'll be back and finish my supper in a minute. I want to call Brit right now."

Jennifer nodded her assent. "Go ahead. But you need to tell your brother thank you. It was his idea."

"Will do," she answered over her shoulder as she left the dining room.

"Well, at least part of the damn family is happy," Grandma Rose snorted sarcastically as she got up from the table and waved her arm at all the untouched supper. "Least ways you two won't go hungry, Jake. Looks like there will be enough leftovers to last the entire weekend."

Jake reached his long arm out towards the heaping platter of golden brown chicken and grabbed a plump breast off the top that was almost as big as his huge hand. "There'll be plenty, but don't get no ideas 'bout pickin' up those supper dishes just yet. You all may not be hungry but that don't mean I ain't."

"Are you sure this will be okay, Jake?" Jennifer asked the big man as he tore into another piece of juicy fried chicken. For some reason she was full of anxiety and it manifested itself in the apprehension in her voice.

Jake swallowed his big bite and wiped his mouth on the sleeve of his hickory shirt, temporarily forgetting his table manners. "Don't you fret none, Jennifer," he answered easily. "I'll keep him busy. 'Sides that, there sure as heck ain't no trouble he can get into round here."

Jennifer Baxter shook her head in concession and gave him a smile. "I guess you're right, Jake. There shouldn't be any trouble Willoughby can get into here, is there?"

Chapter Four

WILLOUGHBY WAS DREAMING—THE BEST kind of dream, well, besides the sticky ones—it was a flying dream. When he awoke from such somnolent adventures, he always remembered them—soaring above the trees, over the school or the town, everyone looking up and pointing. No one else could ever fly in his flying dreams; he was the only one. Maybe that was what made them so special. The other thing he always remembered about flying dreams was always having a severe case of morning wood. He never was quite able to figure that one out, maybe it was the way the excitement of the dream manifested itself.

In his dream, he was flying over the Baxter farm. Jake was there, but he didn't see Willoughby; he was driving the herd of black and white Holsteins towards the milking shed. He yelled at Jake, wanting him to see him fly, but the big Indian didn't look up; he was too busy with the cows.

Out over the pastures and fences Willoughby soared on the breeze. The Baxter farm was divided into several different sections by tree-lined fence rows, Grandma Rose and Jake had names for all of them. The North Pasture, the South Pasture, and Jake called one of them The Swamp because of a slow moving channel of water that ran down a gully in the middle of it. The cows liked this place and made it a muddy mess during the wet season. At the upper end of the farm was a patch of timber. The Back Eighty, Grandma called it, because it was at the back end of the farm and there were about eighty acres of healthy timber, most of it Douglas fir. Out of the tops of this healthy second growth rose several towering giants—

old growth residuals that had been left during the first harvest. Like proud parents with their brood gathered about them, they dominated the skyline. Their gray boles were covered with heavy, ridged bark, up to a foot thick near the ground. Massive limbs, some nearly as big in diameter as the young trees growing up around them, jutted from the trunks, hanging low with the tremendous weight they carried.

Like a bird playing tag, Willoughby soared in and around the giants, dipping and diving down to the tops of the smaller trees and then jetting back skyward to the tips of the old growth. Several of the old fellows had dead, spiked tops on them, signs that they were ever so slowly succumbing to age. In the very top of one of these sat a large black bird—a raven.

Willoughby had made the mistake of calling them crows one time when he and Kendall had been watching Jake bring in the cows for milking. One of them had swooped in and landed on the peak of the old barn roof.

"Mister Raven don't take kindly to being called a crow," Jake had told them. As if on cue, the bird became agitated and started hopping with its wings out. A low, raspy squawk came with each hop as the bird danced its way back and forth across the ridge of the barn.

"See," Jake told them as they watched the strange display. "Told ya. They get upset when ya call 'em a crow." He lifted his right hand towards the roof with his palm out and shouted something in a language that neither Kendall nor Willoughby had ever heard him use. The bird hopped to the very end of the roof and looked down, its dark eyes staring intently at them over its large black beak. Jake repeated the strange phrase again. The bird bobbed its head and made a series of deep clicking sounds. When it was finished, it lifted its tail feathers and deposited a load of white bird shit on the barn's rusty red tin roof. It squawked one more time and then flew off.

"We're lucky," Jake said as he went back to prodding the cows through the gate.

"Why's that?" Kendall had asked.

"A lot of times when they get mad they'll fly over you and then take a shit, and trust me, they can dump a load." He boomed out a laugh as Willoughby and his sister were grossed out at the thought.

Willoughby had never thought to ask Jake just exactly what he had said to the bird. Grandma Rose had told them that Jake could speak his native language as well as or better than he spoke English.

When Willoughby saw the raven in his dream, he was surprised when the big bird pushed off the spiked top of the old tree it was on and flew up next to him in the air. It cocked its head towards the boy as they soared along in his dream. The bird was jet black except for a white patch right on top of his head. The bird wanted Willoughby to follow him. The boy didn't know how, but he knew; it was a dream, he just knew. They glided in unison, the boy matching each twist and turn the bird took, riding the air currents this way and that.

Willoughby and the raven swooped down past the firs to a snaking, light green line of hardwoods; he knew he must be flying over the Cascade River which bordered the Baxter property on the east side. They had visited the farm in the summer a few years back, during a time when James Baxter was trying desperately to free himself from the chains of pain-killing drugs and alcohol. His doctor told him a change might do him some good, so they packed up and drove to Oregon. It had been a pleasant stay, at least for a while. They had gone swimming under the old covered bridge spanning the river down the road from his grandma's house. It had been his dad's favorite swimming hole when he had been growing up.

That had been the first time Willoughby had heard about the waterfall, the one the town was named after. Kendall and Willoughby had wanted to go see it—you could actually get to it from the Baxter property—but there hadn't been enough time. Dragging the chains around had been too much for James Baxter. He needed to get help—he needed to go back to San Diego—he needed to go back to his drugs.

As Willoughby and his dream bird friend followed the river channel, the raven with the white patch on his head suddenly broke away and began dropping down in a slow spiral until it suddenly disappeared into the gap between the trees lining each side of the riverbank. Willoughby followed.

When he broke past the trees, he found himself just feet over the river, gliding smoothly over the water. His raven friend seemed to have vanished, but he didn't care, he was having such an amazing dream. The river channel below was narrow but deep, forced into a slot between walls of wet, gray granite. The dark green water picked up speed as it surged through the trough, Willoughby gliding along with it. Then he started to hear the sound. It grew louder and louder as he flew just above the water. Like a freight train at full speed, it roared in his ears until he almost couldn't stand it. Even though he knew it was a dream, it still hurt his ears, yet you weren't supposed to feel pain in a dream. Willoughby wanted to stop, something foreboding was ahead of him. He could feel it, but out of nowhere, the bird was beside him again, urging him on.

The freight train pounded in his head as Willoughby sped along at a frantic pace with the river, his eyes hypnotically glued to the rushing green current below him, and then suddenly, the pounding and the river were gone. Willoughby was encased in a thick, wet mist that chilled him immediately as it wrapped him in a soggy blanket of wet and cold. But what alarmed him most was that the feeling of flying was gone. Willoughby was falling. He tried to regain his ability to fly but it was gone. Down and down he plunged, still cloaked in the clinging, wet mist. He flailed his arms and kicked his legs in panic, for he knew what waited in the unknown below him. Death waited at the bottom; he knew that as sure as he knew his name. When you were dreaming and fell, you never hit the bottom; to hit the bottom meant that you would die. You had to wake up before you hit the bottom.

"Aaauuggh!" Willoughby cried out as he flopped around. He was tangled; something was keeping his arms and legs from moving. "Owww!" he yelled, then cursed as he rose suddenly, cracking his forehead on something hard. He opened his eyes, at first having no idea where he was, but gradually saw things take shape in the dim blue light. The light came from the illuminated numbers on his alarm clock.

"Fuck!" Willoughby cursed again as he freed his arms from the blankets that had wrapped tightly about him as he had thrashed around in his bed. For it was his own bed he found himself in. The dream was gone—he had woken up before he hit the bottom. So he wasn't dead, but he was soaked. Wet and clammy, it was sweat, he could smell it. He had fallen asleep in his jeans, t-shirt, and socks, and they were all stinking wet with perspiration.

He untangled himself from his blankets and managed to sit up, making sure he cleared the headboard when he did. He had cracked his head hard. It was tender to the touch but he didn't feel any blood. A glance at the clock told him that it was almost five in the morning. Sounds from downstairs told him Grandma was already up. She was talking to someone and it wasn't Jake; he would already be in the barn at this time. His mom or his sister, both it sounded like. Yeah, now he remembered. They were all up because they were going to Seattle this morning—going without him.

Things came back to him slowly as he sat there in the dim blue light of his alarm clock. He and his mom had gotten into a fight right there at the supper table in front of Grandma, Kendall, and Jake. His thoughts were fuzzy; he didn't think very clearly this early in the morning. He had said something his mom didn't like and she had yelled at him. She never yelled at him so it must have been something really bad.

"Crap," he said as he started to remember. Grandma Rose had been asking about the fight with Eddie and he had blown his top and said something really ugly and nasty. He knew what he had said, it was bad, but what made it painfully worse was that he said it to Grandma.

Willoughby slipped his legs from under the covers and swung them out over the edge of the bed. He still felt tired. After leaving the dining room table, he had stomped up to his room and had plopped himself face down on his bed (he was sure he had been bawling) and that was it; he had nodded off to dreamland. But man, what a nasty dream it had been! Flying dreams were never bad but that one sure had been.

Flipping on the lamp, he winced as the brightness caught his night eyes. When he adjusted to the light, he changed out of his sweaty clothes into sweatpants and a clean t-shirt. There were spots of sweat on his bed. He would have to wash his sheets after everyone left so they wouldn't think he had wet the bed again. That embarrassing problem hadn't resurfaced since moving to Oregon, but it had happened more than once last year.

He was still sitting on the edge of the bed willing himself awake and still confused about his dream when there was a knock on his door.

"Willoughby?" It was his mom. "Are you up?"

Kicking his wet clothes under the bed, he flipped the blankets over the sweat spot on his mattress. He hoped there wouldn't be a stain.

"Yeah, I'm up. C'mon in."

Jennifer Baxter eased the door open and stepped into Willoughby's bedroom. She must have gotten up early, she was showered and dressed for the trip.

"Hey," he greeted as she stepped in.

"Good morning," she replied. "Can I sit and talk to you for a minute?"

"Sure," he said, motioning towards the chair at his computer desk. It was the only other piece of furniture in the room that you could sit on besides the bed. When you didn't have friends to entertain, you didn't need much.

His mom walked over to the desk, pulled out the chair, spinning it to face him, and sat down. "Willoughby, I want to apologize for what happened at the table. I think we both reacted without thinking and it made for a bad deal."

That made him uncomfortable. It hadn't been her fault, she only reacted the way she did because he had been crude and rude to his grandma, of all people. "It wasn't your fault, Mom. I did it again, and this time I did it to Grandma."

"Willoughby, I…" she started, but he didn't let her finish.

"No, Mom. It's not your fault, no matter what you say. It's just like what happened with Eddie—I react without thinking. I told you—I'm crazy."

"No." She didn't yell, but the tone in her voice was firm with conviction. "I will admit it is a problem, son, but you are not crazy."

"But I…" Willoughby started, but this time it was her turn to stop him.

"No, just let me finish. Let me talk and then it will be your turn. You can say whatever you like, but just let me get what I have to say out. Please?"

Willoughby could hear the emotional edge in her voice. He nodded for her to go ahead.

"I don't know if I have what it takes to fix what is wrong with you or me, Willoughby. But I do know that I have to try. *We* have to try. For all of us. Kendall, your grandma, you, and me. I think I thought that by simply moving here some of what was troubling all of us would just go away and that was wrong. I know I didn't talk it over with you when I made the decision, but I felt I was running out of options living in San Diego."

While his mother wasn't crying yet, Willoughby could tell she was close, and he was just as close as she was. When she stood up and walked to the window and turned her back to him, he was actually thankful. She had been a pretty strong woman over the last couple of years dealing with more than anyone should ever have to. The times he had seen her cry sickened him in a terrible way.

At the window she pulled open the curtain and gazed out into the still dark hours of the morning. "I know now that I was running from things I couldn't deal with and I used you to justify it. It was a very selfish thing to do and I'm sorry. I just couldn't handle the pressure. Every time I went anywhere or did anything in that town, I was reminded of your dad. I couldn't get away from it. It overwhelmed me to the point I would just stand there and bawl, even in the aisle at the grocery store. People would see me coming and think, 'Oh no, here comes the crazy lady.'

"I had a nervous breakdown Willoughby, a bad one. I didn't tell you but Kendall knew. They gave me antidepressants and I guess that is probably the only thing that got me through the lawsuit. I don't know how much you knew of what was going on at that time but it wasn't good. I had to get up there in front of the judge, the lawyers, and the family of that poor woman and her little girl and tell them everything I knew about your dad. His playing days, the injuries that ended his career, and all the crap that followed because of it. I had to relive that nightmare over and over. It almost killed me."

Willoughby wanted her to stop. She had never told this much to him and he didn't like it, mainly because he felt he knew what she was leading up to. He had heard it before, mostly whispered behind his back, but never from her. Deep in his heart, Willoughby knew the truth. He hadn't been blind to all that had gone on with his dad, but to hear it from her would be driving the final nail home that would seal the family's coffin of guilt.

"Mom, don't," he pleaded through tears now flowing freely. "I promise I won't cause you any more trouble. We don't have to talk about this anymore. Please?"

She turned away from the window and sat down on the bed, wrapping both arms tightly around him, and pulling him close. They didn't speak for a long time. They just held each other in the darkness and shed their tears in silence.

It was Willoughby who finally broke the spell. "I need to tell you something, Mom," he told her as they pulled apart. "I'm not as dumb as everybody thinks I am. I know why you had to leave. I could see what it was doing to you. I didn't have to deal with things like you did; I was the poor little boy everyone felt so sorry for. I had my good memories of Dad and that's what I hung onto. I could hide and you couldn't. But I can't hide here and I think that's what scares me the most. But I'm going to try to change, I swear I will. I just don't want to hear the truth about Dad from you. Do you understand that? Please. I'm smart enough to know what the truth is but I just can't hear it from you."

His mother picked up his sweaty t-shirt from the floor and used it to wipe the eyes of both of them. "Then I think both of us have been running long enough. I'll make you a deal. When we think of your dad, we need to concentrate on all the good things he did. He loved his family more than anything; you know that, don't you?"

There were times when Willoughby had questioned that very thing, asking himself many times how people who supposedly loved their families so much could end up hurting them so badly. Maybe it was like one of his teachers in San Diego told him—sometimes bad things happen to good people. But he was starting to believe two very important things, two truths about his dad. The first was the very thing his mother had been trying to tell him when he stopped her. Deep down inside, buried under layers and layers of distorted reality, he had known this truth all along. Willoughby knew the pain his father had been in, both physically and mentally, and he knew the steps his father took to make the pain at least controllable. He also knew it was those very steps that led his father to incoherently speed down a busy city street in the middle of the afternoon, tragically ending not only his own life, but that of an innocent young mother and her six-year-old daughter. That was the hard truth.

The other truth was easier, and it also was just like his mother had said. Willoughby did know that his father loved all of them, and that was the truth he needed to hang onto. That was the truth that would get him, his mother, and his sister through these tough times.

He reached his arms around his mom and gave her another big hug. "Nothing but the good things from now on, Mom. Nothing but the good things."

She smiled and kissed his forehead. "Thank you, Willoughby. Now, we've got to get ready to go. You going to be okay staying behind and helping Jake?"

"I'll be fine, Mom. I'll be down as soon as I brush my teeth. I owe Grandma an apology before she leaves."

When he got downstairs, he was surprised to see Kendall's friend Brittany and his sister on their knees in the front foyer going through their bags and making sure they weren't forgetting anything important. They were only going to be gone for a day and a half but every item seemed critical. Brittany Ellison was a petite blonde with her short hair styled in a cute pixie cut. Everything about her was tiny but perfect—her lips, her ears, her dainty little nose—everything. Willoughby's sister and she made a strange pair. Kendall was athletically built and nearly six feet tall and Brittany wasn't even as tall as Willoughby who was considered short. But Kendall and Brittany had become fast friends from Day One and now were pretty much inseparable, which Willoughby didn't mind at all since he harbored a painful crush on Brittany.

"Hey little bro," Kendall greeted. "Thanks for suggesting to Mom that she give your ticket to Brit. Still won't be as fun without you."

"Right, like I believe that." He actually did believe her, but wouldn't go as far as saying so. "Hey, Brit. How was the game last night?"

"Hey, WB. Kicked butt as usual. Still undefeated." She smiled back at him and his heart fluttered. She had given him the nickname WB; he liked it when she called him that. Brittany stood up and looked quickly towards the kitchen where Jennifer Baxter and Grandma Rose could be heard talking. When she was sure neither of them was likely to walk into the room, she raised her fist out to Willoughby and he responded likewise, she whispered low as they bumped their fists together.

"WB, you are the man. Knocked that piece of shit Eddie into next week. Way to rock."

"Yeah, little bro. Brit thinks you are the greatest," Kendall added. "Here, she wants you to have a little token of her appreciation." Kendall tossed something tiny and black at Willoughby. He grabbed it out of the air and it took him a moment to figure out just exactly what it was. When he did, he wasn't quite sure what to do with it, but Brit took care of that for him. Kendall had tossed him a pair of her friend's thong underwear, a very tiny little piece of sexy black lace and spaghetti straps.

Brittany gave a little shriek as she snatched Willoughby's prize from his hands before he even had time to admire it. "Oh, Kendall, you are so going to pay for that one." She feigned anger as she stuffed the tiny panties back into her bag. "I know some guys at school that will pay good money for a pair of yours."

A slightly embarrassed Willoughby left the two friends playfully threatening each other and went into the kitchen. His mom and grandma were sitting at the kitchen table having coffee.

"Good morning, son." His mom stood up and greeted him as if they hadn't already spoken. "I gotta see if the girls are ready. Rose, we need to be out of here before too long."

"Sit down, Willoughby." Grandma Rose directed him to the spot his mother had just vacated. "Can I get you a cup of hot chocolate?"

"Yeah, that would be fine, Grandma." He sat down as she went about fixing him a cup of her special hot chocolate. There was no instant powder, hot water, or microwave for his grandma. Taking a large glass pitcher from the refrigerator, she poured fresh milk into a saucepan on the big, wood cook stove. Milk did not get any fresher than his grandma's. She busied herself bringing the milk to a boil, stirring constantly to make sure it didn't scorch, while Willoughby helped himself to a couple of her chocolate chip cookies from the always full cookie jar. "I owe you an apology for what happened at the supper table last night, Grandma," he told her. "I didn't mean to use that kind of language and I'm sorry."

She turned and gave him a smile. "Thank you, Willoughby, your apology is accepted. I think we all have moments where we speak without thinking about the consequences." She turned back to stirring her milk. "Do you want me to fix you some breakfast?"

He never had been a big eater early in the morning, much to Grandma Rose's displeasure. She didn't see how people could get through a day of hard work without a good and filling breakfast. "No thanks, Grandma. A couple of cookies and hot chocolate will do me just fine."

"You and Jake get started on that woodpile after he gets the morning's milking chores done and I'll bet about ten o'clock you'll be thinking pretty hard about that good breakfast you passed on." It was her way of telling him he needed to eat something besides cookies. "Got biscuits about ready in the oven and bacon in the fridge. Throw a couple of fried eggs in with that and a man could go all day without being hungry."

He had tried before. As long as he remained in place in Grandma Rose's kitchen, it was a battle he would not win. "Okay Grandma," Willoughby decided to give in without a fight. It was just easier that way. "One egg, one biscuit, and a couple of pieces of bacon. That's all."

"Comin' right up." She grinned as she stirred thick streams of Hershey's chocolate syrup into the steaming milk. "Maybe you can talk that sister of yours and her little friend into eating breakfast before we leave," she said as she placed Willoughby's mug of hot chocolate in front of him. "That Ellison girl is so damn tiny she'd blow away if'n you was to fart hard in her direction."

Willoughby laughed and nearly spit out his first sip of steaming chocolate milk. As Grandma Rose happily went about the task of fixing breakfast, he munched a cookie and washed it down with sips of his chocolate milk. From the big bay kitchen window he could see Jake in the yard between the milking shed and barn. The big Indian had finished the morning's milking session and was putting the Holsteins out to pasture. They would stay there for the day, munching grass and doing what cows did all day long. Light was starting to break on the cool morning and the steam from the bovines' hot breath rose in clouds around Jake as he prodded them along with a short wooden club. His cow pacifier was what he called it.

"I can poke 'em easy, jab 'em hard, or flat knock the stubborn suckers out if they don't cooperate," he bragged. It might have been mostly BS but the cows seemed to have gotten the message. They moved where Jake told them to go.

Willoughby was more than a little intrigued about spending the day working with the big man. Though he and Jake had become much closer of late, with the big man taking him under his wing, for the most part he remained a mystery, never talking much about himself.

"Where did Jake come from, Grandma?" Willoughby asked as he watched him out the window.

The bacon hissed and spat grease as his grandma turned the long strips over in the cast iron skillet. "Well, I'm not rightly sure exactly where he comes from. Never had any reason to ask. Chiloquin, K-Falls, or maybe farther south in Northern California is what I always heard. Don't know if that's right or not and I don't suppose he's going to tell me anytime soon, either. Jake Thompson is a pretty closed man when it comes to his past. All I know is he's been around Spirit Falls for the past thirty years or so. Workin' here and there, mostly loggin' I think. He came to work about ten years ago for your Grandpa Will and me and has been a blessing. Man can do just about anything a body needs him to and do it well."

Willoughby's curiosity about Jake was interrupted as his mom and the two girls burst noisily into the kitchen.

"We're ready Grandma," Kendall announced. "Let's get it on."

"Let's not and eat some breakfast first. Fifteen more minutes won't make a difference as far as your and Brit's shopping plans go. So set." She waved her spatula like a Calvary captain directing troops with his saber. "One egg or two?"

They all opted for one egg, the girls both protesting to no avail. The car wouldn't leave until Grandma had everyone fed—that was the way it was.

Willoughby found his appetite quickly enough. No matter how hungry you didn't think you were, Grandma Rose's biscuits could change that in a hurry. Golden brown on top and flaky when you pulled them apart, with a pat of butter melting quickly in the hot center and a generous spoonful of his grandma's homemade strawberry or raspberry jam, it was hard not to eat more than one. Willoughby managed two along with his egg and bacon.

When the breakfast dishes had been cleared, washed, and dried, a chore that didn't take long when everybody chipped in, they were ready to go. Jennifer and the girls had already loaded their bags in the trunk so there was nothing to do except say good-bye.

"There's plenty more bacon in the fridge and biscuits in the warming rack if Jake wants to eat," Grandma reminded him as they loaded into his mother's Accord. "More than enough cold fried chicken for a couple of meals. You two won't starve. He'll let you know when he's ready to tackle the wood."

"Bye, Willoughby," his mom said, giving him a big hug. "Be careful around that woodpile."

"I'll be fine, Mom. I'm sure Jake won't kill me, least not right off the bat."

"See ya, bro," Kendall shouted from the back seat. "I'll bring you home a surprise from the Pike Street Market."

"Bye WB," Brittany added. "Stay cool."

Willoughby watched them until the Honda turned from the driveway out onto the county road. So that was it. They were gone until late Sunday night and he was at the mercy of a crazed renegade Indian, who was sure to run him through the wood splitter. Well, maybe nothing quite that dramatic. But as the car went out of sight Willoughby felt a sense of deep anxiety. Maybe it was that he hadn't ever been left by his family before, or it could have been the strange dream. Whatever it was it made him uncomfortable. Willoughby forced himself to set his mind to something else. He had a couple of choices to pass his time until Jake took care of the early morning chores and needed his help. He could catch a little bit more sleep but he had plenty of that last night, though it had been rudely interrupted with that stupid flying dream with the dumb raven in it. Saturday morning TV pretty much sucked unless you were into ESPN Gameday and college football, or into stupid kid shows that were about as funny as an overripe pimple. Video games had been out of the question ever since the last time he had gotten in trouble at school for not paying attention. His Xbox 360 was still locked up tight in Grandma's gun cabinet.

Still unsure of what he was going to do, he headed through the gate and up the concrete sidewalk towards the front porch. As he did, an ample breeze blew through the big maples and oaks that dominated the yard, dry leaves skittered across the sidewalk and lawn in front of him, and a flurry of new leaves joined them from the trees. Still, Willoughby would have ignored all of the hints if he hadn't spied the leaf rake looking forlorn and unused propped up against the front porch where he had to walk within an arm's reach of it. It was funny, he hadn't noticed it yesterday.

But it made sense. He had, after all, promised his mom he would turn over a new leaf. His decision had been made.

He went inside and changed into an old pair of Levi's too ragged for school, if there still could be such a thing. He added a t-shirt to go under an older sweatshirt as it wasn't all that warm outside, and he put a thick pair of work socks on his feet. What passed for his work boots (cheap hikers from Walmart) were on the back porch along with several pairs of cotton work gloves Grandma kept on a shelf. After lacing on his boots and finding a pair of gloves that weren't too big for him, he was ready.

The front yard was where Jake found him about an hour and a half later. He had done well—several large piles of leaves dotted the lawn like mini volcanoes.

"Well," Jake said, admiring Willoughby's handiwork, "thought I would find you in the house plopped in front of the tube or something. Pretty decent piece of work."

"Thanks." Willoughby was actually surprised at the amount of leaves he had piled.

"Just don't look up," Jake added. "Gets depressing after ya been workin' hard. I think you're ready for some real work, gloves and all, so why don't you retire that rake and let's get on to bigger n' better things. Something that requires gasoline and oil to get the job done. Man stuff. See ya at the woodpile."

Willoughby hadn't paid much attention when Jake told him not to look up but quickly figured out what the big guy had been talking about after he leaned the leaf rake back up against the porch and shot a glance skyward into the massive canopy of green, yellow, and brown leaves still hanging overhead.

"Shit," he cursed. For as many leaves as he thought he had raked, there were still ten times as many waiting to fall. A big yellow maple leaf mocked him as it drifted slowly down, inches from his face.

When he rounded the corner of the barn where the woodshed was, Willoughby was surprised by the small mountain of wood piled up waiting to be run through the splitter. Jake had been a busy guy with his chainsaw.

"We gotta split all that?" he asked Jake as the big guy maneuvered the rubber tired wood splitter into place near the end of the pile closest to the shed.

"That and half again as much more if you want to keep your balls from freezing off this winter." He bellowed out a laugh. "Got several more windfall to drag down and buck up, then we'll have us a pile."

Jake checked the engine oil in the splitter and after adding gasoline, he fished into his shirt pocket and handed Willoughby a small plastic packet with two soft colorful plugs in it.

"What's this?" Willoughby asked.

"Ear plugs. You don't fire up a piece of power equipment without havin' 'em in. Pinch the end, roll it with your fingers, and screw it into your ear like this," Jake demonstrated. "They'll expand once they're inside the ear cavity. Gotta wear these, too." Out of his back pocket, Jake produced a pair of clear plastic eyewear. "Safety glasses. Same rule. You fire up your equipment, you have your safety gear on."

When Willoughby was properly attired, Jake flicked the switch on the splitter and pushed the choke forward. With one strong pull of the starting rope, the Briggs and Stratton sputtered to life, running smoothly once Jake shut the choke down.

"What do you want me to do?" Willoughby shouted over the engine.

"I'll run the splitter for now," Jake shouted back. "You keep feeding me the wood so I don't have to reach for it. Roll 'em up one right after the other, then keep the split pieces clean outta my way. Toss 'em in a pile over there in front of the shed door. Smooth operation, one right after another. Got it?"

Willoughby nodded his head. Jake had rolled one of the rounds off to the side of the splitter so he could sit on it while he ran the hydraulic lever raising and lowering the splitting ram. He pointed to one of the rounds lying at Willoughby's feet and motioned him to roll it closer. To his surprise, the fourteen-inch-long rounds, ranging from a foot to two feet in diameter, rolled easily on their sides. Once Willoughby had the round close enough for Jake to grab, the big guy sat it upright on the splitting platform and ran the ram down onto it as close to the center as he could. The sharp ram point bit deep into the wood, a crack started to open as more pressure was applied, and then the round popped neatly in two. Up went the ram but before the halves fell away, Jake grabbed them both, spun them around, and dropped the ram again, popping the two halves into quarters. In what hadn't amounted to much more than ten seconds, there were four neat pieces of firewood lying at the base of the splitter.

It didn't take Willoughby long to get the hang of the operation and very quickly the two had a smooth system going. He would get several rounds close enough for Jake to reach, this kept him busy long enough that Willoughby could gather the split pieces and toss them towards the shed. Sometimes Jake would get a piece full of crazy knots or twisted grain—a little tougher to split—but the ram had plenty of hydraulic pressure and ate its way through them all.

Willoughby lost track of time as the process continued to cycle over and over. Though it was a cool and overcast October day, he found himself sweating as he kept ahead of Jake. Suddenly, right in the middle of a split, the engine sputtered several times and died.

"What's wrong?" Willoughby shouted over the engine noise that was no longer there.

"I can hear you son. The machine is off, no need to yell. We're just outta gas."

They took a water break while Jake gassed up the splitter and greased the mechanism that the ram slid up and down on.

"Works pretty slick," Willoughby said as he surveyed the big pile of neatly split wood in front of the shed door. He figured they might have a quarter of it done, but there was a whole lot more left.

"Wood splitter makes for a lot less ache and strain on a man's back," Jake answered as he took a large draught from his water bottle. "Ain't nothin' gets a man down faster 'n a bad back."

The two sat there quietly as they each polished off a bottle of water. Willoughby had wanted to ask Jake some questions, but the big man didn't seem to be too receptive to conversation this morning so he let it be.

Jake stood up and flipped his empty bottle towards the trashcan sitting just outside the shed door. The plastic bottle bounced neatly off the shop wall behind the can and plopped inside.

"Off the backboard," he said as he looked towards his young helper and his empty water bottle. Willoughby stood up and flipped his bottle towards the trashcan. It bounced on the ground two feet away and never even touched the can.

"Air ball, air ball." Jake grinned widely at Willoughby. "What ya say we get back to work. We can stop for lunch after the next tank of fuel or pound it hard 'til we get the job done and have a nice early supper. Your call, Will."

There. Jake had done it again, calling him by his Grandpa's name instead of his own. He wasn't sure if the big guy was even conscious he was doing it, but he certainly didn't care; he liked the name Will whichever way it came about.

"I'm not really all that hungry," Willoughby answered. "Grandma made me eat breakfast. Let's pound it out."

"Now yer talkin'," Jake smiled. "Like the big redneck guy says, 'Let's git er done.'"

They kept after the mountain of rounds, pausing only to refuel and rehydrate—Jake was big on making sure a guy had plenty of water. The two worked at a consistent pace and the pile got smaller and smaller. Jake moved the wood splitter twice to get it closer to where the wood was, saving Willoughby time feeding it. They even swapped jobs for a while, Jake allowing his helper to run the ram. Willoughby thought it was pretty cool, but he wasn't able to wrestle the bigger rounds into the splitter as easily as Jake did. Everything rolled into one long afternoon and suddenly Willoughby found himself looking at the last round. He rolled it triumphantly over to Jake and gave him a thumbs up as he ran it through the splitter. Willoughby tossed the last pieces into the now big pile in front of the shed door as Jake shut the splitter down.

Willoughby was dead tired but it was a good feeling. It probably had been the most work he had done in his entire life.

"Ya done good, Will," Jake complimented as he wheeled the splitter back into the tool shed. "Your grandma thought we'd be two days a gettin' that pile done. I think she owes us an apple pie. How about we go get cleaned up 'n take on them leftovers from supper last night? Should be plenty bein' I was 'bout the only one seemed to have much of an appetite. See ya in 'bout an hour?"

Willoughby smiled. "Sounds good to me, Jake. See you in an hour." For some strange reason he felt really good—tired, but good. Maybe it was the satisfaction from a good day's work or maybe it was the big guy's company. Maybe it was the way Jake had taken to calling him Will; he could get real used to that. Whatever was going on, Willoughby felt like he hadn't for a long time. It was a feeling he liked.

CHAPTER FIVE

WILLOUGHBY SPENT A LONG TIME IN THE shower letting the hot water run over his aching shoulders, and by the time he shut the water off, he was really starting to prune up. His skin tingled as he toweled off; he was almost too tired and sore to lift his arms up.

That's why they call it work, dumb-ass, he told himself as he finished drying and dressed simply in his sweats and a t-shirt. As he passed through the living room, he flipped on the TV. A local station out of Portland was carrying one of the state's two major college team's football games this afternoon. Willoughby didn't know if it was Oregon or Oregon State and didn't much care. In contrast, most local folks took that stuff pretty seriously; seems like you had to be one or the other but couldn't be both. His grandma loved the Oregon State Beavers, the school in Corvallis, and she absolutely despised the other, located in Eugene. On the other hand, both Willoughby's mom and his sister had become University of Oregon fans since the move from San Diego. The glitzier and higher profile Ducks were tailor-made for them. But it was still football, his father's game, and Willoughby hated it with a passion.

As he passed by the phone on his way to the kitchen, he stopped when he saw the red message light blinking. He hadn't checked it when he came in from working. There was a message from his mother on the answering machine.

"Hey, Willoughby. A little after noon. Made it okay to our hotel. We've got a busy afternoon in front of us and are heading out shortly for the Pike Street Market and the Space Needle." The rest of the

message was the phone and room number of the hotel, followed by a *"Hope you and Jake are doing okay. Love you."* The sound of her voice made him feel even better than he had been feeling—she sounded happy.

"I love you too, Mom," he said softly as he pushed the delete message button.

It had been an understatement when Grandma Rose said there were enough leftovers from last night's supper to feed him and Jake. When he pulled the platter from the refrigerator, Willoughby figured there was enough chicken not only for tonight, but tomorrow's lunch as well. To go along with the chicken were bowls of leftover mashed potatoes, chicken gravy, and green beans. He could heat up some of the biscuits his Grandma baked this morning and they would have a fine meal. That was one other thing about work that Willoughby noticed—it made you hungry.

Willoughby set the table for two as he used the microwave to heat up the leftovers. He was pouring two large glasses of ice-cold milk when he heard Jake coming in from the back porch.

"Hey Jake," Willoughby greeted as the big man ducked his head coming in the kitchen door.

"Will," said Jake, returning his greeting as he worked his big frame into one of the chairs at the table. "Smells mighty good in here."

They were soon plowing their way through a much appreciated meal. They talked a little about the day's work and the future job they had in front of them stacking all of the split wood under cover in the shed. Jake had some more logs to drag down off the hill and he told Willoughby he could ride along on the cat if he wanted; maybe even learn to operate the dozer himself.

The conversation remained simple for the most part. Both were famished, having worked through lunch, and by the time they had helped themselves to second portions there wasn't as much left as Willoughby thought there would be. Finally Jake pushed his plate away from him, leaned back in his chair, and began picking his teeth with a toothpick.

"Don't know why your Grandma don't go to sellin' that fried chicken of hers. Flat puts that Kentucky fellow to shame if you ask me, and if ya don't ask, I'll tell ya anyway."

Willoughby was dying to ask Jake some questions. Though they had developed a pretty good bond between the two of them, the big guy was still pretty much a mystery. Willoughby decided not to let the opportunity go by.

"How did you end up working here at Grandma's farm, Jake?" He blurted the question out and immediately thought it sounded stupid, but Jake didn't seem to notice.

"Well, sure wasn't something I planned." He didn't venture anything else for a minute or so, he just leaned back in his chair and picked at his teeth. Willoughby thought maybe he had been annoyed at the prying question.

"I'm gonna tell you a little story, Will," Jake finally began. "Ain't but two people alive know this story; you're gonna be the third. There's two reasons I'm gonna tell you—one is that I know you'll keep it to yourself, two is that it has to do with your family as much as anything and maybe you got a right to know."

Jake leaned forward in his chair and drained his milk glass in one long gulp. "Fetch me another glass of that moo juice, if you please."

Willoughby grabbed the glass and jumped up from the table while Jake settled back in his chair and made use of a toothpick. He started on his story again after thanking the teen for the re-fill.

"I came to work here on the farm about ten years or so ago. I'd been driftin' in and out of Spirit Falls for a long time. I bummed around some in California and Nevada, workin' oil rigs. Did some loggin' and fishin' out around Crescent City and Yreka, never stayin' too long in one place. Kind of a tramp more or less if'n you know what I mean. Did get married once in Reno. Now as far as dumb-ass moves go, that ranks right up there near the top a the list, but that's another story.

"Anyway, I ended up in Salem. Don't quite remember why I ended up there but I did. I was lookin' for work and a fellow in this bar I was drinkin' in said there was a mill in a place about an hour away called Spirit Falls puttin' on a new crew for the green chain. I never pulled on a chain afore but I knew how it operated and I could pretty much hold my own when it came to production work. So I got directions from the guy and when I sobered up the next day I hitched a couple of rides and ended up here. Went to work at the mill for ol' Cart Anderson who was runnin' things then. Charlie and Curtis was fresh outta high school raising hell and chasin' pussy at that time. Anyway, it was a pretty good job so I rented me a little room up above The Landing, kinda kept to myself, and made a little money. Stayed out of hot water for a while but I got ta drinkin' pretty hard and when you do that trouble will find you sooner or later. Got in a fight, busted a guy up pretty bad, and ended up in jail. Now jail ain't necessary the worse place in the world for a guy like me. They tend to feed ya pretty good and it's a roof over your head but the bad thing is, if you're in jail, you can't work. My bail was pretty high 'cause of the assault charge, and since I didn't have enough set back to make bond and get back to work, I lost my job."

"So you came to work here?"

"Naw, not for another ten years or so, maybe more. Hell, time don't mean much to an old shit like me. I worked a lot of different jobs. Stayed around here mostly 'cause I kinda liked the country. Logged for a while, cut some timber, and drove log truck. Did go to Alaska for a couple of years and logged up there, but man that is nasty country to work outdoors in. Fuckin' bugs so bad up there like to drive a sane man crazy. Anyway, bet you're wonderin' when in the hell I'm gonna get to how I came here ain't ya?"

"No. It's a good story." It was exactly what Willoughby had wanted. The mystery man wasn't nearly as mysterious as he had been ten minutes ago.

"Okay." Jake seemed satisfied. "Long as you ain't bored. Anyway, I had lived around the area on and off for quite a few years and I had seen your grandparents around town. Though we didn't quite run in the same social circles, it's a pretty small town so I knew who they were."

Jake paused for a minute and wet his throat with another long pull of cold milk. "So now we're gonna come to the good part, my young friend. I'm gonna tell you about the first time I had the good fortune to meet your Grandma Rose and Grandpa Will. Now I say good fortune 'cause eventually that was what came out of it but when that first meeting happened there weren't nothin' good or fortunate about it.

"I think it was a Saturday, maybe. Hell, I don't remember all that good but I'd been drinkin' at The Landing. Case you ain't noticed, drinkin' used to be my number one hobby; I practiced hard and was pretty damn good at it. Anyway, I had started way afore noon and was getting a pretty good buzz on and for some reason I decided to walk down to The Alibi to see what was going on there. Now you know The Alibi is on the other end of town from The Landing so I had to walk a ways to get there. Well, I had to take a goddamn piss. It came on all of a sudden and I couldn't hold the damn thing. I had to go. So I went 'round the back of Evert's Feed and Seed where they park to load up the trucks. Well there was this damn red Ford pickup sitting there all by itself, didn't look like no one was around to me, so I just walked up behind it and hung out big Jim and let 'er go. After I drained the ol' mule I zip myself up'n turn around to leave and there's this guy standing there with a sack of chicken feed slung over his shoulder and this little gal no bigger'n a pint standing behind him."

"Grandpa and Grandma?"

"Sure as shit was. Now I gotta tell you sumthin' else Will, and I don't mean to be a braggin' but it's a known fact. I'm a pretty big guy as things go and pretty damn good at fightin' as well. Had more than my share of scrapes and proud to say I only got my ass kicked one time in my whole life. One time. You believe that?"

Willoughby was pretty sure Jake was telling the truth. He didn't know anyone any bigger and he had heard enough stories to know the part about him being a badass when it came to fighting was probably every bit the truth. "I believe it, Jake."

"Good. Don't want you to be a thinkin' I'm fillin' you full of bullshit. So anyway, I turn around like I said and there's this guy a standin' there. Your grandpa. Now you know your Grandpa Will was a pretty big guy hisself. 'Bout six foot four, hard and lean from all them years a workin' on farms and ranches. But I'm still bigger and thought I was a whole lot tougher so I wasn't too worried about things. I did have a good buzz on and an attitude to go with it, so instead of sayin', "Scuse me folks, but I had to go pretty damn bad, 'I just said, 'What the fuck you lookin' at?'"

Willoughby could just imagine the sight. "You said that to Grandpa?"

"Yeah, I did," Jake answered. "The alcohol doin' the talkin' more than me 'cause I usually ain't so rude, but yeah, that's what I said."

"What'd Grandpa do?"

"Well, he flipped that big ol' bag a chicken feed into the back of the truck and says, kinda real quiet and polite like, "I'd appreciate it if you wouldn't talk that way in front of my wife here."

Jake paused for a minute in his story, picking up his milk glass and downing its remaining contents in one swallow. He stared intensely at the empty glass, turning it around a couple of times in his hand. To Willoughby it was as if he was seeing something in its surface, a vision of something remembered.

"What did you do then?" The question broke Jake's concentration, and he put the glass down.

"Well, like I said, I thought I was a pretty tough guy and wasn't goin' to let no farmer tell me what to do and I told him that. I don't remember exactly what I said but there musta been some more words in there he didn't much care for."

"Did you and Grandpa Will get into a fight?"

Jake smiled. "To make the story a mite shorter, you know when I said I only had my ass kicked one time in my entire life? Well, that was the time. All I remember was reaching out to grab your Grandpa—that was usually my way of gettin' the best of somebody—get my big paws on 'em and not let go. Pound 'im a few times, maybe a knee or an elbow, whatever worked. Only your grandpa had other notions. I don't think I ever got a good lick in on him but he got plenty in on me. Knocked my ass out cold. All I remembered after that was comin' to face down in the gravel behind the feed store. Your grandpa and grandma were already gone."

"But how come Grandpa let you come to work on the farm if you and him got into a fight?" The story Jake had just told him only led to more questions.

"That's somethin' I don't think I ever figured out, Will. I didn't run into him or your grandma again 'til about a year later. I don't know exactly why but that was the day my life changed completely. You can call it luck, fate, or whatever, I got my own notion of what it was, but I think I would have been dead if it hadn't been for them, and I'm bein' as truthful to ya as I can be."

Willoughby didn't doubt it; he could not mistake the sincerity in his voice. There was something about the way he spoke and the look on his scarred face that left no question.

"What happened?"

"I ran into a couple of old buddies a mine and we went on a bender. Drank hard for a couple of days straight. Cheap whiskey. Somehow we ended up out on the Skunk Creek loggin' road about six or seven miles from here. There it was fuckin' January and we're out in the woods in the middle of the night. I was so drunk I don't know exactly what happened, but my 'buddies' so to speak, ended up leavin' my ass out there. It was cold—rain mixed with snow and me in my cowboy boots, jeans, and a fuckin' t-shirt."

"That's all?" Willoughby could only imagine how cold that must have been.

"That's it. Good friends weren't they? I just started walkin'. It was a miracle that I walked the right way, but that was the first of a couple of lucky things that went in my favor. I finally came out on the county road and kept walkin' towards town. But me bein' dressed like I was with the cold and sleet a comin' down the whole time, I ended up gettin' a hypo hernia."

"You mean hypothermia?"

"Whatever. Where ya get so cold and wet your body starts shuttin' down, that's what I had. I couldn't go no farther. I just gave up.

Laid down in a fuckin' ditch and waited to die…just waited to die…"
Jake let his words tail off into nothing. He just sat there staring, a
far-off look in his eyes.

"But you didn't die, Jake," Willoughby finally said quietly, after
an uncomfortable silence.

"No, no I didn't, Will. That's where the story gets a mite strange,
the fate or luck thing. Your dad ever tell you about a big black lab
he used to have?"

"Titus? Is that the one?" Willoughby's dad had told him about
the dog.

"Yeah. That's him. Big ol' black brute. Anyway, your dad was
gone off to college then, it was just your grandma and grandpa here.
The ditch I ended up layin' down and waitin' to die in was right
out there in front of the driveway by your mailbox. That ol' dog
musta heard me or something cause damn if he didn't come out
there sniffin' around and find me. He went back to this house and
scratched and barked at the front door until he woke your grandpa
up, musta been about two o'clock in the morning. Your grandpa
gets up and he don't know what the hell is goin' on but he knows
ol' Titus is bothered by somethin', so he gets his clothes on, grabs
a gun 'n a flashlight, and follows the dog."

"And he found you?"

"Yep. Lo and behold, your grandpa found a half-dead drunk
Indian out at the front of his driveway layin' in a ditch full of freezin'
water with a bad case of hippo thermos. Got me outta the ditch
and damn if he didn't carry me back to the house, me bein' as big
as I am. Shit, he musta been sixty-five then at least, all the way to
the fuckin' house."

"Did they call an ambulance for you?"

"No, damn if they didn't. But your grandma, she knew what to
do. Got my body temperature back up and got me in bed. I woke
up a couple of days later, no idea of where I was or how I got there."

"Did they know you were the guy who tried to beat up Grandpa?"

"I'm sure they did, but they never said a word about it. I recognized them when I finally got back to my senses. Your grandma fed me, got me some clothes that fit, got me back on my feet. I tell you what, Will, those two and that damn dog saved my life that night. I know that sure as I'm a sittin' here talkin' to you."

"So you stayed here and went to work?"

Jake smiled. "Naw, weren't quite that simple. Your grandpa asked me where I wanted to go and I said he could take me into town if'n he would. We loaded up in that ol' red truck, I told Rose thank you for savin' my ass, and me 'n your grandpa headed for town. Kind of a quiet ride, made a little small talk I guess, but I think I was kinda scared of your grandpa in a way."

Willoughby had a hard time believing Jake was afraid of anything. "You were scared of him after he saved your life?"

"It wasn't scared in that kinda way. Maybe that weren't the right word for it—humbled or somethin' like that. Anyway, we pulled up in front of The Landing and I got out and was holdin' the door, gettin' ready to shut it. Now here is where it gets a little strange. If I woulda shut that door and walked into that bar, well, my life would have been totally different, and probably not in a good way. But there was somethin' telling me that I weren't supposed to do that, somethin' in the back of my mind. So instead of sayin' thanks and goodbye, I asked your grandpa if he could use a hand workin' the farm. Blurted it out just like that."

"What did Grandpa say?"

"Well, he didn't say nothin' for awhile. He just looked at me real hard. I thought he was gonna say no but then he said the words that changed my life. He said, 'You quit yer drinkin', right here, right now, and I got a job for you.'"

Jake had that far-off look in his eyes again, like he was remembering the moment. Willoughby could have sworn there was moisture in his eyes.

"I got back in that pickup and never took me another drop a drink since."

Neither said anything for a while. Willoughby had the impression that the telling of the story had been hard for Jake, and inside he was immensely thrilled and awed that the big guy had chosen to do so.

"What ya think there, Will?" Jake finally asked. "Was it luck? Fate?"

Willoughby just shook his head. "I don't know what you call it, Jake, but I'm sure glad it happened."

"Yeah, you and me both. I owe your grandma and grandpa everything. I was a worthless drunk, but they seen somethin' in me worth savin'. I gotta admit that it was hard. Those first few days, your grandpa would roust me out at four in the morning, me wantin' a drink so fuckin' bad. But I kept my word. There was somethin' about them, somethin' about this place. I asked you if it was luck or fate that saved my ass, well I got my own opinion 'bout that if'n you want to hear it."

Willoughby did want to hear it. He felt a kinship to the big Indian. It felt to him like he and Jake had shared a lot of the same frustrations.

"What do you think it was?"

"Well, like I said, I ain't a religious person but I am a spiritual person. You know the difference?"

Willoughby wasn't all that sure but he said so anyway. "Kinda."

"Well, us Indians, we are spiritual by heritage, the spirit world plays a big part in almost every native tribal culture there is—spirits of their ancestors, evil spirits, animal spirits. These spirits play a big part in how our lives go, they guide you on the path so to speak, and it can be a path to good and happiness or it can be a path to the other side. There are little things along the way what determine which it's going to be. For the most part, my spirit guide got me all screwed up. Couldn't hold a job or a family. I was a drunk. That's how my world went until…"

"Until you got back in my grandpa's truck?"

Jake smiled. "Exactly. Just that little step. Somethin' that didn't seem to amount to nothin' at the time was a life changer. And I'll tell you another thing. There's another reason my spirit led me here to your grandma and grandpa's."

"What was that?"

"This place here, your grandma and grandpa's farm—it's a spiritual place for Indians, a sacred place."

Willoughby wasn't quite sure what Jake meant. "What's so sacred about the farm?"

"Well, it took me a while to put two and two together, but one day I finally realized why this place seemed to be different. I could always feel it, feel the presence of things being not normal." Jake paused, giving his words a chance to sink in, then asked, "Do you know about the waterfall, Will?"

Willoughby knew of it. It was hard to live in a place called Spirit Falls without knowing about the town's namesake. He also knew that it was located on the upper end of his grandma's property. "I've heard about it. Mom said that we were gonna take a drive some day and look at it from the county road."

"Well that's one way but you can get a lot closer if you walk to it across the property. But it's a lot more than just a sightseeing attraction, Will. Spirit Falls is what makes this place sacred."

"How's that?"

"Well, a long time ago the salmon used to run up this river. That was before they put in the Elk Ridge Dam back in thirty-five. Millions of salmon, so thick you could walk across the river on 'em. My ancestors used to come over the mountains every year and harvest the salmon. They'd catch tons of 'em and they built big racks outta alder to dry 'em on so they could pack 'em back across the mountains and have a supply of food for the winter when the game got scarce. They used to set up camp right here on this place down by the river. Spend the summer catchin' and dryin' fish and tradin' with the valley tribes for Camas root and willow baskets and lots of other stuff. My people brought arrowheads with 'em to trade. Valley tribes didn't have the obsidian to make good points like my ancestors did so they traded for 'em. They did that for hundreds of years and that's why this place was so sacred. The place of the salmon. The salmon kept my people alive during the winter—the spirit of the salmon was strong in them."

Willoughby was impressed. He could visualize the pastures

being one large Indian encampment with lodges and campfires and racks upon racks of drying salmon. "My dad said they used to find a lot of arrowheads around here."

"Yeah they did. Other stuff, too. When I started to get interested in the history of this place your grandpa and grandma gave me the stuff they had found over the years. I thought that was pretty nice of 'em. I guess they figured since most of it belonged to my ancestors anyway, maybe I ought to have it. You wanna see some of it?"

"Yeah, I'd like to see it."

Jake stood up, towering over the table and his young friend. "C'mon."

Willoughby followed Jake out the back porch and into the quiet night. A layer of fog hugged the yard where the cold night air met the warmer ground. The big light mounted on the pole next to the hay barn threw an eerie luminescence across the landscape and created pockets of dark shadows. Willoughby was startled when a large black shape crossed the light near the top of the pole and disappeared into the blackness.

Jake's trailer was parked at the side of the big hay barn, not visible from the main house. When they rounded the corner of the barn they were in complete darkness.

"Damn bulb is burned outta my porch light. Wait here and I'll get some light on. Wouldn't want you to fall off the damn steps."

He did as Jake told him and waited. It wasn't long before Jake was able to get an inside light on, enabling Willoughby to see well enough to navigate the steps and enter the trailer.

"Welcome to my humble abode," Jake greeted as Willoughby entered.

The inside of the trailer was small and Jake's towering frame seemed to make it even smaller. A bar separated the kitchen from the living room that was furnished with a single couch. A small coffee table and another small table shoved against the wall with a flat screen TV sitting on it completed the room.

"Make yourself at home," Jake welcomed. "You'll have to excuse all the clutter."

The furnishings were simple and alone were enough to fill the tiny living room, but it was the "clutter" as Jake called it, that caught Willoughby's attention.

There were artifacts and antiques everywhere. Bookshelves lined the trailer's wall, crammed with all sorts of interesting things. Strange rocks, crystals, pieces of petrified wood. One shelf was full of what Willoughby thought were different sizes of river rock until he got a closer look. They were bowls. Each rock had a deep depression in it, made from years and years of grinding corn, roots, and other things. The pestles, long gray cylinders of river rock that were used to do the grinding, lay next to the bowls.

"Most of those came from the place here," Jake said as he saw the boy's interest. "Your grandpa found some of them. Like I said, this used to be where the tribes camped when they came over the mountains in the summer to catch the salmon." Jake pointed to a small bowl, barely larger than a baseball.

"I think this little one here was used to mix up medicinal powders. Willow bark for pain medication, different kinds of roots, and other stuff. Probably belonged to a medicine woman or sumthin."

Jake picked up the pestle, which was a little over four inches long and about the diameter of one of Jake's fat fingers. He demonstrated to Willoughby how they would have placed the dried roots or bark into the mortar and ground it into powder using the stone pestle.

Willoughby was amazed. "How did they make these things?"

"They just looked along the gravel bars for the right kind of river stone and picked one that already had some kind of natural depression in the top of it. Then they'd find a long, cylinder-shaped rock like this for a pestle, start to use it, and as the years went on, the depression would wallow out and get bigger. I found this little one here 'bout four or five years ago down along the riverbank below the falls. We had a pretty wet winter that year and the high water had exposed a lot of the bank. Walkin' along and there it was, pretty as could be. I was tickled as hell when I picked that thing up. Never thought in a million years that I would find that damn pestle but I took two steps and there it was, pointin' at me like a finger."

"Wow, that was lucky," Willoughby said as he turned the little round bowl in his hands, imagining an old medicine woman using it to grind her bark and roots into healing powders.

"Maybe," Jake answered, "but like I said, I think this place is sacred and things don't just happen here by luck. Here, take a look at this stuff." He stepped over to another bookcase where a large, polished and lacquered wooden box with several drawers sat. Willoughby thought it was a big jewelry box.

"Look at these babies," Jake said as he pulled open the first drawer.

"Whoaa!" Willoughby exclaimed. Inside the black velvet lined drawer were arrowheads, most of them smaller than a quarter.

"Look at the workmanship on those things," Jake said as he reached in and pulled one out. "I think this one is made out of crystal or somethin' like that," he said as he held it up. "They're bird points. Can you imagine the work it took for a knapper to make that?"

"A what?" Willoughby asked.

"A knapper," Jake said as he handed the tiny point to Willoughby. "That's what they called the guys that made arrowheads, knives, and spear points. It's called knapping. They use a really hard piece of stone to chip off tiny flakes of obsidian, flint, or other things to make these points. They made these little notches near the top to fasten to the shafts."

The arrowhead was perfectly shaped and very sharp as Willoughby tried the point out on his finger.

"Sharp, eh?" Jake said. "Obsidian was the best for arrow and spearheads. They could flake it off and get a razor-sharp edge."

He took the tiny bird point from Willoughby and laid it back in with the others. "Look at these," Jake said as he pulled open another drawer. This one held much bigger points. Jake took one out that was long and narrow.

"A spear point," he said as he handed the deadly looking thing to Willoughby. "Probably used it to hunt deer and elk. Or maybe unwanted settlers," he said and grinned.

Willoughby inspected it carefully. He could see each spot where tiny flakes of the black glassy stone had been chipped away to form the six-inch-long point. Jake reached in the drawer and extracted another stone that had a half-round shape.

"This is a skinning tool. They used this to take the hide off the animals."

"You found all of these here?" he asked as he handed the pieces back to Jake.

"Some, not all of them. Your grandma used to find 'em when she was a kid livin' around Bend and Redmond. She gave 'em to me when I started to collect 'em. "Your grandpa found quite a few here, though. He found that spear point up close to where the trail goes to the falls."

Willoughby was fascinated by what Jake had shown him, but the Indian artifacts were just part of the big guy's collection. Along one wall stood a rack of old rifles and shotguns and above that, five swords rested on wooden pegs.

"Whoa, are those real?" he asked.

"Most of 'em," Jake said. He took a sleek, slightly curved black case off the wall mounts, grabbed the tasseled grip, and slid out nearly three feet of shiny steel. The sword sang with a clean, metallic ring as it came free.

"Wow! This is so cool!" Willoughby exclaimed as he admired the sleek weapon.

"Samurai," Jake explained. "A real officer's sword, not one a' those that was mass produced after the war started." He offered the weapon to Willoughby. "Easy now. That thing is sharp as you could ever imagine."

Willoughby grasped the sword carefully with both hands firmly on the grip, and held it out in front of him. It was just a little heavy but he could feel its solid balance and workmanship.

"Supposed to be that the craftsmen who made the true Samurai blades folded and hammered the steel a thousand times afore they were finished. Most of the ones brought home by servicemen after the war was over weren't like this. I had it checked out by a dealer in Vegas after I got it. This one here's the real deal."

Willoughby relished the feel of the deadly weapon. "This is so cool. Can you imagine fighting with this thing?"

Jake laughed. "Well, it might look cool in a movie or somethin' Will, but I don't think getting your arms or head hacked off would be a very pleasant thing. I mean, guns kill just the same, but fighting with weapons like this is a lot more up close and personal." He reached up and took another sword off the wall mount. It was massive.

"Try this one."

Willoughby traded weapons but when he grabbed the sword's huge grip with both hands, he could barely hold the thing up off the ground for any length of time at all. The blade was nearly five feet long. "I've never seen a sword so big."

"Well, this one ain't real but it's supposed to be a true replica of ones they used to use. It's called a Claymore. Ain't you ever seen the movie *Braveheart*?"

Willoughby shook his head, he hadn't.

"Big Scottish guy, William Wallace. He fought the English with a sword just like that. He was supposed to be damn near as big as me. Good movie 'cept for havin' Mel Gibson playin' the Wallace part. That guy wouldn't a come to the real Wallace's crotch."

Jake replaced the Samurai sword on the wall and took the heavy great sword from Willoughby. The big Indian gripped the pommel in his huge hands and held the blade out in front of him. Even though the weapon was nearly as tall as the teen, it looked like it fit Jake perfectly.

"He must have been a big guy," Willoughby said as he warily stepped back from Jake, who filled the tiny living room with his towering presence. For a brief moment, a terrifying realistic vision flashed through the boy's mind. He could hear men shouting, horses screamed in anger and fright. Metal on metal rang in his ears accompanied by the guttural grunts of men fighting for their lives. And then he saw Jake, or at least it kinda looked like the big guy, younger maybe. The man's shoulder-length hair was black and kept out of his eyes with a braided leather headband, and he was wearing a short-sleeved shirt that looked like it was made of tiny metal rings. On his left arm he carried a big round shield with a nasty looking point sticking out of the middle, and in his right hand was a huge sword, just like the one Jake had, but this guy was holding it in one hand like it was nothing. He strode towards Willoughby and raised the mighty sword high up over his head.

Willoughby stepped back and nearly fell over the coffee table.

"Whoa there, son," said Jake as his booming laugh filled the tiny trailer. "I ain't gonna hit you with the damn thing."

Willoughby forced a smile but inside, his heart was still pounding furiously. The vision had been far too real.

Jake put the sword back on the wall much to Willoughby's relief. The two spent another hour looking at all of Jake's collectibles. Along with the Samurai and Scottish swords were two real cavalry swords and a replica of what Jake called a scimitar, a strange looking thing with a curved blade. Jake also had quite a number of antique guns, Winchesters mostly, but a few military weapons as well. One shelf held an impressive array of knives and bayonets.

"How'd you get all this stuff?" Willoughby asked as they examined Jake's collection.

Jake laughed again. "Well, some of it I came by honestly, and then some of it by other ways if you know what I mean?" Willoughby thought he did. "Didn't have too much afore I came to your grandma and grandpa's, cause I never really had a place you'd call home but I always had an interest in old weapons and such. The Indian stuff I started to collect after your grandpa showed me the things he had found here and I got to pokin' around the history of this place. Some of the stuff I bought when I started collecting my inheritance."

"Inheritance?"

Jake grinned. "Casino money. Don't like to spend too much time in the damn things cause they can get you broke in a hurry. But when I finally got settled here and got an official address I started getting this mail that said that me bein' a full-blood member of the

94

Klamath tribe and all, I was entitled to share in the proceeds from their investments. Hell, suited me just fine. Ain't nothin like free money. But I was kinda glad I never got any afore I came here. I'da just drank it all away. Instead, I started collectin' this stuff. Don't know what I'm gonna do with it all—kinda outgrown my trailer here."

They were looking at more guns and some of the knives and bayonets when Willoughby started to feel a funny sort of itch on the back of his neck. It was a strange feeling like someone—or something—was watching him. Jake was showing him a Model 1894 Winchester 30-30 when Willoughby slowly craned his neck around. Immediately he spotted the source of his discomfort. There it was, as high in the corner of the small living room as you could get and so obvious Willoughby was surprised he hadn't noticed it until now. Standing nearly two feet high it stared down at the boy from its perch, piercing jet black eyes glaring at him over a long ebony beak, with a white splotch looking like someone had dripped white paint onto its head—a raven. It sat there without moving; it just watched.

"That's Patch. Kinda takes you by surprise, don't he?" Jake asked as he noticed his young friend had spotted the bird.

"Is he alive?" Willoughby asked.

Jake shook his head and laughed. "Naw. Though it's a pretty damn good taxidermy job, don't ya think?"

Willoughby did think. He stepped across the living room to the corner where the bird sat silently on its corner perch. He swore he could see the eyes follow him across the room. "It's the bird that was in my dream last night. He had exactly the same white patch on his head."

Jake put the Winchester back in the rack with the others and stepped next to Willoughby who was staring up at the raven. "Patch was in your dream?"

"Last night." Willoughby remembered the flying dream. "It was stupid."

"Dreams aren't stupid, Will," Jake said as he reached up and took the mounted bird off the corner shelf it sat on. "You want a soda or somethin'?" he asked as he moved to the small kitchen and placed Patch down on the table.

"Sure," Willoughby answered, sitting down at one of the only two chairs. The bird watched his every move. "Where'd this come from?" he asked Jake as he and the bird stared intently at each other.

"Well, he was here afore I came," Jake replied as he sat a can of cola down in front of Willoughby and sat at the table's other chair.

"Your grandpa and grandma both said they used to see 'im around. But after I got here, he started showin' up regular like whenever I was out workin'. I'd be out cutting wood or herdin' the cows and there he'd be, just a watchin'. Kinda like he's doin' now."

The bird was watching.

"Ravens all kinda look alike but with that white mark on his forehead, he was an easy one to spot. That's why I gave 'im the name Patch. Kinda fits, huh?"

Willoughby thought it did fit, but there was something more about Patch, something that poked at the boy. "It does look like the bird that was in my dream. It was weird, kinda like I was supposed to follow him."

"Did he take you to the falls?"

The question shocked Willoughby. How could Jake have guessed that?

"Yeah…yeah, he did."

"Did the same thing to me first day I ran into him 'cept it weren't no dream," Jake said. "I had the cat up near the old growth patch draggin' some windfall off the hill. I had hooked the chokers up and was gettin' ready to head down when I felt somethin' funny like, like somethin' was watchin' me. I turned around and sittin' on top of a stump was this big ol' raven with a white patch on his head. I ignored him for a while but he kept actin' real funny, bouncing around, bobbin his head and makin' these clickin' sounds. I even threw a chunk a wood at 'im but he dodged it and kept actin' weird. I don't know what it was but I got this feelin' I was supposed to follow him."

Willoughby had the same feeling in his dream. "So what did you do?"

Jake shrugged. "Only one thing to do—I followed 'im. He'd fly ahead a ways and sit and wait for me. I'd just about catch up to 'im and he'd fly out front again. I followed him up through the old growth in the back eighty and came out on this old trail I never seed afore. Kept on following that damn bird and the next thing I know I'm standin' next to the river just up from where it goes over the edge of the falls. I had never been there before and I gotta tell you, Will, I didn't like it much."

"Are you afraid of the water?" Willoughby couldn't imagine Jake being afraid of anything.

"Naw, weren't the water. Hell, I done a lot a commercial fishin' in my time. It was that place, the top of the falls. It made me feel real funny. Vertigo or somethin' like that. Yah, that's what ya call it, vertigo."

Willoughby hadn't heard of it. "Vertigo?"

"Yeah. It's where ya get really dizzy and think the world is spinnin' around ya. I thought I was gonna fall over into the river. Hell, I woulda went right over that damn waterfall. I didn't like it, somethin' weird 'bout the place. I got the hell outta there."

"What about Patch?"

"He disappeared, but showed back up the next day while I was doin' chores. Kinda just made 'isself welcome round the farm. I'd be workin' at some job and I'd get this feelin' like somebody was a watchin' me and there that son of a bitch would be. Just a watchin'. He'd run all the other birds off if they tried to come around. Wanted the whole place for 'isself I guess. Stayed around for a lotta years that big ol' bird did."

"What happened to him?"

Jake was quiet for a moment, twisting the cola can around in his huge hands and staring at it like he had never seen such a thing before.

"Well, that's kind of a strange story in itself. Your grandpa and I were in the milk shed doin' the morning's milkin' when this feelin' kinda came over me like somethin' wasn't right. I tried to focus on the work but it kept gnawin' at my insides, ya know what I mean?"

Willoughby did. In a strange way it was almost as if he knew where Jake was going with his story. He had felt the same way before.

"After we got done with the milkin', your grandpa said he wasn't feelin' all that good and was goin' into the house and set a spell. He was headin' out the shed door and he turned to me and said, "Jake, anything ever happens to me, you make me a promise, okay?"

"I said, 'Sure Will, you know I'd do anything for you.' And that there's the honest God's truth son. I woulda done anything for your grandpa and grandma. He looked me square in the eye and got all serious like and said, 'Jake, you take care of Rose and the farm. Don't you let this place go under. Only promise I'd ever ask of ya.'

"I gotta tell ya, Will, I thought that was really strange. Your grandpa musta been close to seventy but he was as healthy as any man I knew. He could do the work of three young guys any time. So I just kinda shrugged and told him he could count on me. He grinned that big ol' grin of his and reached out to shake on it. Like to nearly crushed my fuckin' hand with that big ol' paw a his, and my hands ain't none too small."

Willoughby knew what was coming next. Two years earlier he had been getting ready for school when he had felt the same uneasiness Jake had described, a foreboding deep inside that wouldn't go away. When he turned to leave his bedroom that morning, his dad was standing in the doorway.

"Hey Dad," he had greeted, surprised that his father was up that early. James Baxter was deep in the throes of addiction and usually comatose at this time of the day.

"Hey son," he had said. They had made small talk, he asked about school and grades and such, things they hadn't talked about in a long time. When Willoughby's mom called from downstairs that breakfast was ready, James Baxter did something else he hadn't done in a long while—he hugged his son and told him he loved him. That was the last thing Willoughby's father had ever said to him.

He died at one o'clock that afternoon. Willoughby guessed where Jake's story was headed.

"That was the day Grandpa died, wasn't it?"

Jake looked at him and nodded. "He went on into the house while I finished the morning's chores. When I got done, I still had this bad feelin' I couldn't shake. I went for a walk; it just seemed like what I should do. I went up to the back eighty to the place where I first saw Patch, and there he was, just a sittin' on that same old stump lookin' like he always did, but I could tell from a distance that there was somethin' different."

"What was he doing?" Willoughby knew the story was going to get strange.

Jake turned the cola can around and around in his hands, a far-off look in his eyes. "Weren't doin' nothin', just sittin' and starin'. Funny thing 'bout it was, he was dead."

"Dead?"

Jake nodded again. "Honest to God truth Will, that bird was sittin' straight up, eyes wide open but he never moved a mite. I walked right up to 'im and picked 'im up. Wasn't even cold. Damndest thing I ever saw, him sittin' up like that bein' dead. I was gonna bury 'im, but I thought it wouldn't be the same if'n ol' Patch wasn't around so I knew this guy in town what was a taxidermy so I made up my mind ta take 'im there. I had just got back down off the hill when I heard your grandma a yellin' for me—your grandpa had a heart attack."

Willoughby knew the story. Jake had performed CPR until the ambulance arrived but Will Baxter had never regained consciousness.

Jake leaned back in his chair and laced his huge hands behind his head. "Worst day a my life when your grandpa died. He knew, somehow he knew. But there was one more weird thing happened that day, Will. I had laid that stupid dead Patch on my porch when I heard your Grandma Rose hollerin' for me. Just laid 'im down and left 'im there. When I finally got back to my trailer that evenin', that dead bird was sittin' up on the rail just like I had found 'im on that stump. Sittin' up eyes wide open. No fuckin' lie."

Willoughby didn't think it was a bullshit story at all. He looked at the mounted Patch and imagined the surprise Jake had when he found him upright on the rail of the porch. He swore he could see a sparkle in the bird's glass eyes.

"He's a spirit of some kind, Will," Jake went on. "Knew it the day I met 'im. My ancestors believed in the animal powers and they had a special place for ravens. Called 'em the Tricksters 'cause they were so smart. I believe ol' Mr. Patch here has somethin' to do with this place around the falls bein' sacred ground and all, like he a ghost of everythin' past. To this day I think every now and then he's a watchin' me with those damn shiny eyes a his."

Willoughby agreed wholeheartedly with Jake on that point, the piercing eyes of Patch seemed to follow every movement. You could almost see them move. "What do you think killed him, Jake?"

"Shit, I don't know. Old age maybe. Damn bird's probably a hunnert years old. Wanna know one more thing that don't make no sense, Will? Take a look at that bird. He's been sittin' up in that corner ever since I got 'im stuffed, not too long after your grandpa died. Go ahead, look at 'im close and tell me what you don't see."

Willoughby did. He stared intently at the mount—the taxidermist had done an excellent job. The man had taken a small piece of log about five inches in diameter that had a stub of a limb sticking out of it and had sanded and varnished the wood to a hard, clear finish before securing the bird's long black claws around the limb. Even without believing Patch was some sort of ancestral spirit, the mount was amazingly lifelike. The white patch, the long ebony feathers, the lighter shaded beak, the claws, and especially Patch's eyes—they all pulsed with life. Nothing about them hinted the bird had died nearly four years ago.

"There's no dust on it," Willoughby said abruptly.

"There ya go," boomed Jake so loudly the dishes in the cupboard rattled. "Put that mount up in that corner the day I brought 'im home and have never taken it down. Not a speck a dust on 'im anywhere. Never been no cobwebs either. Cobwebs in every corner a this place 'ceptin Patch's. Like the spiders are scared of 'im. Explain that one."

Willoughby couldn't.

"It's cause he's a damn sacred spirit a some kind, that's why," the big Indian answered for him. "Him'n this place, the falls. There's somethin' unnatural about it. Fuckin' place is haunted. Ain't no wonder so many people drowned foolin' around there."

That was something else Willoughby hadn't heard. "Drowned?"

Jake nodded. "That's why the County closed the park. See, used to be the road here was one of the only ways to get over to the east side of the mountains. Lots more traffic back in the day. Spirit Falls was a popular place for travelin' folk to stop and take pictures, like Salt Creek Falls on the Willamette Pass and Sahalie on the McKenzie Highway. The County owned the property on the other side of the falls from your grandpa and grandma's and they built a park there. Put in a parkin' lot, some picnic tables and a couple a shitters. Had a viewpoint there at the top of the falls for picture takin'. Wasn't a problem 'til they built the trail so folks could get down to the river below the falls. That's when people started gettin' stupid."

"What happened?" Willoughby was starting to develop a real interest in Spirit Falls. His dad had never talked much about it even though he had grown up on the farm next to it. But for Willoughby, Jake's stories were fascinating and he was trying to picture in his mind what the waterfall looked like.

"They put in a steep-ass trail, cut it damn near straight outta the rock. Built switchbacks and rails and stuff but right off the bat, some guy showin' off for his girlfriend stood on top of one of the rails and fell off, splatterin' his brains out on the rocks. But that weren't the worse part. See, there's a pool at the bottom of the waterfall and then the water goes hard down this chute afore it levels out a mite. Same thing at the top of the falls. There's a damn ten-foot ledge of rock around the pool and the chute and the water is deep and fast with a lot of undercurrents and such. People get too close to the edge, maybe they been a drinkin' or a smokin' weed and sooner or later some dumb ass falls in and there ain't no way to get 'em out.

Pick their bodies up downstream later."

The picture in Willoughby's mind was vivid. Though he had never been there, he could visualize the pool and the deadly chute and could imagine a bunch of college guys on a break who stop off to take a piss and hammer down a few more brews before they head on over to Bend. The more they drink, the braver they get, and head down the steep trail and start messing around. Then someone slips on the granite that's wet from the heavy spray or someone gets bumped—in an instant the fun turns into a brutal nightmare. The victim surfaces once, maybe twice, flailing away helplessly against the current only to be jerked under again. His buddies scream at him to hang on. He surfaces one last time and claws in vain for a hand hold on the vertical wall of rock before he finally disappears. Maybe one of his friends does the unthinkable and goes in after him, only to suffer the same fate. Jake interrupted Willoughby's morbid scenario.

"The family of some woman that fell in and drowned finally sued the County, said it was negligent for not protecting the public. After that, they took out the picnic tables and shitters, made the trail so ya couldn't use it anymore, and blocked off the parkin' lot. People still can hike in and see the falls, but the County put up a warning sign telling 'em to stay out. Guess they figured that was the best they could do. Didn't stop people from bein' stupid though. I remember a time when I was doin' some volunteer work for the fire department. Guy fell in around the first week of April or so when the water was still pretty high from snow melt. Didn't find him until July, wrapped up in a logjam just up the river from Stewart's Bridge. Man, that was nasty work. Guy was bloated up and his skin was all white-lookin'. I remember he didn't have any eyes left, like somethin' ate 'em."

Willoughby didn't want to visualize a picture that vivid. "So you think all this happens 'cause this is sacred ground?" he asked. "Like it has some kinda curse on it?"

The big guy gave him a toothy grin. "Hell, Will, I don't know. Makes ya wonder though, don't it? Gotta admit all that stuff with ol' Patch here makes for a damn strange story."

It did make for a strange story but he'd had about enough stories for one night. He yawned hard as Jake replaced Patch in his corner perch. Willoughby's body was telling him it had been a long day, probably the hardest he ever had as far as actual physical labor went. He would sleep hard tonight.

"I'm gonna call it a night Jake. What's the plan for tomorrow?"

"You're off the hook as far as work goes," The big Indian answered. "When I get done with the morning's milkin' I gotta go to Corvallis. They got a big tractor junk yard there that's open on Sunday. I need to find a PTO drive shaft for the John Deere. Got a couple of other errands to run for your grandma so it'll probably be late afternoon afore I get back. You're welcome to ride along if'n you want to."

Willoughby declined. If Jake had no plans for work, his idea of tomorrow morning would include a fairly late wake up time. As he was getting ready to head out the trailer door, he took one last look up at Patch—the bird's eyes stared down at him hard. The Trickster, that's what Jake had said the Indians called the big black birds. He could feel something, something hiding behind those dark eyes. The Trickster…Willoughby thought it fit.

"Mystery, mischief, and mayhem."

"What?" Willoughby asked as Jake's words broke the spell.

"You're wonderin' bout ol' Patch there. I don't think either one of us is crazy, Will. There is somethin' about that bird, somethin' about this place. You feel it the same way I do, don't you?"

Willoughby wasn't sure what it was he felt other than tired. It was starting to get more than a little confusing and it must have shown on his face. Jake didn't press him anymore.

"Go get some sleep, Will. You did a good piece of work today and I'm gonna tell your mom how much I appreciate your help. See ya tomorrow."

"Yeah. Good night, Jake. See you in the morning."

As Willoughby stepped off the porch and into the foggy night he could still feel it—the bird was watching.

Chapter Six

FOR THE FIRST TIME IN A WHILE WILLOUGHBY had slept without dreaming; another plus for hard labor—a good night's sleep. Pulling his covers around him, he rolled over, fully intending to take advantage of the fact that Jake didn't have any work plans for him today. But suddenly he sat up and checked his clock and was relieved when he saw that it wasn't six yet. Jake would still be getting his morning milking chores done and Willoughby wanted to make sure he got to talk to the big guy before he left to go to Corvallis hunting tractor parts. He had a plan in mind for the day but he would need permission from Jake before he followed through with it. He just hoped he wouldn't say no.

His bedroom was cold and he fought the desire to roll back into the encompassing warmth of his covers for another half hour or so. Sure as shit if he did he would oversleep and miss Jake, so he forced the temptation from his mind and instead pushed himself to a sitting position on the edge of the bed. Goosebumps and shivers assailed his bare legs as he hurried to get his socks and sweats on. He still hadn't shaken free of his San Diego mild weather habits entirely, but a few more mornings like this one, with its definite cold edge to it, might just do the trick.

After a quick trip to the bathroom, Willoughby checked the big wood stove in the living room, and was relieved when he pulled the damper open and saw the coals spring to life. His grandma had showed him and his sister how to stoke the night fire up with the right kind of wood so there would be a good bed of coals with which to get the morning fire started. Some dry kindling, topped off with a couple of pieces of seasoned wood, and the fire took off nicely. Much better than trying to get a blaze started from scratch—a job he hadn't quite mastered yet.

It was a slightly different story with the woodstove in the kitchen, but with a little effort and a minimal amount of smoke, he soon had it going as well, with water heating in the big pot. Rose and Jennifer Baxter were big coffee drinkers and had allowed Kendall and Willoughby to take up the habit, but it wasn't coffee from a can or instant from a jar for them—instead it was fresh beans worked through a grinder and a French press. Willoughby loved the smell of freshly ground coffee and was gradually getting used to the taste, but his mother would allow him and his sister only a cup, maybe two on a weekend morning, but absolutely no caffeine-induced late school nights for them.

Willoughby had the kitchen warmed up, the coffee ready, and was in the process of heating up some leftover biscuits when he finally heard Jake sliding the heavy twin doors to the milking shed closed as he finished up his chores. He stuck his head out the back porch and hollered, "Hey, Jake. Got some hot coffee on."

Jake responded with a wave and after a quick rinse of his cow-shit-covered boots at the outside faucet, he was soon settled in at the kitchen table nursing a hot cup.

"You're gonna make some woman a mighty fine husband you keep gettin' handy around the kitchen like ya are." He smiled as Willoughby slid him a couple of hot biscuits on a plate.

Willoughby returned the smile as he heaped his coffee with a couple of spoonfuls of hot cocoa mix. He had decided on mocha for his morning kick.

"Two days in a row up at a damn decent hour. Looks like yer gettin' shed of them city ways to me, son."

Willoughby took Jake's ribbing in stride. He wasn't real sure how to broach the subject of his plan to the big guy, but Jake made it easy for him.

"You sure you don't want to come with me to get those tractor parts? Might be kinda borin' fer you, lessin' yer just gonna sit 'n play video games all day."

Willoughby shook his head as he stirred his mocha. "Mom's got the Xbox locked in the gun cabinet in Grandma's bedroom. Fallout from the last time I got in trouble. Thanks for the offer to go, Jake, but I was wonderin' if it would be okay if I hiked to the waterfall today while you're gone?" There, the question was out.

Jake didn't answer for a moment; he just stirred and stared at the coffee in his cup. "You wanna hike to the falls?" he finally looked up and asked, as if he wasn't sure he had heard the question right.

Willoughby was relieved the answer hadn't been no immediately; he thought that was a good sign at least. "Yeah, I mean if you think it would be all right. I'd be careful and all and it wouldn't take that long, would it?"

"Naw," Jake shook his head, but Willoughby could sense some hesitation in the big Indian's voice. "It ain't a bad hike from here, just don't know what your mom and grandma would think about me lettin' you go off by yourself."

It wasn't a 'Yes' but the door had been opened just a crack. Willoughby, expecting just that kind of response, was ready to jam a wedge in. "They won't care, Jake. Heck, Grandma has been telling me I need to get out and do more things like that anyway. She thinks I sit around the house too much as it is, and I know Mom wouldn't care. That's why you guys bought me the pack and stuff wasn't it? I mean going for a hike, or watchin' TV all day? That's a no-brainer." The crack in the door had just been opened a bit wider.

"Well,I won't argue that I ain't heard that from both your mom and grandma. Don't suppose it would hurt for you to hike there, since you don't even have to leave the property to do it. But that falls ain't no place to be foolin' around. I'll tell ya how to get to the bottom and ya can look at it from there. Ain't no goin' to the top of the thing, ya hear?"

It was exactly what Willoughby had in mind. He just wanted to look at the falls and the view from the bottom would do the trick. "Absolutely. No need to worry about that, Jake."

The big man sipped his coffee and looked over the rim at Willoughby. "Mind what I said, son. The falls is a fine place for sight seein' but people always seem to push it a bit and don't settle for just lookin' at the thing. Remember 'bout all the folk who end up dead there? I'm sure they weren't doin' nuthin' but lookin' at the falls. But like I also said afore, that place is strange and things happen there that don't normally happen at other places."

Willoughby could hear a slight bit of reluctance creeping into Jake's voice and was afraid he was going to change his mind. "I'll remember what you said, Jake," he promised. "I won't go anywhere close to it. I'll just get a good viewpoint from below and look at it from there. I'll take my camera and get some good pictures of it to show Mom and Grandma."

"I 'spose they'd like that. Just so's you don't make me look like a damn idiot and get yourself hurt or sumthin'. Stay away from the river edge and the slick rock. You fall and break an arm or a leg and your mom and grandma will skin this ol' Indian alive."

The two of them laughed, but down deep Willoughby was positive that if he hurt himself, Jake's prediction wouldn't be too far off. He made himself a mental promise to be extra careful. Jake was going out on a limb for him and he didn't want to get the big guy in any trouble. "I swear I'll be careful, Jake," he reassured with as much sincerity as he could muster. "I won't get either of us in trouble."

Jake started spreading his biscuits with butter and jam. "Good 'nuff. Now do me a favor, son, and grab a travel mug from the cupboard and fill it with coffee whiles I polish off these biscuits. I gotta get on the road."

A half-hour later, Willoughby stood at the gate watching the taillights of the old red Ford make the corner onto the county road. Daylight was just starting to push the dark back and a layer of fog enveloped the farm as the warmer air came in contact with the cold ground. As Willoughby watched the pickup disappear, he suddenly realized something—for the first time he could remember since they had come to the farm—he was alone.

As he returned to the porch, a sense of uneasiness settled deep into the pit of his stomach, the old farmhouse suddenly looming larger and spookier than it ever had. He chided himself for being a pussy as he shut the door behind him. What would Jake think if he knew he was scared to be by himself? He just needed to keep busy; the morning light would soon be out in full and chase the shadows away.

Part of the problem was the big house was way too quiet. He flicked the TV in the living room on and the unsettling silence was replaced by the voices of the ESPN Sports Center team recounting Saturday's college football contests. His mom, sister, and grandma spent the weekends wrapped around football of some sort. Friday night high school, Saturday college, and then Sunday with the Pros—it never ended, much to Willoughby's displeasure. Despite Willoughby's aversion to anything football, he was outnumbered and outgunned on the weekends. He thought about turning the channel just to spite them since they were gone, but the familiar voices eased his tension somewhat so he decided to leave it alone.

After cleaning up what little mess he and Jake had made of his grandma's kitchen, Willoughby returned to his bedroom and started preparing for his hike. He was excited about the waterfall; Jake's stories had added an air of mystery about the place that stirred his imagination. He could see himself finding an artifact or arrowhead or maybe even something more spectacular.

He dressed comfortably but warmly enough for the weather. There wasn't any chance of rain today according to the forecast. Foggy in the morning and then cloudy with a slight chance of sun later sounded to Willoughby like a perfect fall day for a hike, and figured jeans, t-shirt, and sweatshirt would be sufficient. He opted for his sneakers instead of his cheap hikers but did put on a pair of thick socks; they would keep his feet warm even if his sneakers were to get damp.

After he was dressed, he pulled his backpack out of his closet. This wasn't the same school pack that had been Eddie Anderson's downfall, but an actual hiking backpack his grandma had gotten him for his birthday just after they arrived from San Diego. She had picked it up at the new Cabela's store in Eugene. That was one reason Willoughby had been sure a hike to the falls would be acceptable as far as his grandma was concerned. His mom might not see things exactly the same, but Grandma Rose thought a boy his age should be out exploring the world instead of watching it on TV. After buying the pack, she and Jake had filled it with items they thought were critical for anyone venturing out into the Oregon wild. Inside one of the pack's individual pouches were a small flashlight and a waterproof container with matches and a Bic lighter. Jake had added a light rain poncho and a small 4' x 8' plastic tarp that folded up compactly at the bottom of the main chamber. To go along with the other weather related gear, Jake had rolled up a chunk of solid Doug fir pitch inside a section of newspaper. Cut from the heart of an old stump, it gave off a heady petroleum smell that Willoughby loved. After Grandma Rose had given him the pack, Jake had shown him how and where to look for Doug fir pitch and how to get a good fire going in the wet Oregon woods.

"Take yer knife or yer ax and slice off a few slivers of that pitch. Have yer other wood ready to go afore you put a match to it, that way you won't have to scramble around while the pitch is burnin' up. Start slow and small with yer other wood—don't even matter if'n it's wet. That pitch'll burn hot enough to get it burnin' long as ya don't smother it. Add another sliver or two if'n ya need it. Ain't nuthin' stop you from gettin' a fire going if you use that stuff like yer supposed to. People don't understand how and what to do when they get lost out here; end up dyin' for no reason."

Jake's next contribution after the pitch was a ziplock bag containing a handful of paper towels, Jake's answer to the critical "ass wiping in the woods" problem. He had explained to Willoughby the paper towels were handier because they could be used in a variety of ways besides wiping your ass, but for that all-important task, they were critical.

"Ain't nothin' worse than takin' a dump in the brush and havin' to wipe yer ass with moss or leaves," he had stated emphatically. "Makes your crack feel greasy and itch like a son offa bitch the rest of the day. So don't get caught without ass wipe. Hell, no more'n you know 'bout the woods you'd probably wipe with poison oak."

A side pouch contained a couple of energy bars, chocolate and peanut butter. While not as tasty as a candy bar, they supposedly carried more nutritional value, which would come in handy in case of a forced prolonged stay in the woods. The last thing inside the big pouch was a birthday present from his sister—a small Gerber camping ax with a sheath. His pocketknife, a Buck folding model that had been his dad's, was inside his jeans pocket.

Willoughby tried the pack on and after adjusting the various straps, he was surprised how comfortable the thing was. It was overkill for the hike he was planning, but it felt good to know the stuff was in there. He thought about adding some extra clothes but he really wasn't going to be far from home.

The last item Willoughby packed was another one of Jake's contributions. Early in the summer Grandma Rose had mentioned the possibility of giving Willoughby one of his grandpa's rifles, a 22, but his mother had vetoed the idea, at least for a while. The thought of Willoughby and a gun just wasn't something she wanted to deal with. His grandma had argued that every boy living in the Oregon woods should at least learn how to handle a gun. Jennifer Baxter wasn't totally against it, but she felt he hadn't gotten familiarized enough with basic life here to go that far. An agreement was reached where Jake would start to teach the boy and his sister the basic principles of safe gun handling. But for the time being, Jake had gotten Willoughby a secondary weapon, one his mother couldn't argue against.

"You can start to hone yer eye on the damn rats in the barn," he told Willoughby as he handed him the slingshot. It was a stainless steel model Jake called a wrist rocket. At first Willoughby thought it was just a little kids' toy, but when Jake took him out behind the barn and had shown him the power and accuracy that could be achieved with a little practice, the boy was impressed and had gotten fairly proficient with it. He had yet to nail one of the big barn rats, but had come close. They were fast and smart but it would only be a matter of time. Jake had given him a supply of ball bearings to use as ammunition.

"Way better'n rocks," he explained as the two of them practiced on soda cans lined up on the fence. "Rocks are too inconsistent in shape and size. They'll do in a pinch but if'n ya want to take them rats down, use these." Jake had given him a leather pouch tied with a rawhide drawstring full of the shiny projectiles. Willoughby stuffed the slingshot and the pouch in the big chamber of the pack.

In the kitchen, he filled his water bottle and packed a half dozen of Grandma Rose's chocolate chip cookies into another ziplock bag before adding two more for good measure. There were three pieces of chicken left over from Friday's dinner and yesterday's lunch, two legs and a thigh, so Willoughby placed them in a ziplock. Cookies and chicken—it probably wasn't what anyone would call a well-balanced meal, but to a teenage boy it was about as good as it could get. After adding a soda and a bag of chips, Willoughby was satisfied and wrapped everything up in a plastic supermarket bag, tied the ends shut, and secured it inside the backpack. The food was not overkill; the energy bars were great for survival, but this wasn't no boy scout adventure. If he was going to go on a hike, he was going to have a good lunch.

Slipping his arms into the pack, he readjusted all the straps; it felt firm and comfortable—he was ready.

Willoughby turned off the TV and lights, made sure the house was secured, and then checked the time, a quarter 'til eight. He was surprising himself; the desire to laze away a weekend morning sleeping in was disappearing right along with his San Diego tan. Like Grandma Rose said, Willoughby was getting "Oregonized."

The fog was still hanging low in the yard between the house and the barn as Willoughby closed the screen door on the back porch and stepped into the cool morning. Satisfied he was dressed appropriately, he made his way between the barn and Jake's trailer to the big metal gate that marked the way to the pastures. He pushed it open just far enough to squeeze himself and his backpack through, double-checking the iron latch when he closed it to make sure it was secure. Jake wouldn't be happy if he had to chase cows down because he forgot to get the gate shut. Once through, he cinched the pack up a notch higher onto his shoulders and headed west up the muddy track through the pasture towards the tree line marking the edge of the Baxter property and the river.

He had to thread his way carefully through this lower part of the road, not that you could actually call it a road. Once he left the packed gravel in front of the barn, it was just a track marked with thick mud and cow manure.

"Cow shit soup" was what Jake called it. Willoughby quickly realized he should have at least worn his cheap hikers instead of his sneakers. The big Indian had told him to always wear footgear suitable for the job but to Jake's way of thinking, any job on the farm meant the thick, black rubber boots both he and Grandma Rose wore when they went out to tend to the chores. But Willoughby had quickly nixed the idea of wearing them. He might live on a farm now but that didn't mean he was going to dress like a farmer.

"Yer choice boy," Jake had shrugged when Willoughby had declined his offer of a pair of the ubiquitous rubber boots. "Just wait 'til ya step in a shit pie with those low tops. Things were made for a basketball court not a fuckin' farm. Wear these and don't worry 'bout where ya step and just hose 'em down when you're done. Reckon a time or two trying to get those things clean and you'll figure it out."

Willoughby didn't want to figure it out today so he slowly and carefully worked his way along patches of ground with the least amount of mud and shit on them, at last coming to another fence and gate which marked what Jake called the upper pasture.

"Crap," Willoughby sighed when he came close to the gate. Not literally cow crap this time, though. There was a standing pool of muddy water blocking his path to the gate post and the wire loop that served as the latch. No way was he going to open it without soaking his feet. He would just have to go through the wire.

The fences on the Baxter ranch were almost all the same—four strands of wicked barbed wired starting one foot off the ground and spaced one foot between strands. One thing Willoughby had learned when his family had moved in was that fences and gates were important—you always shut a gate behind you and you took care of your fences. Jake spent a lot of hours taking care of fences.

"A good fence keeps yer things in and people out," Jake explained as Jennifer and Willoughby had watched him work replacing rotted posts. It was uncovering a fence from invading blackberries that Jake had been working on when he had stopped Eddie Anderson from rearranging Willoughby's facial features.

"Set your posts right and keep your wire tight," Jake preached. "Let posts loosen and the wire sag and the animals won't respect it. Won't take 'em long and they'll have it down."

As far as Willoughby could see, Jake had taken care of this fence pretty well. The wire was tight all right. Good thing he was small. An average sized person would have trouble squeezing through this fence.

Shrugging off the backpack, he slid it through the strands, being careful not to catch the material on one of the sharp barbs. Pushing the second strand of wire down as far as he could (which wasn't much) he put one leg through to the other side and started to ease his body and head under, promptly catching the hood of his sweatshirt on a barb.

"Shit," he cursed as he tried moving his shoulders back out, hoping the material would free itself, but the barb was sharp and had a good grip on his sweatshirt. As he released his right hand to free himself the strand he was pushing down came up just far enough to send another sharp point through his jeans and into the tender flesh on the inside of his legs just below his crotch.

"Owww! Son of a bitch!" he yelped. The pain made him flinch and he jerked his head up as he cursed, promptly catching his uncovered scalp on another barb. "Shit, shit, shit!" More curses and body movement; the barb in his leg sunk in a little deeper.

"Okay, okay, slow down," Willoughby prodded himself out loud. He eased back just a little to move his scalp away from its contact with the barb, something warm and wet started to trickle down his forehead—that one had drawn blood. Moving his right hand back to the strand he pushed down hard. The wire was tight, but Willoughby finally got enough room to free the barb poking into his inner thigh. Moving much slower this time, he managed to get his right leg onto the ground and then slowly brought his left leg through. With his body outside the wire, he eased the strand back up and finally was able to free his hands, quickly finding where the barb had caught the hood of the sweatshirt.

It hadn't been a very good way to start his hike. A quick swipe of his arm across his forehead revealed a fairly good amount of blood on the sleeve of his sweatshirt. It was one of his older ones—San Diego Chargers, of course—but he still hoped the stain would wash out. He unzipped one of the small compartments on his backpack and withdrew the ziplock with the paper towels. Jake had been absolutely right, they did come in handy for more than just wiping your butt. He used a little water from his bottle to moisten one and cleaned his forehead. After a minute of direct pressure, the wound in his scalp stopped bleeding.

Willoughby shouldered his pack and started along the logging road running across the upper pasture towards the old growth timber, vowing to find a better place to cross the next time he came to a fence. It didn't take him long to traverse the two hundred yard wide upper pasture. Jake hadn't turned the cows out here for a while so the minefield of cow patties wasn't as bad to navigate. Willoughby quickly spotted the landmark Jake had told him to look for.

"Follow the loggin' road 'cross the pasture to the fence," Jake had explained. "When you get there, turn upstream. You know which way is upstream, son?" Willoughby wasn't sure if he had been joking or not.

"Stay on the inside of the fence; it's easier going. You'll see the Old One, a big fire-scarred fir standin' all by itself. When you get to that tree, cross there. That's where the trail that'll take you down to the river starts. Ain't nobody been that way for a while so it might be a bit brushed up, but look and you'll find it. Brings you out a hundred yards or so below the falls and it ain't bad goin' along the bank there. Get ya fairly close to the bottom."

114

The "Old One" as Jake called it, hadn't been hard to spot. Willoughby had seen it just after crossing the fence where he had gotten stuck, towering over everything else around it. Separated from its brethren in what Jake called "The Old Growth Forty" the silent sentinel stood alone.

Willoughby had always been fascinated by big trees. The only things that rivaled the old growth fir, hemlock, and cedar forests of the northwest were the redwoods and sequoias of Northern California. Magnificent, beautiful, and to Willoughby, always mysterious in their looming silence.

The tree here was an "eight footer" as Jake had called it, referring to its diameter at what would be stump height. It had been one of many on the three hundred sixty acre claim that made up the original Baxter homestead. Though magnificent to behold, they were nonetheless a formidable challenge for the hardy folk who, after the Indians, were the first to settle the land flanking the west side of the Cascade Mountain Range. Cutting, grubbing, and burning acre after backbreaking acre to get land clear enough for crops, livestock, homes, and towns had been a monumental feat. Most of the old growth on private land was now gone, replaced by second and third growth industrial forests, the remainder locked away from most harvest on Forest Service and BLM lands; the Baxter forty acres of old growth were an anomaly.

"Won't nobody be touching that timber," Jake had stated to Willoughby as he explained the history of the Northwest logging industry. "And I reckon that's a good thing. The old growth got used for a true purpose, built the houses for a country that was doin' a heap a growin' after WWII, but the times changed things. Got enough of the smaller stuff to feed the mills. Builds good houses and it's still cheap. That patch a yer grandma's is sumthin' ya don't see much on private folks' land. Her 'n yer grandad took a little out now and then to help pay a few bills but they kept it pretty intact. Just 'tween you 'n me, I think they had kind of a spiritual thing goin' on with the trees, the land, and the history of this place. Somethin' kept 'em from cuttin' that piece. Coulda' made 'em some damn good money but they never did give in."

Willoughby walked up to the base of the giant. Some of its massive roots had been exposed by wind and rain and one of them made a perfect bench. He sat down and leaned his head back, taking in the majesty of his host towering into the sky above him.

The tree was indeed an "old one." Its massive limbs, the lower ones bigger than the standing trees around it, drooped heavy and low. Long individual strands of moss draped lazily towards the ground, some of them at least thirty or more feet in length. Like nature's tinsel, they adorned the heavy branches. "The Old Man's beard" Jake called the strange looking moss. He had also explained how the bark was more than a foot thick on some of the big firs, and as Willoughby ran his hand over its coarse, ridged texture he didn't doubt it. Black scars, reaching nearly fifty feet up the tree gave mute testimony to a fire that had gotten away from an unattended camp at the County campground thirty years ago.

"Bad dry season that year," Jake explained. "Some dumbass left a campfire goin' what got away and burned a couple hundred acres afore it got it stopped. Burned some a yer grandpa's timber."

But the thick bark of the old fir had protected it then. It had also withstood the Columbus Day windstorm, which had ravaged the Northwest in 1963 and felled many of its brethren. It now stood alone among the much smaller fir, hemlock, and hardwood that had since grown up around it. It had stood here for hundreds of years. An image came to Willoughby as he sat there, an image of a young Indian boy about his age, sitting in this same spot, craning his head skyward as he too pondered the wonder of nature's creation.

A breeze stirred the big tree's branches and rustled the lighter limbs of the small trees nearby as Willoughby's mind wandered. As he stared upward, mesmerized, the tree seemed to turn, slowly at first, and then it began to pick up speed. Faster and faster it spun until things no longer maintained their shape and blended together in a blur. Willoughby was suddenly very lightheaded and more than a touch dizzy, nearly toppling over before he regained enough control to force himself to look back down towards the ground.

116

Nausea racked him as he fought the urge to puke. He put his head down between his legs and tried to recover by taking deep breaths. Slowly the dizziness left him and the world settled back down to normal. But just as it did, the tree whispered, *"Willlloughbyyyy."*

"What?" he asked aloud, standing up abruptly. Big mistake. The blood flow to his brain had been screwed up enough as it was and standing up suddenly like he did after a bad case of vertigo hadn't been very smart. The world around him lit up in a flash of brilliant light and then just as quickly plunged into blackness. Willoughby toppled backwards over the root, landing with a thud on his back, temporarily out cold.

There was no recollection of how much time he lay there on his back with his legs draped over the huge root of the tree; it probably hadn't been more than a minute. When he finally opened his eyes he wasn't quite sure what had happened, but it slowly came back to him.

"Jeez," he chastised himself, "that was dumb." But it didn't seem dumb; he heard what he heard. It had sounded like the tree said his name as plain as day. That was why he had stood up so quickly.

Willoughby pulled his legs over the root and forced himself to a sitting position, hoping that he hadn't smashed his food as he lay atop his backpack. He sat there quietly for a few moments, listening intently, almost as if waiting to hear something else.

But the Old One was silent. It had to have been the wind and the sudden case of vertigo was his conclusion. As if lending credence to his wind theory, the long, drooping tendrils of moss stirred again in the breeze. But while it made more sense than the tree talking to him, it didn't ease the discomfort he felt—it had sounded so real.

As he sat there recovering from his fainting spell, Willoughby contemplated putting an end to the hike. It hadn't started off well, he could still feel the spots where the fence barbs had cut into his flesh, and the passing out thing was not good at all. Maybe it was better just to sit in the house and watch TV all day. Probably a whole lot safer, too.

Willoughby wrestled with what to do; it was easy enough to

quit the hike. There was nobody around to say anything about it, but he really didn't want Jake to think he was a pussy. But this was the first time he had ever done anything like this on his own and no one would blame him for being just a touch apprehensive. It was all making for an interesting debate going on inside his head until a funny itch started at the back of his neck—the kind of itch you feel when somebody is watching you from behind.

Slowly Willoughby turned his head, relieved when he saw nothing but the fence, and beyond it, the brush and more trees. His first thought was that his mind had played another trick on him, just like thinking the tree had spoken his name, but just as he got comfortable with that explanation, he saw it.

It hadn't been some*one* watching him, it had been some*thing*. On one of the big tree's lowest hanging branches, a mere twenty feet away from where he was sitting, perched a very large black bird. It leaned slightly forward, its dark eyes intently watching him.

It was a raven. Willoughby knew it immediately. While the bird's presence startled him there normally would have been no reason for concern, but there was something else about this bird that churned his stomach acid and fueled his uneasiness…he had seen it before. As sure as he was sitting at the base of the old fir, the bird perched on the branch above him was Patch. There was no mistaking the white splotch splattered across its head. It had just been last night when he and Jake had sat at the kitchen table in the trailer with the very same bird sitting in front of them.

It's not possible, his mind tried to reason with him. Patch was a dead relic from the taxidermist's table. But the bird sitting twenty feet from him was anything but dead. As if in response to Willoughby's confusion it cocked its head at an angle and presented the patch even more clearly.

"*See*" the bird seemed to be telling him, "*it is me.*" At least it hadn't talked out loud like the tree had.

Willoughby stood up slowly, trying not to scare the intruder away, even though he wouldn't have minded; it was starting to creep him out. But the bird didn't fly. It stayed on the big limb and stared at the confused boy, cocking its head from one side to the other.

"Patch?" Willoughby called out softly; it just seemed the thing to do at the present.

"Aaawwwck," the bird squawked, bobbing its white-splotched head up and down. Was that a yes? But before Willoughby had time to answer his own question, the bird suddenly flew off the fir limb and landed on a twisted vine maple across the fence from where Willoughby stood.

"Aaawwwck," it squawked and bobbed. Just below where the bird sat, Willoughby could see a slight opening in the brush. It was the trail he was looking for—just beyond the fir where Jake had said it was.

Willoughby made his way to the fence and stood staring at the brush-choked head of the trail that would take him to the falls. Patch, or the bird that looked just like him, had shown him the way. The apprehension of whether he should or shouldn't continue the hike was forgotten as Willoughby went back to the task at hand—crossing the fence again. The raven bobbed his head in accordance.

Being a little smarter this time due to the fact his inner thigh and his head still smarted from the earlier encounter with the wire, Willoughby eased his backpack through the wire and then removed his sweatshirt and tossed it over. Pain is a great teacher and this time he made it through the barbed wire unscathed, but when he stood up, the raven was gone. Willoughby scanned the sky and then looked back to the branches of the old fir, but there was no trace of the bird. As suddenly as the raven had made an appearance, it had disappeared.

Wow, Willoughby mused to himself, *that was weird*. It was a story to tell Jake when he got back. It might be a tale some would shake their heads at but Willoughby had a feeling the big guy would understand. The Tricksters—that was what Jake told him Indians had nicknamed ravens. Willoughby was thinking they deserved it.

The start of the trail down to the river was overgrown with blackberry bushes but Willoughby could see that someone, probably Jake with his machete, had cut the vines back a couple of years ago. New creepers had edged their way back in, but a few feet beyond the encroachment of blackberries, the trail looked as if it cleared considerably once inside the forest canopy.

Willoughby tied the sweatshirt around his waist instead of putting it back on. The walk had warmed him significantly and the fall sun had edged over the treetops. He wiggled into the straps of his pack and took one last look at the big fir tree. As he gazed wonderingly at the worn and fire-scarred bark of the trunk and up into the branches thicker than his waist, another wave of uneasiness passed over him. It nagged at him, both the incident of hearing his name whispered and the strangeness of the raven who looked like Patch.

"It's a strange place and funny things happen round here," Jake had said. Willoughby would now vouch for that. Strange and then some. But for some reason, though the circumstances of it still nagged, the incident had also steeled him to complete the rest of the hike.

He shrugged his shoulders in resignation as he pushed past the vine trailers blocking his way to the trail. Once inside the tree canopy, the sunlight was blocked for the most part and the path wandered downhill into the twilight of the river canyon. The waterfall was close, he could hear it, but as Willoughby plunged down the trail, an unwanted question crept into his mind. It had been a very strange start to his adventure—what other strange things would he find?

CHAPTER SEVEN

ONCE INSIDE THE CANOPY, WILLOUGHBY found the trail fairly easy to traverse; the heavy brush, including the nasty Himalayan blackberry vines, didn't grow in deep shade. The trees, a mix of conifer and hardwoods, grew thick and close in the wet confines of the river gorge, and had choked the life-giving sun from the plants that needed it. But there were plenty of species for which the dark of the closed canopy was an environment well-suited for their survival.

Ferns, several varieties, huddled in small communities in the thick mulch under the trees. Rhododendrons, whose brilliant pink blossoms would splash the dark wood with color in the spring, grew hearty and tall. Their root systems dug deep in the rich loam while their trunks stretched high for what little sunlight was able to force a path through the tight canopy. Vine maple, a smaller cousin to the bigleaf maples and also well suited to life in the understory, challenged the rhododendron for living room. It wasn't hard for Willoughby to understand why the Indians chose to make their camp away from the river; the place, though filled with vibrant life, had a dark and dreary feel about it.

Through this twilight environment, the path wound its way steadily down towards the river. Steep and muddy in parts, Willoughby was forced to watch his footing out of fear of slipping and falling and in an attempt to keep his tennis shoes as clean as he could. He was somewhat surprised that the path was easy to follow, owing more to the fact that it was trafficked heavily by game animals instead of human feet. Close enough now to hear

the sound of the river, he caught glimpses of it through the trees, flashes of white water hinting at the force of its flow. The powerful river rushed through the boulder-strewn canyon into which Willoughby was descending and didn't ease up until just above the old Stewart Covered Bridge.

The trail skirted firs and hemlocks, cedars, maples, and alders, a typical cross section of what grew in the riparian areas along the river channels in Western Oregon and Washington. The carpet of decayed needles and leaves lay thick beneath his feet and to Willoughby, the place had an unpleasant, musky smell. It was also noticeably chillier here than it had been up in the sunlit pasture, and he paused at the base of a huge old growth stump to put his sweatshirt back on.

As he pulled his sweatshirt on, he noticed notches in the bark of the stump a couple of feet over head height. Jake had a name for those notches, and he had shown Willoughby several like it in the forty acres above the upper pasture. Springboard notches, that was what the big guy had called them. Timber fallers long ago, before the advent of power saws, had chipped out these notches and driven steel tipped planks into them to stand upon as they chopped away the undercut with axes and then felled the tree with their long crosscut saws. Jake had explained that they did this to get above the swell of the stump, which could add much more work to the falling process. Willoughby stared hard at the notches above his head, trying to visualize a man standing there as the giant tree went over. Jake had never said if the men jumped or simply rode the planks as the tree crashed down. He would have to ask him.

The sweatshirt put the chill of the dark and damp canyon to bay and Willoughby resumed his hike. He was pleased when the path started to level out. He had reached the bottom of the gorge and the river was just off to his left. The conifers gradually gave way to more hardwood and Willoughby soon broke through the trees and found himself standing on the bank of the Cascade River.

The river was about twenty yards wide, separated from the tree line on either side by gravel bars and expanses of river rock, giving evidence to how high the water ran at its peak flow, swollen with the spring rains and snowmelt from the high Cascades. It now ran dark green with plenty of white water as it pounded through the boulder-strewn channel. That there were very few opportunities here to swim or fish was Willoughby's first impression. Kayakers might like it if they weren't too concerned about all of the large rocks intersecting the water flow, but it ran too fast for much else.

Willoughby listened closely. The flow of the river made quite a bit of noise but he could hear something else. A bend in the river a couple of hundred yards ahead made it impossible to see too far but he could hear it—a freight train roar in the not far distance. It was the waterfall.

The gravel bar and rocky shore made for fairly easy going and Willoughby found no need to re-enter the trees and find the trail. All he had to do was head upstream and he would find it. Contrary to what Jake had teased, he did know which way was upstream, and he started off in the right direction. Easy going on a long gravel bar brought him around the bend in short order, the thunderous sound gaining in intensity with every step. Around a clump of willow clinging to the rocky bank and there it was—his first view of the waterfall.

Spirit Falls plunged off a vertical face in the center of a huge basalt bowl and made a straight drop to a deep pool below. At seventy-two feet it was not one of the higher waterfalls in the state, but was still impressive in its own right.

From the pool, the river funneled into a chute hewn by the eroding power of water over the last few million years. It had cut a deep and narrow channel and flowed away from the pool for a hundred yards before widening out. Jake had explained how the river funneled into the same type of chute above the falls, increasing its velocity and flow in the same way water in a big pipe would do if it were suddenly forced into a smaller one. Willoughby had viewed numerous waterfalls on his trips from California through Oregon, but never from a point this close; the waterfall was no more than the length of a football field away, at the most. The gravel bar on which he was walking ended suddenly against the flat expanse of solid basalt that formed both sides of the channel and from what Willoughby could tell, it would take him almost right up under the thing, and while he had never envisioned getting that close, that was what he fully intended to do.

The path along the basalt wasn't nearly as flat and navigable as Willoughby had thought at first. As he ventured out on its charcoal gray surface, he soon found numerous cracks and fissures in the rock that he could not cross, and he was forced to go around them, but doing so took him close to the edge of the chute and the rock glistened wet with spray. It appeared slick, so he took a couple of tentative steps, checking his footing. Satisfied the rubber tread of his sneakers seemed to grip the wet rock fairly well, he minded himself that he would just need to be careful, especially as he got closer to the edge.

Willoughby worked his way tentatively along, planting each foot securely. The mist from the falls became heavier as he got closer and was starting to dampen his sweatshirt considerably. He wouldn't be able to stay too long without getting totally wet, not something he wanted to do. It might be pleasant on a hot summer day but it was about forty degrees shy of that today.

When he got to within about twenty yards from the bottom of the waterfall Willoughby decided he was close enough. He didn't think Jake, his mom or his grandma would be happy if he told them he how far he had come. The mist was now as heavy as a good Oregon rain and he was already feeling wet through his sweatshirt. He flipped up his hood, his hair already soaked, and water dripping into his face. Besides the wet, the roar was deafening, alluding to the enormous power of the water as it slammed into the pool. It churned and frothed with a whirlpool effect as it gathered energy for its downstream run. As the flow came out of the pool, it picked up speed and power as it charged down through the basalt chute. It would be absolutely unforgiving if someone were to make a mistake and find themselves caught in the deadly cataract. Even a total moron wouldn't deliberately try to challenge the torrent.

Yet every so often, as Jake had said, someone did end up in the thing and searchers would usually find them a mile or so downstream, extremely unpleasant to look at once they were discovered. Willoughby remembered clearly the big guy's story about helping to pull a college student out after a tragic spring break drinking party.

"It's pretty bad when you fish a body out what been in water for a couple of weeks," he had graphically informed Willoughby. "All bloated up and pasty white lookin.'"

But he hadn't stopped there. "When they get the shit beat out of them on the rocks in that river it really looks gross. Arms and legs all broke 'n twisted. Face all smashed in. That poor guy looked like a creature from hell twenty times over. And all 'cause him and a bunch of his buddies got drunk up in the viewpoint parkin' lot and decided they wanted to get a closer look at the water." Willoughby could see the disgust on Jake's face as he went on with the morbid story. "Water don't look no different up close than it does from a fuckin' distance.

"Kid's parents came up from Salem and stayed for a week," he went on. "Out tryin' to find their boy. Had an official search on but that had to be called off after a couple of days when they didn't find him. They don't have the money to keep after somethin' like that. But the kid's parents stuck it out for a while longer before they had to hang it up. I remember seein' 'em a couple of times in the Bunkhouse Café. Pretty pathetic."

Jake had gotten Willoughby's attention and had finally gotten around to the point he was trying to make.

"I'm tellin' ya boy," he had stated emphatically, "when you go to look at the falls, stay the hell away from the water. Two weeks after that poor couple gave up lookin' for their son, a couple of hikers spotted the kid's body hung up in a big pile of debris where the river sweeps around Beaver Point. I went and helped the fire department fish him out. Nasty, nasty, nasty."

Willoughby stopped well short of the edge. It dropped off a good eight or ten feet to the water and he wasn't going to press his luck. Like Jake had said, it didn't look any different being up close than it did from farther back.

As he surveyed the landscape across the river, he could see up the cliff to the chain-link fence that marked the viewpoint area and blocked off access to the old trail leading down. It didn't take much of an imagination (and he had a dandy one) to visualize a group of college guys out rippin' it up. Starting in the parking lot, with each beer chugged giving them more bravado, they would finally decide to scramble down the cliff face to the bottom and get closer to the river.

Willoughby could see them, whooping and hollering, throwing beer cans in the water and making assholes of themselves. Then, for whatever reason, shoving each other around in horseplay, making a dare as to who could get closest to the water, or maybe just being so drunk they didn't even realize where they were—and then one of them goes over the edge. A quick scream, his buddies taking an intoxicated moment to figure out just exactly what was going on, but with those brief seconds of hesitation, it's already too late. The boy disappears in the churning whiteness, pops up for a brief moment, giving his friends an uncomprehending look of shock and confusion, and then he is gone. Hours later, as the State Police officer takes down their stories, the remainder of the group give garbled accounts of what they think might have happened. All they are keenly aware of was that they were partying, knocking back a few brews and then…their friend was history. It's something that will haunt all of them forever.

Willoughby shuddered and took an involuntary step back away from the edge. That had been all too real. It was as if he was seeing the thing go down on TV. But as quickly as he broke the spell of one vision, it was replaced by an even more poignant one. His mom, sister, and grandma standing together at the fence in the parking lot looking down at the killing river while an officer explained to them over the roar of the falls how there probably isn't much hope of finding his body. It will turn up later, the man explains. That's how it is when people don't respect the river. The trooper gives his condolences and then leaves them to their grief. Jake is there, shaking his head and telling them how it was his fault. He had warned Willoughby about getting to close to the water. He should never have let him go on that hike by himself.

"Screw that," Willoughby said aloud, breaking free of the temporary spell that had been cast over him. Jake had been right, there was something strange about this place and it was starting to give him the creeps. It had been cool seeing the waterfall but that was enough. The whole thing with the stupid bird, the tree he thought was talking to him, and now the vivid visions here at the falls—not what he had in mind.

Turning away from the river and its disturbing images, Willoughby hustled himself away from the dampening spray and backtracked to the gravel bar, finding a nice flat rock to rest upon. He had fulfilled his goal of making it to the waterfall and figured the accomplishment deserved a decent lunch. Shrugging off his pack he briefly entertained the idea of making a fire and drying himself a bit but decided against the effort. Away from the spray, he would dry off quick enough. He would do lunch and then head on back to the farm.

Unbuckling the straps on his pack, he fished out the chicken, cookies, bag of chips, and his soda, and was soon enjoying his repast with an excellent, and safe, view of the waterfall as a backdrop. Away from the proximity of the soaking mist and the deadly chute, he was feeling pretty pleased with himself, imagining his mom and grandma would likewise appreciate his efforts helping Jake and the fact he was not just sitting around the house all day but getting out and enjoying some healthy physical activity outdoors.

Willoughby polished off the chicken and his bag of chips and had just tipped his head back to take a large swallow of his soft drink when a black blur flapped past him. Startled, he pulled the can back just as he was starting to drink, causing a shot of soda to course up his nostrils. Willoughby snorted as the carbonation tickled his nose into a series of sneezes, shooting out sprays of snot and soda.

"Shit!" Willoughby cursed between sneezes. He was just about to wonder what the hell had just happened when he spied the source of his trouble sitting on a rock a mere ten feet away—it was Patch.

"Aawwkk," the raven greeted, bobbing his head excitedly.

"Patch! You stupid bird," an irritated Willoughby coughed, still trying to recover from soda up his nose. "What the hell are you doing here?" The bird bobbed his head a couple more times, made a strange clicking sound, and cocked his head sideways as if asking his own question.

Willoughby was pretty sure the bird was not a reincarnation of the stuffed troublemaker sitting high in the corner of the living room in Jake's trailer, but it was an eerie enough coincidence that he called him by the name anyway. He was going to make the big guy explain this one to him. But same bird or not, there was a big raven sitting within spitting distance of him and acting as if he was used to being this close to humans all the time.

The two stared intently at each other before "Patch" clicked and cocked his head again. Willoughby had the funny feeling the bird wanted something.

"What do you want?" he ventured. "Some cookie?"

Another series of clicks, more bobs of the white patched head. That was definitely a 'yes.' Willoughby broke one of the chocolate chip cookies in half and tossed it towards the bird, where it landed at the base of the rock. The raven hopped down, snatched up the treat, and flapped back up to the top where it began pecking the cookie into bite sized morsels with its oversized beak.

The boy watched, fascinated. The bird was acting just like a pet. When it polished off the last bite, it looked back towards his host and again cocked his patched head.

Willoughby was going to flip him the other half of the cookie when he suddenly had an idea, a bizarre idea.

"Tell you what," he started, "answer me one question and I'll give you the other half of the cookie." He held it out teasingly towards the bird. "Tell me the truth and I'll give it to you—are you Patch?"

The raven cocked his head first to one side and then the other, as if considering the question. "Aawwk," it finally squawked and bobbed its head up and down several times.

As absurd as it seemed, Willoughby was certain the bird had understood and had just given an affirmative answer. "Well, son of a bitch," he quietly cursed in surprise as he fulfilled his promise and flipped the bird the other half of the cookie.

He couldn't wait to hear Jake's take on all of this. The big guy had mentioned some strange occurrences in his dealings with the bird and this was going to rank right up there with the best of them. Definitely strange. He was about to break another cookie in half when Patch flapped his large wings and hopped excitedly up and down on the rock.

"Aaawwwck," it rasped again loudly in its croaky raven voice. Then, as abruptly as it had flown in, the bird took off. Willoughby was expecting to see the bird disappear when it surprised him and flapped onto the limb of a vine maple where the riverbank met the tree line. Patch squawked again several times and flapped his wings.

The bird's antics were totally confusing until Willoughby noticed the faint outline of a path just behind where Patch sat, heading up the steep bank. It climbed at a sharp angle for fifty or sixty feet or so before breaking onto what seemed to be a fairly wide natural rock ledge. From where he sat, it looked as if it went straight to the top of the basalt bowl. It dawned on him clear as a bell—the raven was showing him the trail to the top of the waterfall.

Willoughby hesitated. Jake had been explicit with his instructions not to go to the top of the falls. The thought of doing so hadn't crossed his mind until Patch had made his scene, but there it was, beaconing him plain as day. The thought of viewing the waterfall from the top suddenly loomed large as an intriguing possibility.

But he still wasn't sure. Willoughby had a queasy feeling in his gut, knowing he wouldn't be able to lie to Jake if he was asked about it. There were two little gremlins sitting on his shoulders. The good little Willoughby gremlin was speaking in a calm and collected voice, telling him to listen to what Jake had said—it was too dangerous to go to the top of the falls. The other, the bad Willoughby gremlin, screamed in defiance, "Bullshit! It would be cool to see the falls from the top. Hell, babies and their mommas could look at the thing from down here—what a pussy!"

Willoughby was confused. And then there was Patch. What was the bird's part in all of this? Didn't Jake call the raven a trickster? Yeah, that was it. He said the raven was a trickster and a mischief maker.

"Aawwwk," the bird squawked in protest from his new perch, obviously not liking to be stereotyped.

But apart from the battle the voices on his shoulder were waging, there was another, and a much more logical reason to take the trail to the top—he could go home that way. If the plan was to return anyhow, and he already had seen what there was to see coming in, why not get a new perspective? Jake had told him enough to know that he would come out on the same fence line so there certainly wasn't much of a chance of getting lost. The trail seemed passable enough and it wasn't like he was going to put himself in any danger. He would get to the top, take a look, and then head home. The good little Willoughby was brushed off his shoulder and unceremoniously dumped. Patch squawked happily.

He slipped into his pack and made some adjustments to the shoulder straps. It looked like he would need both hands to navigate this first piece of the new route and he couldn't afford to have the pack slip down from his shoulders and get in his way. The bank was steep and slippery but there were rock outcrops he could use as footholds and several vine maple bushes growing out of cracks that he could pull himself up with. Satisfied with the boy's choice, Patch fluttered to the ledge and loudly voiced his approval.

For a while at least it went smoothly, other than getting his jeans and the elbows of his sweatshirt a little wetter and muddier than they had been. Another good reason for taking the shortest way home, the spray from the waterfall had dampened his clothes and he was starting to get cold. The quicker he could get out of the canyon the sooner he could get dried off. His decision was starting to make total sense to him now.

With a grunt and a heave he pulled himself up over the edge, finally getting a closeup view of the ledge he was planning to traverse to the top. Slick. That was the first thing that struck him. It was slick, as was everything here in the bowl. The angle the ledge took up the cliff face was steeper than it had looked from down below and it also wasn't as wide; another error in judgment.

Willoughby studied the ledge carefully, briefly entertaining the thought of backtracking and tossing this idea out the window but he decided against it. All he had to do was be careful. If he hugged the rock and took it slow, he could make it. At least there were no obstructions to go over or around. Patch flapped to the edge of the bowl and squawked him on.

Willoughby pushed his face close to the rock wall, trying hard not to look down, and started to edge himself cautiously upward. Double checking his handholds and making sure of each placement of his feet before moving, he inched forward. The wet rock was covered with a slimy green residue, another thing he hadn't counted on. Water dripped continuously into his face, coming from clumps of clinging wet moss on the rock overhead. Stopping his climb, he carefully released one hand and pulled the hood of his sweatshirt up. It would at least keep some of the water out of his face. Slowly he inched himself ahead.

Willoughby allowed himself a quick glance across the river to the viewpoint, still being very careful not to look down. Something he hadn't given any thought to was the chance someone might be witnessing his little adventure. Someone like his mother who would come unfrigging glued if she could see him clinging precariously to a ridiculously narrow and wet rock ledge high above the boulder strewn riverbed. The thought prodded him to move faster, cautiously but still a little quicker. His mom was a long way from here but that didn't mean there wouldn't be someone who knew her or recognized him and wouldn't tattle.

The ledge veered slightly to his left, bringing him closer to the thundering water as it plunged over the basalt lip, roaring like a jet fighter as hundreds of thousands of gallons of water hammered into the pool below. Willoughby was getting a much more up close and personal look than he had ever imagined. The spray was making the ledge far more hazardous, now more like a drenching rain, soaking him and everything around. Still Willoughby persevered, knowing he must be getting close. Pulling his face from the wall, he risked a peek.

Shock and disbelief hit him like a wet blanket. There, just a few feet above him, was a final geological hitch to his travel plans. The ledge ended suddenly in a vertical wall just over head-high, standing in mute mockery as the last obstacle between him and the top.

"Fuck," Willoughby cursed loudly, as if trying to be heard over the cacophony of the waterfall. Why hadn't he been able to see such an obvious blockage from below? Panic grabbed him with its cold fingers harder than he was gripping the ledge. Stuck. Stuck on a slick, narrow ledge dangerously close to a seventy-foot drop-off to what would be a sure death. Absolute fear crept into his stomach, threatening to loosen his bowels as he pressed his face into the wet granite. Tears joined the water running in streams down his face.

Settle down and think, he admonished himself. He was far too committed to try and back down—he didn't even think it was possible. It had been totally stupid to attempt to come this way. Over and over he cursed himself and Patch—where was that fucking bird anyhow—somewhere high in a tree laughing at his plight?

None of that matters, dumbfuck, he cursed again. It didn't matter. There had to be a way to get out of his predicament and Willoughby was positive it lay forward instead of back. Resolutely he forced himself out of his self-induced paralysis and edged onward until he was up against the blocking ledge. Cautiously he worked his left hand up and over the lip, feeling for a handhold.

There, he encouraged himself as the sound of the waterfall hammered hard at his ears and the wet chill soaked through his clothes, *a crack in the basalt.* His hands were starting to numb with cold but he wedged his left one into the narrow gap in the rock and gripped hard. Ever so slowly Willoughby freed his other hand, working it up and over into the same crack. Satisfied with his handgrips he searched to find one for his foot. Inching his right leg up the face of the slimy wall, he found a toehold. It wasn't much, but he thought it would do; a slip of the foot would not be good here.

Willoughby took a couple of deep breaths and gathered himself, knowing once he started up he had to keep going. Pulling with his arms and pushing with his right foot, he drew himself up until he was looking over the top of the ledge. But he started to panic; he wasn't strong enough to pull his weight over the top. Desperately he hung on for all he was worth as he struggled to work his left leg up, searching for another toehold. Just as he felt his grip starting to slip, he found it. One last heave and push and he was over.

Willoughby rolled across the flat basalt until he was comfortably away from the edge before scrambling to his feet. His arms ached from the strain and his hands were so numb he could barely feel them. He was soaking wet clear through and his legs wobbled from the stress, but he had made it.

As he took stock of his surroundings he found himself standing on a broad, flat expanse of dark gray basalt identical to the one bordering the chute below, the water flowing dark and green over the lip of the bowl only a few feet from where he stood. Too close. Here he was at the top of the falls, exactly where Jake had told him not to be. It had been a very stupid choice.

But it was already better. Moving away from the edge of the falls and out of the heavy mist, Willoughby immediately started to feel a misguided sense of accomplishment. It had been a harrowing climb and it had taken a lot out of him, but he had made it after all—damn if he hadn't done it! But he wasn't about to tell anyone, especially the big guy. Jake would not be happy.

Working his way to a flat and semi dry rock away from the water's edge and the thundering racket, he decided to rest. Soaked to the skin and muddy to boot, he made a mental note to get things cleaned up before his mom came home. Wet and muddy clothes would be a prime target for unwanted questions, but all in all, he was feeling pretty pleased with himself. Getting up that ledge had been a challenge.

The raven was nowhere to be seen, which was okay with him. The trickster. Damn if that friggin' bird hadn't nearly gotten him in a lot of trouble. It had been Patch that prompted the climb up the ledge. The whole thing was weird but he would have to be careful what he told Jake. The big Indian didn't need to know about the harrowing climb to the top of the falls.

As he was scanning the trees and bank for signs of his black nemesis, he spotted the trail that would take him back up to the top of the canyon. It was steeper than the one he had come down, but at least it looked to be shorter.

But Willoughby didn't feel the pressing need to hurry anymore, already feeling much more comfortable. His sweatshirt and jeans were wet, but his body had started to warm up, now that he was away from the soaking spray, so he couldn't see any reason not to do a little exploring. Stay away from water, like Jake had warned, and there wouldn't be any problem.

Since upstream was really the only place he could go, that was the direction he headed. The terrain was nearly identical to what it was at the bottom of the falls. Basalt bedrock on both sides of the river formed the channel the water funneled through. But up-river about fifty yards, the formation came to an end and the river channel broadened out to more than twice the width of the chute.

Willoughby could see how this geographical anomaly gave Spirit Falls its ferocity. Like a hose with an adjustable nozzle, when water was forced through a smaller opening it came out the other side with more power.

But as the flat bedrock ended, so did his easy going. The canyon rose up from the river sharply on either side and the passable bank simply petered out. He had come to the end of his exploration. Nothing left to do but head up the trail and make his way back to the pasture and home.

But as he walked back along the channel, picking his way past the flotsam that high water events had left scattered about, he couldn't help but contemplate the river and the tragic legacy of those who hadn't respected its lethal combination of speed and power. A morbid thought wormed its way into his mind, making him wonder if anyone had ever actually fallen into the water above the waterfall and gone over its edge.

Wow, Willoughby mused aloud. The concept he was considering was both scary and highly intriguing at the same time. Jake, when telling him about those unfortunates who had ended up drowning over the years, had never said anything about somebody going over from the top. There were obvious signs people came up here, beer cans, fast food wrappers, and the remnants of party fires on the opposite bank. If people had been drunk or stupid enough to fall in down below, surely someone over the years would have done the same from up here. Willoughby's curiosity was pumping now. He would ask Jake when he got home, being careful with his words so it wouldn't give away the fact he had disobeyed orders and come to the top anyway.

But there was one thing he could do and he wouldn't have to wait to talk to Jake. While walking past the many chunks of debris deposited by winter's high water events, Willoughby had developed another idea. He could actually see for himself just what happened to something (or someone) that went over the top of Spirit Falls.

To accomplish the experiment he needed to do two things. One, select the chunk of wood that would best serve as the victim in his test. There was a name for that he knew; he had learned a little from his class science experiments. A control element, that's what it was called. Select the control element that would take the place of an actual human, and toss it into the channel. The second part of his experiment would be to beat the control element back to the edge of the waterfall before it went over. The whole point of the process was being able to see what happened. Of course, with any scientific endeavor there were always hazards to consider. All of this had to be accomplished without endangering himself.

Safety First—the sign hanging over the lab area in his science class warned students to be careful during their experiments. The science teacher, Mr. Poop, well, it was actually Mr. Stroup, was adamant about safety.

Willoughby carefully thought over his plan, checking for hidden dangers along the bedrock chute. Stepping in a crack or a hole and going down hard on the solid rock would not be cool. But the path was level enough and not near as wet and slick as below. The water was running fast but he was sure he could beat the control element to a safe viewing spot a few feet back from the edge of the falls.

"We must always consider your safety, boys and girls," Mr. Poop admonished in his squeaky voice. "We always conduct our experiments with the utmost caution in mind."

Good advice, Willoughby thought to himself. Even from a jerk like Mr. Poop. He would conduct his experiment with safety first.

Willoughby scanned his path and settled on an observation point near where he had come up over the ledge. It offered him a good view of the falls and the pool below, but was far enough from the edge for safety purposes. Now he needed to select his victim, or rather, his control element. There was a good pile to choose from just upstream.

The first piece of wood he pulled from the pile was a chunk of fir, or it might have been hemlock, about twenty-four inches long and as big around as a football. *Too small,* Willoughby thought, tossing it aside. But it did cause him to pause for a moment. If he chose a big piece, he was going to have to get close to the edge of the chute

136

in order to get it into the water. That was not cool. He decided he would have to sacrifice size in order to stay back from the edge.

Willoughby pulled several pieces from the debris pile but tossed them aside for various reasons. He had just decided he would have to do without a human-sized piece when he spotted it—laying there the whole time and he hadn't even noticed—his control element. About five feet long and human shaped, well, kind of, except that it had no legs and only one limb that would have to suffice for an arm, but hey, you couldn't have everything. It had a head and a neck, thick but still a neck, and a torso. Okay, maybe you had to use your imagination a bit, but it would do. The best thing about it was that it had to be more along the lines of what a real person would weigh. While too heavy to pick up, Willoughby was sure he could just roll it into the river. Perfect.

Willoughby walked over to the chunk of wood, being very wary of his footing. This was as close to the chute and the river as he had been. Cautiously, he peered over the edge.

The channel was deep, much more so than he had thought. The power of the water had carved itself a significant notch in the basalt over its long history. No wonder there was so much water going over the falls. The edge of the chute was about five feet high and Willoughby guessed the water was at least fifteen or twenty feet deep. Multiply that by the channel's thirty feet of width and, while he sucked at math, he figured it was a hell of a lot of water going real fast. Willoughby backed away from the edge of the dark and deadly green water, certain of one thing—if you ever had the misfortune to get into that, you would never get out.

He tested the chunk with his foot, certain he could get it to the edge without too much effort, its weight being less than he thought it would be. As he started to take his backpack off, he thought better of it. He cinched the shoulder harness tight and fastened the chest strap, tying the loose end into a firm granny knot to keep it from flopping around and getting in his way. He wasn't sure how fast the wood would move once it got into the water, but the way the current was flowing, he thought he might need to move quickly.

"Okay Eddie, time's up." It seemed appropriate to give his control element a name and it was the first one that popped into his head. A psychiatrist might have determined there was some kind of deep, subconscious reason for choosing that one but Willoughby didn't care. It was a science experiment, not a psychiatric one.

Willoughby gave Eddie a hard push with his right foot. It rolled easily, just as he thought it would, but only once. The short limb serving as the one arm stopped it dead in its tracks. He was going to have to get closer and roll it one more time.

Willoughby took two small but prudently cautious steps towards the control element, now only slightly more than a foot away from the edge. Dropping to his knees he grasped Eddie under his torso; he would have to lift and push at the same time to get Eddie to roll past the arm/limb poking out. Willoughby grunted and heaved; wooden Eddie seemed to be aware of his fate and hesitated slightly before rolling into the water with a rewarding splash.

"Yeah!" Willoughby shouted excitedly. He stood quickly as he would now have to hurry to his viewpoint because Eddie was already well under way. But as he turned, he plowed directly into a mass of flapping black wings and feathers.

"Kraawwwk," screamed the raven as its heavy black wings beat around the startled boy's head and its talons clawed towards his face.

"Fuck!" Willoughby added his screams to the cries of the crazed bird; instinctively flinging his arms up to protect his face.

"Krawwwk! Krawwwk!" Viciously the raven's heavy wings pounded at the boy's head, trying to rake his claws across his face. In a desperate attempt to put some space between himself and his assailant, Willoughby unwittingly took a step back…into nothing but air.

He hit the water, landing flat on his back. Fortunately the fall was not much over a few feet, but the cold liquid was an instant shock to his system. He took a nose full of water and came up sputtering, coughing, and flailing his arms. He could feel the power of the current as it gathered him in and propelled him downstream, the bulk of his backpack working as a detriment as its mass caught the water. Willoughby knew he was quickly running out of time.

Panic started to take over as he tried to take a few strokes and kick his legs but it was useless, the force of the water was far too strong to swim against. He thrust out with his hands and felt the cold slime of the rock wall, his fingers dug and clawed in desperation as he search for anything to grab hold of which might stop or even slow his momentum. His fingers slipped into a deep crack and he gripped the slick rock for all he was worth and fought to get his other hand jammed in alongside it. For a moment it stopped him but the current swung his body into the rock wall and forced him under the water. Willoughby held his breath and tried to bring his head to the surface but the power of the water kept forcing him down, his pack once again doing him in as it acted like a sail against the wind, the water trying to rip it off his shoulders. He was weakening fast and his arms felt like they were being ripped out of their sockets. His fingers started to slip, one hand let go and then the other. He was able to get his head up out of the water but he could feel the increased surge of the river as it closed the distance. Time was up. In the next instant, the river tossed Willoughby into the air like a candy bar wrapper from a car window.

Time and space became irrelevant as he shot feet first into a whiteout of water spray and foam; the mind-numbing jet fighter roar of the waterfall overwhelming his senses. The first thing that raced through his mind, besides the incredibly unbelievable fact that he had been dumb enough to go to the top of the falls and fall in, was that he needed to land feet first. Somehow, this became his focus as he plunged towards the pool below.

Not counting the fact he had been unlucky enough to go over the thing in the first place, there were two things that saved Willoughby from the consequences of a fall to the water from seventy-two feet. One was that he did manage to land feet first. The second was simply due to the characteristics of the water in the pool at the bottom. A fall at that distance to a smooth, flat surface like a lake would be roughly akin to landing on concrete, but the surface of the pool was churning and agitated water, full of air molecules.

This considerably lessened the impact of his fall. It would be the drowning part that he needed to worry about.

As it was, the backpack caused him the most grief. He had been thinking clearly enough to get a good lungful of air before impact, but when he hit the water, the pack was nearly ripped forcibly from his body. He entered the water with his fists clenched and arms folded tight into his body but they were ripped hard up over his head sending an instant surge of excruciating pain through his right shoulder.

Incredibly enough, as far as he fell and as hard as he hit the water, he shot almost immediately back to the churning surface. A cry of pain escaped his lips as his head broke free of the water, but it was short-lived. Willoughby was shocked that he came up as quickly as he had but he no more than broke the surface when the whirlpool-like current of the fast moving river snatched him like a giant hand and immediately pulled him back under. He barely had time to get a breath as he plunged down into the depths of the pool. Panic began to set in as he realized he was being pulled not only to the bottom, but the current was sucking him under a ledge and into an opening in the rock. He kicked his legs and flailed with his good arm to try and slow his descent but to no avail, his head slammed hard against the rock and he felt himself slipping into unconsciousness. In the millisecond before he slipped into darkness, Willoughby knew he was going to die.

Chapter Eight

THEODORE HURD CLEARED HIS THROAT directly into the microphone, the rasping cough reverberating through the cavernous gymnasium, immediately grabbing the standing room only crowd's attention. He allowed the buzz of conversation a few seconds to die down before he started.

"Ladies and gentlemen, students and faculty of Spirit Falls High School." The balding principal was grateful for his one semester public oratory class he had taken as a whim at Oregon State University in Corvallis. He knew just how and when to pause for maximum effect.

"It is indeed, with great sadness and a heavy heart, that I welcome you today to these hallowed halls of learning. It is fitting that this be the chosen place for us to come together, as a school and a community, in mourning one of this town's most beloved citizens."

Another well-placed pause for effect. He was doing great. Already he could hear the sobs and sniffles.

"A devoted and loving son, brother, and grandson, an illustrious and gifted student, a cherished and dear friend to all."

The volume of weeping and crying was rising. Time to raise his own voice level to maintain his control over the gathered mass.

"A young man with the whole world at his doorstep. A world that can now only ponder in tormenting sadness what great things might have been. We can but wonder. Would politics have been his destiny? The Senate? Governorship? Perhaps even the Presidency? Maybe science would have been his calling—making world changing discoveries that would have placed him alongside Galileo,

Newton, and Einstein."

Theodore Hurd was on a roll. He had really cranked up the volume a couple of notches when he dropped those three names. The crowd hung on his every word. But he knew it wasn't just his oratorical brilliance that had them enraptured. No, it wasn't that hard when your subject was larger than life itself.

"But no, fate has dictated that it was not meant to be." Back to a softer tone. Great speech givers throughout history had used this up and down roller coaster of syntax to perfection to capture the undivided attention of their audience.

"Indeed it has instead given us just a taste of the greatness that would have been Willoughby Baxter's lasting legacy."

As Mr. Hurd placed an emotion-rousing accent to Willoughby's name there was a surge in the audible grief responses from the varying segments making up the overflow crowd. Groups of teenage girls sobbed unabashedly. His immediate family—mother, sister, and grandma—kept a more subdued, if nonetheless heart-wrenching composure. Groups of former teachers, business owners, movers and shakers of the town, the mayor, local representatives, and county commissioners bowed their heads with tears rolling down their ruddy cheeks. This was indeed a day of grief for Spirit Falls.

Mr. Hurd had allowed just the right amount of pause. The effect of Willoughby's name had grabbed the crowd's emotional drawstrings and cinched them tight. "We all are overwhelmed with the tremendous sense of loss; the tremendous sense of incomprehension of what has transpired." Mr. Hurd was now getting caught up in the moment, adding his tears to the mix with electric effect.

"WHY?" He slammed his fist against the lectern, snapping everyone's head up to immediate attention. *Wow,* he thought. *That was good.* "Why, I ask you again. Why are we brought to this moment? Why are we brought to this apex of monumental grief and unbearable sadness?" Mr. Hurd's words rang out over the transfixed crowd as he let his rhetorical question echo off the walls of the gymnasium.

"Because the little shit ass didn't pay a damn bit of friggin' attention to what I told him. That's why."

A huge gasp rose from the crowd, blended together as one shocked voice as they all spun to see from where the blasphemous words had been uttered.

Standing at the double doors to the Spirit Falls High School gymnasium was a tall, lanky figure, bathed in shadow, as all the lights in the building had been dimmed for effect—more of Theodore Hurd's stage theatrics.

Stunned silence from the stricken crowd greeted the newcomer. Murmurs started quickly through the gathering. Who was this? Why would he say those things about their beloved Willoughby?

Jake "Tall Bear" Thompson strode out of the shadows into full view. His voice, powerful, commanding, and full of unabated contempt swept over the gym.

"Hell and shitfire." The words spat out like cobra venom. "Don't even know what the fuck the majority of ya all are doing here anyway. Only ones who cared much about the boy was his family and a few others." His steely glare cowed the crowd, challenging any intervention.

"Most of you didn't treat him worth a damn crap since the day the poor kid moved here. Everyone spectin' him to be some sort of reincarnation of his dad. Picked on and bullied was what he got from most of you. Disappointed he wasn't some sort of fuckin' jock."

The tall Indian scanned the crowd, searching out any who might challenge his words. None dared. "But I guess the little asshole has had the last laugh in this whole matter."

The crowed looked around at each other in total disbelief. What was this crazy Indian saying anyway? Jake saw their shock. It was time to drop his bombshell.

"You just don't get it do ya?" he continued on. "Well I'll let you in on a little surprise. This will come as a shock to those of you who really did care for Willoughby. He will be truly sorry for causing you this grief. As for the rest of you bleedin' heart hypocrites—put this in your pipe and suck on it."

Jake made timely use of the pause as well as Principal Hurd had.

"The joke is on you—the boy ain't dead. Do you friggin' idiots hear me? I said, THE BOY AIN'T DEAD."

WILLOUGHBY STIRRED. SOMETHING HAD WOKE HIM. A DREAM; HE had been having a bad dream. He had thought he heard a voice... Jake's voice. But where? Had he heard Jake say he wasn't dead? Why would Jake say that? As he stirred himself to consciousness he came to a realization that he was cold, wet, and his body ached in a hundred different places, and almost instantly understood why; he had gone over the waterfall. Gone over the waterfall and he wasn't friggin' dead.

But as he tried to move, excruciating pain shot through his right shoulder, nearly causing him to lose consciousness. Immediately he halted the effort; he couldn't handle too many more of those. It was obvious that something was severely wrong, and he was going to have to take things very slow and very easy.

Willoughby took stock of the situation. He was lying on a bed of very uncomfortable rock, several of which were jamming into his sore ribs. The fact that he was still partially lying in the water was pretty obvious as the bottom half of his body was completely numb with cold. It also appeared to be nighttime, leading him to wonder how long he had been lying there.

He raised his head slowly, painfully aware that sharp, quick movements brought unwanted results. As his eyes adjusted to the dim light he could see smooth, round river rock everywhere and a few scattered pieces of driftwood lying within arm's reach. A few feet in front of him was a wet rock wall; he must be lying on the riverbank downstream from the falls. The roar was still audible but it was somehow different, muffled. His first inclination was that he had been carried quite a ways downstream, but there was something that wasn't quite right. The one thing he did know was that he needed to do more than just lift his head a couple of inches; he needed to get out of the water.

Willoughby was lying on his stomach with his left arm stretched out in front of him, partially cushioning his head. His right was folded underneath his body; that was where the majority of the pain came from when he had tried to move. Something was very wrong with his shoulder, but he was going to have to try and move as his body was really starting to feel the adverse effects of lying in cold water.

Ever so slowly he began to work the right arm from under his body, anticipating the electric shock of pain with every movement. It wasn't long in coming. A sledgehammer blow of searing pain shot through his shoulder, forcing him to cry out in agony from its sheer intensity. Something in his right shoulder was out of place—dislocated. He had never seen a dislocation but had certainly heard about it, remembering his dad telling stories of ugly occurrences on the football field; big, tough football players screaming for someone to put whatever joint was affected back into its place.

But there wasn't anyone here to help him get his shoulder back in its place, it was something he was going to have to do on his own or he was going to be in trouble. The numbing cold was bringing on uncontrollable shivers—*hypothermia*—the body starting to shut down trying to protect itself from the cold. Willoughby quickly came to the realization he was going to have to move—dislocated shoulder or not. Reaching out with his free left hand he felt around until he finally grasped a river rock that seemed to be fairly well anchored. He would pull hard with his left arm and at the same time try to roll over onto his left side and free his right arm. It was going to have to be fast. If he tried to do it slowly, the pain would stop him. It was going to have to be all or nothing. He counted to three, pulled hard, and rolled to his left.

Willoughby screamed as the brutal shock tore through his shoulder but amazingly enough, over the sound of his own discomfort, came the distinct pop of his shoulder going back into place. Immediately the pain started to subside.

As he lay there panting, with his face buried in the wet river rock, the intensity of the pain rapidly diminished, leaving behind a dull ache. While the shoulder pain wasn't as severe, he could now feel all the other places in which his battered body hurt. But at least he was sure he could move now.

Gently Willoughby tested the right arm and was grateful when he got no more than a little discomfort in return. Slowly, pulling himself forward in little increments, he inched his body out of the numbingly cold water. Standing was out of the question; there was barely any feeling in his legs. The combination of lying on the hard rock and the effect of cold water had turned them into dead, wet weight. The only thing he could feel was the tight wetness of his jeans.

Pulling himself a few feet over softball sized river rock, he was relieved when he found himself on a gravel bar with much smaller rock and sand on it. Hard, but still much better than what he had been lying on.

This was the first opportunity Willoughby had to raise his head and look around, and when he did, he found another big surprise. There had been plenty enough of those for the day, but they just kept on coming. He was in a cave. He could tell that because there was just enough light coming from the water to infuse the darkness with a small bit of illumination.

The ceiling was not more than ten feet at its apex, and the whole room was about thirty feet wide. Roughly half of the room's space was water, with river rock, the small sandbar where he lay, and scattered pieces of driftwood making up the rest. He could see the diffused light coming from an opening under the water in the wall directly across from him. It suddenly dawned on him where he was and what had happened.

Willoughby lay his head back onto the gravel, the strain of looking around being more than he could stand for any period of time. He remembered the struggle against the powerful current of the river just after he had made the plunge over the falls. Holy shit. Over the frigging falls. How was he going to explain that one? A voice in his head had told him to breathe and land feet first. After he had gotten what air he could into his lungs, he had briefly popped to the surface before being dragged back under immediately. Hitting his head more than a few times was something he could certainly remember; he had the bumps and cuts to prove it. It must have been when he was being sucked through the tunnel that it led to a cave. That's where he had to be—in a cave under the waterfall.

Willoughby was racked by a sudden onslaught of shivering spasms. He was soaked to the bone and the hypothermia was sapping what little strength he had left. With a lot of effort and more than a lot of pain, he managed to force himself into a sitting position. It wasn't an easy task with the wetness of his clothes adding pounds of weight to his frame and his pack still strapped securely to his back. At least he hadn't lost that. The fact that the pack had stayed on his back the whole time and made it into the cave with him was a surprise. He was fortunate that he had tied the chest straps into a knot.

With cold, stiff fingers he worked at the knot, finally getting it undone. When the knot was free, he undid the chest and waist buckles and slipped the pack off his back. It wasn't that heavy but the relief he felt being shed of its weight instantly made him feel better and improved his situation. Now he could move about more easily.

Opening the flaps of the main chamber, he pulled out its contents and laid them in the gravel, pleasantly surprised to find things not as wet as he thought they might be. The waterproof Cabela's backpack his mother and grandma had paid extra money for had lived up to its guarantee.

Flipping on the beam of the flashlight, he surveyed the interior of the cave, noticing a little more detail. Rocks, water, and an occasional chunk of driftwood were his only companions. He switched the light off, mindful of the need to preserve batteries. The minuscule amount of light seeping in from the pool would allow him to move about, not that there was much need to.

His first order of business was to try to dry out his clothes; not a simple task without a fire. He thought briefly about using his pitch and what bits of wet wood were lying about the cave to kindle one, but he wasn't sure how much air it would use up. Being dry but then dying for lack of oxygen wasn't a good trade off. He would have to wring the chilling wetness from his clothes the best he could.

Willoughby struggled out of his clothes, not an easy task with all of the pain and numbing cold he was dealing with, but soon he was standing completely naked, surprised it wasn't as uncomfortable as having the wet clothes next to his skin. Unwrapping the cheap rain poncho Jake had given him, he slipped it over his head, then wrapped the rest of his body in the brown plastic tarp. The plastic was initially cold against his skin but Willoughby's body heat soon started to reassert itself. Sitting cross-legged, Indian-style, he fished out his first aid kit and swallowed three ibuprofen, chasing them down with a pull from his water bottle. Then he set about the task of getting the water out of his clothes.

Starting with his underwear and socks, Willoughby wrung until his hands and arms ached and until he was able to get them fairly free of water. He laid his socks aside but slipped his underwear back on. They were cold and clammy against his skin but they were clothes. Discomfort was something he could put up with; being caught naked scared him to death. Even tucked away in a cave under a waterfall, the phobia was strong.

The t-shirt and sweatshirt came next; the muscles in his hands and arms burned by the time he wrung what wetness he could from them. He laid those aside on the rocks with his socks. The only things left to go now were his Levis and his sneakers. Willoughby decided to work on his shoes and let the jeans go for a while; their tougher fabric would not wring easily and he wanted to give his hands and arms time to recover. His tennis shoes presented a different problem. He couldn't squeeze hard enough to get the water out, so he took a different approach—he simply reached in and pulled the insoles free. Having them out made the process of wringing the water from them quite simple.

The process of getting as much water out of his clothes as he could had occupied Willoughby's mind and kept him from thinking about his real predicament, but the beast finally raised its ugly head. After having achieved a comfort level that allowed him to feel better about his physical state, a bad case of mental anguish rapidly took over the boy's train of thought. An overriding question had begun to gnaw away at his meager defense mechanisms...

How am I going to get outta here? It was time to think about it. The first thing that confused him was that he had no real sense of where "here" truly was. The inclination that he was trapped in a cave under the waterfall was the best he could come up with but was it fact? It just led to more questions.

Why had no one ever discovered the existence of a cave behind Spirit Falls? Jake certainly had never said anything about it and he was as close to an expert on the waterfall and things happening around it that Willoughby knew of. The fact that the muffled but still intense sound he was hearing had to be the waterfall added credence to being under the damn thing. But overriding all of the questions surging through Willoughby's mind was one sure thought—*If I'm in a cave under the waterfall, getting out is not going to be easy.* The process of getting in had almost killed him. He was almost certain that trying to go out the same way would finish the job.

Thinking about his predicament was starting to overwhelm him to the point of tears and he mentally chastised himself to stay strong. There was one obvious fact he would force himself to concentrate on—after all he had gone through, at least he was alive, and sooner or later people would start to look for him.

The thought made him feel better. Strangely enough, it also made him feel just a tad bit hungry. The chicken, chips, and soda he had consumed for lunch seemed like forever ago and the gnawing in his stomach was going to have to be addressed. But he didn't want to get carried away. After all, he had no idea how long it would take for the searchers to figure out where he was. The food he had left might just have to last for a while.

Willoughby took stock of what there was—four cookies, and two energy bars. While it was a struggle to bypass Grandma's cookies, he decided to go easy and eat part of an energy bar. It would help to ease the pang in his stomach and maybe give him the energy to focus on his situation.

There it was again, his situation. It just wouldn't go away. But he shoved the thought back inside and focused on his snack. Unwrapping one of the bars, he broke it in half, pleased to see that they had survived without getting wet. Carefully he wrapped up the remainder and put it and the other bar in the ziplock with the rest of his cookies.

As Willoughby sat there slowly chewing, he contemplated on how long he had been gone. It had been late morning when he left. Taking into account walking slowly and stopping a couple of times, he thought it had taken a half hour, maybe forty minutes, to get to the falls. Dallying there, eating his lunch and then the trek up the ledge had consumed another forty-five. With what he knew, Willoughby calculated he had gone over the falls sometime around noon. Jake was supposed to be home at two and was expecting to see Willoughby when he did. What wasn't known was how long he had been out cold. That piece of the puzzle made things a little tougher, but he was sure enough time had passed that the big guy was looking for him.

Jake. Damn, he was going to be pissed. His warning had been very clear. Willoughby was absolutely not to go to the top of the falls, and yet he had done just that. To top that, he had fallen in. No, not just fallen in. He had fallen in and gone right over the falls. How was he going to explain that? Then there was the whole story about the fucking bird—it had been Patch. That damn bird had been responsible for the whole thing.

Willoughby shook his head; he didn't think anyone but Jake would believe that part of it. But it was all a moot point now and could be dealt with later. He was sure Jake would be searching for him and when he couldn't find him, he would get help. But as much as that notion made him feel better, it also brought about another question—how would they find him in the cave? They would think he had drowned and been swept downstream. That's where they would look if they didn't find him on the trail anywhere.

Willoughby started to panic. No one would be able to find him in this cave. Maybe they were already looking, maybe they were just outside. Frustration and fear overwhelmed him and the tears started to flow. He started to yell for all he was worth.

"Help! Can anyone hear me? Helllp! Helllp!" He didn't know how long he kept it up, only stopping when he was nearly hoarse. But his only response was the muffled roar of the waterfall and the water lapping the rocks inches away from his feet; that, and the disheartening sound of his own sobs.

Willoughby suddenly felt completely drained—the half energy bar had done nothing for him. He wanted to sleep, to rest. He wanted to wake up in his own bed and laugh at what a stupid dream he was having.

Stuffing his possessions back into the pack, he slipped the rain poncho on and wrapped himself in the tarp. The wrung-out underwear was damp against his skin but he was warm enough. His body hurt in a thousand places and the gravel bar made for an uncomfortable bed but exhaustion was taking over. Willoughby lay his head down on his wet pack, taking care not to smash what food he had left and pulled his knees tight to his chest; a smaller package would allow his body heat to work better for him.

The waterfall thundered on overhead, its muffled, monotone roar broken only by the water slapping at the rocks. His body wanted so desperately to give itself in to sleep but his mind was still clicking. They had to be looking for him by now. Jake would figure it out. The Indian was a woodsman; he could track exactly where Willoughby had gone. Muddy sneaker tracks would show his progress up the ledge. But once Jake tracked him to the top, then what? Would there be any evidence that he had gone (or been forced) over the falls? Maybe Jake would see that fucking raven. He would know something strange was going on if he were to see Patch, the bird that was supposed to be dead and stuffed high in a corner of Jake's trailer. No one else would understand but Jake. Patch was tied to the mystery of Spirit Falls somehow.

But as he lay there huddled in damp clothes and plastic, fighting for every ounce of warmth he could, it wasn't the surrealism surrounding the raven bothering Willoughby most, it was the nagging certainty that no one else knew of the existence of the cave. His train of thought kept coming back to that single point. Everyone that had gone into the water and drowned had been swept downstream. That was where the search would focus. It would do no good to shout and holler on the outside or on the inside. Spirit Falls would allow nothing but its own voice to be heard. The search party would look but for how long? How long would his mother, sister, and grandma be able to hold on to the hope that he just might be alive?

There was nothing about his predicament that gave him any sort of hope, but an exhausted Willoughby was too tired to cry. With a final thought to his family, his battered and exhausted mind and body finally gave in to sleep.

CHAPTER NINE

"WAKE UP, WILLOUGHBY. WILLOUGHBY, wake up."

His inner voice was really being a nagging bitch this morning, but Willoughby wasn't ready to get up yet. He was still tired and school was the last place he felt like going. It was school he was supposed to be going to this morning, or was it? And what the hell was that noise?

As he rolled over, trying to get comfortable, something hard immediately jammed into his aching side. His eyes popped open. *Shit.* He wasn't in his bed and he wasn't going to school this morning; he didn't even know if it was morning. He was still in the cave, wrapped up in the cheap rain poncho and tarp, aching cold, and feeling every bump, bruise, and scrape. The noise was the sound of the waterfall, dulled to a muffled roar by who knew how many feet of solid rock. A dull throb reminded him of the dislocated shoulder, one he had painfully put back in place himself. The hard thing jamming into his back was a river rock, which he pulled out from underneath him and flipped into the water.

The water. Willoughby sat up quickly as the gravity of his situation flooded back over him in bone chilling clarity, much to the dismay of his battered body, as the sudden movement brought unwanted results in the form of sharp pain.

Everything came back to him—trapped in the cave with the deadly water between him and home. His thoughts turned immediately to his family; they would be frantic by now. Jake would have started looking for him Sunday afternoon; his family scheduled to be home late that night. Willoughby had no track of time, but there was still a tiny bit of light coming in through the water. It was either late Sunday afternoon or he had been in this cave all night, which was his inclination.

What a mess. His mom, sister, grandma—Jake. It sickened him to think what they were going through. They would assume the worst—that he had drowned, and there was no way he could let them know he was all right. If he had only listened to what Jake had said. What an idiot he was.

Tears were getting ready to flow but he fought them back. At least he was not dead and he had options. His biggest challenge was staring him in the face not more than a couple of feet away—the only barrier between him and his agonized family. The pool leading to the wall and then the opening that led to the way out. It was visible only a couple of feet under the water. But how far did it go before it came out into the river? He remembered going under the ledge and being sucked into the cave. It was the last thing before he hit his head and became unconscious.

The water lapped lazily against the dark wet of the river rock; water which had nearly drowned him before depositing him abruptly into this subterranean holding cell. But that was it; that was his way out. Willoughby knew he could wait for quite a while, hoping those on the outside could figure out where he was and mount a rescue. His meager bit of food he could make last and the biggest thing that usually killed people was lack of water. That was certainly not an issue. But could they figure out where he was?

When he contemplated his option a wave of nausea crashed in the pit of his delicate stomach, nearly causing him to puke. The thought of trying to get back out on his own terrified him. He had no idea how far back in the cave he was. The fact that there was a small bit of light filtering in from the water gave him some hope, but the thought of trying to reverse what he went through to get here was not a pleasant one. The sensation of near drowning wasn't something he wanted to experience again, and he had an uneasy feeling that luck had somehow played a big part in his survival the first time. Could he even hold his breath long enough to get out? And then what? Jake had said the current was unforgiving and that was where people had drowned. In the fast water below the pool. If he did have the ability to go out through the underwater cave would he then just drown in the whitewater? He had to admit to himself that he was scared of trying that way…very scared. No. Trying to go back out that way was something he would do only when he had given up any and all hope that they might find him. It just wasn't something he had the nerve to try just yet. If he waited, they just might send a diver down to see if his body had hung up on something under the water. Wouldn't that be something? The diver pops out into the cave looking for a pasty, bloated body and lo and behold—Willoughby is sitting there waiting.

He shook his head. *Like that's really going to happen.* The thought was a teasing bit of hope that dissipated as quickly as it had come, leaving him only more depressed, cold, and aching. He had to do something besides sit and feel sorry for himself. Unwinding the rain poncho, he got to his knees. Every joint and muscle in his body screamed in protest with some sort of ailment or stiffness. The fall had been brutal, though mitigated by the condition of the water, it had still been seventy-plus feet, and he had banged against the rock numerous times as he was sucked into the cave. Slowly and carefully he struggled to his feet, trying to stretch out some of his aches and pains. His legs were wobbly but it still felt good to stand.

Surely it had been hours since he had gone over the falls and ended up here. Was it Monday? If it was, everyone would be out looking by now; the Search and Rescue folk scouring the river-bank. They could be just outside, calling his name, but he knew that whether they were calling from the outside or he was scream-ing from the inside, the constant roar of the waterfall would make hearing anything absolutely impossible.

But he was alive and he had to keep telling himself that. No matter how dismal things seemed to be—he was alive. He was also pretty damn hungry again. He had eaten part of an energy bar before going to sleep but his stomach remembered none of it. Fishing the other half of the energy bar out from the pack, he polished it off in three bites and thought about eating another, but if he was going to be in here for a while, he needed to save it. He knelt down and with his cupped hands, drank from the river; the water was cold and tasted remarkably good. It had tried to kill him but could be the thing that actually helps him survive, for a while, anyway. At least the irony of the whole thing was something he couldn't taste.

Willoughby stood back up and started stretching the kinks out of his arms and legs, trying to get his blood circulating through his chilled extremities, when his body suddenly reminded him of another issue, one that needed to be addressed very soon. He had to go to the bathroom. And not just a piss call either. Most definitely a hearty number two was in order, and fairly quickly.

Nature was not going to take a back seat just because he was in a tough situation. Damn, he hated having to squat and crap. A guy needed to be comfortable when he was doing important business like that. But wishing for the comfort of a warm toilet seat wasn't going to get him anywhere. And now he had that funny, queasy cramp-thing going, the one that said, *you'd better figure this out in a hurry or else.*

Willoughby grabbed the ziplock bag with the paper towels from the backpack. He needed to find a good spot; somewhere he could bury it at least. If he was going to be here for a while, like maybe forever, he didn't want to have to smell his own crap.

The cave wasn't very big; he had checked it out with his flashlight before. He would just have to find a corner away from the gravel bar. The rest of the cave was mostly river rock and this little patch of gravel and sand seemed to be the most comfortable spot he was going to find. Since he had no idea of just how long this may be his cell, he might as well keep things tidy.

Grabbing the flashlight, Willoughby flipped it on and shone it around, looking for his outhouse-to-be. The Mini Maglite wasn't very big but it didn't take much to light up the interior of the cave. As he had noticed before, it was pretty featureless but at the far end from his gravel patch, maybe twenty feet away, there was a large boulder. About three feet high and semi egg shaped, it looked as if it had been part of the ceiling at one time. There appeared to be space enough between it and the cave wall that he could do his business; maybe not "out of smell" but at least out of sight.

Willoughby slipped his underwear off; squatting was uncomfortable enough and it would be easier not having any clothes in his way. Making his way carefully across the slick river rock and over to the boulder, he shone the light into the space between it and the cave wall, hoping at least for some sand and gravel there with which to bury his crap.

But what he saw stopped him short and made him suck in his breath, temporarily making him forget his pressing need. There was a hole. A small one, maybe two feet high and a little narrower in width, but from his angle it seemed to go back in a ways. Getting down on his knees, he peered cautiously inside, half afraid there just might be something in there. The light showed him an irregularly shaped tunnel, just a crack basically, but one that went in about ten feet or so and then made a right corner—one that was big enough for him to crawl through!

Willoughby backed out from behind the boulder and stood up, his heart pounding and his mind racing. He hadn't thought about the possibility of there being another way of escape other than going back out under the water. The chance of this crack going all the way through to the outside was a long shot at best but he knew he was going to have to try it. If it went just around the corner and ended then he was no worse off than he was right now. The bad thing would be to get way in and have it dead end; he would have to back out unless by chance it opened enough for him to turn around. Still, he was excited; it was better than just sitting there.

But his excitement was tempered by another wave of cramps, a reminder of the urgent business to attend to. Going around to the opposite side of the boulder from his newfound hole, he rolled a football-sized river rock out of its bed and squatted just in time. When he was done he rolled the rock back into place.

Willoughby dressed quickly, not even minding that his jeans

weren't dry. Rolling up his poncho and tarp, he made sure everything except the flashlight was secure in his pack. He was about ready to climb into the straps when he realized that the crack probably wasn't big enough for him to go through with the pack on his back. No matter. He would push it along in front of him.

When he got back on his knees in front of the hole, Willoughby silently said a prayer though he certainly wasn't what you would call religious. His mother and sister hadn't started going to church regularly until after his dad had died and they had moved to Spirit Falls, but his mom had never insisted he accompany them. But still Willoughby was hoping for a miracle, and it certainly wouldn't hurt to suck up a bit to the guy upstairs.

Pushing the pack into the hole in front of him, Willoughby squeezed his body in behind. Immediately he realized that it wasn't going to be an easy task. It was going to be a belly crawl unless the crack got bigger and with the pack in his way, he was going to have a hard time seeing what was in front of him. But other than the water, it was his only hope, tough going or not; he pushed ahead.

There were rocks on the floor to crawl over and water dripped everywhere but with effort he got to the first bend. He forced his pack around and crawled forward so he could see what was ahead, breathing a sigh of relief when the light showed another twenty-foot stretch of passable going before his tunnel disappeared around another corner. *So far, so good,* he thought.

Unfortunately for Willoughby the crack showed no signs of getting bigger. It was push the pack ahead and crawl, push the pack ahead and crawl. He was starting to fall into a rhythm but it was taking its toll. He kept bumping his head on the uneven ceiling and rocks ground their way into his ribs and scraped at his knees and elbows. Water dripped constantly from above him and on several occasions he was forced to belly crawl through standing puddles. His clothes, which he had so painstakingly wrung the water from, were now wet and muddy.

Willoughby had come far enough now that he began to fear that the tunnel would suddenly come to a dead end and he would have to reverse his way out. What was waiting for him if he had to do that was the daunting prospect of either trying to do the water route or wait for help, neither very pleasant to think about. The one thing this had going for it was he was still moving. Moving towards what he had no idea.

Exhaustion forced him to stop numerous times to rest. While he knew he wasn't making very much progress distance-wise, it had to have been more than a couple of hours since he had first crawled into the hole. In a weak effort to keep his mind from dwelling on the seriousness of his situation he tried to think about how far a guy could crawl in an hour. Surely a hundred yards or more at the speed he was moving. But his attempt to keep his mind focused on something else, quickly got lost in the tangled mess that was Willoughby's sense of time. It had gotten sidetracked when he went over the falls, and with no concept of how long he may have been out cold, there was nothing for him to form a time tracking relationship with.

What the fuck difference does it make anyway? Just keep going, he angrily prodded himself. So he did, but the going seemed to be getting tougher. More and more rocks lay in his way; some he could move, others he had to work himself over or around. Twice he came to sections of the passage so constricted he could barely worm his slender frame through. While he had never considered himself to be claustrophobic, the sense of being squeezed to death in this tiny crack in the earth was growing ever more intense. Panic was close; its dark tendrils probed for an opening in Willoughby's battered frame of mind.

After squirming and wiggling his way through one particularly tight passage that nearly peeled his sweatshirt off, exhaustion and despair finally caught up with him. Switching the flashlight off in an effort to save the batteries, he lay there in absolute pitch black darkness with his battered head resting on his pack. Heaving sobs wracked his body as Willoughby succumbed to an overwhelming sense of hopelessness. He didn't think he could go on, and going back seemed to be a mind-numbing impossibility. A big part of him wanted to just give in; to go to sleep here in this damp crack of a tomb and never wake up. It would be so easy to just allow himself to let go of that precious little flutter of a heartbeat that maintained his tenuous grip on life. So easy to just give it over and be done with this futile struggle; so easy to…

That's pure bullshit.

Willoughby jerked his head up with the surprising interjection of Jake's voice into his contemplated mental surrender and was promptly rewarded with another crack of his head against the jagged ceiling.

"Ouch!" he cursed into the black nothingness as he switched the flashlight back on. A probe with his free hand quickly found a warm stickiness spreading on a patch of scalp.

"Thanks, Jake. That one hurt." He cursed aloud at the chastising but nonexistent persona of the big Indian.

As depressing as his situation was, Willoughby was buoyed by the fact that there seemed to be some sort of mental bond between him and the big guy that kept manifesting itself. He wasn't sure if it was just a trick his stressed brain was playing on him or if there truly was a presence of Jake's spirit with him, but it really didn't matter; it was reassuring in any case. The feeling that he wasn't totally alone helped banish the ghosts of self-destruction that had started creeping into his subconscious. If Jake's spirit, or whatever, was along for the ride, it was okay with him. In this case, two was definitely good company. The sobs stopped as he regained his composure. Willoughby pressed ahead.

On and on he crawled forward, foot by agonizing foot, his body screaming in protest. The tunnel showed no sign of opening up other than a couple of short stretches where he had enough room to get to his knees, giving his belly at least a little relief. If he could just get to a spot where he could at least sit, that would be something.

Willoughby stopped again after another particularly tight stretch of passage. He was simply exhausted and desperately needed to rest; at least for a while. While he didn't relish having to sleep in what amounted to little more than a terribly long coffin, it was

going to be necessary. His body was giving out on him. Water…
he was exceedingly thirsty. The dust and grit was now caking his
face, getting into his eyes, and coating his nostrils. Willoughby
propped his light up on a rock and fished in his pack for his water
bottle, deciding to swallow some ibuprofen while he was at it.
Every movement was difficult within the constricted space. He
could barely raise his head far enough to get a drink, and did so
very cautiously, avoiding another nasty encounter with the tunnel
ceiling. It was amazing how good plain water could taste when you
were in need of it.

Willoughby took a healthy swallow and then another smaller
one to wash down his ibuprofen. His water bottle was now only
three quarters of the way full; he would have to conserve. It had
been awhile since he had crawled through any standing puddles
or steady drips enough to replenish his water supply. It had been
nothing but dry and dusty conditions for quite some time.

It hit him like a brick. When had the conditions in the passage
changed? Willoughby couldn't remember. He had crawled for so
long he hadn't even noticed, but change it had. His hope rose. Did
it mean something? Had he gotten away from the river? Is that why
conditions had dried out?

But Willoughby's mind was as tired as his body was and trying
to rationalize anything was hopeless. He didn't know what the
change meant, if anything. He must have crawled at least a mile, he
thought. A mile on his friggin' belly—a mile. Despair began to take
over again. The hope and excitement he had felt when he found the
tunnel now seemed like it had just been another mistake, one of a
long line of them since he had left the house however long ago. It
had been one screw-up right after another.

As he was putting his water bottle back into his pack, Willoughby was thinking things couldn't be much worse than they
were right at the moment, but when he flicked the light on and
peered at the passage ahead, he found that things could indeed get
worse, and very quickly. Praying for a glimpse of something more
than the tight confines of his tunnel, not more than ten feet ahead

of him was just what he had hoped he wouldn't see—a rock fall was blocking the passage.

"Fuck!" screamed Willoughby bitterly. He couldn't believe it—not after he had come this far. But there it was nonetheless. It looked as if a section of the ceiling had fallen in, leaving no way around or over.

Willoughby switched the flashlight off and lay there in the darkness. He had fought back the urge to cry on several occasions as the task of maneuvering the passage had nearly gotten the best of him, but critical mass had just been reached. The tears flowed fast and heavy and he made no effort to chastise himself into stopping. The brutal, numbing exhaustion he had been feeling just had a heavy layer of despair dumped on top of it. It had certainly been a possibility going in that he could run into this very situation, he had known that, but to actually have it manifest itself was still an overwhelming shock. Backtracking—it had been no easy feat going forward but it was going to be a real bitch going out backwards.

Holy shit. I don't think I can do it, Willoughby cried to himself as he buried his dirt-and-dust-caked face in the fold of his arm, mixing it to a slimy mud with his tears. He must have gone over a mile—to have to do it backwards—no way.

But there was another way out. It had poked its ugly head from a crack in his sanity once before but he had pushed it back into the dark pit from which it crawled. It was the thought that isn't supposed to come to a fourteen-year-old, no matter what the circumstances.

Just think a bit about the logic of it. Willoughby couldn't tell whose voice was talking. Was it his own?

You should have been dead anyway, it was luck that cheated death the first time. You don't go over a waterfall like that and live to tell about it. The voice was strong, but there had to be a catch to it. You couldn't just lay your head down and will yourself to die… or could you?

No. You have to hurt yourself to die. It was a different voice. Willoughby didn't recognize that one either. He was going absolutely crazy. He flipped the light back on. As tired as he was he didn't to want to spend any more time in the claustrophobic confines of this passage to nowhere and just let insanity take over.

He had resigned himself to start the unpleasant task of backing out when he shone his flashlight on the ceiling above the rock blockage. That was when he noticed what appeared to be some space between the rock fall and the top of the passage. Curious, he pushed his pack and himself forward until he was at the edge of the rock pile. Lifting himself up as far as he could, he shown the light on the opening. Though he couldn't tell for sure, it looked as though the passage might just keep going beyond the pile of rock in front of him. The rocks for the most part were ones he thought he could move; if he could get enough of them out of the way, he might just be able to get through to the other side. The idea was more appealing than the thought of trying to go backwards the way he came.

Willoughby pushed his pack as far to the side of him as he could get it. It was going to be tight; he was going to have to move a lot of rock in order to get enough room to squeeze himself through. He wedged the flashlight into a crack beside him so it shone on the task in front of him. It wouldn't have been much of a pile had it been outside with room to just toss the rocks aside, but this was a different story; every rock was going to have to be moved in behind him somehow. He grabbed a football-sized rock and worked it around to the side. When he had it far enough past his body, he pulled his right leg up enough so he could use his foot and was able to push the rock back down into the passage.

"One down and a friggin' truckload to go" he said aloud to the mute rock walls. He kept working. Small rocks he could just give a slight flip and get them behind him, though once he managed to bounce one off the wall and it ricocheted into his flashlight. He nearly panicked when the light clattered down and flipped suddenly off, leaving him enveloped in the folds of absolute darkness. His relief was immense as he groped in the blackness and finally found it; flipping the switch and getting the result he hoped for with no apparent damage to the glass or bulb. *Tough light*, he thought as he wedged it back into its spot on the wall, vowing never to buy anything but that brand again.

Willoughby kept working. Twice he was forced to stop and with his feet, work the mounting pile of rock down the passage behind him. If he didn't keep the material worked back as far as he could, he would run out of room before he got through. As he pushed the pile into the narrow passageway, it suddenly occurred to him that he just might have to do this all over again if the tunnel came to another dead end. It was an unpleasant thought but he didn't let it stop him from working. The waterfall and the cave hadn't whipped him yet and he wasn't about to give up. The thought of home and his family pushed Willoughby on. Never in a million years had he thought he would miss everything so much as he did right now. Laboring deep within the constricting confines of his would-be tomb, Willoughby made himself a promise: if he could manage this seemingly insurmountable task, he would never again treat those in his life as if they didn't matter.

The atmosphere in the crack had changed considerably. Moving the rocks had created a dust cloud and since it had nowhere else to go, it settled on Willoughby like a blanket, getting into his eyes and his throat. It was gritty and dry. He tried to rub the gunk off his face and out of his eyes with the sleeve of his sweatshirt but there wasn't a clean piece to be found. The dust cloud hung about him like a dirty curtain, making it harder for him to breathe. That, in turn, made him wonder about air. Would he run out?

But none of his physical discomforts or the sobering thought of possibly running out of air, made him stop working. He had developed a rhythm of sorts that was serving him well. Reaching out above his head with one or both hands he would find a rock, move it down past his body, and kick it down out of the way with his feet. It was slow, but he thought he was making headway, and so far he had encountered nothing that he couldn't move. The smaller gravel and dirt he just left and would smooth out and crawl over when he had a hole big enough to fit him and his pack through. He was now working with his eyes shut most of the time; the grit and dust were really starting to bother him.

As Willoughby reached out for the next rock, he was mildly surprised when he grabbed onto one whose surface had a smooth and completely different texture than the ones he had been handling. He was even more surprised when he noticed its lack of weight as he worked it out from amongst the others. It really didn't feel like a rock, so as he brought it past his head, he opened his eyes to see just what it was that he was holding. There, in the dusty haze not more than six inches from his face, a human skull grinned at him.

Willoughby did three things all at once. He let out a totally god-awful scream, he dropped the skull, and he threw his head back before he attempted to scoot backward and away from the hideous, pasty white monstrosity he had been holding.

"Owww!" he screamed again as the top of his head took in another painful reminder of the confined space in which he was in. Backing away from the skull wasn't an option either as he found himself blocked by the rock pile he had created.

"Holy crap!" he cursed, wedging himself as far away from the nasty object as he could. Which, given the circumstances of Willoughby's current position, wasn't nearly far enough. Now, not more than a couple of feet away, the skull lay in the dust of the cave floor, glaring at the terrified teen with its haunted, hollow eyes. Willoughby's racing heart was in his throat as he helplessly stared back.

Gradually he started to calm himself. As terrifying as it was to look at, it also sent a torrent of thoughts through Willoughby's battered mind. This had been a living human being at one time. He, or she, had been in the same position Willoughby now found himself; crawling through the constricted space of this cave crack when the ceiling had collapsed. Immediately it made him wonder if this person had been crawling in from the opposite direction or had come in the same way as he had and was attempting to crawl back out.

Willoughby reached up and pulled his flashlight from its crack in the rock. Shining the light on the pile where he had fished the skull from, he could see more bone and rotted clothing. As much as he dreaded touching the bones, he had to get past that pile. The find, though terrible in its content, had opened up hope. It looked like there was a fifty-fifty chance that this person had been coming in from the other way, and right now, to Willoughby, those were pretty damn good odds.

He directed the beam of his flashlight back onto the skull. Now, past his initial shock, it didn't appear to be so frightening. He wished it would quit grinning at him with that morbid, toothy smile but he figured that without skin and lips that was what you ended up with. He wondered again if it was male or female. Male he guessed, though he had no real reason to do so.

"Bob," Willoughby said aloud, "I think I'll call you Bob." There was no response. It seemed not much would surprise him anymore after what he had been through, but had the skull voiced protest at the name he had been given, Willoughby thought his heart may have just stopped right then and there. As lonely as this hole was, he was glad his new acquaintance hadn't talked back to him.

"How did you get in here, Bob?" Willoughby continued. "I sure hope it wasn't the same way I came in. That would really suck. But if you didn't come in that way, then I need to find out just where you did come in at."

Carrying on a conversation with a dead pile of bones was totally crazy, but he was also past the point of giving a crap about that. He needed to know what Bob knew. If there was a way out of here, Willoughby needed to know where it was.

"I'm sorry you got killed when the rock fell in and I hope you didn't have to lie there and suffer a whole bunch. That would not have been cool."

A vivid picture went through Willoughby's mind of himself being buried as he crawled through the narrow tunnel. He shuddered at the thought of dying in such a manner; all alone without anyone knowing where you were at. It made him wonder if this person had left a family back at home, maybe even in Spirit Falls; people who had worried and searched for days, maybe even weeks. People who had cried and mourned at a funeral with no body, people who never stopped wondering what had happened to their loved one, people just like his mom, sister, and grandma.

Willoughby shook the notion out of his head. He needed to get past this and see if there was indeed another way out of here. It wasn't a time to fret about things that didn't have to be—not if he could help it. He had lost his fear of the skull by this time. Gently, he moved it to the side and started moving more rocks. He decided to work on the upper part of the rock fall and keep away, as much as he could, from the rest of Bob's bones. If he could manage to work the upper part down he just might create an opening large enough for him to crawl through. He would leave the rest of Bob buried under the rock, but he made the skull a promise: "If I ever get out of here I will tell people back at home where you are at. Maybe somebody might know who you are, do a forensic test or something, and figure out who your family is. They will come and get you and give you a proper burial."

As he placed his flashlight back up into the crack in the rock, Willoughby caught a glimpse of something shiny reflecting off the beam of light, buried in the sand and gravel where he had excavated Bob's skull. Carefully he brushed the loose material away, exposing more bones. It was an arm and hand this time, but more than just that. Clutched in the grip of Bob's finger bones was a piece of what appeared to be glass about six inches long and a little bigger around than a hot dog. As he brushed it free of dirt, he noticed it tapered to a point and that it had several smooth sides. Gently, as if he were trying to pull something out of the hand of someone who was sleeping, he pulled it free and held it up into the light. It wasn't glass, it was a piece of crystal. Willoughby had seen crystals before but never one like this. Bob must have found it and had been carrying it when the ceiling collapsed. Maybe that's why he had been in the cave in the first place, hunting for crystals.

Willoughby reached for his backpack and unzipped one of the side pouches and placed his find inside. He didn't figure Bob would be missing it anyhow. He wondered briefly what else he might find if he looked, but his overriding desire to get the heck out of the cave vetoed the idea. He brushed sand and gravel back over the exposed arm and hand bones and continued working on his escape hole.

Gradually, as Willoughby kept pulling rocks down and pushing them as best he could into the diminishing space behind him, the space at the top of the rock pile began to open up. When he got to where he thought he had enough room, he worked his pack around and pushed it through the hole. It rolled down the other side and out of sight. He breathed a sigh of relief—there must be space on the other side. Willoughby grabbed his flashlight and shone it on the grinning skull that had been watching the teen's progress with hollow eyes. "Well Bob, here goes nothing. Rest in peace. I made a promise. I'll tell people where you are if I get out, and I hope you don't mind that I took the crystal. It's actually pretty cool. My friend Jake will like it."

Willoughby pulled and belly-dragged himself up over the rock pile. The space he had created wasn't much more than a foot high at the most. He wasn't very big, but he was going to have to suck himself into an even smaller package to fit. Scraping his back on the ceiling, he wiggled his torso through the opening. The going was tough and there was a moment when Willoughby thought he might have gotten himself stuck but he kept pulling and wiggling and finally forced his way through.

Relieved as he was to be past the cave-in, he was even more comforted when he saw the passage ahead. It wasn't any taller or wider, but it kept going and that was what he wanted to see.

Willoughby crawled on in an almost trance-like state; exhaustion and pain had shoved all but the bare basics to the back of his weary mind. Push the pack ahead and drag his body forward, push and drag. It was all he could think of. Foot by agonizing foot he kept going until thirst finally forced a halt. The dust and grit had turned his throat into a piece of coarse grit sandpaper. He fished his water bottle from his pack and was confronted by another terrifying reality. As if he needed anything else to give him concern, he was running out of water. The dry, dusty condition he had been in for quite some time had forced him to take several drinks and now there were only a couple of swallows left. The cave behind the waterfall, with its pool of cold, clear water might have well been a thousand miles behind him. Every exposed spot of skin was raw and dirty and his eyes were tormenting him. And now he was nearly out of water. Willoughby wasn't sure how much more of this he could take.

As he dragged himself across a sandy stretch of the cave floor, his body suddenly gave out and he lay there panting—he could go no farther. Whatever lay ahead of him would just have to wait. Flipping the flashlight off, he was almost thankful for the total darkness that enveloped him. It was like having the lid closed on his coffin. Beat, battered, and mentally overwhelmed, Willoughby surrendered to sheer exhaustion.

CHAPTER TEN

WILLOUGHBY STIRRED AWAKE. THERE WAS no surprise this time; he absolutely knew where he was. No dream—it wasn't his warm comfortable bed he was lying in. He didn't even try to open his eyes, caked as they were with grit and sand. His lips were cracked and his mouth felt like he had chewed a mouthful of dirt. There was no attempt to roll or re-adjust his position as there was no single place on his body that didn't hurt. But as uncomfortable as he was, it was that irritating sound that bothered him the most. Not just bothersome—it pissed him off. Why couldn't a guy as mentally and physically beat as he was at least sleep without interruption? But no, that was too much to ask. He had to be bombarded by an annoying drip.

It took Willoughby a moment to process that thought. His mind was so exhausted he was having trouble understanding why it was important, other than it had interrupted his much-needed rest. The sound of dripping water. A sliver of recognition offered itself and Willoughby mentally grabbed hold of it. Dripping water. There had been no noise other than that of his own making ever since he had left the wet part of the tunnel behind, but there it was. Willoughby could hear the distinct sound of water dripping ahead of him.

He flipped his light on and shone it down the passage. The tunnel made a bend to the right ten feet ahead. Willoughby forced himself onward with nothing but sheer willpower, though his mind had been re-energized by the sound, his body wasn't as responsive, but with each push and drag the sound became clearer. He stopped once to listen and convince himself his mind wasn't playing tricks.

But it was there. After working himself around the tight bend in the crack, Willoughby's light illuminated a much different picture than the one he had become so used to seeing. Not more than twenty feet ahead of him, the crack opened up.

Willoughby pushed ahead with a burst of adrenalin—even his exhausted body could not help but respond to this new development. The thought of being able to sit or maybe even stand up was nearly as powerful of an incentive to forge ahead as the sound of water. When he had covered the last few feet, he pushed his pack ahead of him and it disappeared; the sound of it dropping to a stop in the darkness was reassuring. At least it wasn't an abyss of some sort. He dragged himself to the edge of the crack and flashed his light into a large room. The pack had rolled down a short bank about five feet high and was now resting on a flat, wide floor. But what Willoughby saw ahead of him, next to the opposite wall of the cave brought tears to his beleaguered eyes; a small pool of dark water, fed by a steady drip from the cave ceiling.

With one final effort Willoughby pulled himself up and over the edge where he immediately tumbled down the bank, dropping his flashlight and rolling right over the top of his pack in the process. His body agonized in protest but Willoughby pushed himself to his hands and knees and pawed after his light. The water lay just ahead, beckoning to him. While he was aware that he had enough room to stand, Willoughby chose not to try, afraid he would fall if he did. Instead, he covered the last bit of distance on his hands and knees until he was at the edge of the pool. Before taking a drink, Willoughby cupped his hands into the water and splashed it over his dirt-encrusted face and cracked lips. Its coolness was a shock to his system but he couldn't remember when just washing his face had ever felt so good. He sipped the water; it had a brackish, metal taste to it but could have been a mud hole as far as he was concerned. He slurped it down. Only when he had killed the rasping dryness in his throat did he pull himself back. His stomach nearly revolted at the onslaught of too much liquid with nothing else inside him, but he managed to hold it back. He relaxed somewhat and splashed more of the soothing water over his face and head; it was an immense relief to get rid of the abrasive grit and grime. Willoughby pushed back away from the life-giving pool and rested on his knees, finally allowing himself to relax and let the reality of the moment set in; he wasn't going to die of thirst in that stupid tunnel after all.

His stomach kept trying to revolt. Hunger had now taken the place of the overwhelming thirst that had been driving Willoughby's psyche. His belly churned from his overindulgence on the mineral-tinged water; he needed to get something else down there for his stomach acid to work on or soon he was going to be puking. Crawling back across the cave floor, which was surprisingly smooth, he retrieved his pack, and fished out the other half of the energy bar he had consumed earlier. Willoughby forced himself to chew slowly. The urge to wolf it down was strong but when the first bite got to his stomach, he nearly barfed it back up.

Easy does it, he mentally cautioned himself. As he savored his remaining bites, he flashed the light around his newfound cavern. It was more than twice as big as the cave behind the waterfall. The tunnel had deposited him at the end of the long room, the ceiling was maybe twenty feet at its highest point. Stretching some forty or fifty feet beyond him and the pool, the tunnel disappeared around a corner.

Willoughby knew enough to know that this one wasn't a limestone cave because there were no stalactites or stalagmites, one which grew from the floor and one which grew from the ceiling; he forgot which was which. Jake had told him of gold mines thirty miles or so from Spirit Falls up in the Cascades but Willoughby knew this wasn't a mine shaft. There was no conformity to the cave and he certainly couldn't have traveled that far.

Sitting there thinking, as the last bite of his energy bar collided with the water in his stomach, Willoughby tried to remember if Jake or his grandma had ever mentioned any caves around Spirit Falls. He didn't think natural caves were common in this area. There were some pretty cool ones down around Grants Pass that he had visited once, and he had read about the lava caves in central Oregon, but a cave like this would have gotten attention from the locals. But those thoughts gave way to a feeling of uneasiness; no one had ever said anything about a cave behind the waterfall, either. Putting one and one together wasn't adding up well. If no one had ever mentioned there being a cave like this around, then it probably was because there was no way in or out of it. Though his situation had improved considerably—he had water and could now at least stand up—he was painfully aware that he might still be trapped.

Willoughby flushed the troubling thoughts from his mind and slowly pushed himself to his feet, something he hadn't done since he began his long crawl through the tunnel. His legs were wobbly and he got a little lightheaded but it felt good to finally be able to stretch his tired muscles. He pointed the beam of his flashlight at the small hole in the cave wall from which he had emerged—he made a vow that there would be no going back that way. It sent a shiver through him as he contemplated on what he had been through and it also made him think about Bob. He had to have stood in this very spot and made the decision to go in the way Willoughby had just come out. It had been a fateful choice that hadn't worked out well for Bob, but it steeled the boy's resolve. Some way or another he was going to find a different way out. He was convinced that Bob had come in from somewhere other than the waterfall and he was going to find it. Hell, they might even name the cave after him when he got home and told them about it.

Willoughby grabbed his pack and walked to the pool. He had an overwhelming urge to explore around the corner but he wanted to fill his water bottle first. Had he done that before he left the pool behind the waterfall, he wouldn't have suffered quite as much. Thirst was a powerful teacher.

With his water bottle full and after another healthy drink, Willoughby flipped his light towards the passage; forty feet ahead it disappeared with a sharp left turn around a jutting elbow of rock. His anxiety was jumping out of his throat; the fear of being faced with another dead end was daunting. Images of Bob, whoever he or she might have been, kept popping into his head. Had he been exploring the narrow tunnel to see where it went or was he trying to get back out to the cave behind the waterfall after experiencing the shock of a dead end? Was Willoughby going to be faced with the same dilemma? He wasn't sure he could handle it.

Willoughby shouldered his pack, took a deep breath, and started slowly towards the corner. When he rounded the point of rock he let out a sigh of relief; his light illuminated a clear passage for another forty feet or so. The ceiling had dropped considerably but he could still walk without bending over or having to revert back to crawling on his hands and knees.

So far so good, Willoughby congratulated himself. He was so thrilled with the fact that the tunnel kept on going that he nearly walked right past the articles lying against the cave wall, just inside the crook of the rock elbow.

Willoughby had been shining the light down the passage when the outside edge of his peripheral vision caught sight of something that looked out of place a few feet to his left. Startled, he quickly flipped the light into the corner.

There, just inside a nook formed by the rocky outcrop, was a pack, a long, rolled-up bundle that might have been a blanket, and some sort of round pizza pan-sized thing leaning against the wall.

"Son of a bitch!" Willoughby exclaimed out loud as he immediately realized what it was. This had to have been where Bob had left his gear as he had taken the fateful venture into the hole that Willoughby had just emerged from. Sitting there just as he had left it, fully intending to come back and get it after he had explored the tunnel.

Willoughby dropped his own pack and stepped over to where the pieces of equipment waited in vain for the owner who would never return. A heavy sadness crept over the teen as he went to his knees to have a closer look. He felt a sudden surge of kinship with his dead counterpart lying alone back in that dirty crack in the earth, buried under a ton of rock and dirt. He couldn't help but wonder if that was to be his fate. Would someone years from now find his pack lying against the wall?

Willoughby forced the unpleasant thoughts from his head and examined his find. The stuff looked old. The pack looked like it was made of canvas, kind of like what the old boy scout packs used to be made of, but it also appeared to be homemade. The thin straps looked like they had been sewn into the body of the pack by hand, with uneven stitches of a coarse thread tied at the ends. The straps also had no adjustment whatsoever to them. There was only a big chamber, no handy little side pouches to stow your smaller gear in, and the flap over the chamber was tied by pieces of bootlace-sized leather. There wasn't a single piece of metal or plastic on this homemade backpack at all—no zippers, no grommets, nothing. But one thing Willoughby could see was that it had stuff in it. The whole thing was attached to a pack frame of wood bound by leather strips. To Willoughby's surprise, neither the wood nor the leather appeared to have suffered much from rot.

Carefully he took one of the straps and lifted the pack off the cave floor. It wasn't too heavy but it thudded back into the dust with a clunk as the strap he had grabbed onto promptly broke. While the wood, leather and canvas seemed to have fared well, the stitches were a different story.

Definitely been here for a while, he mused as he tugged at the tie downs. Folding the flap back, he peered cautiously inside with his light. So far he hadn't found any bats, blind spiders, bugs, or other critters inside the cave but if there were any, he thought the old pack would be a great place for them to hide.

To his relief nothing with legs or wings came jumping out at him. What he did see was clothes. Or at least he thought they were clothes. He lifted the first article out—a rough-looking brown shirt of some kind, with short sleeves and a ragged neck opening. It felt like it was made of the same sort of canvas the pack was made of. Willoughby clamped his flashlight between his knees and held the heavy garment up with both hands. It almost looked like it would fit him, maybe just a touch bigger; Bob evidently hadn't been a big person. As he examined it, a powerful dank muskiness assailed his nose.

"Whew! Man, that stinks." He grimaced as he dropped the smelly shirt to the side. A few more articles of strange looking clothing followed—two pieces that looked like undershirts and a pair of thick padded things that had to be socks, though Willoughby had never seen any quite like them. The last was a heavier garment made of the same heavy canvas as the pack—it appeared to be a poncho with a hood on it. Willoughby shook the dust out of it and held it up. It reeked with the same mustiness as the rest of the clothes but he thought if he aired it out, it might be useful if it didn't fall apart. He still had no idea if he was going to get out of this cave and it wouldn't hurt to have some extra covering. All the articles of clothing had the same distinct characteristic that Willoughby couldn't help but wonder about—there was no color other than dirty light brown and there weren't any manufacturers' tags or markings on any of it.

The next item Willoughby pulled from the pack was a small, black iron pot with a lid on it. It looked a lot like some of the pots and pans his grandma had hanging around her old wood cook stove, what she called cast iron. He lifted off the lid and peered inside.

"Rocks?" he questioned aloud when he saw what was inside the pot. *Why would anyone carry rocks around inside a cook pot?* Reaching in, he pulled one out; it crumbled into dirty black powder in his hand. He realized quickly what the objects were—biscuits. He dumped the rest of them out onto the cave floor. There was one other chunk of something black that looked different than the others. He picked it up; it was about as big as his fist and hard, dang near hard as a rock and it didn't crumble the way the biscuits had. He scraped the chunk with his thumbnail and was surprised when a piece peeled off under his nail. He held it to his nose and smelled it.

"Ughh." His nose recoiled in protest. It was cheese. Nasty old friggin' cheese. He dropped it to the floor with the biscuits and wiped his thumb on his pants. "That's so gross." As hungry as he was he didn't think eating really old biscuits and cheese would be good for him. Setting the pot on the floor, he reached back into the pack.

The next thing to come out was a leather pouch, its top tied with rawhide laces. Willoughby undid the ties and carefully poured the contents of the pouch onto the folded poncho he had laid on the floor. He recognized two of the items immediately; whetstones. One was about the length of his hand and half as wide and the other slightly smaller. Both looked well used.

Willoughby set them aside and turned his attention to the third item in the pouch, a small rectangle of dark, polished wood about three inches high and maybe four long. At first he thought it was just a solid piece of wood until he examined it more closely in the beam of his flashlight. He could just make out the hairline cracks on both ends. Willoughby pushed on one end of the rectangle and to his delight, a drawer popped open. Lying inside was another piece of irregularly shaped stone and a small round piece of metal about as long as his index finger and tapering to a chisel like point. This would have perplexed him if he had not remembered two of the items lying on the bookcase in Jake's trailer that he had questioned the big Indian about. It was a piece of flint and a metal striker. Holding the flint with one hand, he struck the point of the metal downward against it; a shower of bright sparks rewarded his effort.

"Whoa! That's friggin' cool!" Willoughby exclaimed aloud as he laid the flint and striker back into the box and slid the drawer shut. Things were starting to come into perspective as to the age of the things he had found. If the striker and flint were an indication, along with the homemade look of the pack and the clothes, this stuff was old. That meant that Bob and his gear had been down here for a long time. Maybe before Spirit Falls had even been a town. If he ever got out of here, the people back home were going to be mighty interested in what he had found. He placed the items back into their pouch and set them next to the cook pot.

There was one more thing left in the pack: another pouch. Though smaller than the one with the fire starting material and the sharpening stones, it was surprisingly much heavier. Willoughby untied the laces and emptied the bag onto the poncho. He sucked in his breath with an audible hiss as the contents clinked out onto the canvas. A pile of gold and silver coins sparkled and gleamed back at the boy in the harsh glare of his flashlight.

"Whoa, again!" He smiled as he picked up one of the gold pieces. Son of a bitch if he hadn't found some actual friggin' treasure! They were too heavy to be fake, especially the gold ones. This was the real thing!

Willoughby had never seen anything quite like what he held in front of his face. There was no marking on the piece at all and he could see that it also wasn't perfectly round like a regular coin would be. There was an indented cross on each coin that divided it into four equal pieces; that confused him for just a moment until he saw that there were half and quarter pieces of gold and silver coins in his pile as well. Whoever had used this as currency had a simple way of making change.

There wasn't much that had gone right for Willoughby since he went over the waterfall. Bruised, battered, and very fortunate not to be dead, he was still stuck in this cave but now he couldn't help but crack a big smile. This was really a piece of good luck. The pile wasn't big but Willoughby was sure this stuff was valuable. Thoughts coursed through his head about the possible origin of his find.

Maybe it was Spanish Conquistadors or whatever they were called, he thought. He had studied those guys in history class. Maybe that's who Bob was. It really didn't matter. He had a gut feeling that when he got out of here, this pile in front of him was going to make his family rich. Well, maybe not totally millionaire-type rich, but it was damn well going to bring in some much needed money. Maybe enough to even get him a four-wheeler—that would really kick ass.

Willoughby counted the coins as he fed them back into the leather pouch, hoping it would hold together. Thirty-one full gold pieces, three half, and seven quarter pieces. Of the silver, he had twelve full pieces, two halves, and five quarter pieces. Unzipping the larger of the two auxiliary pouches on the back of his pack he took out the large ziplock baggie that held his paper towels. He put the bag of coins inside and tucked it lovingly back into his pack, stuffing the towels securely around it.

The old pack was empty now, yielding no more treasure. He stuffed the clothes back inside except for the big poncho type thing; he wasn't going to lug the pack around just to have it fall apart on him. When he came back with people to fulfill his promise to Bob, he would take it out then. Willoughby scooted over on his knees and turned his attention to the bed roll, or at least that's what he thought it was. It looked like a thick wool blanket. His grandma had a couple of those around her house but he didn't care much for them because they were scratchy. As he put his hands on the dusty roll he realized that there was something hard and lumpy wrapped up inside. His curiosity jumped another level—something else old and valuable? As he started to unroll it, a big chunk of the blanket came off in his hands, not having fared too well with age. But Willoughby was in a hurry to see what was inside, and he wasn't too concerned about tearing a rotten old blanket. Giving it a flip, he rolled it the rest of the way open.

"Shit!" he swore as the blanket revealed its treasure. Lying in front of him was a sword—an honest to God, Lord of the Rings, friggin' sword!

Willoughby settled back onto his knees as he gazed in absolute awe at the weapon lying on the rotted bedroll. It was about thirty-six inches long overall and was in a black case. A scabbard, he remembered, that was the name for it. It was attached to some sort of harness-looking contraption that appeared to be made out of leather. But it was the handle of the sword that grabbed the teen's attention.

Starting at the point where the blade entered the scabbard, two shiny metal protrusions jutted out four inches to either side and angled slightly back towards the rest of the handle. Willoughby figured that they guarded the hands that were on the grip. At the end of each were the identical heads of some sort of animal. He leaned closer and highlighted the figures in the beam of his light. Dragons. The heads were no bigger than a half dollar but intricately carved. While he was no expert on metalworking, he knew the detail he was looking at was the work of an extremely talented individual. Willoughby had never seen anything like it. The heads of both beasts were directed right towards the point of the sword; right to where the intended recipient of the blade would be.

From the hand guards, the main portion of the grip looked to be bone but as he eyed it more closely, he was sure what he was looking at was actually ivory. Willoughby remembered the two carved pieces of walrus tusk sitting on Jake's knickknack shelf; a mother polar bear and cub. The handle of the sword was made of the same stuff, he was certain. *Illegal.* Jake had said that it was illegal to make anything from ivory anymore. There were no carvings on the grip at all, just metal rivets holding the handle to the blade.

But at the very end of the grip was something that once again made the teen suck his breath in. Half again the size of the carved dragons was what looked to him like the talons of a bird, done in the same intricate workmanship as the dragons. Two talons spread out like fingers from the ivory grip, and clutched tightly in the grasp of these claws was something that caught Willoughby's gaze and wouldn't let go. It held him so hard it made his eyes water. A red stone as big around as a chicken egg glared back at him.

Willoughby had never seen an actual ruby, but he had seen enough pictures to know that this was what one would look like. Sure, they could make things like this out of glass and sell them as ornaments and mementos in any gift shop, but the teen had a feeling deep inside his gut that this was the real thing. This stuff was too old for fake glass. He couldn't take his eyes off it. It kept pulling his head closer and closer, drawing him in. Deep inside the stone, something was happening. A swirl of liquid fire spun like a tiny, glowing tornado.

It pulled Willoughby's face closer, until his nose was nearly touching the talons that gripped the strange red stone. His eyes began to water profusely. The glowing core seemed to be getting brighter and brighter as it forced him to look deep inside its fiery heart. It almost seemed to be—alive. Willoughby finally managed to blink, and when he did, the spell was broken.

"What the hell!" he exclaimed, leaning back and rubbing the tears from his eyes with his dirty sleeves. When he looked again, the swirl of fire had dimmed, now barely visible deep in the heart of the red stone.

The experience had shaken him. *Man, I must be going friggin' crazy!* he thought, trying to come to grips with what had just happened. Besides nearly frying his eyes right out of his head, his mouth and throat had become parched and dry. Fetching the water bottle from his pack, he took a healthy swig, following it with another. Despite its metallic taste, water had never gone down so good. He took another drink; he would refill it from the pool before he moved on. Willoughby's eyes wandered back to his prize.

This was going to set the whole damn town on end when he came out of the cave with this stuff. Hell, it would probably even get national attention. People would come from all over to see the sword. Willoughby didn't know if the red stone was a real jewel or not but it didn't matter. With that freaky, swirly fire thing going on inside it would catch people's attention, and it just might be worth money—a whole shit pile of it.

But that meant selling the sword. A strange possessiveness swept over Willoughby, shoving aside any thought of being made wealthy by his find. *No. The sword was his and he didn't want anyone else to touch it.* The coins he would part with, that would help out his mom and grandma. But the sword was his.

Willoughby set aside his water bottle and propped his flashlight on top of his pack so it shone on the stunning weapon. Reaching out, he gripped the scabbard and lifted it up off the rotted blanket. It was heavy, but not as heavy as he thought it would be. Its weight and length seemed a perfect fit for him. He reached out with his right hand and in one smooth motion, grabbed the ivory handle just in front of the glistening jewel and started to pull the blade from its sheath.

With a brilliant flash of searing light Willoughby's confined cave world exploded. An electric jolt shot up his arm, immediately causing him to drop the sword in a clatter on the rock floor. With his arm totally numb from shoulder to finger tips and his eyes temporarily blinded by the flash, he stepped backward and promptly tripped over his pack. The flashlight clattered to the floor and flipped off. Willoughby landed with a thud on his butt, enveloped by the total darkness of the cave.

CHAPTER ELEVEN

N O! DAEMON RHUE SAT UP SUDDENLY IN HIS bed, flinging his coverlet from his sweating body. For a moment he didn't know where he was, but quickly his protective instinct took over and restored calm to his body and mind.

It's nothing but a dream. Settling himself with controlled deep breaths, he checked his surroundings; it was his tower room and he was in his bed—all was as it should be. But something troubling had wakened him from his sleep. It wasn't a common type of ill he was experiencing, not an ill that you could cure with an apothecary's powder or potion. It was instead a deep-seated uneasiness; a gnawing discomfort that all was not as well as it appeared to be. He had sensed something, something that should not be there, and it bothered him.

Throwing his legs free from the warm clutches of the bed covers, he quickly slipped on his slippers and donned the heavy robe hanging from a hook near his bed. An irritating glance at the stone fireplace gave him one clue as to why he was feeling out of sorts. The fire had gone out in the hearth, and fall Arturan mornings could be uncomfortably chilly. He cinched the drawstring of the robe tightly, with more than a slight sense of irritation.

"You miserable little whoreson." Daemon's harsh voice echoed unheard as he strode purposely across the cold stone floor of the tower room that served as his personal living quarters. Grabbing a small rope hanging next to the heavy door leading to the stairwell, he gave it several violent tugs. Cleverly hidden inside the tower walls this simple communication system was delivering an alarming message to his personal servant quartered in a small room just below his. The uneasy feeling that had awakened him on this cold morning was going to cause the poor boy much suffering at the hands of his temperamental master.

Daemon Rhue wasn't the sort of man someone would immediately be afraid of if meeting him suddenly on a darkened night. Built small of stature, as were most Torbekians, he had the light brown-toned skin of a man used to sun-drenched southern climates. Black shoulder length hair, straight and greasy looking, framed his hawk-like face and flanked a dark beard clustered on his sharp chin, tapering to a sharp point after about four inches in length. There wasn't much to give a man cause to be wary until you met his eyes. They were evil eyes that people said would pierce a good man's heart. Indeed, it was hard for one to tell what color his eyes were; it was nearly impossible to stare into them long enough to do so. It was whispered that only a person with as much evil inside as that of the Arturan first council to the king himself could hold his gaze for more than a second or two.

What his stature failed to convey, and what his eyes hinted at, was a dangerous man who used predator-like cunning and a ruthless heart to make up for his lack of physical size. Daemon Rhue was a man who did whatever it took to get what he wanted and who did whatever it took to hold onto it once it was his.

Crossing the tower room, he drew open another heavy wooden door and stepped out onto the balcony beyond. A bone-gnawing blast of wind assailed him immediately, causing him to pull the thick robe even more tightly about his lean body—another shivering reminder of the many things he hated about this wretched land.

But regardless of the omnipresent cold wind blowing out of the eastern mountains at this time of year, it was to this vantage point that Daemon Rhue came faithfully every morning upon rising. The balcony encircled the tower but its only door opened directly to the south, and not by any accident of architecture. Southward lay Torbek—Rhue's home—it was towards his homeland that he longingly gazed each and every morning.

His view was unsurpassed by any other in this portion of the country. The great city of Tiernon, the largest in Artura, stretched out beneath him. The castle, of which his tower was its highest point, lay on the edge of a high plateau overlooking the city and the river Tier. It was this city and its river traffic that had brought him to this place nearly a decade ago. First as an ambassador, then, after years of carefully planned maneuvering, first council, second in power only to the king, Edmund Daine. That Daemon Rhue had come this far was a testament to both his resourcefulness, and his ruthlessness. A decade of careful role playing, loyalties bought, extortions carried out, and people in high places that were perceived as roadblocks stealthily eliminated. And for the last two years his greatest accomplishment—the surreptitious eroding of the king's mental capacity to the extent that now he, Daemon Rhue, was truly the one in control of this country. His task was nearly complete, the final elements falling into place. He hoped his master would be pleased.

With amazing clarity, the sounds and smells of the great city, shaking from its slumber and stirring to life hundreds of feet below, assailed his senses: Greetings being exchanged and the clop of horse- and ox-driven wagons clattering along to the open stalls of the market delivering the late season produce from the farms and the slabs of beef, hog, and mutton from the slaughter pens just outside the city's wall; The calls of the fishmongers pushing their handcarts up from the quay, loaded with the previous day's catch; The booted tramp and harsh shouts of the morning foot patrol as they rousted the unfortunate drunks from the doorways of the whorehouses and alleyways behind the taverns; The heady aroma of the morning's strong coffee and tea being brewed blended with the aroma of freshly baked bread; The nastiness of the night's chamber pots being emptied into the open sewers and the pungent odor of the stables; The smell of wood being kindled to fire in a cold hearth; And all the other sounds and smells of a great city stretching itself awake to meet the day.

Daemon Rhue snapped his attention back to the moment. The

smell of wood smoke coming from a fireplace was none other than his own. That mangy little bastard had snuck in while he was out on the balcony and was attempting to rectify his mistake. He decided to postpone the boy's misery at least for the moment; he needed to think, to clear his head. There was something, a presence bothering him that he couldn't quite grasp; and very few things slipped the grasp of Daemon Rhue.

He placed both hands on the stone of the waist-high retaining wall surrounding the balcony. Bowing his head and closing his eyes, he cleared his mind. The sounds of the city, the sound of his servant preparing the fire, even the whistle of the wind around the corners of the tower, all faded to nothingness as he took complete control of his thought process. Daemon Rhue stopped breathing—this was one of the first things he had learned from his master. Complete control. That meant everything. In this condition, his body functions slowed to a death-like state.

He allowed himself a few seconds of emptiness before starting his search. Then he began. The first probe went towards the south, his home and that of his master. He needed to discern if it had been Lord Taul trying to contact him, though he truly didn't think such was the case. His master was far more powerful than he and contact from that source usually came in a mind-flash of light and pain. No, Daemon Rhue determined quickly that there was no trace of his master trying to summon him.

Drawing his mind probe back from the south he sent it off in other directions but stopped after several tries. The effort was draining him. If he knew what he was looking for he could have narrowed the search's scope, but whatever it was it had been small and strangely foreign to him. But there had been a definite power tinge to it, and that nagged him.

Giving in, he willed himself back to the present. His legs sagged as his body struggled to restore itself. *This is not good,* he mentally chastised himself as he slowly regained control of his functions. That he hadn't been strong enough to sustain the mind probes was an irritation to him. He needed to concentrate more on stretching the boundaries of his power, but there was always so much to deal with in this cursed place that he hadn't time to keep his abilities sharpened to their maximum effectiveness. He was confident when Lord Taul did contact him he would not be pleased that he had slipped. Things were coming together according to his master's plan and this was no time for a mistake.

Daemon Rhue closed his eyes, widened his stance, and settled his hands together in front of his stomach. Slowly he began taking deep breaths, inhaling the cold air slowly through his nose, filling his abdomen first before his lungs. When he reached maximum capacity, he slowly exhaled through his mouth, settling his body and mind as he did. A simple exercise in control, and control was critical to everything about Daemon Rhue, especially now that things were moving fast. It was odd to think events were finally quickly coming to a climax after ten years of moving at a snail's pace.

But we are not there yet, he reminded himself as he continued his controlled breathing. The timing of each step was critical and he needed to make sure the next one went according to schedule. Others were involved in the process and he needed to make sure they understood their roles, and understood that none would be spared if things went wrong. He needed to talk to Steyr.

When Daemon Rhue stepped back into the tower room he found his servant nervously adding more pieces of dry kindling to the flames that had taken hold in the fireplace. The boy was usually concerned about using too much kindling as the effort it took to get firewood up to this lofty tower room demanded that he be conservative with it. But this morning was different and he needed to make haste. When the summoning bell had rudely awakened him from his slumber, the boy immediately realized his error. Fear now overcame any hesitation about using too much dry kindling.

"Well, good morning to you my fine lad," Daemon's voice greeted from behind.

Startled, the boy turned immediately and bowed low. "A good morning to you Lord Rhue," he stammered. "I-I-I beg your Lordship's pardon for neglecting the fire." He kept his eyes glued to the floor. "I hope that it caused you no discomfort sire. I did not think the morn would rise so cold."

At thirteen years old, and large for his age, the boy, had he the courage to stand up straight, would have been as tall as the man standing before him. But absolute, bowel-loosening fear had control over him. He dared not look this man in the eye.

"Do I ask so much of you that you cannot find the time to tend to my fire?" Daemon's voice was surprisingly pleasant and soothing. Not what the lad was expecting.

"N-no, my Lordship sir," the boy replied meekly. His eyes remained glued to the floor.

"Very well then. Come now. Finish your task so you can fetch me some breakfast. It does a man ill to be both cold and hungry."

The tone of his master's voice gently pushed the lad's fear aside. It was almost as if the man had chuckled as he spoke. Relief flooded through him as he rose. The boy made himself a mental note to repay his master for the lenience that had been shown him.

"Yes, my Lord Rhue, I…"

Smmackk! The echo of the blow bounced off the bare stone of the tower walls as Daemon Rhue's bony hand brutally struck the hapless servant boy full across his cheek. The speed and force behind the unsuspected blow sent the boy crashing backward, cracking his head hard against the fireplace. No sooner had he slumped sideways into a dazed heap when a slipper-coated foot lifted him off the floor with a vicious kick to his exposed ribs.

The boy was desperately gasping for air as Daemon reached down and grabbed him by his hair, jerking his head up.

"Heed my words and heed them well boy," Daemon hissed into the lad's face. "That is only the beginning of your suffering if you offer me any more of your pig-headed Arturan insolence. I'll make you wish your street-slut of a mother had never shit you out in the gutter."

He shoved the boy's head to the floor. "Now go and fetch me that fat, worthless pig that calls himself a physician. I want him here with no dallying. Bring me my breakfast when you return and it had better not be cold."

The sobbing boy, bleeding from a nasty gash to his head and holding his bruised ribs, pulled himself up and staggered out the door, stumbling down the many tower steps as fast as the pain would allow.

Returning to his balcony, hundreds of feet above the castle courtyard, Daemon Rhue watched the terrified boy's progress, suddenly aware of how much better he felt. The uneasiness and anxiety of the early morning had faded in the perverse and sadistic pleasure derived from the brutal exhibit of his power.

Forgetting the servant boy, he turned his attention to a large table pushed to one side of the tower room. One of the few plain furnishings he allowed himself, it was cluttered with parchment and paper communiqués from his many henchman scattered strategically throughout the country. Daemon's network of spies and bought officials was vast. By monitoring every aspect of what was going on in all parts of Artura, he could detect any wavering of the absolute control he held over its people. By ruthlessly dealing with any of those fool enough to stray out of line, he maintained his grip on his power.

Pulling up a stool, he sat down. Though there were many on the table, he usually scrutinized every document. There were tallies from tax collectors and treasury accounts, harbor reports of vessels coming and going, and detailed cargo ledgers. But most important of all were the personal reports from spies detailing special circumstances involving those who needed to be occasionally reminded of who was in control. These he enjoyed reading. The quirky sexual habits of supposedly proper lords and ladies; the scandalous behavior by key government ministers and officials; people whose lives were controlled by addiction; people who could be bought and controlled with gold, sex, or drugs—all were valuable tools in this deadly game he played.

But today was different; there was something else he needed to attend to. He turned his eyes to a worn hard-leather tube lying in front of him. Daemon Rhue knew its contents; reports from the commander of the Arturan army. For nearly two years now they had been fighting alongside Torbekian troops, their former enemies, trying to eradicate the unruly Uthans from their homeland in the mountainous waste between Torbek and Dazor. The Uthans were a seminomadic tribe who scratched a meager living from one of the most desolate places imaginable. While they were a threat to no one, they would swear no fealty either. That made them a useful tool for Daemon Rhue. Not that there were pressing reasons for military action against them; it had all been a ploy to keep the Arturan army and its meddlesome Commander out of the way. All of this conveniently and very neatly done under the auspices of the treaty Daemon Rhue himself had forged between the two countries nearly ten years ago.

Pulling the cap of one end of the tube, he spilled the contents onto the table. Most of the reports were written in the tiny space-saving hand of the scribes. Reports on skirmishes, requests for supplies, and casualty lists—lots of casualty lists. But Daemon cared little for those, especially the casualty lists. The more dead Arturans, the better. They weren't what he was looking for today. He quickly spotted what he sought, a heavy parchment envelope sealed with a blotch of red wax. On this wax was an imprint of two broadswords crossed over the head of a wolf—the personal seal of Artemis Thoryl, Commander of the Arturan army and closest friend to King Edmond himself. Daemon ripped open the wax seal and extracted the letters inside. It was these in which he was keenly interested. He needed to search for any hints and clues that the cagey old veteran of a soldier might have that something was not quite right back in his homeland.

Written in the sprawling hand of Commander Thoryl, they were personal letters intended for the king's eyes only, but it had been a long time since Edmond Daine had seen any communiqués from his friend. A cruel smile broke across Rhue's thin lips. He began to read.

Greetings my King and dearest friend,

May these letters find you in better health than has been

reported. Your well being concerns me greatly and it is with great distress that I cannot be at your side. But here, in this blasted land that a lizard would not fight over, is where my Lord says that I must be, and as your most loyal and obedient servant it is here I will stay, attempting with all my effort to bring this war, if that is what it may be called, to an end.

You know my heart, my Lord. I have been by your side at the head of your troops in battle for nearly forty years now. You and I have sat over many a field table by candlelight and planned strategies against our enemies that would bring us victory. And what glorious victories we have had together. We have also buried many of our comrades on the battlefield and returned their broken swords and shields to their weeping families, that it might lift their heavy hearts when they hear of the bravery and sacrifice given by their husbands, brothers, and sons.

It is upon this bond we have forged as brothers-in-arms; and more so as true friends, that I implore you to listen once again to my plea.

My Lord, there is something dreadfully wrong with this situation in which we find ourselves. This is not a war being fought like any other that I have been part of. If you were of good enough health to be here with me, as I know you would if you were able, you would witness this for yourself. This is not an enemy that chooses to stand and fight anywhere. It has been a full two years since we crossed the River Tier and marched into the eastern wastes along the border of Torbek and Dazor. Three armies, my Lord, have yet to bring these rebels to heel.

I realize that our treaty binds us to this joint endeavor with our two former enemies, but there seems to be little true cooperation here. If we are indeed allies then why is there reluctance for the armies of Torbek and Dazor to cross their respective borders in order to bring this hardy folk to task?

One stays on their side and the other does the same. You have given me orders that I must remit to the command of General Ortair, and he has ordered me not to cross into Dazor. Instead, he has me chasing these bandits to and fro along hundreds of miles of the most desolate earth a man can imagine.

Indeed our casualty lists do not lie heavy with those who have fallen in the heat of combat, but rather those who have succumbed to sickness and disease. Our food is poor at best, oft rotted and unfit for consumption by the time it reaches us. That we must depend on a Minister of Supply from Torbek is another matter which grieves me deeply but formal complaints to General Ortair come back with the same answer—it is the same food that his troops eat and they do not complain. If I believed that to be true I would be ashamed of my complaints but some of our men who have had the rare opportunity to be in the Torbekian camps tell another story. They say they have witnessed fresh vegetables, fresh meat, and indeed fruit in the mess kitchens of our 'allies.' The only thing fresh our men have here is the scraggly goats they take—even those are better than the meat rations we receive. The water, from what few wells and waterholes there are, is tainted and vile, and must be boiled before consumed lest a nasty affliction of a man's bowels renders him unfit for duty days and weeks at a time.

The rebels, on the other hand, thrive in this waste. What is here that is worth fighting over? It is my understanding, talking to those fighters that we have been able to capture, that they have lived here in this place for hundreds of years bothering no one. They are perfectly content raising their ragged goats and what few crops they can in the small valleys that have enough water to do so. Yet both the Torbekians and the Dazorians say that these folk cause mischief and mayhem enough that it requires the armies of three nations to bring them to task?

My Lord, I am just repeating myself when I tell you here that this all makes no tactical sense to this old warhorse. Our foe uses hit and run attacks that never allow us to overwhelm them with force of arms. They pop up, draw our troops in for a skirmish and then disappear into the mountains, only to resurface in a different location to repeat the process. To chase them into those mountains is to commit suicide, for they are steep and as rugged as any. Narrow trails bordered by sheer rock walls hundreds of feet high are a death trap for soldiers who must traverse them on foot as they are too narrow and rugged for horse.

In what few times we have been able to catch numbers of these fighters in a position where they must cross arms with us, they have proven themselves to be a worthy adversary and often choose to die fighting rather than surrender. It is a trait that I have found, in my many years of combat, to be common with people who care passionately for the land which they call home.

So friend Edmund, and I choose to dispense with the formalities of title to bring my point home, I find myself in an uncomfortable position. I have within the past few months repeatedly asked General Ortair, and his counterpart on the Dazorian side of the mountains, Commander El'nin, for a meeting to discuss what I firmly believe is a necessary change in strategy. But each time my requests are denied for the same reasons. They say this war is being administered on a plan agreed on by Supreme Overlord Taul, Sultan Kala'un of Dazor and yourself and there is no room for deviance. If that is indeed true then I must say that we labor and die here for naught because that is exactly what adherence to this ridiculous plan is going to get us. My history with you has taught me this type of warfare is not something that you would commit your beloved troops to if you were completely aware of its implications and its utter futility.

My Lord I beg your forgiveness for allowing my frustrations

to spill onto this paper but it is concern for the welfare of our men wasting away here in this forsaken land for an endeavor that neither they, nor I, understand. It is this concern that has steeled my resolve to take actions that may be deemed contrary to this 'plan.' I have met with my field commanders and together we have evolved an approach to this stalemate in which we are mired; one that will allow us to at least start giving us some momentum dealing with these insurgents, if that is what they truly are. I am telling you this with the full understanding that my actions may be deemed insubordinate and as Commander of your forces I alone bear the responsibility.

I will not submit the details of this strategy to the pages of this letter. Instead, I am dispatching two of my most trusted advisors, men that you are familiar with and know of their unquestionable loyalty. The message they will deliver is one for your ears alone and they will speak to you directly or will abandon the effort and return, at which time I must make judgment about our situation. If these men, brave, trusted and loyal sons of Artura, cannot gain a private audience with our King on my behalf then I must conclude that events have come to pass that will require me to make some difficult choices.

Edmund, I implore you one more time. You are my friend. What is going on? This is so unlike you. Your return letters, the few that I have received, are cold, distant, and bear no resemblance to the man I grew up with and would lay down my life for. If there is a reason you have changed your opinion of me, then at least allow a small courtesy and say so.

My Lord I have laid my heart bare within the confines of these pages. I await your answer.

Your Obedient Servant,

Artemis Thoryl

Daemon Rhue laid the last page of the letter aside; it was as he had suspected. The old fox was starting to get suspicious. The letter was dated over a month ago. Artemis Thoryl would by now have already dispatched his men to visit the king. It was a good thing he had doubled the amount of eyes watching over the slobbering old fool. No one could get close to Edmond without Daemon Rhue knowing about it, not even the king's young daughter Alicia. But Artemis Thoryl would have warned the two men he sent of just that sort of thing. They would have entered the city in disguise and watched for opportunities. If they were good, and Daemon Rhue had no reason to expect they were not, they would see the spies watching the king's every move. Mayhap they had already begun their return to their Commander to report their findings?

Daemon Rhue stood up from the table and strode to the fire, trying to let its heat comfort him while he contemplated the situation. But the warmth of the flames did little to dispel the chilling uneasiness he felt. Things were going to have to come together quickly; he had spent too much time and too much effort to be thwarted now. He needed to talk to Steyr and after that they would do what he had been dreading for some time, contact his lord and master, Kenric Taul.

CHAPTER TWELVE

WHILE DAEMON RHUE WENT BACK TO STUDY-
ing the disturbing contents of the letter from Commander
Thoryl, his bruised and battered young servant was hurrying along
as quickly as he could. His ribs ached with every hurried step and
the dried blood clotted uncleaned on his scalp but the young boy
was aware that his suffering would be ten times over if he failed to
quickly do his master's bidding.

Down the many steps of Daemon Rhue's tower and out into the
vast inner ward he hurried—past scullion boys and kitchen maids
as they went about their chores preparing to feed the masses who
called the castle home; past soldiers and stable hands; past bakers
and cook's apprentices; past hearth tenders and delivery boys. Like a
crag bear, those enormous furred denizens which lived in the rocky
clefts of the great mountains, rousing from a long winter's nap, the
great castle stirred and stretched itself awake.

Castle Daine sat high above the city on a plateau separated
from the land next to it by a yawning chasm. This natural feature
made the castle an island in itself—and an impregnable one. A
single causeway, one that could send trespassers plunging to the
jagged bottom of the chasm in the blink of an eye and the pull of
a lever, connected it to the mainland. The causeway was fortified,
heavily guarded, and barred from any type of traffic unless officially
authorized by the king, or his first council.

All traffic in and out of the castle did so via the city of Tiernon,
clustered around the base of the plateau next to the great River
Tier. For five hundred years this fortress had been the home of the

Daines, ancestors of King Edmond. It had withstood attacks and sieges by vast armies led by great generals but had never fallen. It had watched the city and docks clustered at its feet burn to the ground three times but still stood in defiance. Castle Daine had been built to survive. Ordered into construction by Bayen the Bold, the first king of a united Artura, it had taken fifty years and three more kings to see it to final construction.

But while it had been great and mighty men who had envisioned its glory and power, it was not the Daines who had engineered and constructed this masterpiece of stone. Few men had the ingenuity to haul the massive granite blocks from the quarries a mile away and the engineering skills to lift them into place. Few men had the genius to harness the power of the great river to turn the giant capstans, originally designed to haul stone from the quarries but which now hauled wains full of goods and people up the tram road from the city to the castle. Few men had the skill to bring into being the mightiest engines of war that had ever existed—the Twin Sisters of Chaos.

Sitting atop a battlement overlooking the river, these throwing machines could hurl death and destruction upon any invader attempting to navigate the river or attack the castle by land. It was the cunning of men who foresaw the need for such a mighty fortress with all of its ingenious devices, but it was dwarves who were its master engineers and builders.

But the suffering boy who scurried across the inner ward in the smoky twilight of early morning cared little for dead kings, mighty castles, or dwarves. His mind was fixed upon his immediate task— doing his master's bidding. Many of the people he hurried past gave the lad nods or hellos but he paid none of them any attention lest they idle him with small talk. His master's spies were everywhere and he feared being reported as dallying from his errand. Haste was his only friend when it came to fulfilling his master's wishes.

On the far side of the great inner ward, directly across from Daemon Rhue's tower, the boy came to a huge set of timbered doors, nearly as thick as he was tall, high and wide enough for large ox-drawn wains to pass through. These doors, now open wide, marked the entrance to the vast subterranean network of passages and rooms that housed the great castle's support functions. Built underground for safety in time of war, there were storerooms and granaries, water reservoirs and stables, blacksmith forges and armories. Castle Daine could withstand a long siege even if the city were to fall. As important as the underground was for supplying and storing the material necessary for survival, equally so were the tunnels that connected to strategic parts of the city and those that were escape routes to the outside. These had sections that could be sealed off, trapping an enemy that might manage to fight its way within. Once the trap doors were sprung, water or burning oil could be directed inside, bringing death to those unfortunate enough to find themselves trapped. Once again, it was the ingenuity of dwarves at work. The knowledge of this subterranean maze was now a well-guarded secret of a select few, only to be made known when dire straits called for drastic measures, or for more nefarious and clandestine purposes.

Through the doors and down the ramp the boy entered the perpetual twilight of the underground city. Along the main passage, dimly lit by scores of black smoke belching oil lamps, he passed the many whose duties demanded they toil deep in this nether land. Many of these folk rarely saw the natural light, entering well before dawn and not leaving until the sun had dropped beyond the horizon. They spent their entire lives in service to the king in these shadowy corridors.

The boy had been here on numerous occasions and knew the way, soon coming to a passage and set of steps leading to a lower level. This entry was guarded by a stout pair of well-armed soldiers. Recognizing him, they allowed him to pass, well aware of the wrath of the lad's master.

This lower level was even more dimly lit and stifling than the first. Though there were shafts and vents whose purpose it was to allow ventilation from the surface, they were deliberately small; it wouldn't due to have them large enough to allow a determined enemy to slide down and gain access, so the passage of fresh air was minimal at best.

There was also much less activity at this level. The rooms the boy passed were mostly storerooms, some of which looked as if they hadn't been opened for years, though he did pass another boy whose job it was to keep the lamps filled. He grunted a quick greeting as they passed; the other responding with a grunt of his own while pumping oil into the lamps from a large wheeled barrel. Both had learned the hard way that there was no time for idle talk when you had a job to do.

Just past the lamp boy, he came to an intersection with an ominous barred door looming directly in front of him. On either side of the door sat two surly looking guards and just to his right, through an unguarded door, the boy could hear the grunts, snores, and farts of several more. This was a place the boy dreaded; the entrance to the dungeons and torture chambers.

For many years this area of the castle had remained unused. King Edmund had little tolerance for inhuman methods of treating people involving rat and flea infested cells, chains and manacles, and deadly instruments whose only purpose was to inflict pain and suffering. While firm with those who chose to disregard Arturan laws, a sturdy jail above ground had served the king well enough.

But all that had changed after the appointment of Daemon Rhue as first council. Lord Rhue had reopened the dungeons and put them to more use than had ever been imagined. They had come in handy during his unrelenting quest for power and control. Under the premise of protecting the king, he had been able to round up many of those who sought to stand in the way of his ambitions, using forgery and false witness bought with the king's own gold or done in by various other forms of lies, treachery, and deceit. All these tools were used to perfection by Rhue and his henchmen, ensuring a steady stream of traffic through those dreaded doors. Many souls whose only crime was loyalty to country and king were never heard from again once they passed beyond this point.

The guards ignored the boy's presence as he pulled the hood

of his tattered cloak over his head and darted down the passage to his left. This was not only to help ward off the damp chill of this wretched place but to muffle any dreadful sounds that might pass beyond the barred doors. It was never too early in the morning for the head torturer to be at work; after all, he was one of First Council Rhue's highest paid henchmen.

The boy hurried down a tunnel more dreary than any of the others, there being few lamps here to push back the darkness. The air was fetid and foul and water dripped from the walls and ceiling. A scuffling noise made him jump with fright as shadows flittered across the floor in front of him—rats.

Finally he came to a small, undistinguished door lit by a single smoky lamp. No guards were needed here, for this was the abode of the man who, with the exception of Daemon Rhue, was perhaps the most hated and feared in Artura.

His name was Steyr, and his title was Personal Physician to the king. But to most people he was a mystery. Even though he worked in the castle and tended to the king, few ever saw him and those who were unfortunate enough to do so were usually disturbed by the encounter. People were afraid of Steyr. Whereas Daemon Rhue instilled terror in people by violent and ruthless acts, the fear they had of the Physician was of the kind that oozed from places dark and evil. The kind of fear one has when passing an old burial ground on a fog shrouded night; the kind of fear children have when they are wakened from sleep by strange noises, those which make them hide under their blankets and pray for the light of morning to come. That was the kind of fear the name Steyr had on people.

It was at this man's door that Lord Rhue's servant finally found himself. He hesitated slightly before knocking, he had been here before but fear still seized him with its icy grip. The urge to run away was strong but his fear of the man behind the door was offset by the knowledge of the fate awaiting him if he failed to do his master's bidding.

With his trembling hand he reached towards the skull-shaped knocker on the door; it swung open just as he was about to touch the brass handle. The boy nearly swooned at the sight of the grotesque apparition in front of him. Steyr's appearance always had the same effect on the boy—terrifying and repulsive. Standing just beyond the door in the flickering light of a small fire burning in a brazier, he was a pale, obese man, naked except for a small and filthy coverlet that he held about his waist. His torso and legs were pasty white and he was hairless except for a wispy dirty brown fringe clustered about his ears and temples. A bulbous nose and saggy jowls accented the pale bulging orbs that were his eyes, the byproduct of many years spent underground in the darkness. As the boy stood there in front of this appalling sight, a sickening sweet smell emanated from within the dark bowels of Steyr's room, nearly causing the boy to vomit. It was not just the appearance of the man which caused the boy to feel so nauseated, it was rumored that Steyr practiced magic—dark, evil magic deep within his abode. The boy had reason to fear; people disappeared after visits to this realm, never to be heard from again. But as grotesque as the physician was, and not withstanding all of the evil practices he was rumored to be associated with, he was nonetheless one of the few who now had direct access to the ailing King Edmond.

When Steyr saw it was only a servant boy standing at his door, he dropped the coverlet, exposing his fat belly and the flaccid penis dangling between his fleshy white legs. The obese man put his hands on his hips and thrust his groin forward, a smirk of satisfaction crossed his lips when he noticed the boy could not help but steal a glance at the shriveled prick hanging there.

"Well? Are you going to explain why it is I find you at my door at this hour of the morning or are you going to just stand there and stare like the idiot you are?" Steyr's voice echoed in the passage.

The boy fought his fear and found his voice. He wanted to get this over with and get away from this man as quickly as he could.

"My master Lord Rhue commands your presence in the tower immediately." The words came out choked and weak.

"Hhhmmph," Steyr snorted. "So I am to come running like an obedient dog, eh?" He rattled off a deep, mucous-filled cough and spat a gooey glob of snot at the boy's feet. "Very well then. Run and tell his Lordship that I will hasten to his command." The deep sarcasm was lost on the servant.

The boy was about to turn and depart when a soft, whimpering sound coming from beyond Steyr caused him to look past the fat man and into the room. His eyes had become acclimated to the dim light and he could now see a young girl huddled in a clump of filthy bed robes on the hard pallet that served as the physician's bed. Long brown hair, tousled and matted, flanked a smudged and tear-stained face. Her shoulders were bare and she clutched the robes about her tiny breasts. The boy recognized her as one of the scullery maids who worked in the castle's kitchen. Yesterday she had tossed him a warm biscuit as he fetched Lord Rhue's supper. She was always a happy and smiling girl and the boy had secretly grown quite fond of her. Although he wasn't very bright, he knew very well why she was down here in this horrid place.

A sharp finger jabbed hard into his chest and immediately refocused his attention back to the man in front of him. "Your wandering eyes are going to get you into a lot of trouble, brat." Steyr's harsh voice snapped away the images coursing through the boy's mind of what vile things the man might be doing to his pretty little friend deep in this wretched pit.

But before he could react to Steyr's warning, the fat man slammed his hand up into the startled boy's crotch, grabbing his testicles and squeezing. The boy doubled over, nearly blacking out from the gut-wrenching pain, but Steyr's other hand reached out quickly and snatched a handful of the boy's hair, jerking his head up and pulling his face within a stinking breath of his own. Steyr's flaccid penis stirred to life between his fat legs as the delight in the boy's suffering aroused him; he was thoroughly enjoying this.

"Maybe you would like to take her place?" he hissed, squeezing the hapless lad's balls tighter as he pulled him close. Steyr pressed his lips against the boy's ear. "You'd like that wouldn't you?" he whispered. "Yesss, I believe you would." With a hideous cackle, Steyr jerked the boy inside, twisting him around and slamming him face down on a table. Steyr ground his hips against the boy's backside, his erection now full and hard. The young servant cried out in agony as Steyr bit hard on his ear lobe and continued to squeeze his testicles.

"Now listen closely you miserable little piece of goat shit. You'll tell Lord Rhue that I will be there shortly and say nothing else. Do you understand?" The boy nodded as best he could. "Good," Steyr hissed into the lad's now bleeding ear. He slammed his hips hard into the boy's rear, putting emphasis on his warning. "Now be gone from my sight before I decide to give your little ass a pounding you will not soon forget."

Steyr pulled the boy upright and gave him a vicious shove out the door, flinging him hard against the opposite wall. Though he was in a significant amount of pain, the lad was in an instant tearing down the passage, trying to put as much room between himself and the madman as he could.

"Come back for more any time my good fellow," the fat physician's voice cackled in laughter after him. "The great Lord Rhue commands and we all jump to obey." Steyr's voice dripped with venomous sarcasm as he slammed the door shut. The young girl in his bed whimpered and clutched the dirty coverlet tighter against her naked body as he turned towards her…

"I alone hold the key to his success but he treats me like a servant who empties his slop bucket." Ignoring the girl for the time being he grabbed a dark, lacquered box from a shelf. Pulling up a chair, he sat down at the table he had bent the boy over. "You would not understand my pretty," Steyr spoke absently as he busied himself with the contents of the box. "Consider yourself fortunate that you are good for nothing but chopping onions and tending to a man's prick."

With an apothecary's mortar and pestle Steyr ground a cherry pit-sized piece of chalky looking substance to a fine powder. When he had finished he took a tiny silver spoon and heaped a small amount onto a smooth rectangle of polished marble. With a thin blade, he spread the powder into a line.

"My precious master would be nothing more than a minor Torbekian politician were it not for me. With my assistance, alone he stands at the right hand of the king, but does he give credit to my skill? No. He treats me like a dog. Command and I will come to lick his boots."

Steyr took a short hollow tube made from the quill of an owl out of his box. Putting it to a nostril he bent over the marble and inhaled half of the powder, his face contorting in agony as the drug assailed the nerve endings in his nose, searing its way to his brain. He sniffed hard, making sure he lost none of the precious powder before repeating the process with the other nostril; again his face grimaced with pain.

"But we shall see my lovely. We shall see who comes out of this game the victor," he sniffled. Steyr stood up from the table and turned towards the girl cowering in his filthy bed. The drug was coursing through his bloodstream, energizing his fat body into a state of readiness and he reveled in its power. Walking to the night-stand he raised a half-full wine bottle to his fat lips and drained it in a single pull. Trickles of the burgundy liquid dripped from the corners of his mouth and ran in rivulets down his fat cheeks. "Oops, none left, my sweet," he giggled maniacally, tossing the empty bottle into a dark corner. Reaching down he grasped the coverlet and ripped it from the quaking girl's hands. In vain she tried to cover her nakedness from the leering man. "But not to worry. I have something else for you, little one. My Lord has summoned but for now another master will be served." Steyr knelt on the bed beside the girl and grabbed his erection in his hand. "Your young friend has aroused my deviate inclination. Roll over—now!"

When the girl hesitated, his hand shot out and he slapped her viciously across her unprotected face. When he pulled his fist back to strike her again, she involuntarily threw her hands up, exposing her nakedness to his lust. In an instant, he grabbed her by the arm with one hand and forced his other between her legs. With an easy flip, he had her on her stomach. He threw himself on her back, forcing her legs apart as he did. Helpless against his onslaught, she buried her face into the filthy covers. "Oh, don't give up now, my sweet. It feels better when you squirm," Steyr cackled with glee as he buried his face into her neck and bit her hard, drawing blood. Her screams of pain mixed with his fiendish laughter echoed throughout the bowels of the underground as he brutally forced his way into her.

Chapter Thirteen

Artemis Thoryl threw back the flap of his tent and stepped from under the awning and out into the sand. Half-naked to the waist and in bare feet, the cold, desert morning air welcomed his exposed skin with a cool caress. A big man even by Arturan standards, standing a head higher than the average, his well-muscled body served as testimony to years of hard physical exercise and training for war. Powerful legs, rising from the bared feet like tree trunks, supported an upper torso without an ounce of fat on it. Broad shoulders served as a sturdy fulcrum for arms massive enough to wield his great two-handed broadsword.

Indeed his body, tanned to near bronze by two years in the desert sun, appeared that of a much younger man, even after a closer look revealed the many scars tattooing his chest, back, and arms. But it wasn't until you looked at his face that one could sense the true depth of the man's age. Worry lines across his face mapped decades of stress and struggle until they ran headlong into the sword scar running from his right temple, across the corner of his eye and down and across his cheek until it disappeared into a thick beard now more gray than black. Bed-tousled, shoulder length hair matched the color of his beard and framed the worn face with its blue eyes. Eyes that, if they could speak, could sum up Artemis Thoryl in simple terms, tired and troubled.

A decent night's sleep had escaped him—again. Never a man to capture more than a few hours, he could not even manage that anymore; worry and stress make for poor bed partners. Bronsen, his personal attendant, had noticed. The man was concerned enough to even suggest sleeping powders. But powders or potions would not solve the problem of sleepless nights for Artemis Thoryl. A change was necessary for what troubled the weary man, and today was the day he was going to start bringing about that change. The implications of his plan were going to be very unwelcome for many, and would probably bring about the end of a long and illustrious career, but he had resigned himself to accepting that.

He closed his eyes and inhaled a deep breath of the cold morning air. One of the few things he found to enjoy in this harsh environment was this time of the morning, before the sun peeked its brazen head over the eastern mountains and began to cook the landscape into misery. Sage, juniper, and greasewood greeted him with their soothing blend of aromas; smells that would disappear all too quickly with the heat of the coming day.

Still breathing deeply through his nose, he stretched his arms towards the yet unlit eastern sky, allowing his tight muscles to stretch themselves to their maximum. Slowly he began rotating the arms in wide, slow circles, still keeping them stretched. As he did so, he kept breathing deeply and slowly in through his nose, directing the cool air into his abdomen and filling it completely before allowing his lungs to fill. Once he had filled his air reservoirs, he began letting the air out through his mouth in a slow, steady stream. He repeated the process nine more times along with the arm stretches. Not until he had exhaled the last breath did he drop his arms to his side and open his eyes.

"A good morning to you, General. I hope you slept well," a familiar voice greeted from behind. "Will you take your tea out here this morning?"

"No to the quality of my sleep and yes to the tea, Bronsen. And a good morning to you as well." He turned to face the voice and was not surprised when he found the cup of tea already being held out to him, its welcoming heat colliding head on with the frosty morning air in a steamy cloud.

"Thank you, Bronsen." The old warrior smiled as he accepted the proffered cup. "I don't know what I would do without you. Come sit, and take your tea with me."

"You would survive just as you did before I came to serve you, thirty years ago tomorrow to be exact."

The two men pulled battered camp stools from the side of the tent and sat with their hands wrapped around the steaming cups of tea. They could not have been more unalike sitting together in the morning twilight. Bronsen, already dressed in a simple faded blue tunic and brown trousers, the color of the general's personal staff, was a small man in comparison. He kept his brown hair close cropped and it held no gray even though his age was not much less than the man he served; a complete lack of facial hair made him appear even younger. Slightly built, it was a trait people often mistook for a sure sign that he was weak and could be bullied. A serious and potentially fatal mistake for any man who sought to test him, for Bronsen was cat quick and well trained in the more subversive and secret ways of defense. No less than four knives were hidden on him at any time, sharpened to an edge keen enough to split a hair down the middle. At twenty paces, a man could blink and Bronsen could pin his eyelid shut before it had a chance to reopen. His green eyes sparkled with intensity and awareness, darting to and fro, searching for that which might go unnoticed by others. From the time he was old enough to walk and talk he had been trained to serve and to protect, and now was dedicated completely to the man he shared his morning tea with.

"Thirty years ago tomorrow Bronsen?" Artemis Thoryl questioned softly after he had enjoyed a long sip. "It's hard to believe that it has been that long."

"Indeed it has my Lord. If you will remember I joined your staff during the height of the Bayen campaign. Right after the unfortunate incident with Lucien."

Artemis Thoryl shook his head, sighed heavily, and took another sip of his tea. "Ahhh yes. Now I remember. Poor Lucien; took a blade meant for me. I dishonor the man's name by allowing myself to forget that moment. If not for his bravery those stinking pirates would have had me."

"Lucien was honored that he could do so, my Lord. It is what we are born for and in our order there is no greater honor than to die protecting the one we choose to serve."

The commander stood up from his stool and drained the dregs of his teacup. He laid his huge hand gently on the smaller man's shoulder. "And for that dedication I am thoroughly grateful Bronsen. I don't tell you often enough but I sincerely trust you know the truth in those words. You yourself have saved my life twice."

The smaller man stood up, took the general's empty cup, and gave him a smile. "All in a day's work, my Lord. It is a dangerous profession we have chosen for ourselves. Maybe we should have taken up winemaking."

"Winemaking, ha," the general chuckled, finally allowing a broad smile to push the worry lines away for a brief moment. "I am sure you would have saved me from a horrible death by many a bad vintage. Come, help me get ready for the day. The camp stirs and there is important business at hand. The captains are here, I presume?"

"Yes, sire," Bronsen nodded as he held the flap of the tent open. "They arrived at the outrider camp last night. They have kept out of sight as you ordered and will join us as soon as you are ready."

"Good. And Minister Denron?"

"Our Torbekian liaison is not expected to arrive back in camp until later tomorrow night. But since he is not known for his trustworthiness, I have taken the liberty of installing another layer in the security perimeter. Should he return unexpectedly we will have ample warning, sire."

The general stopped just inside the dimly lit tent and turned to somberly face his old friend. "You have done well, Bronsen," he sighed. "That little bastard is going to be a big problem once he realizes we are changing the rules. You must help me keep him in the dark for as long as we can."

"I will see to it, Commander," the smaller man nodded. "But while I know it is not to your taste, I must remind you of my 'special' talents. All you have to do is give me the word and I can eliminate the problem of Minister Denron."

There was a long silence between the two men as they held each other's gaze, both keenly aware of the gravity and implication of Bronsen's statement.

"Let us hope it does not come to that my friend. While this be a dangerous game we play I will not bring murder into it—at least not yet."

"Very well, sire. I will find other ways to keep the blinders on that horse's ass."

The general laughed softly and clapped his huge hand gently on the man's shoulder. "That's the wrong end for blinders my friend but I know I can count on you to keep him out of our way. I fear this gamble may not work out as planned, Bronsen. If this breaks badly you will be named guilty by association as will the rest of the staff. We are placing our hopes on two elements, neither of which is a sure thing. Number one—we must bring about quick and successful results here on the battlefield. If that part of the plan fails, we are doomed. Number two—we have been out of touch with the council. We know things have changed at home and what mood we find when, and if, we get back there to explain ourselves we do not know. The best I can hope for is that our venture will garner enough success that it will be hard for the powers that be to overlook. When I am called to task for what may be construed as treasonous behavior, I at least hope to be able to use success to show the council that this 'plan' we have been forced to adhere to over the last two years is absolutely worthless."

"Surely the king will see that you have been forced into this position sire? He could not call you a traitor."

"With the king I am not sure of anything anymore, Bronsen," said the general, shaking his head sadly. "He is not the man who wanted so desperately to ride beside us as we left the gates of Tiernon two years ago. The man who answers my letters—when he does answer them—is cold and distant. A change has come over him."

"There are perhaps many issues at home to deal with sire. We have, after all, been gone for a long time. Maybe things are not well within the council itself, if you know what I mean?"

"That I do, Bronsen. That I do. I am afraid that little weasel, Rhue, has been playing his own brand of politics for quite a while, and we both realize there are too many of the council members who have a weak moral fiber. But I know Edmund as well as you know me. We have been friends since childhood and have fought side by side on many battlefields. It was I who placed his father's bloody sword in his hands and lay the crown on his head after we routed the Torbekians on the Goran Heights during the first war. The man who had the strength and courage to unite the warlords under one banner is not the same one who sits on the throne now my friend. Something has happened to him. That is one of the reasons I have initiated this strategy. When I am called home to be held accountable for my breach of the alliance I am going to find out for myself exactly which way the wind blows in Artura."

Bronsen laid his hand on top of the general's. "And I will be at your side when you do sire. For good or for bad, I am your man."

"I am counting on that, friend. Now, before we stir the pot, we must first light the fire. Call the staff together."

The commanders filed in one by one, eight in all, and assembled themselves around the general's great oak table which occupied a big portion of his personal tent. A modest sleeping pallet and a single chair were the only other pieces of furniture. The table was the one luxury the man allowed himself and it had traveled with his army many thousands of miles. Designed to come apart and be reassembled quickly, it was around this table that the commanders of the Arturan army plotted their strategies. Across its broad and scarred surface were sprawled several maps and it was to these maps the attention of the group was immediately drawn as they crowded the table. Excited conversation soon followed as the men quickly realized what they were looking at. Artemis Thoryl leaned heavily against the table and allowed their fervent discussion to continue unabated for a moment or two longer before he reined them in.

"Commanders." His voice rose clear and commanding above the din. Silence was immediate as the eight men snapped their attention to their leader. The general paused as he surveyed the group gathered around him. All were dressed alike, light short-sleeved tunics and trousers of a slightly heavier material tucked into canvas and leather boots, all a pale tan color closely matching the desert environment in which they operated. Each wore a worn hard-leather hauberk crossed at the chest by a sword buckler also of leather. These bucklers were of a design that allowed the great broadswords favored by Arturans to ride across the owner's back and not hang down at the side where its length and weight would serve as an encumbrance. The grips of these mighty weapons rode just above the shoulder and could be drawn in an instant by one trained to do so. Riding at each man's hip was a short version of the sword riding at their backs, in fact, they were matched sets; identical to the finest detail.

Though none stood as tall as General Thoryl, they were all fair-sized men representing a mix of ages. Two stood out as being on the complete opposite end of the age spectrum. It was to the youngest of these the general spoke first.

"I bid you welcome to this table Captain, excuse me, Commander Ferrin. Congratulations on your appointment, though I speak with a heavy heart when I say that. Commander Aeose was an old comrade. His loss was a blow to me personally but I take comfort from the fact that I believe you are up to the task of replacing him."

All eyes now turned to the young man at the far end of the table from the general. Barely in his twenties, Thad Ferrin's appearance was in sharp contrast to the grizzled warriors who surrounded him. His shoulder length black hair was tied back into a braided ponytail at the nape of his neck and a leather headband crossed his brow. Deep blue eyes burned with intensity and highlighted a smooth, handsome face void of facial hair. He gave the group a short nod of acknowledgement and slapped the closed fist of his right hand over his heart.

"Thank you, General Thoryl. I am honored by your faith in me and pledge to uphold the tradition of the Aeose Regiment."

"If you want to uphold the tradition of the Aeose Regiment son, do it a favor and grow a damn beard. I've seen baby butts with more hair than you." The somber tone of the moment was broken as the group broke into hearty laughter. The general himself could not resist a broad smile towards the man who spoke.

Even at a table of rough-hewn and battle-hardened veteran soldiers, this man stood out. His hair was totally gray and stuck out wildly in all directions matched by an equally wild gray beard that might have hung nearly to the middle of his chest had it been straight. Bits of sticks and dried grass clung to the unruly mass, giving the whole thing a nest-like appearance. The only color in the matted beard was from the dark brown trails of tobacco juice that ran past his lips, streaked his beard, and then disappeared from sight into the tangled mess. A single eye peered out from under bushy eyebrows, while a hollow scarred socket flanked the other side of a nose permanently deformed after being broken numerous times. He grinned even wider, showing what few yellowed and rotted teeth he had left swimming in a mouthful of brown juice and partially chewed tobacco.

"Give the lad time Oren, give the lad time." The general smiled as the laughter subsided. "The stress of command will make him old enough in a hurry. Let us just hope he doesn't end up looking like you."

He turned to the young man at the opposite end of the table. "And for you lad, it is no longer the Aeose Regiment. It is now the Ferrin Regiment. The new standards are being sewn as we speak and those of Commander Aeose will be taken back to the hall of warriors in Tiernon and hung with honor beside those who have fallen before him." There were nods of assent and words of congratulations from around the table.

"Now back to business," the general ordered as he slid one of the maps in front of him. "Do my old eyes deceive me or do I see you are all heartily interested in these little beauties we have here on the table? We first crossed the River Tier over two years ago, and entered into this 'cooperative endeavor' as the politicians have referred to it. Since then we have asked our allies repeatedly to provide us with accurate maps of this country so we might develop an offensive strategy that would bring this so-called insurgency to an end." He paused and scanned the eyes of the men surrounding the table. Satisfied he had their undivided attention, he continued.

"Every time we have been told either there were no maps or that none were needed to defeat the rebels. We have also asked numerous times why we have been hamstrung with a policy that will not allow us to go into the border mountains and root out our foe. To that question we have been told that this is a 'sensitive' issue and that it is in the best interest of ourselves and our allies to defer the strategy of running this war to my counterpart, General Ortair." The mention of the Torbekian army's commander brought a few derisive snorts from around the table. The general continued.

"Indeed, I have been reminded more times than I care to count, that the pursuance of this war is based on a plan formulated and agreed to by Sultan Kala'un of Dazor, Supreme Overlord Taul of Torbek, and King Edmond."

"Long live the king." The salute from those around the table was unanimous but noticeably reserved in its tone. A nuance not lost on Artemis Thoryl.

"So for the past two years we have been chasing the rebels back and forth along this line," he said, as he traced his meaty forefinger across the map in front of him. "From the Kasseri Pass north to the village of Dosen. Two hundred miles. Our area of operations." There were more derisive sniggers from around the table.

"The rebel forces use hit and run tactics and well-planned ambushes exclusively. They hit us hard and then melt into the mountains on one of their many escape routes. By the terms of our agreement we are not allowed to enter into those mountains in pursuit. Thus we find ourselves in the same situation we encountered on the day we arrived in this blasted land, except for the fact that we are now a much smaller force." He looked up from the map and scanned the faces of his commanders. "And that, at least for the near future, will not change."

214

This brought an immediate response from the group, all of them loudly voicing their displeasure simultaneously. The general held his hand up and the protests skidded to a halt. "I am well aware of what the situation is my friends, and I feel no better about it than yourselves." He motioned towards the man on his immediate right, a thick burl of a fellow whose bushy, brown beard and mustache contrasted his completely bald head. "I have asked Commander Kane to give us a complete update on our troop strength and our overall logistical situation. Commander?"

"General," the man nodded somberly, "as of yesterday, our fit for duty roster stands at less than 60 percent." This brought more gasps and protests from around the table.

The general's hand came up again. "Let him continue."

"To date we have lost over four hundred men. To lose that many in a battle would be one thing, but as you all know, most of these have succumbed to this 'desert scourge' that we cannot seem to escape." The commander cleared his throat.

"That count does not include the ambush of the fresh water party three nights ago."

Reactions from around the table were quick and vehement. Artemis Thoryl held up his hands in a plea for calm. "Commanders, please." He nodded towards the man.

"Two more men died this morning from wounds received during the ambush, bringing the total killed to twenty three."

A simmering silence settled over the men surrounding the table, but under that layer burned a fire in their eyes. Their anger was palpable and it did not escape the gaze of their general.

"The circumstances surrounding the catastrophe at the well vexes us all. To have a mole in our midst while we suffer from so many other calamities troubles me to no end. I hope my orders concerning the scheduling of all future work parties have been carried out?"

The men nodded in assent. "Good. Until we figure out the identity of our spy, we must be cautious. Now please continue."

Commander Kane nodded. "We sent so many wounded and

sick back on the last caravan that we had to steal four of the quartermaster's supply wains to carry them all." He paused for a moment before continuing. The mood around the table was somber.

"The two mounted regiments sit at below 50 percent due to the loss of horse. Unfortunately, it seems they are more prone to this blasted sickness than we are. At least we can make foot troops out of those who have no mount. It didn't help when you sent your personal guard back to Artura, sire."

"I am aware of that Commander. Go on."

"As I said about the horses. The worst thing we battle is this disease. The hospital tents are overrun and the physicians are nearly out of potions and powders to treat them. The gravediggers dig at least four new graves every day. We get no more medicine than we do reinforcements." He was starting to get agitated, but continued. "The medical supplies are the worst of it, though we are low on nearly everything. If it's made of leather and wood, it is sorely in need of good grease and oil. This dryness sucks the life out of everything. The wainwrights are having as many problems as the tackers. We have taken to rendering those blasted goats but they make no better grease than they do as food. And food? The supply train from the Torbekians is overdue again and foraging is becoming a problem. The hunting parties have to be so large for protection against attack they scare what little game there is away." He slammed his fist hard against the table. "So where are the replacements and material promised from home?" The men at the table raised their brows at the outburst. Commander Kane quickly realized his miscue. "I am sorry, General. I meant no disrespect."

"Thank you, Commander. No need for an apology and no disrespect taken. You are concerned as we all are." The general turned away from the table and walked over to a pouch hanging from the tent's only chair. He opened the flap, extracted several rolls of parchment, and brought them back.

"I have sent countless communiqués home asking the same question and these are the responses I get. We were promised a steady supply of reinforcements, both men and horse, and the material necessary to facilitate this war effort. Yet two years later we have received very little and much of what we have gotten has been useless."

"The supply of winter boots was a blessing. I was wondering how I was going to keep my feet warm in this place." The sarcasm drooled like the tobacco spit from the lips of Oren Rand, the grizzled one-eyed veteran, but succeeded in forcing grins from those around the table, including the general.

"Yes, they were. Does anyone need a pair? I didn't think so. We ask for grease and food and we get winter boots." He shook the handful of parchment in front of the group.

"Like I said. These are the responses from Minister Pol." He began to throw them on the table one by one. "The material is unavailable due to procurement problems. The last supply train was attacked and looted by bandits. And this one I really like. Due to the funding cutbacks for the army, initiated by Lord Rhue, there aren't any new recruits. Request for replacement troops at this time is denied." He threw the remainder on the table. "And the excuses go on and on."

Oren Rand skewed his face in disgust. "I don't think you brought us here General to tell us things were going to be the same as usual. You don't like the way this war is being fought and we don't like the way this war is being fought. So what do you intend to do about it?"

The general nodded and sighed heavily. "You are right Oren. That is not the reason I asked you here this morning. My purpose is twofold. First, I brought you here to offer you all an apology."

Everyone around the table started to protest at the same time. The general's statement had caught them off guard.

"Let me finish, friends. Please, let me finish." The group again fell silent. The tone in the general's voice more than hinted of something very important he was trying to impart to them.

"I am an old warrior and have never lived anything other than a soldier's life since I was old enough to walk. And what is a soldier taught to do from the moment he decides to take up the sword in defense of King and country?" The general looked around the table and directly into the eyes of each man before he continued. "He is taught to obey orders. He is taught to believe so unquestionably in the chain of command that he would march himself off a cliff if that is what his orders told him to do. Without this absolute obedience, there would be only chaos on the battlefield. An Arturan soldier believes in those who have been deemed worthy enough to bear the grave responsibility of leading men into battle. He believes in you."

There was complete silence around the table. Sounds of an army rising to meet the dawning of another day filtered into the tent. The very men the general was talking about were going about their assigned tasks as they had done every single day of their military career; they were following orders. It was an appropriate backdrop for the general's speech.

"The Arturan soldier believes in you," the general repeated, "and in turn, you have believed in me. Each of you has earned the positions of command you now hold. The Arturan army does not hand out promotions because of who a man's father is or how much money his family has. Promotions have to be earned. You have all earned your command not by just valor on the battlefield, but by exhibiting an ability to lead men. To lead men forward into the fire, into the smoke, into the screams of men and horse, into the blood and carnage of war. You have earned the respect and loyalty of the men you lead. They follow you because an Arturan soldier has faith that his commanders are making the right decisions. So I ask, what do you do for your men to prove that faith is justified? Oren?"

The old warrior grunted and turned his head to spit out a mouthful of tobacco, then, remembering whose tent it was, swallowed it instead. "No sense in wasting a good chew." He grinned. "I do just as any good commander worth his salt does, General, I take damn good care of my men."

"Exactly. I expected no other answer from you, Oren. Thank you. That is what you all do, you take care of those who put their trust in you. It is that kind of trust, respect, and loyalty that has always given us the upper hand in battle, even when the odds have been against us. You have all been with me on many campaigns and have served me well because you have faith in my leadership, and I in turn have always put my faith in the leadership of our King." Artemis Thoryl paused a long moment before taking an audible deep breath, preparing himself for what he was about to say next.

"I have faithfully served three generations of Daines. I swore my oath to King Edmond's grandfather Raymond. I earned my commander's rank under Edmond the First and now have served his son, our King, as his general for nigh twenty years. Never once in that time have I questioned his orders—until now."

The men turned and looked at each other around the table, almost as if to gain reassurance as to what they had just heard. The general gave them what they were looking for.

"Yes my friends, you heard me right. I no longer believe King Edmond is capable of making the decisions that will lead us to victory in this war. In fact, I have come to believe that we are not even expected to win this war at all. I think our sole purpose here is to be kept conveniently out of the way."

"Do you realize the implications of what you are saying General?"

"Absolutely Commander Meril, I do. I would not be standing here if I thought there was any doubt about my suspicions. You know me—I am not a man who rushes to act without careful consideration of what the consequences might be. You are all aware of the total futility of what we do here. There isn't one of you who haven't declared to me your frustration with the way this action is being orchestrated by our 'allies.' It has infected the men as well. They know we are not fighting this war in a manner which will allow us to achieve victory."

"Frustration yes, General. But to the point of going against the king's orders? That is a dangerous path."

"A dangerous path indeed, Commander Palner. One that I would not ask any of you to march down without giving you more information. About six months ago, I started to realize the responses I was getting from the king to my personal requests were not those of the man I have stood side by side with for so many years. You all know that the best way to measure a man's heart is to stand beside him in the heat of battle. There is nothing that will tell you faster if he is the man you believe him to be. I will say to you all—the man I fought beside and who I served for all these years is not the same man who now sits on the throne of Artura and I am willing to risk my career to find out what is truly going on back home. My apology to you stems from the fact that I should have acted sooner. I am sorry I have let you down. It is like Commander Oren said; you take care of those who believe in you. That I have failed to do."

"General." The newest commander, Thad Ferrin, spoke. "Please excuse me if I speak plainly. While I realize that my position here at this honored table may not hold the same weight as my fellow commanders, I must say that we all are experienced enough to know this is not the way to win a war. But isn't the alliance to blame for this situation? You are following the orders of General Ortair who states he is adhering directly to the plan formed by the Tripartite. You certainly cannot be blamed for its failures."

"You are right, Commander Ferrin. We are following the orders of General Ortair, instructed to do so by our King, to show good faith that we are a trustworthy partner in this tripartite peace alliance. But I will tell you something that has been puzzling me more and more lately about our allies. I fought against Jaran Ortair in both Torbekian conflicts. He nearly succeeded in defeating us on several occasions. Sheik Tariq El'nin I have also had the great displeasure of fighting against in a war. And I can tell you this with certainty—they are both shrewd men and understand the art of warfare. If either of them wanted to bring these rebels under control, it would have already been done."

The men looked at each other with confusion on their faces. Grizzled Oren Rand finally asked the question that was on all their minds.

"General. If you will excuse a worn out old dog of a soldier, don't beat around the bush. Are you saying this is all a conspiracy of some kind? One that includes our own king?"

The atmosphere around the table was tense as they awaited the general's answer. The gravity of the old veteran's words filled the tent with an atmosphere of foreboding and anxiety—its grim burden wearing heavily on their faces. Artemis Thoryl closed his eyes and took a long pause before answering.

"What I am saying my friends, is that I believe King Edmond is no longer in control of the situation at home. I know the words I speak will be considered treasonous and that any of you, as loyal subjects of his majesty, have a right to challenge me for a violation of my oath. What I ask of you now is to listen to the evidence I am about to present to you. When I am finished, I am going to leave my fate, and perhaps the fate of our army and country, in your hands. We have reached a fork in the road and the eight of you will decide on which path we will embark."

There was absolute silence around the table, even Oren Rand, never known to be at a loss for words, was dumbstruck.

"Bronsen." The general's attendant flipped back the flap of the tent and stepped in. He had obviously been waiting just outside. "Have Captains Berne and Thoryl arrived yet? These men here are waiting for some answers."

"They have indeed, General. I will bring them immediately."

Like a bee's nest struck by a rock, a buzz of excited conversation rose from around the table. It was obvious the two names had stirred the interest of the men. Artemis Thoryl held up his great hands.

"Commanders, please. You have questions that will be answered in full. I know the presence of these men is a surprise to you but it is as it must be. The need for secrecy is absolute if we are going to get to the bottom of this."

All eyes snapped quickly to the front of the tent and hands reached instinctively for their swords when two men stepped in, dressed identically in loose fitting, sand colored robes tied at the waist. Drab-colored turbans wrapped about their heads, completely obscuring their faces—typical dress of their desert foes, the Uthans.

"Settle your sword arms, Commanders. There is no cause for alarm," the general calmly admonished as the newcomers stepped up to the table. "You all know the two captains, I presume?" Greetings of recognition were finally exchanged as the men unwrapped their faces. "I know you all believed that I sent my personal guard and their captains home months ago. That was a ruse perpetuated by the events of which we have been discussing this morning, and for misleading you, I apologize." The general returned to the map on the table before him. "Instead of returning home, I ordered them to a position here, in the mountains, beyond the northernmost edge of our operational zone. I had to send them that far north to avoid detection. From there they were able to undertake their assignment out of sight and mind."

"And just exactly what was that assignment General?" Commander Rand asked gruffly.

"Patience Oren, patience. There were two assignments and I am going to let the captains themselves explain to you what those were. Captain Thoryl?"

The taller of the two young men nodded to those around the table. Though most of his features were covered by desert garb, his handsome face, covered with several days of unshaved stubble, bore a remarkable resemblance to the general.

"Commanders, father, it is good to see you all again." Artemis Thoryl smiled in return as his son, Captain Kenner Thoryl, pointed to the map.

"As the general stated, we took up a position deep in the mountains in a natural formation the Uthans call the Rake. It is a vast and uninhabitable area of rock spines, spires, and narrow canyons honeycombed with caves. It is also riddled with boiling pits of stinking mud and steam vents which will cook a man and his horse if they are too close when they erupt, and they tend to do so without warning. It is not a place you would want to take a contingent unless complete secrecy is what you were searching for. The Uthans will not venture there. Their Shamans tell them it is the home of Loka the Lizard God, one of the most evil deities in their religion. While it certainly made for a trying existence, it did allow us the opportunity to operate undetected." The men around the table listened intently as Kenner continued.

"We quickly found that maintaining our horse in such a hostile environment was impossible so we were forced to split our force and send half farther north to find adequate water and feed. As you all well know, these blasted mountains do not lend themselves for horse anyway, so it did not disrupt our mission. That mission Commanders, was chiefly to gather information. We were ordered to avoid direct contact with the Uthans and anyone else if at all possible. For the most part, we were successful, though we did manage to find a Dazorian trader with a loose tongue and even looser scruples who, for coin and drink, gave us very valuable information. It is by his hand these maps came to us."

"You found a Dazorian trader on this side of the mountains?" The question came from Oren Rand.

"Your pardon Commander, but I did not say we were on this side of the mountains."

The response from around the table was immediate. "Let the lad finish my friends." Artemis Thoryl steered the conversation back to his son.

"Some of us did indeed find our way to the Dazorian side of the mountains but let me go back to our mission. We found a large cave in the Rake suitable for use as a base and from there broke up into four patrols of eight, leaving a contingent behind as reserve in case the worse befell us. Two of those patrols stuck to the mountains, scouting Uthan villages and trails while two crossed the divide into Dazor. One squad traveled south to shadow the Dazorian army while the other, which included myself, went deep into Dazor proper."

There was a buzz of conversation as Captain Thoryl paused in his narrative. They had all been told the tripartite agreement did not allow any excursion across the mountains which formed the border between the two countries of Torbek and Dazor. The young Captain's admission was a serious breach of protocol.

Oren Rand swallowed another mouthful of chewing tobacco. "And just how did you find our allies on this little excursion of yours, Kenner?"

Captain Thoryl looked towards his father who gave him a nod. "We found things quite different than we have been led to believe for the past two years, Commander Rand. Other than the fact that a Dazorian army is indeed camped on the east side of the Kasseri Pass, we found very little evidence of a war going on. In fact, we encountered Uthans and the nomadic Dazor tribesmen trading as if they were the best of friends." Eyebrows raised around the table. The young Captain continued.

"The patrol that shadowed the Dazorian army found them to be comfortably encamped around a lush oasis with plenty of good water and well supplied with food. Our men witnessed no combat patrols and no evidence of any activity at all mounted against the rebels."

More buzz around the table. "What do you make of all this, General?" Commander Rand spat.

"It is the very reason I sent them out, Oren," replied the general. "My gut feeling that something was rotten about this campaign has been gnawing at me for quite some time. But there is more to hear. Tell them about the other patrols, Captain."

Kenner Thoryl continued. "The two squads sent out to spy on the Uthan villages and their trail systems found similar circumstances as those we found on the Dazorian side of the mountains. For months they watched, but only in the villages close to our active perimeter did we find rebel fighters. Those villages deeper into the mountains show no war activity at all. Indeed they go about daily life as if this conflict did not even exist."

A flurry of questions erupted around the table with all of the Commanders trying to speak at once.

"Please," Artemis Thoryl's powerful voice rose above the tumult, "hear the rest of it." The men around the table quieted and returned their gaze to the young man.

"In the main Uthan village of Costa, which is located near enough to the Kasseri Pass as to be a major concern if this were a real war, one of the patrols was able to discern, on several different occasions, the coming and going of men identified as hailing from both Torbek and Dazor."

The men looked at each other in disbelief. Confusion etched with shock on their faces.

"Thank you, Captain Thoryl," the general spoke solemnly. "I know you all have questions but there is more for you to hear. I would like to take this opportunity to say that the men entrusted for this operation suffered greatly in their quest to gather and bring this information back to us. They endured the harshest of conditions and their lives were at peril every moment. In fact, one of the patrols disappeared and was never heard from again. But there is another part to this. I will now ask Captain Berne to speak."

"General, commanders." Tanner Berne nodded to the gathering. Smaller than Kenner Thoryl by half a head, his dark hair and features were also discolored by dust and the ravages of spending too much time in the blistering sun. The toll of rugged existence in the Rake had aged both young men considerably.

"Captains Lando Berk, Kellen Thoryl, and I were instructed by the general to continue on after the main body reached the Rake. Our destination—Tiernon." More buzz from around the table.

"We did not traverse the main routes, and instead swung north to the village of Whitewater where the River Tier drops out of the mountains. Commander Darwin, I believe that is your hometown?"

Another tired looking veteran, nearly as gnarled and grizzled as Oren Rand nodded wearily. "It has been a long time since I was able to call that place home, son."

The young man nodded. "At Whitewater we played the part of out of work soldiers and were able to hire on with a work party rafting logs to the mill at Stonebridge. Fortunately, no one there knew who we were and people did not ask a lot of questions. It appears that out of work soldiers are not uncommon in Artura as of late. From Stonebridge we worked our way slowly to Tiernon. One of the tasks given us by General Thoryl was to listen and observe the plain folk, gauge their feelings as to what has been going on within the country."

"And you found?" This came from Commander Esten Hard-wyck.

"Frustration and worry at the least. Anger and near open rebellion at the worst," Captain Byrne answered.

"That seems to be directly at odds with the way things were when we marched from the gates of Tiernon over two years ago."

"Overwhelmingly so, Commander Meril," the young man continued. "Ever increasing taxes, lack of work, suppression of the rights of minorities, dwarves and trolls particularly being singled out. It appears most of these oppressive measures started soon after General Thoryl crossed the River Tier bound for the Waste. But as bad as they are, things took a turn for the worse by two recent decrees supposedly coming from the throne. The reason for there being so many out of work soldiers? The first decree disbanded most of the standing army remaining in Artura."

The table erupted, the anger of hardened soldiers burst forth in a fury of shouts and curses. The clamor was great enough to cause Bronsen to hurry into his general's tent with alarm. It took General Thoryl a while to calm the men this time. When they quieted down, Commander Rand was the first to speak.

"This confirms your suspicions, does it not General? The man we know and fought beside for many a conflict would never disband his army."

"It does indeed, Oren." General Thoryl sighed heavily, worry lines furrowed deep across his troubled face. "I knew things were bad, but that goes beyond anything I might have guessed. You said something about two decrees, Captain Berne?"

"Yes, General," the young man nodded. "The second decree is an extension of the first. Along with the disbanding of the army, all pensions, past and future, have been eliminated."

This time the men were too stunned for an outburst. They looked at each other trying to comprehend what they had just heard. In total disbelief, they turned to their general.

Artemis Thoryl rested his huge hands on the table, leaned his weight forward, dropped his head, and closed his eyes. He looked as if an unseen load had suddenly been thrust upon his broad shoulders, a weight that even a man such as he could hardly bear. There was a long period of uncomfortable silence before he raised his head and spoke.

"It seems we have an answer to the question of reinforcement. How long ago since these decrees were enacted Captain?"

"Six months, General."

"Six months, yet I have here a response from Procurement Minister Pol concerning reinforcements dated less than two months ago. He hints at nothing as momentous as the dismantling of the army, instead he states only that there were some minor funding cutbacks."

"The shit is so deep at home General we can smell it from here." Oren Rand spat a thick wad of chew onto the sand floor, his deliberate lack of manners now an obvious reflection on the disturbing news. "The question becomes, what are we going to do about it?"

"That is why I have brought you all here, Oren. But this new information causes me to rethink my original plan. If things have deteriorated as far as they seem at home, then we may not have enough time. What else can you tell us Captain? Were you able to make the contacts within the Ministry like I asked?"

The young Captain nodded. "Yes, sir. We made contact with Derric Lynn, Captain Berk's father-in-law. He was able to give us a great deal of information. The most important seems to be the issue of the king's health. Minister Lynn said that King Edmond has not been out of the castle since just after the army marched. He manages to be present at Council sessions but is in such a state that he does not speak and spends most of his time asleep on his throne. The minister said that for quite some time the business of government has been administered by the elder council in the king's stead, General."

Artemis Thoryl nodded. "Which is as it should be by Arturan law. If the king is incapacitated and cannot govern then the elder council acts for him."

"But there is a part of that situation of which I have not yet spoken, General. It was made clear to me by Minister Lynn, and his opinion was backed by others who Captain Berk and I were able to talk to. The minister was adamant that you understand."

"Then by all means, tell me Captain. What is it that he wants me to be aware of?"

The young man cleared his throat, as if the words he needed to say had become lodged. "It appears that the country is not in the hands of the elder council at all, General. There is one man who controls everything; he has even created a new position within the Government. He calls himself first council to the king and nothing happens without his assent. It is said that he has absolute control over a majority of the elder council and thusly controls their actions."

Artemis Thoryl looked grim as he digested the young man's words. There was absolute quiet around the table as the commanders eyed their leader.

"You can stop there Captain Berne. You do not have to tell me who is behind this for I know the man's name all too well, and I curse myself for not having seen the ramifications of his increasing power years ago. I was just an old fool of a soldier who did not care for the workings of politics. I have failed in my duty to my king and my country."

"You were not the only one guilty of failing to see what was going on within the castle walls, General," Commander Hardwyck said. "But unlike you, I have paid a bit more attention to the inner workings of Arturan politics. As you know, I was thinking of giving up my commander's rank and accepting a permanent position within the Ministry just before the orders came to march. I thought it might be a good place for an old warhorse to put himself out to pasture, so to speak. I too saw the rising power of the man in question but like yourself was not inclined to act, not that it would have done any good. From the moment he began appearing beside our good King, the notion of his mere presence chilled me. When the time came to choose between politics and a saddle, he made my decision to return to soldiering an easy one. Being anywhere close to the man makes my sword hand itch. I will not hesitate to speak his name but I will curse it in the same breath. Artura is being controlled exclusively by that Torbekian weasel Daemon Rhue. Back to Oren's question, General, what are we going to do about it?"

Artemis Thoryl studied the faces of each soldier around the table, old veterans like Oren Rand, Esten Hardwyck, and Thedric Darwin. Men with whom he had slept on the same hard ground and ate from the same pot of camp stew, men who had stood beside him while swords clashed and men died. Young men like Captains Berne and his own son Kenner, men to whose future leadership Artura would come to depend. What he saw did not despair him. While his heart was heavy with the ill news from home, he could look about the table and take pride that these were the sort of men who could be counted on when the time came. And while he was unsure of what the right course of action might be, Artemis Thoryl was sure they were all going to be needed very soon.

"That question has no easy answer, Commander," he began. "As good soldiers must, we have to look at the hard truth which confronts us. Kellen and Captain Berk have stayed in Tiernon and will be giving me as many updates as time and distance allow, but we are a long way from home and any action we take will have constraints built around it that will hinder any effect we may have. Compounding that is the fact that whatever we do that counters our orders will put us under the shadow of treason. This I was willing to accept at least for myself with the plan I had intended to implement. I did not send these young men out on their hazardous mission just for a lark. My plan was to challenge all of what we have been adhering to for the last two years and cause such an uproar and protest from our allies that I would be recalled to Artura. There I would have had a chance to see for myself the things our young Captain has been describing. It would have ended my military career but it was something I felt I had to do. But this news tells me that things are much worse at home than I thought and my plan has come too late."

The general drew himself up to his full height, cutting an impressive figure even around a table full of impressive men. His eyes were intense and none could turn away from them. His voice was firm, belying the emotion that filled his heart.

"My friends, we do not have to be politicians to realize what is going to happen very soon in our country. With the army disbanded and set adrift with no pensions, we have now thousands of men with no way to support their families. Idle soldiers without the discipline of rank and file are trouble of the highest order, ripe for banditry and discord. How are they to pay the high taxes now implemented? It is a stew for disaster whose ingredients have been slowly and cunningly stirred in, while those of us who should have seen what was going on failed to do so.

"That we have been sent here to keep us out of the way while subterfuge undermines the foundation of Artura is something on which I think we would all agree, but it does not change the immediate situation. King Edmond labored long and hard to establish the security at home that we have come to expect. It was he who united our country, the one who brought the warlords together and had them put aside petty squabbles for the good of the nation. It was by that act and his guidance we defeated Torbek and Dazor in two long and bitter wars. But while he was as good and as brave a soldier as any, we also know of his abhorrence to the effects of war, and his brokered peace with our enemies was something he was proud of."

"But what has become of that man, General?" Oren Rand questioned gruffly. "It is apparent that he no longer guides our nation but in his stead allows a Torbekian rat to steer her to destruction."

His bitterness and anger echoed through the tent. The men at the table quietly chewed on the words of their comrade, words weighing heavy upon already troubled emotions.

"I can only imagine at the depths of deceit and lies Edmond has been subjected to, Oren. For him to have sunk as low as this right under the noses of so many good Arturans points to deception on a grand scale. From what Captain Berne has told us, the king's mental capacity is all but gone and with Rhue's control of the elder council, it was quite easy to remove any obstacles in the way of him taking control. That we find ourselves hamstrung here in this waste must have been a big part of his plan."

The general paused and stared intently into the faces of the men around the table. "We may be late my friends, but rest assured we will not stand idly by any longer. We now have information we never had before and can formulate a new plan that hopefully will get us out of this quagmire we find ourselves in. Captains Berk and Thoryl have stayed behind in Tiernon to monitor the situation and seek out those who might understand what is going on, and they will be willing to act when the time comes."

"You know their lives will be forfeit if Rhue and the rest of those bastards who had a hand in this find them out General."

Artemis Thoryl sighed and nodded. "They understand the perils of their mission, Oren They are soldiers and will give their lives if need be in the line of duty. We cannot worry about them. For now, what we must do is come up with a new plan. My friends, we are talking no less than civil war if we choose to go against our orders from Tiernon and I do not ask you lightly to think about this and consider the consequences. We will—"

The general's statement was cut off by the sound of a commotion just outside the tent. The eyes of the men snapped to the front and their hands reached for their swords. The flap of the tent was thrown back and Bronsen stepped in.

"Your pardon, General, but that extra measure of security I spoke of this morning seems to have been timely in its execution. Minister Denron is at the outer perimeter and quite angry at being temporarily detained."

A weary frown broke across Artemis Thoryl's worn face. "Timely indeed, Bronsen, and I commend you for your foresight. Commanders, this meeting must come to an end. Captains Berne and Thoryl you must disappear. I will get in touch with you later. Our Torbekian liaison must not see you here."

The two young men threw the trailing folds of their turbans over their faces and disappeared from the tent. The commanders looked to their general.

"The rest of you can stay," he said, nodding to them. "Your hunch was correct, Bronsen. Did the minister mention as to why he has arrived a day early?"

Bronsen shook his head. "No, General. The messenger stated only that he is in an agitated state and is demanding to be brought to you immediately."

General Thoryl sighed heavily. "Very well. Let us see what our allies are up to now. Let him come, Bronsen. Commander Ferrin, would you be so good as to roll up these maps and put them out of sight? The presence of such things that supposedly do not exist might excite the good minister and we do not want to tip our hand quite yet."

The young commander hurriedly did his general's bidding and the maps were safely out of sight when another commotion again focused the men's attention to the front of the tent. A squeaky, high pitched voice was making quite a fuss.

"I will be following up on this matter Bronsen; you can be assured of that. I am the duly appointed representative of Supreme Lord Taul and will not be treated as a common bandit."

Bronsen stepped into the general's tent and held the flap open for a small, mouse-looking man who closely followed. His white, loose-fitting, desert robes were tied at the waist with an ornate, embroidered sash and highlighted the man's dark features. His turban was held in place by a matching headband, its gold and jeweled centerpiece sparkling in mock contrast to the unadorned raiment of the Arturan soldiers. Rings clustered about the man's bony fingers and around his neck, gold chains clinked in gilded protest as the man's head bent ever so slightly in acknowledgement to the general. The Torbekian minister looked as if he had just left an exquisite party.

"General Thoryl. I must protest this outrage. Your man here has had me detained for no reason and I demand he be held accountable for his actions."

"Relax, Minister Denron," the general answered wearily, doing his best to conceal the scorn he held for the Torbekian.

"Bronsen was just following my orders. I had perimeter security changed and they were not notified of your unexpected arrival. You were, after all, not due back until the morrow. Bronsen, would you please get the minister a glass of wine so he may wash the dust from his throat?" Bronsen nodded and let the flap close behind him. "Your surprise visit has found us in the midst of a staff meeting. You know my Commanders, Minister?" The Torbekian looked as if he had just noticed the eight soldiers gathered about the table; men whose contempt was not concealed near as well as the general's. The minister's attitude immediately changed—his condescending tone dropped as he nodded.

"Commanders, I bid you greeting." None of the men missed the sly smile that crept across the mousy man's thin lips. "It is fortuitous that I find you all gathered at the general's tent for I bring you momentous news."

Artemis Thoryl had already grown impatient with the man even though he had just entered his tent. The smarmy Tae Denron served as liaison between the headquarters of Torbekian General Jaran Ortair and the Arturans, a sharp but unremovable thorn in their side. It had long been suspected by General Thoryl and others that Minister Denron was more spy than liaison but they had been saddled with the man regardless. The irritation was obvious in the general's voice.

"What is this momentous news you have for us, Minister? My Commanders have an army to look after and their time is needed elsewhere."

"But my dear General Thoryl, this is nothing short of the gift you have been asking for," the man fawned. "I bear orders from General Ortair." Slipping his hand into the folds of his robe, he extracted a roll of parchment, handing it to Commander Ferrin, who was closest. The orders were quickly passed down the table to the general who unrolled them and began to read. His brow quickly furrowed in concern.

"You see, General?" Minister Denron continued, his voice dripping with the syrup of unveiled sarcasm. "Is this not the very thing you have demanded for months?"

Artemis Thoryl did not answer, continuing to read. Finally, his face clouded with worry and shock, he looked up from the parchment. The minister did not wait for him to speak.

"General Ortair has commanded me to return immediately when you have received your orders. Time is paramount, General. You can see why I was so upset by being detained."

Artemis Thoryl nodded glumly. "Return to General Ortair, Minister, and tell him that we march immediately." The surprised commanders looked to him in shocked surprise but remained silent as the general held up his hand. "You may go, Minister. Like you said, time is paramount."

Tae Denron nodded. "The future will be a glorious one for us all, General. May your army distinguish itself on the battlefield."

With a slight bow, he turned. Bronsen held out a goblet of wine as the Torbekian walked past, but the offer was ignored. Instead the surly minister glowered at him and stalked out of the tent. The Commanders started to all speak at once but the general again silenced the table with his hand. He gave Bronsen a nod towards the tent flap and he ducked out quickly behind the Torbekian. After a brief moment, Bronsen returned.

"He is gone, sire."

"Commanders," the general pleaded as he was immediately bombarded by questions, "let me speak." When the men had regained their composure, he continued, waving the rolled parchment in front of him.

"The orders from General Ortair state that a large rebel force has been spotted mustering deep within the mountains and it appears they are readying for a major assault. We are to proceed immediately in strength to join with our allies at the mouth of the Kasseri Pass. General Ortair says the situation is critical and speed is of the utmost importance."

"But General, this makes no sense." The voice of Oren Rand rose above the din.

"I am as concerned as you are, Oren, but for now, we cannot

disregard this order. All other plans will have to wait. Commanders, attention!" General Thoryl searched the eyes of each man that surrounded the table.

"My friends. For the moment, I will not attempt to decipher the untimely coincidence of this situation. We have been summoned and must respond. We will do our duty, at least for now. It will be a long march to the Pass and we have much to do to get ready. As much as it disturbs me, we must put the conversation we have just had to rest and get about our business. Commander Hardwyck, instruct the drummers to beat the troops to general quarters. We have the better part of the day in front of us and I want the bulk of the army ready to march within the hour. Oren, tell the quartermaster the supply train can catch up with us when we make camp tonight. You are all dismissed."

The men slapped their fists across their chests and hurried from the tent, leaving only the general and Bronsen.

"You are troubled, General?" Bronsen asked quietly after the last man had gone.

The general sighed as he flipped the rolled parchment onto the table. Outside, the drums thumped a heavy cadence, joined in harmony by the sound of the camp preparing to march. Men shouted orders; horses screamed with excitement; armor, swords, and spears rattled. The sound of men preparing to march towards war flooded through the thin tent walls.

"Troubled, perplexed, concerned. You could say that I am all of those things right at the moment."

"But I agree that you have no choice," Bronsen continued. "To ignore General Ortair's direct command at this time would be unthinkable." He walked over to a stand near the tent's sleeping pallet where the general's sword, his light desert chain mail, and his battle helm hung at the ready

"Come, sire, I shall help you dress."

Artemis Thoryl walked over to the stand where his aide waited and placed his hand on the smaller man's shoulders. "Thank you Bronsen, but I want you to write a note as I dress myself."

The man nodded. "Yes, sire. Who am I to address this note to?"

"Address it to my son and Captain Berne. They will not like it but I do not want them to march with us. I have an uneasy feeling about this whole thing. I don't know, maybe I suffer from the same malady all soldiers do when battle approaches. The twisting knot deep inside that makes you wonder if there is an arrow or spear that is marked for you."

"But you do not fear death, sire. I have been at your side for thirty years now and it is not that which gives you concern."

"You know me too well, Bronsen." Artemis Thoryl sighed deeply as he sat down on the dressing stool. "You are right. There is something about all of this that forebodes ill. Something I cannot put my finger to. Why this? Why now? I thought I had a plan that would at least give some direction to this ill-gotten war of ours, but just as I prepare to implement it, the situation changes in a heartbeat. Is this just bad luck or destiny? What do you make of it?"

As the general dressed, Bronsen fetched writing materials from a chest nearby. He pulled a stool up close. "I do not believe much in luck, General, and I do not attempt to guess about destiny. We must ride down the road to meet it head on and find out what it has in store for us."

The general sighed again. "The road to destiny. Down that road lies the inevitable fork, Bronsen. One of which is life and the other death. Which one will it be for you and I, eh? Which one will it be?"

Chapter Fourteen

DAEMON RHUE NERVOUSLY PACED THE FLOOR of his tower, always apprehensive when the time came to contact his master. Not only did the act itself drain him physically, leaving him cramped and nauseous, but he could never be certain that Kenric Taul would not be angry at him for some reason. If there was one thing Daemon Rhue knew all too well, it was the consequences of arousing his Lord's ire. Even at this distance, the man's power was incredible. He shuddered, recalling the last time he had run afoul of his master's quick temper. It had left him a shivering wreck on this very floor, too weak to crawl to the garderobe and cleanse himself of his own excrement after the excruciating pain had caused him to lose control of his bodily functions. But as frightful as the man's power could be, it intrigued him just the same. Daemon Rhue longed for the time when he too had the skill and strength to reach across such distances and inflict such pain and suffering on those who displeased him—to even be able to kill. A rap on the door snapped him back to the moment.

"Enter Steyr. You took your own sweet time as usual."

The physician pushed open the heavy door of the tower room and stepped inside. Breathing heavily, his face flushed with the exertion of climbing the many steps up to Daemon Rhue's tower, the fat man was too winded to answer.

"Why is it that a man capable of concocting a powder that can keep his puny prick erect for hours at a time can't manage to come up with one that would give him energy enough to obey his master's commands in an acceptable time? Can you answer me that, Steyr?"

"Forgive me, sire," the fat man panted as he struggled to catch his breath. "I came as soon as that miserable servant gave me your message. I believe he deliberately dallied along the way and should be punished severely, your Lordship."

"Spare me the excuses and lies you fat bag of shit. The boy was back with my breakfast in half the time it took you to get here. The only one who dallied was you. I am sure you had your nose stuck up the crotch of some kitchen maid barely old enough to bleed. Or is it the baker's boys who catch your fancy these days? Never mind. Are you prepared?"

"Yes, my Lord." The physician huffed as he pulled out a bag from the pocket of his robe and walked to the table still strewn with the communiqués and letters the first council had been reading earlier. He sat down on the stool and opened the drawstring of the pouch, carefully removing a smooth piece of slate slightly bigger than his hand, a small thin blade, and several corked porcelain vials. "Are you ready, my Lord?"

"Prepare your powders and listen to me. I may not be able to tell you what I need to afterwards. And make doubly sure you mix the proper amounts. I swear Steyr, that I will have you strung up and every inch of skin flayed off that fat ass of yours if I get as sick as I did the last time."

"But sire, please! I have explained that it is the combination of the powders, the use of the crystals, and the amount of time you must hold the connection with Lord Taul that weakens you so. I have no control over that."

"Then you had better get with that witch of yours and figure out what it takes to control it or I will replace you both. Do you understand?"

The man nodded meekly and turned his attention back to the contents of the pouch.

Daemon Rhue continued while Steyr worked. "Good. Mix and listen carefully. Things are coming to a head faster than I had anticipated. Artemis Thoryl is growing suspicious and is planning something. What exactly it is I do not know and I doubt that fool

Denron knows anything either. I will inform my master of the situation and I am sure he will want us to act soon. Everything is in place here, though I did want a little more time to be sure that slobbering idiot of a king is completely under control. He is under control, is he not?"

Steyr looked up from the slate where he had been concentrating and nodded vigorously in assent, breaking into a murderous smile. "Edmond is the least of our worries, sire. He is utterly without a thought unless you put it there. A puppet under your complete control is what you wanted your Lordship, and on that one I have not failed. I beg you to just remember your promise after this is finished."

"I have not forgotten, Steyr. I might even watch some of the nasty little things you have in store for our dear little princess. What of General Holt and the cabinet ministers? Any foreseeable problems there?"

"None, your Lordship," Steyr answered as he pulled corks from the vials and poured the contents of each onto the slate.

"With the 'untimely' scandal and death of Minister Rando, all the pieces have fallen into place. I have ordered the key elements to be prepared at any given moment and have taken steps to be sure they are painfully aware that no failure will be tolerated."

"They are not the only ones who need fear failure, Steyr, I remind you of that."

Steyr nodded grimly as he finished mixing the powders together and measured them equally into piles. With the blade, he drew the powder out into two long, thick lines. "All is ready, my Lord. Will Master Taul be expecting you?"

"Probably not, but this is something that cannot wait. Let us hope the link will find him in his library."

Daemon Rhue walked across the room to a large wooden chest located at the foot of his sparse bed. It was secured with a heavy iron lock which he opened with a key fastened to a chain around his neck. From inside, he extracted an embroidered carpet roll which he handed to Steyr. Then, reaching carefully into the depths of the chest with both hands, he brought out a black lacquered box. Smaller than a loaf of bread, the box appeared to have no visible seams, locks, or hinges—anything that might suggest a means to open it. Daemon Rhue held it almost caressingly out in front of him. The lacquered finish seemed to glow with an ebony luminescence.

Carefully he carried the box to the center of the tower room where Steyr had unrolled the carpet. Daemon Rhue sat down with his feet tucked under and his knees splayed out in a meditative position with the box directly in front of him.

"I am ready."

Steyr knelt down by his master's side and held out the slate with the two lines of mixed powder on it.

"Must it always be done this way?" Daemon asked as he took a small quill tube from the physician's hand. "Can't you just mix it with a liquid?"

"I am sorry, your Lordship. Through the nostrils is the quickest and most direct way to the brain. The witch says it must be done this way or she cannot guarantee its effectiveness."

"Hmmphh," Daemon grunted. "I think Mogga just delights in trying to blow the top of my head off. One of these days, I am going to have an accounting with her. Do you have the antidote ready?"

"Yes, my Lord. It is ready."

"Good. Don't let me hit the floor when this is through. Do you understand?"

Without waiting for an answer, Daemon Rhue bent down with the tube in his right hand and pressed his left nostril shut with his left index finger. He inhaled one line of powder deeply into his right nostril and then quickly shifted hands and repeated the process through his left. Steyr barely had time to grab the implements out of the man's hands before the first spasm rocked Daemon Rhue violently. His facial and neck muscles corded up and seemed ready to explode as his eyes bulged nearly out of their sockets. His teeth ground together as his lips pulled out into a maniacal grin by the intense contraction of the surrounding muscles.

Daemon Rhue was rocked by three more violent spasms before

he seemed to regain some semblance of control. After he settled and was able to reestablish normal breathing, he turned his attention to the box. He reached out and settled both of his hands on the surface, placing his two thumbs together in the middle and splaying his fingers out over the edges. With eyes closed and body now settled into a deep, rhythmic breathing pattern, the fingers moved ever so slightly, searching for the hidden triggers which only his experienced fingers could find and manipulate with just the right amount of pressure. When he was satisfied that he had the proper position, he carefully tensed his fingers—the box popped open.

Lying inside, on a bed of exquisite black velvet, lay two crystal shards. Each was near the length of an average man's hand and their slightly unequal hexagon form was a little bigger around than a broomstick handle, tapering to a finite point. Except for their color, they were nearly mirror images of the other. The one on the left was a deep, fire-orange hue with streaks of blood-red running through it; it almost seemed to hiss in kinship to flame and fire. On the other side of the box was an aqua-blue gem that looked as if it had been sculpted of the purest ice.

Daemon Rhue reached into the box and gently lifted a shard into each hand. Resting his wrists on his knees, he faced the points of each crystal directly towards the other, about two finger widths apart. The color of each shard hummed with intensity as the points lined up. Each of Daemon Rhue's hands glowed with the color of its cradled gem. He closed his eyes, slowed his breathing, and bent his mind inward towards the crystals.

"Sacred elements of earth—shard born of fire—shard born of water. Join your power together with your sister elements now flowing through my blood. Complete the circle and give me the strength needed to form the link—seek the master."

Daemon Rhue brought the tips of the crystals together; the darkness of his mind exploded into a flashing brilliance of pain and light—and then he was gone.

"WELL?" THE VOICE FLOATED BODYLESS. DAEMON RHUE WAS

afraid to open his eyes just yet; he had learned the hard way the mind-crippling shock of doing so. He needed to let the intensity die down a bit, so instead he focused on the voice, trying to detect a tonal quality that might hint at the speaker's mood.

"This had better be important, Rhue. I do not like unscheduled interruptions. What is it that you want?"

Daemon Rhue opened his eyes slowly. This part was always hard for him to get used to; his mind told him he was in the great library of his master's keep, high above the city of Sectos, capitol of Torbek, and the grandest city in the known world—his ancestral home. But he knew his comatose body was still sitting on the floor of the cold tower room in Tiernon, watched over by his awed physician. Slowly his spirits came alive with the sensual exhilaration brought on by the successful manipulation of such power—this was what he sought—this was magic.

He was floating bodiless as his other senses adjusted themselves to the great room in which he found himself. As his eyes came into focus, he could see his master sitting at his reading desk, a thick dusty tome propped open on a stand in front of him. His olfactory sense was assailed with the muskiness of old leather, ancient parchment, and dust. Bookshelves rising five times a man's height lined the walls of the great domed room. Steps and permanent scaffolds granted access to the upper reaches. This was a room built for knowledge and gaining the worlds' knowledge, both light and dark, was the goal of the man seated at the plain wooden reading table, a man for whom knowledge was power, and power was absolute.

Though seated, it wasn't hard to tell Kenric Taul was a very large man—unique among Torbekians for they were by nature slightly built. He would have stood two heads taller than Daemon Rhue had they stood side by side. His shoulders were broad and the gap at the neck of his robe hinted at a massive chest. With the bronze toned skin of a Torbekian, he was dressed in an unassuming, white, floor-length robe, tied at the middle with a dark sash. Plain leather sandals covered his big feet and his well-muscled arms were folded casually across his chest. The robe was sleeveless but the arms were anything but bare. At the top of each shoulder where it disappeared into the folds of the robe began the body of a terrifying serpent tattoo. The tail started at the top of his shoulder, their bodies wound down and around the man's arms, ending with their heads raised and fangs bared at the joining of the wrist and hand. The viper's fangs looked real enough to kill.

Though his facial features had the traits common to his race, with thin lips, small ears and nose, there was one other thing besides his abnormal size that made him stand out amongst Torbekians—he was completely void of any body hair at all. Tattoos instead lined his smooth face; from cheeks to temples on up to his shaved head. Mystical symbols, runes, ancient images—these were the adornments that covered the skin of the man Daemon Rhue now faced. It was a fearsome appearance and one not gained by accident.

"Surely you have recovered enough to speak, Rhue? If you were stronger in your skills, you would not be forcing me to wait."

Daemon Rhue finally found his tongue. "I beg your forgiveness Master Taul. I would not have bothered you with this visit if I did not believe it was necessary."

"Very well, let us hear this matter of importance that troubles you so. I do hope you are not going to tell me that there is a problem with our plan? There is no problem is there, Rhue?"

"N-no Master, the plans are going well. All the elements are in place as you specified. The concern that brings me here is a communication I received from General Thoryl in the last batch of dispatches."

"You mean a dispatch meant for the king, don't you?"

"Well...yes, of course. Nothing gets through to the king that is not screened by myself."

"So what does the great general tell his king that troubles you so? More concern over the absence of men and supplies?" Lord Taul's voice was laden with sarcasm.

"That, as usual Master, but it is what he hints at that bothers me. While he doesn't say exactly what his intentions are, he speaks of a plan he is going to put into motion that will change the nature of the conflict. It has always been the general's blind loyalty to his king that was the cornerstone of our plan. If it has come to the point where he is going to take it upon himself to deviate from that plan, it means that we can no longer count on him performing as we expect."

Kenric Taul leaned back in his chair and folded his arms. "Well, well, so the good general is finally letting his suspicions force him into action. It doesn't surprise me as much as it has you, Rhue. The man is no fool. Artemis Thoryl didn't defeat us in the last two wars because he was stupid. It was just a matter of time before he became a problem. That we got two years out of him is a wonder to me."

"So what do you intend to do, Master? For the coup to succeed we must eliminate any interference from General Thoryl and the Arturan army."

"Rhue, you worry like an old woman. Do you think I am not in control here? I have been aware of his change in thinking for quite some time now. Denron has kept me well-informed. While I realize that the minister is not a man you put much faith in, he has done well nonetheless. He has kept me posted on the General's behavior, though of late it hasn't been so easy. The general's man Bronsen has proven to be quite a great nuisance. He has had Denron followed and watched for the last several weeks."

"So you have a plan, Master?"

"When do I not have a plan, Rhue? Did you leave your intelligence back behind with your body? Do not anger me with your insolence. I have plotted every detail of this retribution for ten years and I will not be denied my vengeance because some worn out warrior starts to question the nature of things."

"I beg your forgiveness, Master. I meant no dis—"

"Shut up, Rhue, and spare me your groveling. We have the general right where we want him and he will cause no concern on your end."

Kenric Taul stood up and strode over to a large map located on one of the few spaces of the wall not covered with bookshelves. "Are you strong enough with the link to hold it while I show you why you should not be concerned? Do you forget what happened the last time your power faded before I was done with you?"

"Yes, Master Taul, I can hold the link," Daemon Rhue stammered. He did remember all too well. "I have been working on strengthening my will as you commanded."

"Good. Now float yourself over here and let me show you something which you should already be aware of."

Daemon Rhue willed his bodiless essence over to the map at which his master was standing. Normally moving about during an audience with Lord Taul wasn't something he had to do. Though it was a drain on the mind power that held the link, Daemon knew this was no time to show weakness in front of the man who held the balance of life or death in his hands. Not being strong enough to hold the link at such a crucial time would be suicide. As he had told Steyr moments before he made the connection, failure at any turn now would be unacceptable to Kenric Taul.

"Lucky for you Rhue that you have gotten stronger. Now look at this." He jabbed his finger into a spot on the map. Daemon knew this map well, for it was twin to the one hanging on the wall of his tower. Lord Taul was pointing to Tiernon.

"From Tiernon, east up the river to the bridge at Stonegate. Two weeks of hard travel for horsemen, let alone an entire army." He ran his finger south from the town along the edge of the mountain range.

"Three more weeks across the Waste to General Thoryl's base camp. Even if he were to start to move, it would take his army over a month to get back to Tiernon. That is why we chose to send him there if you will recall. Besides, I do not intend on there being anything left of the Arturan army to cause you any problems."

"So you intend on moving the timetable ahead, Master?" Daemon's bodiless voice queried.

"Come now. You came here knowing that is exactly what I intend to do. Why must you always play the fool? I have already notified General Ortair and Sultan El'nin of the situation and they are preparing as we speak. I will not allow Thoryl time to activate any kind of plan."

"What of Jenga Batu, Master? Do you trust him to do his part?"

"Batu is a narrow-minded man, Rhue. He can see no farther than the gold I have waved in front of his face. With that and the promise of amnesty for him and the rest of the Uthan rabble, he will do his part. Besides, General Ortair has added some extra incentive that will guarantee the rebel performs exactly as expected. He has Batu's wife and daughter."

"That is good to hear, Master. Batu is a treacherous dog; we may need the extra leverage to keep him collared on the leash."

"Batu will serve his purpose. When we have finished wiping out the last of the once glorious Arturan army we will give him his wife and child, give him his gold and his amnesty, and then we will kill them also."

"Master, you have thought of everything. You are truly worthy of your destiny as Overlord of both Torbek and Artura. I will be ready to act once you give the signal. The king is completely under our control as are the remaining troops in and around Tiernon. We know which of the Arturan ministers will attempt to move against us and are prepared to deal with them."

"Don't just deal with them, Rhue!" Lord Taul slammed his fist down on the table next to him. "Make an example out of them and their families. Arturans are hard-headed brutes. Do not hesitate to shed enough of their blood to get the point across to the rest of them. Do you understand?"

"Yes, Master. I understand fully."

"Good. Once we control Tiernon and the river to Ansrak we will consolidate our forces and move against any left who oppose us. Now, you can go."

Daemon Rhue was relieved. His strength was waning quickly and he did not want to fade, but there was one more important thing of which he needed to speak to his Lord. "Forgive me, Master, but there is another reason I came to you today, if I may?"

"Very well. Be quick and be off, Rhue. I have things that need doing and so do you." The irritation in Kenric Taul's voice was almost enough for Rhue to forgo the rest of what he had come for and will himself back to Tiernon. But the uneasiness he had woken with this morning could not be forgotten and pushed aside.

"My Lord, I felt a disruption…something…I am not quite sure, but I believe I sensed a ripple, Master. A ripple of magic."

"Magic?" Kenric Taul had turned again facing the map but spun quickly about to face his diminishing disciple. The one word had grabbed his complete attention.

"Coming from where?" he demanded. "Are you sure it wasn't the witch?"

"No, Master. I know Mogga's power trace; it is quite distinct. This was different. While the ripple itself was very weak, there was a sense of strength behind it, dormant, but still there. It felt…it felt like the power of the Old Ones, sire."

"Utter nonsense. You must have been having gas pains, Rhue. There are none of the Old Ones left. Theron was the last and he has been dead for years."

"That is just the thing that bothers me, Master. Had it been someone actually trying to use the magic I would have been able to tell immediately. Mogga also would have been alerted and she would have contacted me. But while I distinctly felt the ripple of the magic's power it was not like there was an attempt to wield it. It was almost as if…as if it had just woken up."

"Hmmm." The change in Kenric Taul's tone was significant. It was obvious that he wasn't as ready to dismiss his vassal's concerns as he was moments ago.

"It probably has an explanation. There are elements of the old magic left. Probably buried within that miserable dark of a forest that Mogga lives in. There may also be those who might have knowledge of its use but none would dare to actually attempt to wield it. We have accounted for and disposed of the ones who might have threatened us. Nonetheless, it will serve us to remain vigilant. Inform the witch of your concerns and have her be wary. Move quickly against any who may be even slightly guilty of suspected use of magic. Do you understand?"

"Yes, Master. It will be as you command."

"Very well. Don't fail me, Rhue. I want those ignorant barbarians brought under my heel. Too long have they sat across that river and humiliated us with their control of the trade traffic. You don't know how much I have had to suffer with the ruse of this 'alliance.' To be forced to sit at that bastard Edmond's table and sign that peace treaty ten years ago was the lowest point in my life. As I lay down that pen, I made a promise that I would extract the most ruthless revenge possible against Artura and the scum who live there no matter how long it took. I will strip it of all riches and make them suffer. They will know who the master race is and the more of them I have to kill to get them to accept that, the better it will be."

Kenric Taul moved closer to the shimmering Daemon Rhue, bringing his face close to that of the man's ethereal image. Like the flame of a candle struggling to survive a strong breeze, the form flickered and wavered; the hold on the link was weakening.

"You have served me well, Rhue," Taul's voice hissed. "But there is something I want to show you. A small reminder of that which awaits any who dare cross or fail me." Kenric Taul clapped his large hands together and a servant immediately appeared from a curtained hallway and bowed his head low.

"Have the guards bring me Daureg."

"Yes my Lord Taul." The man turned and disappeared as quickly as he had arrived.

"You remember Daureg, don't you?" Kenric Taul asked.

The name was familiar to Daemon Rhue. It had been a long time ago, when he had called Sectos home, but he did remember. "Mica Daureg? Does his family not control the spice and wine trade, my Lord?"

"*Did* control the spice and wine trade, Rhue." Taul smiled. "It seems Daureg and his relatives sought to make themselves richer by skimming the profit destined for my coffers. Though they were one of the wealthiest families in Torbek, it seems they were not satisfied with what they had and started stealing a little over a year ago. But as with all who dare cross me, they were found out."

A commotion in the hall grabbed their attention as two burly guards appeared dragging a naked and shackled wretch between them. They dropped the man to his knees in front of Kenric Taul.

"Well, well. How are we today, Daureg?" Taul said, mocking the prostrate form.

The man never raised his head. Daemon Rhue could see visible signs of severe torture about the man's body. He remembered Daureg as being a rotund man who loved rich food, fine spirits, and dice. There was not much of that man groveling on the floor in front of Kenric Taul now.

"P-please my Lord Taul," the man pleaded in a tormented voice barely above a whisper. He did not raise his head. "I beg of you. Spare my family. They had nothing to do with this. It was my own greed and love of gambling that brought about my wickedness. Do what you will with me but they are innocent, my Master. Innocent."

"Guilty by association, my dear Daureg," Kenric Taul answered coldly. "Besides, I believe it was your brother doing the bookkeeping, was it not? And was it not your uncle and cousin who tampered with the cargo tallies? No, no my dear Daureg. Your family is guilty and the guilty will be punished, but you have the good fortune to find me in a rather magnanimous mood today."

"My Lord?" The weak voice rising from the floor was tinged with a tiny bit of hope, but Daemon Rhue knew that the man groveling at his master's feet could not see the look in Lord Taul's eyes. There was no compassion, only evil.

"Yes, my good man. I am going to spare some of your family," Taul continued sarcastically. "I do fear it is too late to spare that fat brother of yours. Alas, he did not survive the pit. It seems my dogs were in a particularly foul mood this morning and made short work of him. But you will be delighted to know that I am going to spare the rest of your family."

"Th-th-thank you Master Taul," Daureg whispered. Daemon Rhue thought he could hear the man sobbing.

"You are the greatest ruler in the world. All shall hear of your compassion and sing your praise. You will release them?"

"Release them? Oh my, my. I did not say I was going to release them. I just said I was going to let them live. Your uncle and your cousin have been sold as galley slaves. They will spend the rest of their miserable lives chained to an oar. But it should gladden your heart to know that I ordered they be chained together. Keeping the family intact as you might say. As for your lovely wife and young daughter, I have plans to keep them together also; they will work the finer brothels. It seems some men are willing to pay a premium for a mother-daughter combination. It should take them only ten years or so to pay off the debt you have incurred for them with your greed, Daureg."

Daemon Rhue winced, struggling to hold his connection as his master continued the sadistic torment. He had never gone this long and was fearful of losing his strength. It would not bode well, given the mood his master was in at the moment.

"Oh, and your son. He is about ten, is he not, Daureg?" Kenric Taul continued. "He is a fine looking boy. I have decided to place him in one of the brothels on the waterfront. It does seem that sailors often prefer the pleasures of that sort."

Mica Daureg, once known as the richest man in Sectos, second only to Supreme Lord Taul of course, lay prostrated and broken on the floor, his body heaving with great sobs of despair. His cherished family was destined to live the remainder of their shattered lives in misery and tormented shame because of his penchant for drink and the wiles of dice and cards. There was now only one thing left.

"Stand him up," Taul ordered the two guards. Daureg was hauled roughly to his feet. Daemon Rhue had never seen quite such a pathetic figure. He would learn from this demonstration of sheer and absolute power that his master was exhibiting. To break a man, it was often enough to work on his family instead, while he was still capable of understanding the full implications of what was being done to them. Daemon Rhue could be as brutal as anyone, but his master was showing him a somewhat different approach to pain and suffering; it was interesting.

Kenric Taul stepped in front of Daureg and reached out with

his massive arms and gripped the man's head with both of his huge hands.

"Release him," he ordered the two guards. As they stepped back and away, Rhue was amazed that the man's still oversized body did not drop even an inch as his Master Taul held Daureg out in front of him with no more effort than a man would exert holding a small child. This was indeed the most powerful man on the face of the earth.

"Your precious family will spend the rest of their miserable lives paying the price of your folly, Daureg," Kenric Taul hissed as he stared into the tormented and tear-filled eyes of the broken man. "No one cheats or steals from me. Your uncle and cousin will think of you as they feel the lash of the oar master's whip. Your son will think of his father's greed as he finds another stinking drunk sailor stumbling to his bed. And your lovely wife and beautiful daughter, I may even visit them myself before they begin their new careers as whores. Take those thoughts with you, Daureg. Take the agony of their future and hold on to it as you take your last breath. Let their misery mix with the pain you are about to receive. Let me introduce you to my little pets." With those chilling words, Kenric Taul closed his eyes and began to concentrate.

Daemon Rhue stared in both horror and wonder as the serpent tattoos around the muscular arms of Kenric Taul began to writhe and pulse with life. Mica Daureg could see them, too, and his eyes bulged in absolute fear. Slowly the heads of the serpents began to lift from Taul's forearms and slither their way ever so close to the face of the hapless man. They pulled their heads up and opened their serpent mouths revealing their curved fangs dripping with venom. Their forked tongues flicked out, tasting and savoring the fear of the victim in front of them. It was the last terrifying thing Mica Daureg saw before both serpents drove their fangs deep into the corners of his eye sockets just above the cheekbones.

Screams the likes of which Daemon Rhue had never heard echoed off the walls of the library. The two burly guards stepped back in shock as the man's body squirmed in agony, locked in the vice-like grip of those huge hands. His legs kicked and his arms flailed but to no avail. The muscles in Taul's massive forearms bulged and his veins pulsed with energy as the tattoo serpents pumped their fatal venom. Then it was over.

The serpents withdrew their fangs from the dead eyes and pulled their heads back from Daureg's face. Their bodies stopped their motion and they faded back to their place of rest on their master's forearms. Taul dropped the lifeless body onto the floor.

"Get this out of my sight," Taul ordered the guards.

"Take off his head and mount it on a pole where everyone can see it. Let it serve to remind people who holds the supreme power of life or death. Throw his body to my dogs." When the body had been dragged off, he turned to the ethereal form of Daemon Rhue.

"Do you realize what failure can get you Rhue? You have done well so far but let this serve as a reminder of the alternative. Finish this endeavor successfully and you will reap rewards beyond your wildest dreams. Fail, and…well…I think you understand. Now go."

"Yes, my Lord." Daemon Rhue did as his master commanded and began to allow the hold on the link to subside. It was none too quick in coming for his power was waning fast. As he began the mind drift back to his body on the floor in his tower room in Tiernon, he hoped Steyr was standing ready with the antidote. He was going to be sick—very, very sick.

CHAPTER FIFTEEN

THE DARKNESS SMOTHERED HIM AS HE fought his eyes open. It took him a moment to recollect just what had happened, but the numbness in his right arm brought the memory back quickly enough. He had tried to pull that friggin' sword from its scabbard and the damn thing had electrocuted him. Well, maybe not electrocuted exactly. *Shit.* He wasn't sure what it had done, but his whole arm was tingly and numb. It reminded him of the time when Jake had introduced him to the electric fence.

"Best way in the world to get to know an electric fence is to shake hands with the damn thing." Jake had laughed at the boy's plight. "Now's you know you won't ever have to do it again."

Willoughby groped on his hands and knees in the pitch black in a frantic effort to find his flashlight and was relieved when he closed his hand around it. He snapped it back on and breathed easier when he found it was still working. He cursed himself for not being more careful; to be caught without the light would not be cool.

The sword lay there innocently tucked within the safety of its sheath, almost daring Willoughby to try to pull it out again. But it was the "fool me once thing" and he wasn't about to give it a second try—his arm was still numb. Carefully he pushed it out of the way with his foot towards the old pack; there didn't seem to be any problem with it as long as you weren't trying to pull the damn thing out.

Willoughby turned his attention to the other item lying against the wall of the cave. The pizza pan shaped thing now made sense to him; it had to be a shield. It wasn't as big as he thought a shield might be, no more than eighteen inches or so across. He had always pictured the big kite-looking things from the movies. It first appeared to be made entirely of wood, but a closer inspection instead showed the wood covered with what looked to be hard leather on the outside. Around the edge ran a metal strip that held the two materials together and across the leather on the outside ran metal ribs that met together in the middle. From this junction, a spear-like point protruded from the center about four inches. The shield was not only used to block, but was a weapon itself. Attached to the inside of the shield were a wide leather strip with a crude buckle type fastener and a leather hand grip. It took him a minute, but he figured out the whole thing was designed to keep the shield secure to a man's arm.

Willoughby couldn't resist. Propping the flashlight up on Bob's pack, he slipped his left arm through the leather strap with the buckles. It was loose; Bob's arm must have been bigger than his, but he didn't want to mess with adjusting the strap, fearing the old leather might come apart. Sliding his arm through and gripping the other leather hand grip piece with his left hand, he held the shield out in front of him. While it wasn't overly heavy, he could sense that it would take someone with a lot of training to keep this thing out in front of him for any length of time, all the while fending off blows from swords and axes or whatever. He would have loved to pick up the sword and brandish it, but the shock he had experienced the first time he touched it was still very fresh in his mind. But the fact that he had found all of this cool stuff thrilled him. Swords and shields! How long had it been since anyone had fought with that kind of stuff? *Hell.* He knew that the Pilgrims had landed in America hundreds of years ago with guns; this stuff had to be older than that.

Willoughby cocked his arm and brought the shield up to where his eyes could just see over its edge to the dark of the tunnel in front of him. He could see them coming out of the blackness—Saruman's orcs—Viking raiders—screaming waves of Genghis Khan's horde. He thrust the shield out in front of him, warding off deadly blows and driving the spear point of his shield into the scowling face of his attacker.

As Willoughby waged his make believe battle, his mind drifted back to Jake and the blades hanging on the wall of his trailer. *Won't the big guy be thrilled to death with this stuff?* He fended off another blow and hammered a fatal counterstrike with his own imaginary blade. But he stopped suddenly as a thought sobered him back to reality. He was still stuck in the cave. While things had improved dramatically, he was no longer crawling on his belly in that cramped tunnel, he was not free yet, and that had to be his focus—get out and back to his family. Willoughby slipped the shield off his arm and laid it gently next to the sword. It was time for him to move, to see where this larger tunnel would take him.

But now he was faced with another dilemma; he had more stuff to pack. A brief thought about leaving some of it and coming back after he had explored the passage ahead was short-lived. Willoughby was pretty certain his newfound treasure had a lot of value to it, value that would be very welcome back home, and he was not about to leave it to chance that it might be here when (and if) he was to get back. No, the decision was an easy one. He would find a way to get it all tied down on his back somehow.

But Willoughby quickly found out that having all of it attached to his back was not going to happen. There was too much stuff and the bulky backpack of Bob's was just too cumbersome. Willoughby was just going to have to carry some of it. Using his rope, he secured the shield and sword harness to his pack as best he could. Bob's pot, the money, the crystal shard, and the box with the fire starter materials were all secure inside his own pack. Bob's pack held the clothes, the poncho, and the rotted bedroll. He would carry these.

As he hoisted his pack to his back, he quickly realized he hadn't done a very good job of tying things down. The shield and the sword hung low and created a drag on his back. But it would have to do for now. Willoughby was acutely aware that the batteries of his flashlight could expire at any time and the thought of being stuck inside this hole in the earth in total darkness was not a good one. He puzzled about how Bob had managed. There hadn't been anything that looked like a torch around. How had he done it? But it was just another puzzling riddle that would have to be thought about at another time—he was as ready to go as he could be. His pack sagged and the one of Bob's that he carried was unwieldy but he needed to get moving.

The tunnel was, for the most part, wide and high enough to walk upright but Willoughby quickly found that moving fast was not an option. Low, head-bashing overhangs were common as was an uneven floor strewn with rocks and boulders. Concentrate on one but then stumble into the other, was what he quickly found he was doing. He resigned himself to taking slow and deliberate steps, all the while praying for his light to hold out. And thankfully on one occasion, his light may have even saved his life.

After traversing the cave for what he thought was at least an hour, getting comfortable with checking the ceiling and then the floor before moving, he had come to a particularly low overhang, one that required hunching over to get under it. For twenty feet or so it forced him to duck walk uncomfortably, but at least Willoughby was thankful that it wasn't a belly crawler like the one behind the falls had been. As he finished the tough stretch and was finally able to stand again, he took a couple of steps before he put the light to the cave floor in front of him. None too soon—Willoughby nearly stepped into a gaping dark crack. Only at the last second was he able to stop his momentum from taking him over the edge.

"Whoa!" he shouted as he caught himself and quickly stepped back. Cautiously he eased forward and shone the light into the depths of the crack—the beam disappeared into nothing. He took a softball-sized rock and chucked it in, following the sound of it clattering against the side of the crack until he could no longer hear it.

The crack blocked his path. From one side of the cave to the other, the hole yawned like the maw of a giant worm, ready to suck up anyone and anything. The cave floor on the other side of the crack beckoned to him a mere four feet away. Willoughby was going to have to jump.

He cursed under his breath as he surveyed the obstacle blocking his path. It wasn't that far, but Willoughby was no athlete. His sister probably could have done it from a standing start, but he wasn't his sister. But it made no matter, he was going to have to cross the gap if he wanted to continue; there were no viable alternatives for him.

Willoughby tossed Bob's pack over and it thumped safely to the rock floor beyond. His first inclination was to do the same with his other gear but he nixed it quickly. He feared breaking something, and besides, it just wasn't that far across. Four, maybe five feet? The other side of the gap laughed at him, daring him to jump.

Quit bein' a pussy. The voice was his own but it could have been one of many people. He got called that because that's what he was. He wasn't his dad or even close to being what his sister was. It was true; Willoughby Baxter was nothing but a little pussy. The thought made him mad. He stepped back towards the low overhang, took two steps, and leaped the hole, landing a full three feet beyond the edge like it was nothing.

The leap surprised him given how tired, bruised, and battered he was. Maybe it was because he was just too exhausted to even care anymore but regardless, he had done it. Willoughby shrugged his pack a little higher on his shoulders and picked up Bob's. Crossing the obstacle was a huge relief but he silently said a prayer, hoping there would be no more.

There were no more cracks but there was also no sign of an exit. On and on he went, navigating sections of the passage, some wide and high, others narrow and tight. Willoughby was amazed at the length of the cave; it just kept going on and on. Twice he stumbled into large rooms, one with another waterhole. He drank his fill of the brackish water and made sure his bottle was full.

Willoughby cursed himself for not ever wearing a watch. Time had become nothing in the depths of this hole he was mired in. It had all just become one big jumbled mess of one situation after another since he had fallen over the falls. Crawling, walking, whatever the situation had demanded, he pushed himself on until he suddenly came to an obstacle whose presence he had given absolutely no thought to, but there it was, rearing its demanding head right in front of him. He would have been less surprised to see a dead end, signaling an abrupt and nasty stop to all of his troubles so far, but it was just the opposite—a fork in the tunnel loomed in front of him.

Willoughby peered into each with his light. There wasn't much difference in the two; they both looked the same, one veered slightly to the right and the other slightly to the left, but which to choose? They could both go on forever and if he made the wrong choice, how would he tell? He wanted to cry again; it was one thing right after the other and he had mentally just about come to the end of his strength. The gaping crack he had been able to manage because it hadn't been a choice; to go forward and cross it had been his only path, but this—how was he to tell? He peered into each again, hoping something would come to his worn out mind and say *This is it. This is the way.* But there was nothing.

Which way? Which way? Willoughby stood there, trying to make up his mind, when he felt it. It wasn't strong, and at first he thought his mind was playing tricks on him, but then it was there again. He shone his light on the fork to the right, listening, feeling. *There.* This time there was no wondering—a slight breeze coolly caressed his face. He stumbled into the tunnel and pressed ahead, starting up a slight incline in the cave floor. The breeze got stronger as he moved forward but as he worked his way ahead, the passage became smaller and the rise steeper. Soon he was on his hands and knees, pushing Bob's pack ahead.

Willoughby stopped. The pack had been blocking his vision but as he pushed it aside as far as he could he was rewarded with as pretty a sight as he had seen in…well, he wasn't quite sure, but there it was! Around a sharp bend in the cave was light! Sunlight! He flipped his flashlight off, praying it wasn't a hallucination, and was again rewarded. An opening to the outside world was just ahead around the corner.

Willoughby scrambled forward around the bend, the tunnel narrowing on him as he did, but he was instantly rewarded with the appearance of an opening. About two feet in diameter, it beckoned to him like water to a thirsty man. He fought the sharp incline and the loose rock and gravel that littered the tunnel's floor, pushing Bob's gear in front of him. Willoughby pushed the pack over a slight rise and out the opening; it fell away from him and disappeared. Carefully he peered out the opening, making sure he wasn't on the face of a cliff or something. The glare of the sun was hard on his eyes but when he spied his pack sitting on a flat ledge just below him, he quickly scrambled out through the hole and rolled down a six-foot bank and came to rest next to his pack.

Willoughby had been so ecstatic about finally getting out that he had misjudged the reaction of his eyes to actual sunlight and had been temporarily blinded as he rolled from the opening. But as he lay there shielding his eyes from the glare and paying no mind to the jarring crunch he had landed with, there was only one thought coursing through his tormented mind—he was out!

Though hard on his eyes, a small patch of sunlight was already caressing his bruised and battered body. Rolling to a sitting position, he quickly unbuckled his own pack, slid out from under its cumbersome weight. He then dropped his head between his knees, letting his eyes slowly get used to the light. Tears ran freely down his filthy face, and they weren't from the bright sunlight affecting his cave eyes. He was out.

As he sat there adjusting his eyes and trying to gather himself emotionally, Willoughby tried to estimate how long he had been underground. Sunday morning it had been, around ten or so was his guess, but time had meant absolutely nothing in the cave. He had slept a couple of times but whether it was minutes or hours, he had no clue. Jake would have expected him back no later than supper and would have walked to the falls to check on him when he didn't show. After not finding him anywhere, he might have traveled down the river thinking a worst-case scenario, looking for a body. After that, it would take time for Jake to make the right contacts and get a full-blown search under way. That would not have happened before they ran out of daylight, so it would have been people and flashlights scouring the riverbank and finding nothing.

The phone call. A gnawing chill slithered over him as he thought about it. Jake would have gotten the search party to work first and then made the call. His mom? Grandma? Maybe Jennifer? Which one would have answered? They would have probably been in the hotel room relaxing after an exciting day at the game. Willoughby's overloaded mind dragged him back to a place he didn't want to go; the gut-wrenching realization of a horrible truth. A nightmare scene vividly played itself out in his head. The three people who loved him the most—experiencing disbelief at first, then actually thinking people would be cruel enough to tell you something like that as a joke. And confusion as you start to understand there is really something dreadfully wrong, though you still don't want to believe it. The gut churning nausea arrives as the ugliness of truth sweeps over you like a tsunami. Chaos reigns as his family reacts to their grief. Willoughby remembered.

His reaction was understandable but terribly untimely. Jumping quickly to his feet after he had his head tucked down between his legs to keep the sunlight out of his eyes, was a mistake. A huge mistake. When he stood up, he started to take a step towards his backpack as the blood flowed freely from his brain cells. Willoughby's world turned into an explosion of bright light and then just as quickly plunged into darkness as he started to fall. It felt like one of those slow-motion dream sequences; the kind where you are trying to get your body to do something and you just can't make your limbs respond. Willoughby tried to move his arms out in front of him to protect himself as he went over but it was too little too late. His face and the rocky ground met with sudden and extreme violence.

IT WAS THE STICKY MESS THAT FINALLY STIRRED HIM BACK TO consciousness. As he let his breath out through his nose, it made bloody snot bubbles. He didn't remember slamming his face into the rocky ground but as he lifted his head slightly he could see the gooey dirt and blood pudding congealing in front of him. A couple of drips out of his nose and some running into his eyebrows confirmed the matter. His head and face had taken the brunt of the fall.

Willoughby rolled over onto his back. His first concern—stopping the steady stream of blood running down his face. Tenderly probing his forehead with his hand, he found a pretty good-size cut about an inch over his left eyebrow. Cuts around the forehead and eyes bled pretty good; he had watched enough of the *Ultimate Fighter* to know that. His nose seemed to be the only other source that was doing any serious leaking. What really surprised Willoughby was that it really hadn't hurt that much.

Rolling over to his hands and knees, he crawled to his backpack. Fishing out some paper towels, he tore a sheet in half and folded the pieces into smaller squares, dampening them with water from his bottle. Pressing one against the cut on his forehead and holding the other to his nose, he laid back against the steep bank leading to the cave opening, tilted his head, and tried to relax. In a minute Willoughby had the nosebleed controlled and the blood from the gash in his forehead slowed enough that he was able to get a gauze bandage taped over it; the little first aid kit Jake had given him for his backpack had made itself valuable.

But as much as his bloody head and battered body needed to, Willoughby just couldn't force himself to relax. The pressing urge to find his family and let them know he was still alive was overriding the extreme discomfort he was suffering. While he had no idea where he had come out, he knew the river couldn't be too far away, and that was where they would be looking. If he could just get there, he could also clean himself up.

Willoughby struggled to his feet, taking it much slower this time; he was still a bit woozy. When he was sure that he wasn't going to go down again, he took a good look at his surroundings for the first time since he had tumbled out of the cave. That's when things got very confusing.

The cave opening was at the base of a vertical rock face. Willoughby craned his neck back to try and see how high the rock wall was, but to his surprise, it didn't look like it ended. It gave him a feeling of unsteadiness, tilting his head back so far, so he quickly stopped.

The patch of ground he had landed on coming out of the cave was almost the only patch of flat ground around. There was a short and twisted pine tree ten feet in front of him and then the ground dropped sharply. Willoughby couldn't see much beyond the pine but a side to side reconnaissance revealed a strangely unfamiliar scene, with islands of gnarled pine and twisted fir, clumps of brush and grass isolated by steep rock outcrops, and ledges covering an extremely steep slope. It totally confused him. Willoughby had been around Spirit Falls long enough that he should recognize this place—especially with a cliff as high as the one behind him—but he didn't.

Willoughby shivered; something wasn't right. The look and feel of the place reminded him of the high alpine country around the Cascade mountain passes. Country like this was thirty or forty miles from where he lived. There was also another reason for shivering; there was a definite cold bite to the air. He pulled the hood of his filthy sweatshirt over his head.

Tentatively he walked to the break of the slope where the twisted pine stood and looked over the edge. Willoughby sucked in his breath with an audible hiss, grabbing onto a branch of the pine to steady himself as a wave of vertigo swept over him. He backed immediately away from the edge until he plopped his butt on the slope below the cave opening and fought back the urge to puke.

"No way," he cursed aloud to himself, struggling to keep the meager contents of his stomach in place. "No fucking way."

Willoughby took a couple of deep breaths, trying to calm himself, once again on the verge of a breakdown. His mind raced, trying to come up with an explanation but nothing made any sense. He just couldn't be where he was; he had to take another look. Struggling back onto his unsteady legs, he slowly and deliberately walked back to the tree, making sure he had a good hold on the branch before he looked again.

Willoughby stared out at a vast and foreign landscape. The first thing he realized was that he was very high up on a steep mountain slope. The ground tumbled sharply away from him in stair-steps of ledges, cliffs, and rock outcrops, finally giving way to an ocean of green forest. It was hard for the stunned teen to judge distance but it was a long way to where the divergent landscapes came together. To either side of him, the terrain was the same, and for as far as he could see, the mountains kept rising behind him.

Where the mountain slopes came to an abrupt end, there was nothing but green wood as far as Willoughby could see. Groups of hills, tall enough that their upper reaches were barren of trees, periodically broke the landscape like molehills on a manicured lawn. But what really startled him was that the vast expanse of forest stretched to the horizon. Not only what he saw shocked him, it was what he didn't see. No houses, roads, fields, or even a clearcut.

It made absolutely no sense to him. No way could he have traveled far enough, through the confines of the tunnel behind the waterfall, to come out high on a mountainside in an area such as the one spreading out in front of him. To come out into country like this meant a crawl of thirty plus miles, uphill to boot. Willoughby was bewildered and perplexed. That just couldn't happen.

As confused as he was, he knew what he needed to do—find some people, they would explain where he was. Hopefully someone might have a cell phone so he could at least call home and let his family know he was all right. For about the hundredth time Willoughby cursed the fact he hadn't thought to bring his own cell phone along. But it made no sense to worry about things he couldn't change; he needed to get off this mountainside. But as he scanned the terrain separating him and the woods far below, Willoughby realized that it wasn't going to be an easy task getting down. Besides the steepness of the ground, the areas between the cliffs and the ledges consisted of shale scree that would make for treacherous footing; one misstep and an avalanche of rock would get him to the bottom in a hurry and in pieces. He was going to have to be very careful.

Willoughby left the edge and returned to his gear. He realized quickly he was going to have to take a different approach in order to get off this mountainside, and he wasn't about to leave any of this stuff behind. He was going to need it all secured onto his back in order to keep his hands free to assist his descent. Things were going to get pretty hairy on the way down, of that he had no doubt.

Willoughby re-sorted and retied everything, having to make several attempts before getting a satisfactory result. Bob's canvas pack, bedroll, and clothes were forced inside his own pack, which was soon straining at its seams and zippers. The sword, harness, and shield he re-tied to the outside, trying this time to get the things riding higher upon his shoulders. He was getting apprehensive about his descent down the mountain and wanted no interference. It was an amateur lash-up using the entire thirty feet of rope, but he got the job done.

Once he had things the way he wanted, Willoughby got the pack to his back and re-adjusted the straps to make up for the extra weight he was now carrying; again thankful for Jake's guidance into the selection of a good backpack. The thing was made for hunting and packing gear; the waist, shoulder, and chest straps designed to get the weight up on the carrier's shoulders where it should be. While the sword and shield made the whole thing just a tad bit cumbersome, Willoughby wasn't displeased with the way it felt.

With his pack situated in its optimum position and his hands free there was nothing left to do—it was time to start down. There was a desperate need on his part to find someone, anyone, who could answer his questions about where exactly he was and most importantly, help him find his family.

Willoughby held onto a limb of the wind-racked pine tree and gazed once again at the unfamiliar landscape stretching out in front of him. It was a beautiful picture but one that was haunting the boy regardless. Willoughby was looking at country so completely foreign it made no sense. But there had to be an answer and he wasn't going to find it this high up on the mountainside.

As he gazed out over the vast expanse of country spreading out from the foot of the mountain, he saw something that at least he could partially recognize. Far off to his right, a different shade of green snaked its way through the forest—that brightened his outlook somewhat. It had to mark the river channel, the lighter shade of green suggesting the presence of hardwoods. He had come in via the river and that would be the logical place to start looking for some answers. But judging distance wasn't something he had much practice doing and the fact that the sun was on its way down gave him concern about running out of daylight. He needed to get started.

There was no easy way down so Willoughby took a slow and deliberate approach, zigzagging across the mountainside, gradually making his way down the steep slope without any major incident. By staying out of the scree slides and sticking to the ledges, he was able to make it to the tree line. But as the sun slowly sank over the horizon, pulling the last vestiges of light down with it, a serious dilemma rose in its place. Willoughby was gazing into the depths of a dark, uninviting expanse of forest.

A perplexed Willoughby gazed back at the slope he had just traversed, the towering mountains taking on a golden orange hue as they basked in the last of the sun's rays. Up and up they rose, until they disappeared into the clouds. He didn't remember the Cascades being this impressive. It was inconceivable to him that he could have traveled far enough in the cave to be in unfamiliar territory. While he was a newcomer to the area, he had become pretty knowledgeable of the country within twenty miles of Spirit Falls, but since rolling out of the tunnel on the mountainside he had been looking at a totally unrecognizable landscape. There had to be a good explanation for it but it was escaping him and matters dictated he forget about the issue at the moment for he was facing an issue of another sort. As much as he desperately wanted to find someone and let his family know he was okay, this strange forest in front of him wasn't a place he wanted to be in the dark.

Although it troubled him, there really was no other choice; he would build a fire and spend the night here. Darkness was rolling in fast and he needed to gather some wood or he would be doing it by flashlight and he wasn't sure how long the batteries would last. The Duracells had been put to the test in the cave but they had to be on the downside of their life. It crossed his mind that when this ordeal was done he would write the company a letter and inform them how the batteries kept going and going and going. If nothing else, maybe he would get free batteries for the rest of his life.

Willoughby selected a campsite, a small hollow where two rock outcrops came together. He would put his back to the rock wall and the mountain and face the forest with his fire in between. For whatever reason, he shivered at the idea of having his back to the dark void of towering trees that hovered menacingly twenty yards away.

Surprisingly enough the decision to make camp reenergized him and he threw himself into the task. Shedding his pack, he fished out his camping ax, not an easy chore since repacking his gear for the trip down the mountain. Like it or not he was going to need wood, and plenty of it, to last the night, and there was only one place to get it—the forest.

You don't have to worry about critters in the woods. They will be more scared of you than you are of them. How many times had he heard that one? While the old adage made sense, Willoughby wasn't particularly encouraged by it. Normally he wasn't a punk-assed sissy when it came to going out in the dark, but this was not the countryside close to home. It should have been, but for whatever reason it wasn't, and the woods gave Willoughby a creepy feeling. He had the ax and entertained the idea of taking the sword with him, but the last time he tried to pull the thing out was fresh in his memory; another weird thing that there was no logical reason for. He nixed the sword idea; the ax would have to suffice.

He made his way down the short slope to the edge of the forest. The change was abrupt and startling. He hadn't really given it much notice as he had worked his way down the mountain, but now that he was standing only feet away, he couldn't help but realize the contrast.

Like a giant fence the trunks of the huge trees rose from the grassy slope; a veritable wall of gray-and-brown-barked leviathans.

Willoughby was no stranger to old growth forests; there were plenty within a short distance of Spirit Falls. He thought he recognized firs, cedars, hemlocks, and a couple he wasn't too sure of. But like everything else since he had come out of the cave, what was familiar was also different. Every single tree was massive. The eight-footers Jake talked about as being few and far between seemed to be the norm here.

Monsters. It was weird but that was the way he felt. Something unknown and uncomfortable had a presence within the depths of this forest. He could sense it. Maybe he was still suffering from the effects of his ordeal; trauma such as what he had been through could do weird things to people. Yeah, that had to be it. He might laugh about it later but it was not funny now. There was some vibe sending him a message that it wasn't a good thing to linger near the forest edge, especially in the dark.

Fortunately for Willoughby firewood wasn't hard to find. It lay twenty feet in front of him in the form of a dead top from one of the giant firs that had broken off and crashed down across some rocks, splintering into manageably sized pieces.

In a few trips, Willoughby had enough chunks, dead limbs and bark that would keep a good sized fire going through the night. Besides keeping him warm, as the temperature had dropped con-siderably since the sun went down, he wanted to keep the fire bright in hopes someone might spot it and come to investigate. Rescuers were always looking for a signal fire. Willoughby didn't care who it was; he was in need of human company.

One of the things Jake had taught him well was the art of build-ing a fire in the woods. Using a few slivers of his pitch, Willoughby soon had a nice sized blaze generating plenty of heat and light, the walls of rock surrounding his little hollow acting as good reflec-tors. Rolling out his plastic tarp he placed what was left of Bob's old bedroll down and the canvas poncho on top of that. They were still musty smelling but at least offered a small layer of comfort from the hard, cold rock. Willoughby sat down on the poncho and using the cheap rolled up plastic one for a pillow leaned back against the rock wall; the warmth of the fire and its position between him and the forest finally allowing him a bit of comfort.

As the sun bid the day farewell and dropped completely beyond the trees, pulling a blanket of darkness down over everything, Willoughby treated himself to half an energy bar and a handful of cookie crumbs. The cookies hadn't fared too well but still tasted good. The urge to eat more was strong but he resisted, his food supply now down to one half an energy bar and another small handful of cookie crumbs. Sadly the fried chicken, chips, and soda he had consumed sitting on the riverbank were just a stomach-gnawing memory now.

As he sat and savored his meager dinner, Willoughby took stock of himself and wasn't pleased with what he found. Exhausted and filthy, the smell from his unwashed body overpowered the mustiness of the bedroll and poncho. He had been battered, cut, and bruised and his mind was just as mentally thrashed as his body was physically. The whole situation settled itself heavily on the teen's scrawny shoulders and threatened to smother him with despair. Willoughby tried to keep his spirits up by telling himself he had gotten past the worst. It would be just a matter of time before he found someone or someone found him. They would get him back to his family and then, after what would be a pretty emotional reunion, they could sort this thing out and come up with an explanation for all the strange things that had occurred. It would be an amazing and hard-to-believe story for sure, but when he showed them the relics he had found, they couldn't doubt him—or could they? Maybe he was just insane.

Willoughby swallowed the last bite of energy bar and took a healthy pull from his water bottle, replacing the cardboard chocolate taste with the metallic tang of water from the cave. Deep into the depths of the fire he stared, thinking about his mother, sister, and grandma and all they had been through on his account. This latest episode of his was just another traumatic ride on the Willoughby roller coaster, though he had to admit nothing else had come close to matching this one. But the truth was ugly. He was screwed up in the head and had been since his dad died and couldn't remember much true happiness within his family during the years since. While they made an admirable effort, the bile of bitterness was hard to keep down.

The light from the flames of Willoughby's fire danced and flickered against the rock wall of the hollow, bravely defending his tiny fortress from the gloom of dark and unknowing. Beyond the light, the forest loomed large and threatening.

Come to the dark. Let it take you, it whispered. But Willoughby wasn't about to do that, his hollow and his fire were sanctuary. Jake had taught him to build a fire. Jake had given him the things he needed to survive and right then he made Jake and his family a promise—when he got back, he was going to try as hard as he could to make things better.

Promises. Willoughby's head nodded to his chest as he surrendered to exhaustion. *Promises.* Easy to make, harder to keep, and he had kept none. It was the last thing that crossed his mind as he drifted off into a deep sleep.

Chapter Sixteen

THE BOY SLEPT AND THE WOLVES WATCHED. From their vantage point inside the dark cloak of the forest, they could see the light from the intruder's fire dancing on the rock walls, protecting him on three sides. They would have gone closer but they did not like fire. Unlike most everything else that lived or came into their forest, fire did not fear wolves; fire feared nothing. So they sat and watched instead. Some of the lesser females and young had gotten excited when they first discovered the stranger at the edge of the wood and had begun to act foolishly but the she-wolf settled that nonsense quickly with a sharp nip to their hindquarters and a growl warning them to keep quiet and behave or else.

The human pup looked harmless but the female could sense something that frightened her, more than what she could see or smell. She would have to be careful. There had already been a serious misstep earlier in the day that had cost the pack one of their own and she would face the wrath of her mate because of it; she would not make the same mistake twice.

The pack had been at the river washing off the blood from the morning's kill when they overheard the ravens squawking about the presence of an interloper on the mountainside. It had been a good and bad day for the pack; they had fed themselves until they could eat no more but the hunt had been costly.

They had managed to kill an aging red stag they had been trailing for quite some time. He had separated from his herd, run off by a more powerful young male after a heated battle. The old bull had put up a brave fight, desperately trying to maintain his place as leader, but the haughty youngster had been too big and too strong, and the old one had been vanquished. Injured in one of his hindquarters by a well-placed thrust of the young male's mighty horns, he staggered off into the forest. The females he once mated with and the young he had sired watched him go, unconcerned and uncaring. It was the way of the wild, out with the old, in with the new. The strong survive and the weak perish.

Broken and beaten, the old bull limped off, leaving a trail of blood. He would be on his own now, the herd and its new leader would not tolerate his presence. They would keep him from the good sweet grass in his favorite meadow and not allow him to lick the salt from the mineral springs he loved so much. Solitude and loneliness were now his destiny—but it would be short-lived.

A young male wolf had come across the old stag's blood trail. After following it for a ways to see which direction it led, he rolled in the deer's blood. The heady smell on his fur would get the pack

excited when he told them of his find. The wolf raised his leg and urinated on a clump of fern by the blood trail, he would lead the pack back to this marked spot; they would start the hunt from here.

The dominant she-wolf had been pleased with him; the adolescent male was constantly getting in trouble because he kept trying to mount the young females. This find would put him back in her good graces—at least until he got caught again.

She gathered her pack, fifteen in all; the young pups would join them on this hunt. Born in the spring, they were ready to move on to the next level of their training, but she had to be careful. She had smelled the old bull's blood on the young male's fur. She knew this animal; he had been around for a long time and was a wily old stag and had thwarted many of the pack's hunts by being a smart and fearless leader. Her instincts were sharp; she recognized what the blood meant—the old bull had been ousted and was now on his own.

But her caution was as sharp as her instinct. The youngsters in her pack were excited with the thrill of a hunt, but this was no gangly-legged newborn or decrepit and sickly old female that they hunted. This was a formidable opponent. Though wounded, the old stag was still tough and battle smart, easily capable of hurting or killing one of her youngsters if their excitement led them to make a mistake. Her mate, the great male and true leader of the pack, was off on another errand and would not join them on this hunt but would be greatly displeased if an error caused harm to one of his own. But she wasn't the dominant female for nothing; she had earned her role because she was stronger and smarter than the rest of them. While her mate took the younger females as he pleased, she was still his favorite and he trusted her.

She gathered her pack and together they followed the young male to where he had marked the wounded stag's trail. The amount of blood told her that his wound was severe enough that it would not allow him to travel far; he would be forced to hole up and allow the wound time to fester and then heal. She split the pack, sending a portion to each side of the stag's trail in a flanking maneuver while she and the rest kept to the trail.

They moved quickly, but with carefully controlled stealth and silence through the dark wood. The old stag had been stronger than she anticipated and had rolled in a mud hole, forcing the thick mud and clay into the wound to stem the bleeding. After that, the trail had been much more difficult to follow, but she was just as much an old veteran as he and able to stay on his track.

The pack stopped suddenly at a creek. Flowing strong from recent heavy rain, the trail disappeared with no sign of it on either side. The old warrior had used the creek to his advantage and hid his scent, but which way had he traveled? The young wolves became flustered, darting to and fro, trying to find sign that wasn't there, but the dominant female just sat down on her haunches.

She knew this stream and was checking her memory, trying to recall what the land characteristics were upstream and what they were down. Up, the land was a gentle slope, unencumbered by thick pockets of brush, unbroken by rocky outcrops and boulder patches that would make tough going for the injured stag. This was the direction the other members of her pack wanted to pursue, but she wasn't convinced. Downstream the creek traveled through much the same sort of country for a ways but then dropped suddenly into a gorge hundreds of feet deep. If the old bull went that way, he would have to leave the stream. One direction would lead him back to the river, territory very familiar with the wolf pack. He would not choose that direction. But if the old stag chose to go the other way, he would move into an area of brush-choked ravines, caves and hollows, cliffs and rock formations. The wolf pack called it the Broken Land. While the going there would be hard for the wounded animal, it would also offer him well-hidden sanctuaries where he might rest and heal out of sight. He was wise and had not survived for so long because he always did what was expected. Her intuition was strong; she made her decision.

She barked out a series of orders and the pack turned downstream. When they reached the place where the stream dropped into the gorge, her choice was rewarded when the trail picked up again, heading for the Broken Land.

She spread the pack, interspersing her veterans with the youngsters and keeping the pups trailing safely behind. As the going got more physically challenging, the blood trail became easier to follow. Traversing the rough terrain had re-opened the old stag's wound; he would have to keg up soon or risk bleeding to death.

She stopped; the trail led into a jumbled mass of huge boulders and rock formations. Barking out an order, she gathered her pack and commanded they stay; she would go in herself and see what lay ahead.

Cautiously she entered the maze, her sensitive nose reading the signs. It told her that somewhere within had been the den of a crag bear. Shaggy, solitary creatures, massive and formidable, the pack avoided them when at all possible. But the sign was old and her nose told her the bear had long since gone.

Deeper into the broken warren of rock she went, sniffing and searching, and then in an instant, her senses picked up a strong signal. She lifted her nose and flared her nostrils—he was close. She could smell more than blood now. The old stag had been master of his herd and carried with him the smell which warned other males of his power and dominance. He reeked of strong urine, scat, and the heady musk of his scent glands. In his intense battle with the younger male, these secretions had flowed freely as he threw everything he had into the struggle. It was a smell a roll in a mud hole could not hide and it betrayed him, leading the she-wolf to his hiding place.

Ever so carefully, she poked her head around a jutting corner of rock; he was waiting for her. Luck had finally run out for the cagey old bull. Had he not been wounded in his battle for control of his herd he might have lived his life out in relative safety until he either became sick or lame, but fate had made it not so. He knew he had taken a risky chance when he decided to enter the tumbled and rugged canyon but needed the security it offered. When he found the small box ravine with its tiny spring of fresh water and shallow cave which would protect him from bad weather, he thought he had made the right choice. But he had not recollected the savvy and capable she-wolf who had not been fooled by his tactics. The refuge had now become a trap and he had made the decision to fight and die.

She plopped down on her haunches and watched him carefully. When she was certain he was not going to charge and attempt to get by, she lifted her head to the sky and let out a long and piercing howl, calling the pack to her. Her darting eyes sized up the situation as she waited, knowing the old stag had made the choice to do battle—and to die.

In an instant, her keen senses told her many things. The ravine narrowed and the pack would not be able to press their attack all at the same time; advantage to the stag. His mighty antlers spread high and wide to each side, their tines long and sharp, and when he swung his head they would become deadly weapons; advantage to the stag. His thick and muscled forelegs, capped with sharp hooves, could crush the skull of a wolf in an instant but she saw his hindquarters drooped. His wound had been serious and his rear legs would not bear the weight if he was to rear and attempt to stomp his attackers; advantage to the wolves. The old warrior was breathing heavily—the exhausting fight with the strong young male, the depth of his wound, and the laborious trek to his hiding place had left him physically impaired; advantage to the wolf pack.

Their eyes met and locked on to each other. They had crossed paths before. Her pack had hunted his herd and often been rewarded with a young calf or a lame adult. But many times his caginess thwarted their efforts and forced her pack to look elsewhere for food. When the stag had been younger, he and her mate had gone head to head in a ferocious battle that had ended in stalemate. But he was not the same as he was then, and the she-wolf knew they would be able to take him down. His eyes told her that he too was aware of his fate—but they also warned her of his determination to go down fighting.

The pack gathered round her. Their hunger, the excitement of the coming fray, and the smell of the wounded-but-still-mighty stag whipped them into a frenzy. The she-wolf barked and yipped out orders and two of her more veteran females peeled away and tore off back down the trail. She ordered the youngest of the pack to stay back and spread the rest out as much as the narrow confines of the ravine would allow. Her battle line was in place but still they did not charge.

The old stag shook his head and snorted in defiance, challenging them to come ahead, but still they waited. Unwounded, he might have charged, causing the pack to scatter and maybe allowing him a small chance of escape, but in his state, such a move would only hasten his demise and he was determined not to make it any easier for them. The she-wolf admired his courage and knew he would not leave his position against the rock and allow them to bring him down from behind, which was their favorite way of making a kill.

Time was on the she-wolf's side and as the old stag's heart pumped with excitement his wound bled profusely, draining him of life sustaining energy. Finally, she saw what she was waiting for—the two females she had dispatched earlier had found a way into the rocks above and behind the stag.

The she-wolf began to howl and the pack joined her. Their mournful cries echoed violently off the walls of the ravine, chorusing the death knell for the old stag. He shook his head in answer, snot and foam spraying from his flared nostrils as he boldly bugled his own death song. The wolves charged.

The wolves on the stag's right side closed first and he turned to meet them swinging his mighty head, trying to catch one of them with his horns. But the attack had only been a feint and they stopped just short of the wicked tines and skipped clear. The move opened the bull's left flank to attack, his wounded side. Two of the wolves dove underneath the huge animal and struck at his soft belly and testicles while a third attempted to rip at the hamstrings on the back of his wounded leg, but again the desperate stag swung his head and the wolves were forced to jump clear.

The she-wolf yipped her pack back just out of range of the beast's horns but before he had a chance to settle himself again into a defensive position she sent them charging in again. This time the onslaught met with more success and a strong young male was able sink his powerful jaws deep into the corded muscle at the back of the stag's wounded leg. Deep the long canine teeth sunk into the stag's flesh and the jaws locked into a relentless grip. The stag turned as far as he could, trying to swing his horns into the animal at his rear, but while they were able to make contact he could not bring enough force to bear and dislodge the wolf's hold.

This was the opportunity the she-wolf was looking for. She barked a sharp command and her wolves leaped in from the opposite side and tore at the stag's exposed underside. The stag's dangling male organs, long his pride and the source of his prowess, now made an easy target. He bellowed in agonizing pain as a strong young female wolf latched on and ripped his sack open. But he counter attacked—a vicious kick backward with his foreleg caved in the female's ribcage. She released her hold on his obliterated testicles and howled a high pitched scream of agony—but it was a short one. A well-placed stomp of his unwounded right leg drove his sharp hoof onto her head, crushing her skull.

The she-wolf was furious and barked for an all-out attack. From above and behind, the two females dove on to the back of the stag and latched onto the back of the bull's shaggy neck. More of the pack leaped in on each side and attacked his underbelly and rear quarters. The female who had her skull crushed had ripped the bull's scrotum and opened a gash from which his viscera started to leak out. The frenzied pack ripped and tore at his organs. But he was not done fighting and threw his mighty shoulders and head to and fro, bugling his fury. A swipe of his horns caught a young male and threw him crashing against the rocks; he limped off, wounded and out of the fight. But try as he might, the great stag could not dislodge the wolves that had their powerful jaws locked tightly on him. More wolves latched hold of his hindquarters and he sagged as their weight on his wounded leg became more than he could bear. As his rear went down, he threw his head back, trying to throw the two who rode his shoulders, but when he did, the she-wolf saw her chance.

She had been patient, barking orders and waiting for such an opening. When the old stag's hindquarters went down and he threw his head back, it exposed his throat. With wolves, the throat is a vital spot for any kill and although the shaggy fur around the stag's neck was thick, she was able to lunge and sink her teeth in deep. Powerful jaws whose main function was to smash and break bones did their job and soon began to crush the stag's windpipe, cutting off his air.

Still the old warrior did not succumb but his strength was ebbing fast. His guts were spilling out onto the cold, hard ground and the muscles on the back of his legs had been torn and ripped so he could no longer stand. With wolves on his back and the big she-wolf crushing the life from him with her grip on his neck he fell over in a heap of fur, blood, and guts. When the she-wolf felt his muscles go slack, she gave a mighty rip and tore his throat open. With a last convulsing kick, the stag's life energy left him. The battle was done.

When the wolves were sure their formidable adversary would fight no more, they began their victory howls. They lifted bloody snouts high into the cold air and let the forest and its denizens know of their power and dominance. While the rest of the pack chorused their victory, the she-wolf sniffed the young female who had her scull crushed. Her mate would not be happy at losing a vital member of his pack.

But a kill was a kill and the pack was hungry. At her signal, they tore into the steaming body of the old stag. The young pups came in and greedily began ripping at the deer's tender parts. Long into the day did they feast on fresh and bloody venison. A large kill such as this was important for their survival and they did not waste. Ravens and carrion birds squabbled above in the tree branches, hoping there would be carcass pickings left for them when the pack's hunger was finally sated.

Late in the day, they had left the meager remains of their kill for the birds and lesser predators to fight over and moved to the river closer to their den to drink and clean. It had been there that the she-wolf became aware of the stranger in their territory. Raven talk told her the intruder was human. This surprised her. Humans seldom ventured this deep into the forest and when they did, it was usually in packs. They tended to be fearful and puny creatures when not together in groups large enough to give them protection. Her encounters with them had been scarce but from what she knew, this lone one should be easy prey. While the pack was no longer starving, she must investigate and take this creature out. Her mate would allow no mere human creatures to interlope in his forest.

Darkness had settled in before the pack arrived on the mountainside where the forest stopped and the mountains rose to their cloud-piercing heights. She held them back while she investigated and found they had arrived too late. The human was small but he had fire, and the wolves did not like fire. She crept close, using the dark of the night and the wood to hide herself. While she did not fear this puny creature she was cautious, her sensitive nose had picked up his scent and it was strange, not like any other human she had encountered. This alone was enough to make her wary but when she spied the sharp and shiny thing she became even more so. She remembered back to a time when she and her brothers and sisters had become overly excited about a lone creature wandering in their woods. It came back to her as she lay hiding and watching the human pup sitting at his fire; she remembered all too well.

They had been young and only recently allowed to wander and explore on their own. There were five—herself, two brothers, a half brother and half sister—oh how they had run and played, chasing rabbits and squirrels, and wrestling with each other. It had been a carefree day of fun and frolic. They were wolves after all; their pack was dominant in these woods and they had nothing to fear. The only bad part of the day had been when her stupid half brother had became overly excited during one of their wrestling matches and had tried to mount her. She yipped and bit him in anger and her brothers had rushed to her rescue and made sure the miscreant male understood such behavior was not allowed. When the fur had settled and the offender had licked her face in apology, they had resumed their play. That was when one of her brothers smelled something strange in the air.

They stopped their play and sniffed deep with their snouts. Yes, there was something they weren't familiar with close by. They followed their strong young brother and tried to act like the adult members of their pack as they went on the offensive, moving quickly but quietly through the woods to search out the source of this new scent. They were extremely excited now. Their curiosity had fired their basic instinct to hunt and kill. Though they were young and not fully trained, they wanted to prove themselves; the adults would be proud of them if they could bring down an intruder on their own. Here was a golden opportunity and they weren't about to shy away from it.

The lead brother stopped them suddenly as they drew near the river. Down they went to their bellies and crawled forward cautiously through the thick brush to the edge of a wide gravel bar. Ahead, in the shallow water with its back to them, was a creature the likes of which they had never seen. It stood on two legs as it bent over the water and washed itself. They knew that crag bears and other forest creatures could stand on their hind legs for lengths at a time but when they moved, they would drop to all fours. This creature was different, as it left the water and returned to the shore, it stayed on its hind legs.

They watched in wonder as the creature fumbled with some strange looking things lying next to the rocks. Suddenly it stopped and froze, looking in their direction; it had become aware of their presence.

She had hoped the creature would run. This was the way she knew the pack liked to bring down their prey. When the hunted ran, it was easy for the wolves to come up from behind and bring them down by attacking their rear legs or leaping to their backs. When they forced their prey to stop running, they could attack the throats and soft underbellies, ripping and tearing with their sharp teeth and powerful jaws. Nothing but the biggest crag bears and stags with their great horns could fend off death when the pack worked together.

The youngsters had paid attention as they had watched the hunts from a safe distance and were then allowed to feast after the kill had been brought down. Oh how she loved the taste of fresh meat and blood still warm! Though unfamiliar, this creature in front of them was small and they were wolves—they wanted to kill.

The larger brother had assumed leadership and the rest of them had allowed him to do so. He was strong for his age and would undoubtedly be leader of the pack some day. Growling out orders, he spread them out and they leaped onto the gravel bar as one, showing off their skill and sending a message to the strange one that they knew what they were doing and he should run in fear. At least this was their hope.

But the creature did not run. Instead, it reached to its side with its forepaw and pulled out what the young female thought was a stick. This was at first funny to them—a stick. They feared no stick. They chewed on sticks to sharpen and clean their teeth. But this was a stick the like of which she had never seen nor chewed upon. It was shiny. It gleamed like certain stones she had seen along the riverbank. The sun glinted off the stick's shiny surface and shone into her eyes, causing her to blink in irritation. Still they moved slowly forward, unafraid of this small, strange creature and the shiny stick. They knew at any second their prey would take off running down the gravel bar and then they could thrill with the chase and finally the kill.

But the creature did not run.

"What is it doing?" she whined in wonder as they closed in.

"Shut up," her brother growled in return. She did as ordered and tried to mask the uneasiness that was beginning to creep its way into her brain. Something was not right with this situation, but to show fear and let her brothers and sister down was unthinkable. They would tell the rest of the pack how cowardly she was and she would be laughed at and made to sit with the youngest pups, shamed and shunned.

So she held her place in line as they crept forward. She was getting a good view of the strange creature as they moved towards it. It seemed to have no fur at all except on its head, and very little of that, and was covered in some strange-looking hide that was not its own. What skin of the creature that could be seen was as pale as that of the giant worms that washed out of the riverbanks after the heavy rains and floods. It looked sick and unhealthy and she wondered if it would even be any good to eat.

When they had closed within a couple of leaps of their prey, the strong brother growled out a command to cut off the creature's escape routes. If it was too stupid to run that was fine with him; they would kill it where it stood.

The group came to a halt, the young female on the far end of the line next to the river. But she was confused. There was no odorous fear smell coming from this creature; no sense of panic in its pale face. It eyed each of them in turn and waved the shiny stick. Fear gnawed at her insides, her instinct warning her that this was not right. She wanted to growl at her brothers and tell them they should back off but she knew it would do no good. They wanted to kill; they were wolves and they had to kill.

Her brother peeled his lips back and showed his deadly fangs, letting out a fearsome growl as he did. The others followed suit, hoping to frighten the puny creature. As they faced off in this deadly challenge, the young she-wolf began to sense something else completely foreign to her. A strange sense of power within the shiny stick, a hum of warning only the wolves' keen senses could discern. They could all feel it and they hesitated—what was it?

But just as she thought her brother might call off his attack, he did just the opposite. His killer instinct had overridden his hesitation and he threw caution to the wind.

"Now!" he snarled and leaped forward. But his kin had not been so disaffected by the strange and unafraid creature with the shiny stick that emanated a foreboding hum. Unlike their brave brother, they had let the confusion of the unknown override their youthful bravado. They did not attack.

The brother's leap closed half the distance and his prey closed the rest. With a cry such as they had never heard, it leaped forward to meet the wolf's attack. The young wolf had figured to land atop the creature, its weight and momentum would knock the small thing to the ground where he could rip out its throat, but instead, the shiny thing in his prey's forepaws swung forward and met his attack.

In shock and horror, the young female and her brethren watched as the shiny stick severed her brother's head completely from his body. It rolled in a bloody mass towards her and stopped at her front paws, the lifeless eyes of the brother she had grown up with staring at her in disbelief. The body landed with a thump at the creature's feet where it twitched its death throes. The creature screamed at them in challenging defiance.

Total fear and chaos swept aside any of the false courage she had left and she lost control, yipping and snarling at her remaining brothers and sisters to run, run away from the creature and the shiny stick as fast as they could.

Her bladder emptied and her bowels spewed as she turned and fled. Her other brother and half sister, just as stunned and overwhelmed, added their cries of disbelief and ran after her. But the half brother did not heed their warning and sought to avenge his brother. He charged and the sharp shiny swung again in its deadly arc, catching the half brother in the front shoulder. The creature did not land a blow as effective as the first, but still the sharp stick bit deep into the muscle and tissue of half brother's shoulder, coming to a stop only when it met bone.

A hideous cry of pain filled the air and stopped the other three young wolves who had nearly reached the safety of the riverbank. They whirled in time to see their half brother trying desperately to flee on three legs, his left front dangling uselessly. Blood flowed profusely from a deep and wide gash in his shoulder.

The young female took in the sight and immediately made a rash decision. If she didn't do something, the beast was going to chase her half brother down from behind and the sharp shiny would finish the job it had started. In an apparent suicide run headlong back towards the deadly creature, she bolted as fast as she had ever run in her life, growling and snarling to grab its attention. It whirled towards her, ignoring for the moment the wounded wolf as it struggled to limp away on three good legs. But just as she closed in and the sharp stick was poised for another killing strike, she veered away. She had only meant to draw the creature's attention away from her half brother and in that she was successful. Nimbly she skipped out of the thing's reach and bolted once again for the woods. Relieved, she saw her half-brother join with the others and together they disappeared into the safety of the trees. A quick look over her shoulder told her the creature was not going to pursue them. Still, she ran as fast as she could.

The death of her brother hit the pack hard and her severely wounded half brother had lived for only a short time after. She remembered how badly his shoulder festered and started to stink as the sickness from the wound overtook him. While he was not her favorite, she was saddened with his plight but could not do much to help. She would steal a morsel of flesh from the pack's kill and sneak it to him, even though the dominant she-wolf had warned against it. In his state, he was a liability and the law of the pack was uncompromising; if a member could not hold its own it was put out to die, and finally, with a great deal of pain and suffering, die is what he did.

The she-wolf shivered as she watched the puny human snug against the rock behind the nasty fire. She remembered that fateful experience, the day she learned what a human was and how, even though they were often fearful and weak, they could use weapons with deadly results. This human also had a sharp and shiny stick, she could see it nestled amongst his possessions. Though he looked weak, she had grown to know humans, and knew they could be taken easily enough. But they were also smart and you had to approach the kill differently than you did a stag or an artox. In her years, she had learned that besides the sharp shiny, they used other things that could kill or wound; some from a long distance. No, you had to be smart when it came to humans. She wished her mate was here for he knew them better than any other creature in the forest. He knew of their ways, their weapons, and how best to kill them.

But her mate was not here. Though she had sent word to him of an intruder, she did not think he would get the message in time. No, he was off on important business and she could not count on his help. But she would have to do something; this was their wood and the pack could not allow a lone human to roam free.

As she lay there silently watching from her hiding place, she thought back to earlier in the day. They had made a good kill but had lost a valuable young female in doing so. Her mate would not be happy about that, but if she took this human down that would please him. It looked like it should be an easy kill, unlike the old stag. The human pup had backed himself into a defendable corner but by doing so, had cut off any means of escape. There was the fire to deal with of course, she would have to think on that one, but this human was still just a pup and she had her pack. Yes, she would kill this human and her mate would be pleased. Her attack plan against the old stag had been sound save for the misstep with the young she-wolf. She would come up with another good plan to deal with this one and his fire and the sharp and shiny stick he carried. The boy slept and the wolves watched.

CHAPTER SEVENTEEN

A WET QUIET HAD SETTLED OVER THE SMALL sheltered hollow on the mountainside where Willoughby made his camp. The only thing breaking the silence was the sound of the snaps and pops of wood burning on his campfire. It wasn't really a rain that fell, but instead a steady, drizzling mist that was still managing to soak everything. But Willoughby took no notice, as this was his first night free of the underground and all of the physical and mental torment that had come with it.

While he had no clue as to how long he had actually been stuck in the cave behind the waterfall, he knew it had been way too long. The experience of his father dying so suddenly and all of the suffering and grief that had enveloped the family since, had been hard but it had been different; then, at least he had family around for support. But alone in the cave, it had been a high-speed mental train wreck and physically almost as bad. The last thing that crossed his mind as he sat on Bob's old poncho, his tired head drooping to his chest and the sinister and out-of-place-looking forest lurking just beyond his fire, had been of the things he would do to make amends to his family for the anguish he had caused them. But as he succumbed to total exhaustion, he was painfully aware that he was not home yet and the oppressive weight of loneliness was as heavy as it had ever been in the cave.

It was a burning chunk of wood rolling from its place atop the fire that woke him. For a long moment, nothing that his eyes took in—the wet gray rock surrounding him or the fire, now burnt down and falling apart—registered in his mind. It made no sense to him in the way exhaustive sleep can do, at that first instant of becoming awake. But the reality of where he was, settled in on him as quickly as the mist, which dampened and chilled him through.

Willoughby's body screamed in protest when he tried to move. He had fallen asleep with his head tucked to his chest and his cramped muscles were not happy. The cold and wet air of the mountainside didn't help any either. He couldn't remember ever feeling so sore and it took far more effort than it should have for a fourteen-year-old boy to rouse himself to standing. When he finally managed, he set about shoving the non-burnt ends of wood back into the coals, and after adding a few more chunks and dead limbs, the fire was soon back to its security blanket level. The bright, crackling flames radiating off the rock walls chased away some of the misery but Willoughby still had a gnawing anxiety in his stomach; something didn't feel right. The cold mist had settled about everything and in the dark, he could barely see to the edge of the forest, which was spooky enough in the daylight. The light of morning couldn't come soon enough for him.

Willoughby's mind was functioning in zombie mode and clear thought was escaping him. He should have been excited about his first night out from underground, but the overwhelming negativity of what he had seen yesterday stomped the life out of what optimism there had been. Throughout his ordeal in the cave, he had clung to the logical assumption that if he found a way out, there would be a quick reuniting with his family. But when he had taken in the vast and surreal landscape surrounding him, it threw logic out the window. If he could have just recognized something…anything.

But thinking about the why, the where, and the what the fuck gave him a nasty headache to go along with the rest of his body torments, especially after the face plant he had taken yesterday. Fishing a couple of aspirin from the small first aid kit, he washed them down with a few swallows of the metallic tasting cave water. Only four left. Not an issue if he had come out where he should have, but now?

The water set his stomach to rumbling—another problem—

food. Half an energy bar, a handful of chocolate chip cookie crumbs, and no idea of how long it might have to last. But he needed something so he settled for a small bite of the energy bar and one mouthful of crumbs. Nowhere near enough but it would have to do for now. He chewed slowly. He had heard somewhere that doing that could trick your mind into thinking there was more food than what was there, but Willoughby's mind was screwed up and didn't fall for the trick at all.

The wet mist and the chill of the air made it uncomfortable any distance away from the fire. The embracing heat of the dry firewood had dried his filthy sweatshirt and jeans to some extent, but Willoughby couldn't shake the chill and deep shivers wracking his body. He decided to put Bob's rain poncho to use. It still had the offensive mustiness about it but was warmer and longer and gave him better protection that the cheap one in his pack. The smell he could handle. When he slipped it over his head, he was delightfully surprised as to how well it fit him. It left his arms free but covered him halfway to his knees and had a hood to cover his head. When he cinched the leather tie about the waist you would have been hard-pressed to say that it hadn't been made for him. It was an ironic twist to the whole adventure that Bob had been similar in size to Willoughby.

As tired and worn out as he was, he didn't think he could sleep any more. His wood supply was getting low and he had no idea how long it might be until daylight. The thought of falling asleep and having the fire burn to nothing was unsettling given the cold creepiness that pressed about his sanctuary and the looming murkiness of the forest so close by. But he had fire at least, it would do to keep the night critters back, and then there was the fact that he was not totally unarmed. The sword and shield leaned against his pack and it struck Willoughby as strange that it felt like they belonged there—that they had been meant for him. Though the attempt to draw the blade had produced very unwanted results, it was still reassuring to see it there.

That small bit of reassurance lasted for about five seconds when a mournful howl broke the night like the whistle of a freight train coming to a crossing. Long, strong, and not very far away, the sound caused Willoughby's heart to jump into his throat. The unearthly cry tailed off into the darkness, but as quickly as the first howl tapered off into silence, it was answered by another, this one a just a little farther away than the first.

Willoughby knew the difference between wolves and coyotes. He and Jake often listened to the coyote packs around the farm late at night, especially when the moon was full. Jake said you could tell the difference between the dominant females, males, and the lesser animals in the pack by the tone and pitch of their yips and barks. But Willoughby and Jake had never listened to wolves late at night around the farm because there were none. A few wolves had crossed the far eastern Oregon border from Idaho and often made the news when they were spotted or had taken a farmer's sheep, but wolves on this side of the Cascades? Not for over a hundred years. Yet Willoughby knew what they sounded like. Documentaries about wolves were frequent on Discovery and National Geographic channels, and what he had just heard was a wolf. More than one to be exact. While he was certain of what it was, this was another thing that made absolutely no sense to him—you didn't find wolves on the western side of Oregon.

But whether it made sense or not, the howls had grabbed his undivided attention. Immediately he put more wood on the fire and soon had a good sized crackling blaze going. It was throwing off way more heat than the amount the night chill called for, but more important to Willoughby was the amount of light it was putting out. With the rock ledge at his back reflecting the light towards the forest, he had a fairly well lit view of the space between him and the dark edge of the trees. If something came out of the forest, he would see it.

But then what? The question again filled him with fear, sending an uncontrollable spasm of shivers down his spine and a knot of nausea settled itself in his empty stomach. Willoughby had never in his life had the unfortunate opportunity to experience true fear.

Afraid yes, plenty of times. But he hadn't even had enough time to experience fear when he went over the falls, it had happened all too quickly. And he hadn't been afraid when confronted by Eddie Anderson at the bus stop, even though he knew getting your ass beaten by a much bigger guy was going to hurt. But this was different. It wasn't a "bump in the night" type of fear that manifested itself in the dark loneliness of his bedroom, no, this was something he could feel. This had reached its cold hand deep to his very core and was twisting his insides.

But there wasn't any time to contemplate his fear as another long piercing howl pierced the darkness inside the giant trees and again was answered. Not only were there more but they were closer than before. Amazingly enough the second set of howls snapped Willoughby from his fear-induced trance. A voice in his head spoke to him as clearly as someone standing right next to him; he wasn't sure if it was his own or if it was Jake's but it spurred him to action.

"Keep the fire high. A wolf won't approach a bright fire." It made a lot more sense than standing there crying and damn near ready to shit his pants. Willoughby grabbed several chunks of small, dry wood and added them to his blaze. They would burn fast but would also burn brighter and he had been smart enough to pack plenty of them near his woodpile. He just hoped what he had, would get him through to sunrise.

As he stepped back away from the blistering heat emanating from the now fully-fledged bonfire, Willoughby looked past the rising flames towards the dark tree line and immediately spotted the first set of glowing yellow eyes. He froze, forgetting for the moment the intensity of the heat. The dark, black maw of the forest magnified the intensity of the yellow orbs as they reflected the glow of the fire back towards Willoughby. As he stood transfixed, more pairs of eyes flanked the first set, flicking into view like Christmas lights on a timer. Two, three, four…he quit counting at nine. There were a lot of them, staring at him from the blackness.

Panic started to drive a wedge into his fragile hold on sanity. The fire would not last forever and even if daylight was close, Willoughby did not think it would deter the wolves from coming for him. Jake's comments kept coming back to him.

"They're the smartest animals in the woods and they do things according to a plan," the big guy had said as they sat watching Yellowstone packs work together to bring down an aging bison on a Discovery channel special. Smartest animals or not, Willoughby didn't think it would take much of a plan—wait until the fire burned down and then overwhelm him with a rush. What could he do to stop them?

Wolves. Though he had yet to see anything but their eyes, Willoughby could picture the beasts behind them. Beautiful animals, black, white, and gray. Fluid and graceful. But what had always struck him the most were the eyes—cold and cunning. The eyes of creatures whose whole existence was wrapped up in the constant search for food. An absurd morbidity started to manifest itself in the form of bizarre thoughts—would he still be alive as they started to eat him? Would he taste better than a deer or an elk? It was almost enough to make him laugh. Well, almost. How ironic to have come through everything he had only to wind up being ripped apart as a late night snack.

Oddly enough, the bizarre humor of his situation forced a temporary halt to the rising tide of panic. But as he stood there, Willoughby could sense more, something he couldn't quite put a finger on. The creatures behind the eyes were there to kill him, Willoughby felt that as sure as he had ever felt anything before. It was death staring at him from the trees, but they were not coming any closer, and fire or not, a pack that big would not fear a human all alone. Something was keeping them back within the safety of their forest; something was giving them cause for concern.

Willoughby turned away from the piercing eyes and took one step behind him to his backpack. The handle of the sword was waiting for him. As if he had placed it there at the ready for just such an emergency, it was in the perfect position. Without thinking about possible consequences, he gripped and pulled the sword in one fluid motion, as if he had practiced it over and over thousands of times.

The blade smoothly slid free of its scabbard with a pleasing metallic ring, and as he drew it out, he turned and faced the line of eyes.

Willoughby hadn't given the slightest pause to what had happened the first and only other time he had attempted to draw the sword. This time it felt right. Its weight settled comfortably in his hand, feeling like it belonged there—like it was a part of him. The deadly creatures hidden in the dark recesses of the wood were temporarily forgotten as a feeling of calm purpose chased away his fear. The drawing of the weapon transformed him. Putting his other hand below the other and firmly grasping the leather grip, he held the blade up high in front of him, feeling its power—its life. The energy from the sword coursed down his arms and flowed through his body like an orgasm. Willoughby shuddered with the pleasure of the moment. This weapon was meant for him. He had no idea how or why, and he didn't know a thing about how to use it, but this sword had been waiting for him.

As Willoughby held it up towards the light of the bonfire, the three feet of steel seemed to glow. In the flickering of the firelight, he stood there holding the sword in front of him, glaring over the top of the flame towards the dark shadows where the gleaming eyes glared back. Thoughts and images roared through Willoughby's mind like an action movie trailer at high speed; the sword was strength for the weak; truth against lies; and most important for him—the light of courage against the shadow of fear.

Slowly and deliberately, Willoughby began to settle his body and mind with unhurried, deep breaths, in through his abdomen, to his lungs and slowly out through his nose. With each breath he took, he forced the negative energy of fear back down into its hiding place. He focused his vision, not on the glowing eyes of his unwelcome visitors, but instead, on the weapon that he was holding high in his hands. Its weight balanced perfectly; heavy as it should be for three feet of steel, but heavy in a solid and comfortable way and not overburdening his arms. Equally as amazing was that he actually felt physically stronger. He had never lifted weights or done anything to build up his arms—hell his sister could beat him at arm wrestling with either hand—but Willoughby felt stronger. He felt as if he could swing this sword with power.

Reality reasserted itself as Willoughby's gaze shifted beyond the sloping tangs of the cross guard and into the black maw of the forest where the eyes glowed with intensity. But this reality no longer panicked him with gut-twisting fear. Drawing the sword had wrought an inexplicable transformation and set his mind to one purpose—an adversary confronted him and he would have to deal with it. The sword had taken over his thought process and now instead of fear worrying him into shitting himself, his mind clicked with cold calculations on how an attack by the pack would present itself and how he would respond.

"The spirit of the wolf is strong," Jake had explained to Willoughby as they had sat on the porch in front of the trailer on a warm September evening not more than a month ago.

"The pack is a family group that does everything as a single unit. Raise and train its young, hunt together, and protect each other. They are led by dominant males and females but every member of the pack is important. They are wise and use a lot of tricks to bring down their prey and feed the family. That is why they are important to Indian culture. We respect the wolf."

Right at the moment, Willoughby didn't care whether wolves deserved respect or not. His adrenalin rush was off the charts, the fear replaced by an uncontrolled rage. He wanted them to charge, he wanted to meet them head-on. His body tensed like a spring waiting for release, every muscle poised to swing and slash the blade of his weapon deep into the warm bodies of the wolves. Willoughby was now no more than an animal himself; he wanted to smell and taste blood.

"WHAT ARE YOU WAITING FOR?" he screamed into the darkness, shattering the silence, daring the pack to come out of the shadows.

But they didn't come any closer. Willoughby's primal scream of challenge was answered only by the crack and pop of the fire. Secure in the depths of the darkness, the eyes silently held their ground.

The tsunami of rage and the adrenalin rush that had swept over him when he drew the sword began to ebb and exhaustion began to reassert its claim over his body and mind. As his strength dissipated, the point of the sword began to droop until it rested on the ground and the muscles in his arms and shoulders began to ache.

That was totally fuckin' insane, Willoughby marveled to himself as the last vestiges of his fit evaporated into the mist. But the sword still hummed with energy, reminding him that though the fit had passed, the danger hadn't and it was still a deadly standoff. Willoughby kept his position with the fire between him and the wolves and they kept theirs, hidden just inside the timberline where the darkness veiled all but their eyes. Holding onto the sword had produced a radical change in Willoughby's psyche, and while it kept the fear at bay, it couldn't keep his legs from wobbling. A second enemy now began a flanking move on the boy's defenses—sheer exhaustion was taking over. It was a fight to keep from falling asleep on his feet, but just as this new worry began to manifest itself, the eyes started to disappear.

One by one they vanished into the inky blackness until there was only one pair left staring at him out of the darkness. The yellow orbs seemed to pulse and glow with menacing intensity and while he hadn't noticed it before, Willoughby was aware that these eyes were larger than the others. This was his nemesis—this was the driving force behind the pack and he could feel a malevolence that manifested itself in a palpable form. A tremble coursed through Willoughby's body, forcing him to tighten his grip on the pommel of the sword. A surge of calming strength forced the shivers back as he raised the blade back up and pointed its tip directly between those evil yellow eyes. It brought a response that he wasn't prepared for.

"I see you, human." The words stabbed through the dark like a hiss of cold wind, but it wasn't a trick concocted by his tired mind—the wolf had just spoken to him.

Willoughby didn't budge. As unreal as it was, he did not suspect for one moment that it might be his worn and battered mind playing tricks on him. While he did not know if he was actually hearing the voice or if it was being channeled into his mind, the communication was strong and clear—the beast hidden in the shadows was speaking to him. There was something about it that Willoughby could sense—a power, an energy, something he could feel but didn't understand. But it was also familiar and it quickly came to him; it was the same thing he felt as he held the sword.

"You don't understand, do you?" The voice drifted out of the darkness tinged with a distinct tone of amusement. *"When I sensed your presence, I thought a mighty warrior or mage had entered the woods, but instead I find a puny human youngling wandering lost without its mama. I smell your fear. It clings about you like a pup which has rolled in its own filth."*

The voice that shouldn't be mocked and the sword Willoughby held hummed with energy in response, and while it made no logical sense and defied any reasonable explanation, Willoughby was struck by an instant understanding.

"We're not in Kansas anymore, Toto." It hit him with the force and brutality of a head-on collision as the framework of reality as he knew it disintegrated into nothingness. The seed had been planted the first minute he had come across Bob's pack and the things inside. It had been watered and fertilized after the nasty experience drawing the sword for the first time. It had sprouted into maturity when he came out of the cave and looked out on a landscape so totally unfamiliar, causing him to ask himself over and over how he could have ended up where he was. The truth was in front of him and the truth was ugly and frightening—the world of Willoughby Baxter, and all he believed it to be, was gone—and maybe with it, his chance of ever seeing his family again. But as overwhelming as the concept was, it got shoved quickly into the background as the voice stabbed out of the darkness again.

"You are strange, pup. Not from here, yet you carry a scent that haunts me. I have crossed it before, but it was long ago." The voice paused, inviting Willoughby to answer, so he did.

"Why don't you come into the light where I can see you?" It seemed like a logical question for such an illogical moment.

The yellow eyes blinked. That surprised Willoughby. He had been watching those eyes now for quite some time and this was the first time he had seen a blink. It surprised him even more when the wolf stepped out of the darkness.

Willoughby sucked in his breath. The howls that had announced their arrival had exposed the wolves for what they were, even though they were hidden by the dark of the forest, but the creature that materialized from the shadows and into the edge of the light made his heart skip. It was half again as big as he had expected. Documentaries had always shown them to be of a size similar to very large dogs, but Willoughby swore that if the creature had stopped right in front of him, they would be looking eye to yellow eye. He could put a saddle on this thing. It was mottled gray in color except for the snout, which was pure white, making the large dark nostrils even more striking. Its ears, larger than his hands, stood cocked in Willoughby's direction on the alert. They flanked the intense eyes, which darted to and fro, taking in every nuance of the situation in front of it.

Willoughby held his breath as the beast crept cautiously forward, finally coming to a stop at the bright edge of the fire, no more than thirty feet away. The tip of his sword never wavered from the spot between the animal's eyes. The wolf plopped down on its haunches and the two stared across the fire at each other.

"Is this close enough for you?" it asked. Willoughby couldn't tell if the lips had moved or not but it really didn't matter. This thing was speaking directly to him. He nodded in response; it was close enough.

"You smell like nothing I have ever encountered." The wolf's nostrils flared as it registered the findings back to its brain. *"Humans have an unpleasant stink about them but you carry more than just that. You are different."*

Willoughby was second guessing his decision to ask the wolf closer. It had been better when he hadn't known how big the damn thing was. But like it or not, it was here and it was talking to him.

"Where is here?" Willoughby finally managed to stammer. If

he was crazy enough to carry on a conversation with an animal, he figured he might as well see if he could get some answers to some of his most pressing questions.

The wolf cocked its huge head first one way and then the other, looking confused. *"Here is here,"* it answered after a pause.

It wasn't the answer Willoughby was looking for and it irritated him. "Does here have a name?"

"Here is here and you are where you do not belong. This wood and these mountains are the realm of my pack and we suffer no intrusion, especially by humans. You are a cowardly lot and do not usually venture here unless you have protection in numbers. Even then you are stupid and can be easily fooled and killed, though we take no joy in eating you and often leave most to the scavengers. The ignorant beasts which allow you to ride upon their backs are much more to our liking."

Wow! Willoughby thought. Not only did this thing talk, but it carried on a pretty intelligent conversation. The eating of humans thing he could have done without hearing, but he had a sneaking hunch that for whatever reason, this wolf did not mean to try and kill him. It had sent the rest of the pack away. Why would it do that? He decided to ask.

"What happened to the rest of your pack? Did I scare them off?" Willoughby didn't think it would hurt to act tough and he had spotted something about the wolf that made him think his statement wasn't too far off. While the beast was talking, it kept eyeing the sword intently.

"We feasted well yesterday. If hunger had been gnawing at our bellies we would have taken you down, though I think I would prefer to eat grass over something which stinks as bad as you. But there are others who make this wood their home and they will have an interest in one such as you. I have sent the pack to make contact with my mate and make him aware of your intrusion. His name is Fenrir and he is King of Wolves. I have decided to let him determine your fate. But make no doubt, if you are allowed to live you will wish we had killed you quickly instead."

So the wolf was female. Willoughby took a quick peek between her legs but the way she was sitting he couldn't have told the difference anyway. But it did help to explain some of the bitchy attitude. She had put him on alert. He might get through this encounter, but promised there would be another. But she also told him something which gave him hope—there were other humans somewhere and his best chance of survival would be to find them. Though opportunities to carry on conversations with animals who talked back were pretty rare—as in, never—Willoughby was tired and he wanted this one to be at an end. The coming days would bring on whatever they would but for now, he wanted to rest and he was tired of this threatening she-wolf and her attitude. Her furtive glances towards the sword had given him an idea, and it was time to test it.

"My thinking is that if you thought you could kill me easily you would have done it, but you ain't so sure that I might just be more than meets the eye." Willoughby shifted his weight ever so slightly as he finished his sentence, but it was enough movement that the she-wolf reacted. Her muscles tensed perceptibly and the quick movements of her eyes spoke volumes. She was afraid. He decided to pour it on.

"I didn't come into this place because I wanted to and I plan on getting out of here as quick as I can," Willoughby continued. "It would spare both of us a lot of trouble if you would just let me get gone from here, but if you don't, I will tell you right now that you aren't the only ones capable of killing. In the land I come from, I am a warrior, small, but I carry a mighty sting and I think you know this. I have eaten wolf before and I find them to be stringy and tough. I think you had better get back to the safety of your woods, because I haven't eaten in several days and if I can't find a deer to kill I may just decide that wolf will have to do."

Willoughby played his hand and as he finished his sentence, he raised the sword high and took a quick step towards the she-wolf. It was just as he thought and she had been ready, with a bound she jumped back and to the side. He was amazed as to how much distance she covered in the one leap; amazing and scary when he realized she could have made that same leap and been over the fire and on top of him. It was something he would remember later. She landed nimbly on her feet and with one more leap, disappeared into the sanctuary of the trees. But as quickly as she was gone, the yellow eyes reappeared, blazing with a new fury.

"*We shall meet again, human,*" her wolf voice hissed across the distance. "*And when we do, I shall take great pleasure in watching you die.*" The eyes blinked and she was gone.

Willoughby sighed as he dropped to his knees. He stuck the point of the blade deep into the ground and sagged heavy against it with his head resting on the talons adorning the end of the pommel. Convulsions wracked him as he heaved a bitter gruel of bile, water, and the meager contents of his stomach onto the ground. The taste of the nasty stomach acid brought on more heaves.

He tried pulling himself to his feet, but the second he tried to let his legs hold his weight, they collapsed under him. In the end, he crawled back to his hollow and rested with his legs drawn up and his back against the rock wall. He laid the sword across his lap and rested his head against his knees. Oblivious to anything else, Willoughby gave in to his emotions and overwhelming exhaustion. The tears flowed freely and for a long time as the night wrapped its dark arms around him. The fire settled and a long stream of embers flew brightly on a short-lived voyage into the heavy mist. Far off in the distance, a wolf howled.

Chapter Eighteen

IT WAS THE COLD THAT WOKE WILLOUGHBY this time, no voices in his head, no sense of dread that something was amiss, just the cold. He was lying on his side with his head resting on his arm. Rocks dug in sharply at various points, reminding him with stabs of discomfort that he was sleeping on the ground. The air around him was thick with wet mist; it had dampened his clothes and added a layer of clammy chill to his discomfort.

Working himself to a sitting position, he rubbed his hands across his crusted eyes, an unpleasant smell wafted up to his nose from his crotch, another reminder that he was filthy and really starting to put on a stink. He had lost track of days now but at least he was aware that this had been his first night out of the cave. A glance to the fire showed why it had gotten so uncomfortably cold in his protective hollow, it was completely out except for a few smoldering coals. It had burned down considerably since the intense blaze he had going last night trying to keep the wolves back.

Wolves. Willoughby struggled painfully to his feet as the recollection of what had transpired came rushing back to his disoriented head. There had been wolves just inside the tree line last night. He had built up the fire and drew the sword in an attempt to keep them at bay. A quick glance at Bob's pack gave him a bit of relief; the sword lay nestled safely in its scabbard though he didn't recall putting it back at all. The last thing he remembered was falling asleep with it in his lap. But he didn't waste much time trying to figure it out; trying to do that would just make you crazy.

Wolves. That would have been enough insanity in itself but it hadn't stopped there; what came after had gotten really crazy. Willoughby stood there staring blankly into the misty depths of the forest trying to put a logical explanation on what had, or what he thought had, occurred last night. Was he crazy? He was pretty sure that he hadn't been dreaming. He had distinctly heard the howls even though he knew there were supposedly no wolves in western Oregon. But they had been there—a lot of bright yellow eyes staring at him through the dark; they had come for him and he had been afraid.

But then he had drawn the sword. That was something he could not have dreamed or made up. The recollection was fresh and he could still feel the surge of power and strength. It had made him feel invincible and he had challenged the wolves. The wolves had felt the change about him, of that he was sure. The sword had something they could feel and it had made them afraid, and then they had been gone, all except for one.

The she-wolf had spoken to him. Willoughby still could not remember if her lips had actually moved but the voice had been clear. Clear enough also was her warning—they would be coming back for him.

For Willoughby, the events of the night had done one thing, he was now convinced that he was someplace besides where he should be and he thought he knew the reason behind it all. Jake had unknowingly let the cat out of the bag as far as he was concerned. It was Spirit Falls. It was a sacred place and funny things happened there.

Willoughby pieced together the events since he left the house on Sunday morning however long ago that had been. Things had gotten strange from the very first as he had left Jake and the farm and headed out to visit the falls. He had heard voices and then there were the incidents with the raven. It was the bird that had caused him to go over the falls in the first place. The skeleton and the things he had found, the fact that he recognized nothing about the place after he had gotten out of the cave, and now this. If he wasn't crazy, he was on the verge of it simply because he couldn't figure anything out anymore. Nothing was as it should be and nothing made sense. He needed some help, some human help. Someone to tell him everything was all right.

The inclination to stay put, keep a large fire going and hope someone would find him was strong, it was what anyone involved in search and rescue would say was the right choice. But a sick feeling inside his stomach told him that waiting here would get him nothing except cold nights and possibly more visits from unwelcome guests. The search and rescue angle only made sense if people knew you were missing. If he was somehow in a whole different place, how would anybody know about him? No, he didn't think he could handle sitting and waiting. There was also the issue of food, or lack of it, and his stomach was reminding him of that point right at the moment. There weren't a whole lot of good reasons to stay put as far as he was concerned. Nope. It was time to move.

He would start by finding the river; if he could find the river, he would follow it. You always followed water downstream, Jake had said. Follow any water downstream far enough and you were bound to find somebody. That was good enough advice for him.

Willoughby scattered what was left of the fire coals and helped himself to a bite of his shrinking energy bar and chased its blandness down with a couple of swigs of water. He chewed slowly but when it was gone, he felt little relief from the emptiness and his stomach gurgled in agreement that it was nowhere near enough. Food was going to have to become a priority very soon.

While he was too close to the tall trees to see anything except into the forest, he remembered the snaking ribbon of hardwoods off to the right as he had worked his way down the mountainside. He would follow the tree line for a ways and see if he could find a small stream coming out of the mountains. Logic told him that if he found such a stream and followed it that eventually it would meet the larger one. While he wasn't sure he could even trust logic anymore after what he had been through, it was nonetheless all he had.

Deciding on a plan of action was a good start but as he stowed his gear into his pack, a monkey wrench slid into the drive gears of his train of thought. The wolves. They were gone yes, but where? The answer was not a good one. They had disappeared into the forest, the very forest he was going to have to go into in order to get to the river.

So do I face them in the woods or face them here? Willoughby asked himself. It was an ugly question that had no good answer. They would have less chance sneaking up on him during the day but he wouldn't have the fire advantage to keep them away if he was moving. They would have the advantage of knowing the land; the she-wolf had said this was their territory and there was no reason for him to doubt that. But he did have one ace in the hole; the one thing he had that they did not and they seemed to be afraid of it—the sword.

He looked at it, securely strapped in its harness to his backpack. It was there. Just the very thought of it brightened Willoughby's demeanor and he had to fight the desire to pull it free from its scabbard, remembering the way it had felt last night. But he also reminded himself of what had happened the first time he had tried to pull it out. He hadn't even started to free it when it had knocked him on his ass with an electric shock. What would it be this time? He decided not to chance it. If trouble showed up he would, and hope for the best, but for now, he wasn't going to push his luck.

Willoughby shouldered his pack and looked back up the mountain trying to spot where he thought the cave entrance was but the thick blanket of wet fog obscured everything past a couple of hundred feet. He hoped he could remember how to get back here someday. He wanted to bring help back with him, get into the cave, and retrieve Bob. Willoughby felt he owed him that much. There was a story there; Willoughby just needed to find someone to tell it to.

The original plan of keeping to the open and out of the forest quickly proved unworkable. Too many rock falls, house-sized boulders, and thick patches of scrub brush kept blocking his route, causing him to pause and rethink. It amazed him how there was such a distinct line between the steep, rocky terrain of the mountain and the forest. There was one, then there was the other; the mountain stopped and the massive wall of trees took over. As much as he was uncomfortable with the forest, he was starting to think it was the better option. Sooner or later he was going to have to go in, and as difficult as the going was attempting to keep to the mountain slope, it looked like it was going to be sooner rather than later. Deciding that it was as good a time as any, Willoughby plunged into the forest and entered a totally new world.

The change was absolutely remarkable. The previous night when he had scavenged the wood from the edge of the forest there had been little time and less desire to actually do any exploring, but now that he was into its depths, he was awestruck. Inside was a world of twilight. The trees were so tall and the canopy so thick that very little light filtered through to the forest floor. Willoughby thought he recognized the trees as conifers but they differed from the firs, cedars, and hemlocks around his home. Maybe redwoods or sequoias, their incredible size made him feel small and insignificant and gave the forest an unearthly quality. Thick tendrils of mist snaked their way around the massive gray boles adding an ethereal touch to its eeriness. The earth was soft and spongy with the decay of an ancient forest. It looked and smelled old.

Old, but certainly very much alive. There were a lot of things growing, feeding off the organic smorgasbord of decaying matter. Ferns clumped themselves into colonies and reached their green tips towards what little light filtered down. Willoughby thought he recognized a couple of the species—bracken and sword fern that grew everywhere in the Cascades and the Coast Range. But there were some he had never seen before—one whose stalk twisted upward in a conical spiral until it peaked out at a point higher than Willoughby could reach. That was a common theme with the ferns he was seeing; he had never seen any that grew as tall as these did.

Moss clung to the lower branches of the trees like shredded remnants of a tattered jacket while some trailed down in tender wisps towards the ground, moving ever so slightly with the faint hint of the breeze that managed to wiggle through the protective shield of branches and trunks. The Old Man's Beard, Jake had called the strange, pale green strings that hung down in tinsel-like fashion from the branches of the trees. Since the lowest limbs of the trees didn't start until fifty or sixty feet or so off the ground, these long dangling threads of growth were a strange sight indeed.

But as Willoughby angled his way slowly deeper into the depths of the forest, what caught his eye the most were the mushrooms and toadstools that bunched themselves in the darkest corners and hollows. These fungi were a stunning contrast to the muted gray, brown, and black tones of earth and tree bark, a contrast even to the vibrant green shades of the ferns. They pulsated with such color that Willoughby first thought they were fake. He was totally blown away by what he was seeing. Into cavities formed by giant tree roots, lined into the cracks that formed between deadfalls of wood and the decay of the earth, anywhere there was relief from what little light filtered down, these denizens of dark thrust their painted heads through the humus. There were toadstools, bright yellow and orange monsters with wide-brimmed caps larger in diameter than a pizza pan; tall, cone shaped ones with long, shaggy, blood-red skirts covering chalk-white stalks; and brain-looking orbs of blue-gray matter with veins that seemed to pulse with energy. Willoughby was staring with jaw-dropping wonder at pockets of Alice-in-Wonderland colors set against the somber tones of the forest.

But as amazing as the flora was, it was equally confusing to a tired and bewildered Willoughby. There had been nothing in the twenty-four hours since he had come out of the cave that told him he was close to home. The mountains, the woods, the things growing in the woods, the wolves. Where in the fucking hell was he? Things kept piling up against the thin fabric of sanity deep inside the fragile boy's mind. While he had never contemplated on the true meaning of the word "insanity" before, Willoughby thought he was really getting close to figuring that out.

But he kept moving. As incredible as the spectacle of growth was, he was in no mood to waste time gawking. The going was much easier in the relative openness of the deep wood and Willoughby had an obsession now, in order to make any kind of sense to all of this he was going to have to find a living person. That would be best accomplished by finding the river—find it and follow it until he found someone. It would be the starting point to putting this crazy puzzle of confusion behind him.

As he plunged deep into the depths, the quiet of the wood spooked him; not a peep, whistle or caw from any type of bird, no sound of planes going over. He had been hiking in some of Oregon's beautiful wilderness areas and had still been assailed by the sound of a jet or plane occasionally overhead. So far nothing but deathly quiet, yet Willoughby had the feeling that he was being watched. Looking back over his shoulder to see if he was being followed became part of the process as he forced himself forward. There was nothing to guide him and at times he wasn't sure if he was going the way he had intended. The detours he was forced to take around giant windfalls that loomed before him like stone walls of a fortress threw his sense of direction into a spin; no longer was Willoughby sure that he was traveling in the direction he thought the river lay.

But he pushed on. The ground sloped downhill in the direction he was headed and Willoughby figured down meant away from the mountains and towards the river; it was the only thing he had to go on. With nothing but the sound of his tennis shoes squishing in the soft earth and his own labored breathing keeping him company, he blindly willed himself on. There was a force driving him—something was following him. Furtive glances over his shoulder showed nothing, but he could feel a presence.

Willoughby frantically picked up his pace. Almost at a run, he pushed his tired body ahead until an exposed root caught his foot and he fell headfirst into a clump of red and orange toadstools. A cloud of powder enveloped him as he smashed the delicate fungi apart, getting into his eyes and his nose, forcing him into a sneezing fit. When he pulled himself up, a strange feeling came over him as he tried to wipe the clinging powder from his face and eyes. Sparkles of light danced across his field of vision and everything in front of him pulsed and glowed in an outline of vivid color. As he moved his hand in front of himself, it traced out a jerky pattern like an old stop action camera.

Willoughby grinned wide in amazement, forgetting where he was or what might be chasing him. This was amazing. Dropping the gear he held, he waved his hands in front of his face, marveling at the patterns and color. He lifted his arms high and twirled slowly—it was like he was inside a kaleidoscope. He had never felt so strange yet so vibrantly in tune with everything around him. The trunks of the giant trees swirled in a vortex of color as he spun; the smile on his face so wide it was starting to hurt.

But his hallucinatory fantasy ended as quickly as it had appeared as a searing cramp in his gut viciously slammed him back to reality. Willoughby doubled over in agony. Heaving retches followed quickly as a nasty bitterness worked itself out of his nearly empty stomach and into his mouth. He spit and he puked, trying desperately to rid himself of the vileness.

A warning flashed into his head as the heaving spasms intensified, he was going to puke his insides out. The toadstools! Willoughby grabbed the straps of Bob's pack and stumbled away from the red and orange clump, making it only a dozen feet or so until the next set of cramps doubled him over. Desperately he slipped his own pack to the ground and groped for his water bottle. He had just gotten the cap off when another attack struck, nearly causing him to drop the bottle. As the cramps subsided, he splashed water into his eyes and nose and rinsed his mouth out. Another cramp. The pains were so intense he almost passed out. More rinsing and spitting. Finally, after what seemed an eternity, the spasms subsided.

Willoughby hunched over, dazed and exhausted from the attack. Drool dribbled from his mouth and onto his chin. He became aware of a warm and smelly stickiness in his underwear. In the violent throes of the cramps he had lost control of his bodily functions; he had shit his pants. Too weak to stand, he crawled across the soft humus of the ancient forest floor, trying to put more distance between him and the deadly toadstools. Slowly his strength and senses came back to him.

Wow, he thought as he steadied himself onto his legs, his stomach muscles still on fire from the intense cramping. It had been a hard lesson. He was going to have to pay attention and stay away from the fungi growing in this haven of dark nastiness. The powder that had been released from the toadstools must have had some type of hallucinatory chemical makeup. He looked towards the hollow between the roots of the giant tree where he had fallen into the clump of fungi and smashed them, releasing the deadly powder. He sucked in his breath—the toadstools stood there as if they had never been touched.

More insanity. Willoughby knew what had happened—he had tripped and fell headfirst, smashing the stalks and caps. Yet there they stood, in defiant contrast to what reality told him it should be. But the confusion in his head was replaced by something else—something he could hear. Willoughby cocked his head and listened carefully. Yes. He could make it out now. Off to his left he thought it was—the sound of flowing water!

Quickly forgetting his hallucinogenic encounter and temporarily ignoring the messy uncomfortable feeling in his underwear, he struggled back into his pack and stumbled off in the direction he thought the sound was coming from. It wasn't long before Willoughby could see a slight change in the tree line ahead of him. The towering conifers slowly gave ground to hardwoods and soon he was standing on a high bank overlooking a river. Relief swept over him as he gazed at the landmark that he hoped would be the answer to his ordeal. But his relief was tempered by the sobering fact that he recognized nothing about the river or the landscape surrounding it.

But it was a start. *"Find water and follow it downstream."* Jake's words were reassuring but Willoughby would have been much more relieved if he had seen something he could recognize. But the disappointment of unfamiliarity was secondary to having finally accomplished a goal—he had found the river.

It was bigger than the Cascade River near his home by half again. He tried to think of any place within forty miles or so of

Spirit Falls where he would find a river of this size. The Santiam and its tributaries were south of Spirit Falls by at least twenty miles or so and they were the closest ones he could think of. It was still inconceivable to him that he could have traveled anywhere close to that far.

Keep moving. You do better when you're moving. It was good advice at this point and Willoughby was pleased at least to have given it to himself. It meant that he wasn't totally off the deep end, yet. He was starving, bruised, sore, exhausted, and confused and it would be easy to sit down on a rock by the water and wait, and more than likely start to feel sorry for himself again and start bawling. There was the pressing matter of having to clean up after the mishap in his shorts, but as he stood there on the bank, the urge to move on down the river towards what he hoped would be people was strong.

The trail he was standing on looked slightly used, animal tracks, nothing that appeared to be people prints, but recent rain could have eliminated those if no one had traveled on it for a while. But it was a trail, a trail going downstream in the right direction.

"Shit!" Willoughby shouted aloud as the significance of his discovery dawned on him. It was indeed a trail he was standing on. Why he hadn't noticed it before, he wasn't sure; maybe he had just focused on the river. But lo and behold it was a trail nonetheless.

Another surge of relief got his adrenalin going again. This was the second thing in a row that had worked out to some degree. He had found the river and here was a trail he could follow downstream, and as tired and sore as he was it was enough to put a little bounce in his step as he plunged forward. There was a whole lot of the day left and if the going was good, he could cover a lot of ground. He would stick to the river no matter what. As long as he wasn't in a wilderness area somewhere, he had to find a road, a bridge, a house—something.

The trail kept fairly close to the river and that meant that he was traveling in hardwoods rather than the deep and disturbing gloominess of the big conifer forest. The leaves were turning and many had already fallen and sunlight was actually breaking through the clouds, adding a welcome brightness and warmth in contrast to the deep wood. It was close, and he could feel the forest; its shadowy presence lurking no more than a hundred feet away or so, but thankfully the trail he was on stayed out of its depths. Evidently the animals didn't like it any more than he did.

Willoughby was alert and attentive as he walked. To the trail, the river, its opposite side. As he walked along, he thought he recognized some of the tracks he found on the path. Deer maybe, though the size of the track made him think elk, and smaller animals, raccoon and possum, usual travelers next to a river. But it was the footprints he didn't see that concerned him. Nowhere could he see human tracks. He was looking for anything that said people had been there. A boot or sneaker imprint, beer and soda cans, styrofoam fishing worm containers, McDonalds' wrappers. His grandma hated the fact that people threw their garbage out everywhere but at this point Willoughby would give anything to see a bit of trash.

It was discouraging but he kept walking. The trail meandered, dipping down off the higher bank onto a gravel bar for a ways and then back up. Twice he had to cross side streams that connected with the river, getting his feet wet the second time as he slipped on a rock. The backpack was also giving him trouble. The shield and the sword were cumbersome tied as they were and kept slipping and shifting around, causing him to stop every so often and retie them. But he was making pretty good time, or at least he thought, not having any way to tell. By his guess, he had been walking for several hours since he had left the camp on the mountainside and his feet and legs were starting to protest.

The trail had taken a turn down onto a long sand and gravel bar that was actually enjoying a good bit of sun when he finally decided to take a break. The bit of energy bar he had left had been on his mind for the last couple of hours and his belly had been rumbling uncontrollably, his stomach having completely emptied itself of everything after his last vomiting session. He had made a good effort but now there was a need for rest and since this was the first good sunlit stretch of river he had come across, Willoughby thought it might be a good time to make the best of it.

Finding a nice flat boulder next to the water's edge, he shrugged out of the pack and sat down. The shoes and socks came off and Willoughby wiggled his pale, shriveled toes in relief as the sun caressed them. The sweatshirt was next and as he pulled it off, he was assailed by the unpleasant reminder of his filthy and now soiled body.

"Wooo weee!" He grimaced as he lifted his arms and sniffed his pits. The smell of dirty butt and shit wafted from his jeans. The situation had to be addressed and with the warmth of the sun finally breaking through the gloom, Willoughby made his decision. He peeled off the foul smelling t-shirt and then did the same with his filthy jeans. Taking a quick look around to ensure no one had snuck up on him, the messy and powerfully odorous underwear joined the rest of his clothes in a pile at his feet. He was an extremely self-conscious young man and being naked in the out of doors was something not much to his liking, but on this occasion it felt really good to be shed of his clothes.

Willoughby stretched his arms to the sky and breathed deeply of the clean air while the sun massaged his body with warm tenderness. The combination of the sun's warmth and the stretching he was putting his stressed body through melted many of his minor aches and pains away, as well as it did much of the anxiety he had been feeling about his situation. He had not intended to sit and wait for someone to come along and find him but this place was making him rethink. He could make use of the rest of the day's sun, get some rest, and clean himself up. Hell, what had started out as a miserably cold and uncomfortable morning had turned into a beautiful day, the kind that might find people out on a hike along a pretty stretch of river. If he had any idea to sit and wait in hopes of being found this would be the place to do it, a safe distance away from the dread of the deep forest, though it was still too close. His position also gave him an excellent view of a long stretch of river above and below him.

As Willoughby contemplated his new plan, he took a good look at the area around him for the first time, taking in its beauty. He had been in a hurry when he had first come to the river, the thought of finding people overriding anything else. The colors of the hardwoods seemed much more vibrant and alive than they had been along the stretch of river that Willoughby had walked up, going to the falls so many days ago. Red, yellow, and orange burst from the trees in an array of brilliant fall finery that simply awed him. It had been the same with the colors painting the weird mushrooms and toadstools he had seen in the deep forest. All of them reminding him of something he was trying hard not to dwell on—he just didn't remember things being this way before.

But all that confusion could wait. Right now he had made up his mind to enjoy the sun and this spot along the river and get himself and his clothes as clean as he could. Despite his nakedness, he set to gathering driftwood from the many piles trapped in the cracks of the larger boulders along the stream. Using the combination of the sun and a nice fire, he had a plan to rinse his clothes of as much filth and stink as he could and then dry them. While he was at it, he would do the same with his stinky body. Forgetting the unfamiliarity of his surroundings and the nagging fact that he had seen no sign of people at all, Willoughby set to work.

The fire was the easiest, using just a couple of slivers of his pitch, the driftwood caught easily and soon he had a nice campfire going in a clear spot of sand and gravel next to his flat sitting rock. Attacking a small patch of hardwood saplings next to the riverbank with his Gerber hatchet gave him some forked sticks and cross pieces to use as a drying rack for his clothes. Once those were firmly in place around the fire, he grabbed the stinky pile of filth he had been living in and went to the edge of the water.

The pool was just over head-deep, formed by several large boulders in the stream that separated the water from the main channel and diverted it into the perfect swimming hole, bordered by the sandy gravel where Willoughby had made his fire. The water was brilliantly clear and much to his surprise, several nice-sized fish bolted away from the water's edge into the deeper part of the pool as he walked up to it.

Fish. Their presence reminded him of how hungry he was. He had polished off the last bite of his energy bar as he built his fire but it had done little to curb the rumblings of a very empty stomach. The fish were fairly large, fifteen or sixteen inches at least, he thought. They seemed not too disturbed by his company as they lazily swayed in position against the easy current not more than a few feet away from him. The sight of them gave more credence to an idea he had been wrestling with since he had reached this welcoming spot along the river.

Willoughby was torn between two trains of thought. The first was to keep moving. His need to find people had been his driving force since he had rolled out of the cave high on the mountain yesterday and that hadn't changed. He definitely wanted to find somebody. The second choice was to stay put here by the river. It was what everyone said you should do when lost…stay put. It might have been easier to choose between the two if he had found himself in a place he recognized. How that had happened he wasn't sure, but somehow he had traveled far enough in the cave to come out in unfamiliar territory.

Unfamiliar territory. How unfamiliar was the question that kept creeping its ugly way into his head. The guess he wanted to make was that he had come out in one of the wilderness areas of the Cascades; that would maybe help to explain the absence of any sign of people. But it could be another big problem to overcome. Oregon's wilderness areas were vast and rugged, covering thousands of square miles. He knew there were many well-kept trails used by hikers but he hadn't found one yet. The trail he had discovered was no more than a faint game trail at best, and while he wasn't an experienced woodsman, he thought he could tell the difference. Jake's advice of keeping to a stream and following it seemed logical but it ran contrary to what others said—stay put until people find you. Besides that, Willoughby had no idea of how far he might have to travel. Time and distance—two things he had been unable to get a handle on.

While the wilderness angle might explain some of the consternation he was having about not recognizing anything, there was no explaining the other things that weighed heavily on his mind. Things had been happening that were not supposed to happen. The sword, the wolves—a fucking talking one even. What about those things? This was fantasy movie type stuff. Maybe he had just crawled his way into a whole different fucking world.

But it made no sense to get run over by that train of thought. Instead a powerful gurgle in his belly turned his attention to a more pressing problem—food. Nothing else mattered right at the moment and it settled the issue. He would set up a campsite here as comfortable as he could make it, and keep the fire going high in the hopes that someone would spot it, maybe someone in a plane looking for him. He had plenty of water, no problem there, the weather was tolerable, and now he had spotted food. If he could figure out a way to catch one or two of those fish or kill a small bird or something with his wrist rocket, he would be all right at least for a while. Hell, it even dawned on him that he now had something to cook with. Bob's little pot was stored in his backpack.

It now seemed that staying put at the river, at least for a while, was the better of his two choices and now that he had made it, he set to work with renewed effort to get his clothes and himself as clean as he could. Wading knee deep into the cold water, Willoughby worked on his underwear and t-shirt first, wanting to get them dry and back on as quickly as he could. Running around naked might be something that was fun for some but it didn't thrill him, and a major case of shrinkage reminded him that it wasn't all that warm.

The best he could do was soak his clothes full of water and then wring them out, over and over, until he had gotten out as much filth as possible. The soiled shorts had needed extra attention but after a time, his t-shirt, socks, and underwear were steaming themselves dry on the racks next to the fire. Willoughby turned his attention to his sweatshirt and jeans. They had taken the brunt of his ordeal so far and being of much thicker material, they took more work but before long, they had joined the others on the drying rack.

It was an accomplishment that made him feel good. Getting wrapped up in the work also temporarily kept his mind off his stomach and his predicament. With his clothes taken care of, he returned to the cold water and rinsed his filthy body off as best he could. A small chunk of soap would have been nice, but at least he felt better; cold, but better. His skin tingled and goose bumps set him to shivering but after some warming time near the fire, he was ready to go again. He set about gathering more firewood from the drift piles near his fire. Finding something to eat was what he really wanted to do, but one of Jake's wisdoms told him not to get too far away from his clothes and the fire.

"Turn your back on wet clothes drying around a campfire for very long and you are liable to find them toast," Jake had admonished. It was late last spring, not long after they had moved to his grandma's and they had been burning a big pile of brush and limbs behind the barn. It was a typical cold and wet Oregon day, much more suited to staying indoors and playing Xbox games than working outside, but his mother had insisted that he help. Jake was drying off his wet White Ox cotton work gloves close to the hot fire.

"When they really get to steamin', pull 'em away and turn 'em," he explained. "Been a lot of pissed off loggers what had to finish the day settin' chokers with one or no gloves 'cause they weren't payin' attention."

Willoughby's fire was hot and the steam was pouring off his wet clothes. He minded what the big Indian had said and kept turning and moving them. His stomach would just have to wait a little longer.

After he had gathered as much firewood as he thought would be needed for the coming night, he broke away from his clothes watch long enough to return to the sapling patch where he had cut the poles for his drying rack. Selecting two straight pieces about four feet long and an inch and a half in diameter, he cut them off with his hatchet. When he got back to the fire, he proceeded to sharpen one end of both into a rough point with the ax, finishing with his pocket knife. It was long and slow work but kept him occupied as his clothes dried. Every so often he would put the points into the fire, letting them blacken and then scraped the burned area off with his knife. The fire helped harden the points and after a while he had two serviceable spears.

The fish he had encountered while washing his clothes hadn't seemed spooked by his presence but Willoughby knew he would need to get lucky if he was going to have anything for dinner. He didn't think he could actually spear a trout—that's what he thought they were—but if he could hit one with a solid strike he thought it might stun and disable the fish long enough for him to get it onto the bank. He was sure that he could get a ticket for this type of fishing since he didn't have any sort of license but maybe an understanding game control officer would cut him some slack. Besides, a ticket would be worth it if it meant that someone had found him.

Willoughby moved his clothes away from the fire onto a rock to let the sun continue the drying process, but did put his underwear on. They were closest to being dry and he still was not comfortable running around naked. He slipped on his tennis shoes, he didn't necessarily want to get them wet but the river rock was hard on his feet, and gathered his two spears—he was ready to fish.

They were still there in the pool but catching one would have been much easier with a pole and some bait. The trout were much faster than his spear and with a slight flick of their tails avoided Willoughby's best throws with ease. They simply moved around the pool and after about a half hour or so, the teen was nothing more than frustrated and still even hungrier.

Willoughby surmised that the pool was simply too big and deep for what he was trying to do; he would have to change tactics if he was going to be successful.

Moving downstream, Willoughby searched the eddies and backwaters next to the riverbank and soon spotted what he was looking for. A ledge of rock jutting out of the riverbed forced part of the flowing channel into the bank, carving a shallow, crescent moon-shaped backwater out of the gravel bar, no more than two feet at its deepest. Three fat fish swayed lazily in a foot of water only a couple of feet from shore, giving the boy an ideal opportunity to catch his prey between him and the bank.

As he waded out into the channel, they barely moved with indifference. He moved slowly, one homemade spear in his left hand and the one in his right cocked and ready. No more than ten feet away, the dorsal fins of the three fish broke the surface of the water as they nonchalantly held their place in the easy current. With everything he could muster and a hearty grunt to go with it, Willoughby let fly.

His trajectory was too flat and the spear hit the water and skipped once to the bank, clattering with failure to the rocks. When the concentric rings faded, Willoughby's prey had moved only slightly upstream in a mockingly unconcerned posture. Again he took careful aim and let fly with the second spear.

It was a better throw than the first as far as penetrating the water's surface went but the result was the same; the speed at which the fish reacted to the spear touching the water was too great and once again they moved away ever so slightly. The spear floated with ineffectiveness in the eddy.

"Fuck!" Willoughby shouted. Tears welled in his eyes as he came to grips with the futility of his efforts. There was no way he was going to get a fish with this method. In a gesture of pure frustration, he reached down into the water at his feet, came up with a football-sized river rock and heaved it with two hands at the floating shapes in the water in front of him.

The result was a lesson in simple water displacement and as the splash settled, one of the fish flopped furiously on the gravel bar in front of a stunned Willoughby. It took a moment for his mind to register that the fish was out of the water and in serious danger of flopping itself right back in, but a moment was all he needed as he crossed the water and literally dove on top of the floundering trout. It almost shot out from underneath him but he was able to squeeze his arms in tight and keep the slippery body from getting away. The fish was slimy and cold against his bare skin but Willoughby lay on it until it settled. Once it did, a quick whack to the back of its head with a rock and it was over.

He held up his prize; the fish was fat and heavy, a good eighteen inches long. It was a trout, of that Willoughby was certain, but it wasn't colored like the rainbows that he had caught with Jake in the river below his grandma's house. Its silver sides were dotted with bright red spots and its upper body was dark brown; he hadn't seen anything like this one, but he was sure of one thing—it was dinner.

Setting the fish aside on the gravel bar, Willoughby returned to the water and rinsed the slime, blood, and fish poop from his chest. He was anxious to try his new fishing method out again but he was going to have to do it in another pool; a quick glance told him the other two fish had evidently figured out that they needed to move to safer territory.

Willoughby spotted another good-looking pool similar to the one he had been successful in just downstream. The one fish was going to be great for dinner but where one was good, two would be better, and what he didn't eat tonight would still be good for breakfast. He could taste the trout already.

After securing his trout for carrying as Jake had shown him, by sliding the long end of a forked stick through the gills and sliding the fish down to the fork, Willoughby scrambled over the rocks and gravel bar downstream towards the next pool and hopefully more fish. He was crossing a narrow patch of fine gravel and sand close to the pool's edge when he stopped suddenly. He felt like he had been punched in the gut and had to fight down the nasty bile that rose from his churning stomach. In the sand in front of him were tracks. Big tracks. Lots of big tracks. Lots of big, wolf-looking tracks. Willoughby suddenly lost all interest in fishing.

CHAPTER NINETEEN

FEAR GRIPPED WILLOUGHBY IMMEDIATELY and sent his heart thumping wildly in his chest. While he wasn't a hunter by any stretch of the imagination, he knew the tracks were fresh, probably last night, before or after his encounter with the pack. He fought back a nearly overwhelming urge to run back to his fire and more importantly, the sword.

Calm down and don't panic, he scolded himself while he scanned the riverbank and trees beyond on both sides of the river. When he was satisfied that there was no immediate danger he studied the tracks more closely.

It was impossible to tell just how many animals there had been but it was definitely a lot. There were tracks on tracks and few were very clear. Some went towards the river and some were going the other direction. It wasn't a likely spot for a crossing; the river channel was wide and the current strong enough to make it tricky even for big animals. That they had used this spot to drink was a better likelihood, and the muddy cluster along the edge of the water seemed to add credence to that assumption. It also lead Willoughby to another conclusion—if they were just drinking and not crossing, then it was also very likely that they were still on the same side of the river as he was.

As he studied the tracks, there was one print that stood out from the others, close to where he was standing on the outside edge of the sand bar, deep and clear in the soft silt. He knelt down beside it and placed his right hand inside the track and splayed his fingers wide. With his hand centered inside the paw print as best he could,

Willoughby's spread fingers never touched the sides of the track.

As he knelt there mesmerized by the size of the thing, he had a vision of his encounter last night. Bright yellow eyes, flickering red in the glow of his fire. Deadly eyes. Was this the track of the she-wolf that had spoken to him? Another thought crossed his mind as he squatted beside the huge print. She had mentioned her mate, the true leader of the pack. Was this his sign? Willoughby shuddered. The words the she-wolf had spoken came back to him, "*We will meet again, pup. And when we do, I will enjoy watching you die.*"

Willoughby lifted his hand out of the track; it was shaking. Last night had been as confusing as it had been frightening. He hadn't thought much about the voice today as he had hiked through the woods and along the river; the thought of finding someone had pushed that bit of craziness back into a deep dark corner of his mind. But this track had just pried it out again. At this point, the question of whether he was insane or not made no difference. There were some nasty realities staring him in the face and he needed a plan.

Willoughby headed back towards his campfire, stopping to pick up the two spears he had left at the first fishing hole. His clothes were still damp but he put them all back on except for the sweat-shirt, which he returned to the drying rack. He wasn't sure yet what he was going to do, but he didn't want to be in just his underwear when he did it.

There were two clear choices in front of him—to stay here like he had planned or to move on down the trail. When he had left the mountain this morning, the overriding impulse was to move down the river as far as he could in hopes that he would be lucky enough to find someone. When he had gotten to this spot that changed and staying put seemed like the best plan. Now what? He was sure he had several more hours of daylight left; he could cover quite a few miles if he headed out now. But what if he didn't find anyone before it got dark? That meant making camp and building a fire, two things he had a good head start on here.

Willoughby sat on the flat rock staring into the fire, working the pluses and minuses of each choice over and over again. There were good arguments to be made for each, but there was one minus that threw a nasty shadow over every single plus he could come up with—the wolves.

They were close. Willoughby didn't know how close but he knew that whichever choice he made, there was more than a good chance he was going to encounter them again. If they came, he knew he couldn't outrun them. Wolves couldn't climb trees but if they caught him unexpectedly, they would get him before he could get very far up one. The backpack and its gear would make climbing a tree fast nearly impossible. The river? He had watched the Discovery channel often enough to have an idea that most animals were good swimmers; some just liked it more than others, so that was out. Fire was good; Willoughby thought that was the reason they hadn't gotten any closer last night. Here the fire was already going and he had plenty of wood. If he left this spot he would have to do it all over again before it got dark.

These things rolled through the frail fabric of his mind over and over again and when he finally made his choice he still wasn't convinced it was the best idea, it just seemed like the one that didn't have so many "what if's" attached to it. Using the fire in front of him and the river at his back, he was going to stay where he was for the night.

There was plenty of daylight left and Willoughby decided to put it to good use. As he started working to prepare for possible unwanted guests, he was surprised at how the fear melted away once he got busy. Maybe it had something to do with the fact that the very first thing he did was to untie the sword and shield from his pack. Still hesitant to take it out of the scabbard, he lifted and tested its weight again. There was something about it that made him feel at ease; it had felt so good in his hands when he had drawn it last night. It had made him feel strong. Willoughby wanted to pull it free, to feel that surge of energy again. It was like something new that you had tasted for the first time and it was so good you had to have it again.

But not yet, he cautioned himself. *If they come, when they come.* He left the weapon within easy reach on the flat rock, making sure there would be nothing in his way if he had to get it in a hurry. Knowing it was within reach was comfort enough.

In his excitement, Willoughby had nearly forgotten his fish, but a surging gurgle from his stomach reminded him. Using his pocketknife, he made short work of gutting the fat trout the way Jake had shown him—two intersecting cuts removed the fish's asshole, then he slit the belly open all the way to the gills. Making one more cut where the jawbone was hinged, he stuck his left thumb in to hold the head and using his right thumb, started to pull down slowly towards the tail. With a sucking *"slurrrrp"* the whole piece, the skin with the lower jaw and the fish guts attached, came free and easy, hanging from his thumb. He flicked it out into the river as far as it would go. Laying the fish on a flat rock, he cut off the head and it quickly followed suit into the river. He set to cleaning the large blood cavity running down the backbone. Jake would have been proud; the whole process had taken him no more than just a couple of minutes. He scraped both sides of the fish to remove loose scales and slime and then rinsed it off in the clean water. This baby was ready.

The best way to cook it was something he hadn't thought about. He had Bob's pot in his pack, he could chop the fish into a couple of pieces, add a little water, and cook it that way, but then it would be boiled fish soup. That didn't sound all that appetizing. He needed a fish roasting stick.

After scanning the riverbanks to make sure there wasn't any unwanted company, he grabbed his hatchet and as a second thought, grabbed the sword harness; he didn't want to get too far from it. It took him a few tries to figure out how to strap the thing on, being careful with the old leather straps. There were no easy adjusting fasteners, just straps that you had to retie for any type of adjustment, but he managed to get the contraption secured to what he thought was the right position. With the grip of the sword resting comfortably just above his right shoulder, the stone set at the end of the pommel looked him squarely in the eye when he turned his head. The bulk of the sword angled down across his back and his left butt cheek, protruding just slightly past his body. The waist strap pulled it in tight to his hip and when he moved, it felt comfortable, almost like a natural part of his body. Willoughby marveled at the design and the fact that he and Bob must have been exactly the same size, something that gave him a good feeling. He pushed back the urge to reach up with his right hand and pull the blade free. Something inside told him that when the need arose, it would work just like it was supposed to.

With the harness and sword secure and comfortably strapped to his back, Willoughby returned to the thick patch of hardwood saplings where he had cut his drying rack and spears and quickly found a stem with a fork thick enough to hold his catch as it cooked. There were plenty of tall, straight saplings in the clump and Willoughby cut a dozen of the best; the spears he had fashioned earlier had given him another idea.

With the forks of the stick forced through the back of the trout, he soon had it propped up on a large rock at what he thought was a good cooking distance from the hot fire. As he sat on the flat rock trimming his spears, the delicious smell of the fish cooking soon wafted pleasantly around the campsite. Willoughby's neglected stomach rumbled its approval.

As the fish baked, he trimmed, scraped, and sharpened his spears, all the while his mind playing scenarios of the upcoming encounter with the wolves. At this point it didn't seem like just a possibility; they were going to come, and they were going to come tonight. He whittled away at the green stems with an intense concentration, stopping only to turn his dinner. Questions squirmed and wriggled inside his head like maggots on rotted meat, feeding on the parts weakened by his ordeal. Would they come all at once? Would the fire be enough to keep them back? He was not even sure he could actually kill one if they came for him—he had never killed anything other than a fish. Staying busy helped, but it didn't keep the questions from tormenting him.

The need for food finally broke the spell; the smell was absolutely driving him crazy with want. Pulling the roasting stick away from the fire he checked his prize; overdone in a couple of places and slightly undercooked in others, it still looked and smelled like the grandest gourmet meal in the world. The meat of the fat trout glistened pink and juicy where the skin had peeled itself back.

Willoughby pulled a piece of the crispy browned skin off and popped it into his mouth; it was a little too hot but tasted wonderful. Putting the stick aside to allow the fish to cool a bit, he searched the gravel bar for a flat plate-sized rock. Finding one just the right size, he rinsed it off in the cold water and slid the trout off the stick onto his custom stoneware plate.

The famished teen ate slowly, savoring every mouthful of the flavorful fish meat; nothing went to waste. The bigger chunks peeled away from the backbone with ease and he mixed the well-done pieces in with the not-so-well-done. He ate everything, even the blackened portions of skin, using the tip of his knife to scrape even the tiniest morsels off the bones until there was nothing left. The tail, well, it was crispy looking, but he couldn't quite force himself to chew on the bony appendage. He wasn't quite that hungry.

The transformation was amazing, his whole body felt better now that he had eaten. And while he could have easily devoured another one of the fat trout, it had been a meal to remember. Sure, it was lacking maybe a little salt and pepper or Mrs. Dash but still, he couldn't ever remember anything tasting as good. He flipped the tail and bones into the river and as he rinsed the traces of his meal off his rock plate, he vowed never again to take food for granted. It was also satisfying in another way; lost and alone in the wilderness, he was doing pretty well.

But managing to stay alive by catching your own food and knowing how to build a fire, and surviving what he believed was going to come after it got dark, were two different things, and Willoughby was once again confronted by the seriousness of his situation.

"Local Boy Missing—Possibly Eaten by Wolves." That would be

324

a headline that would make the *Spirit Falls' Weekly Chronicle* fly off the rack at the local Ray's Supermarket. The fact that he had survived the trip over the waterfall would go unnoticed if he got killed by wolves; by wolves that weren't even supposed to be in this part of the country and could talk. He wondered what people would think about that.

There was still plenty of time before the sun went down so Willoughby set to gathering more wood. He was planning on having one heck of a bonfire tonight so he would need plenty. What was concerning him as he worked was what would happen when he fell asleep. He didn't think he could stay up all night, or at least he had never been able to. If he fell asleep, how would he know when they were here, except when it was too late? But as he was pulling a big chunk of driftwood out from a pile, he sent some small rocks clattering across some others; they made a clear and distinct sound as they bounced and rolled across the gravel bar. It gave him an idea.

Starting at the big rock that marked the upper end of the pool and gravel bar, he built a semi-circle of small rock towers. Each was about three feet high and started with a bigger rock at the bottom and getting concentrically smaller as they went up. He took his time, careful to select the right sized rocks so they would balance precariously as the tower went up in height. Just a simple brush of these would bring the pile down with a rattling clatter he thought he could hear over the omnipresent rush of the river. The warning towers were constructed close enough together that he was sure some of them would get knocked over if the animals came onto the gravel bar. It wasn't much, but it would have to do.

What his task did accomplish was to eat up a lot of daylight. As he placed the last stone on top of his last tower, the sun dipped behind the trees. Ready or not; night was coming fast.

Willoughby scrambled to finish the last of his defenses and warning devices and surveyed his campsite. From his campfire he had about thirty feet of shoreline between him and the river; this is where he would place himself with his pack and his sword. To his left was the big rock that marked the upper edge of his gravel bar. He didn't know if they could come over it or not; it was about ten feet high on the upper side and jutted out into the river. The best he could hope for was that they wouldn't get on top of it. To his right he had placed a barrier of his hardwood spears. Sinking the butt end firmly into the sand as far as he could, he propped the spear onto some rocks jutting at a sharp angle outward. Ten of these spaced from the fire to the river made a formidable barrier. Their points were sharp and about chest high to a wolf, if they ran into any of these it would at least slow them down. That left Willoughby with four of the stout spears stuck into the sand close by, ready to throw. With the sword and shield resting on his pack next to him, Willoughby sat down on his flat rock and took a large drink of water from his bottle.

This is absolutely fucking crazy, he thought to himself as he waited. He was fourteen years old and should be in his bedroom playing video games or in the living room watching TV with his sister, waiting for his mom and grandma to put supper on the table. Why was he here? He thought back to what Jake had told him about the waterfall.

Place of Spirits, Willoughby thought as he sat on his flat rock and stared into the fire, wishing he were back on Jake's porch watching brown spit dribble down the old man's chin and listening to stories. *Place of evil spirits for me.*

Dusk was setting in and the sun was sinking rapidly behind the tree line and taking the temperature with it. Soon it would be dark. Willoughby put on his sweatshirt which had dried nicely beside the fire. Come what may he thought, it had been a good day. He had managed to get his clothes and himself acceptably clean, and had managed to catch a nice fish for supper. His family and Jake would be proud of him; if they knew. But they didn't know. Willoughby stared into the glowing depths of the fire, seeing their faces flicker within the heat and flame. His thoughts drifted from the issues at hand.

What would they be doing now? Normally his grandma and mother would be getting dinner ready while his sister did homework at the dining room table. Jake would be in the barn with the cows. Had he been there he would have been in his room paying attention to his Xbox instead of his homework. But this would not be a normal evening for them. Four days? Maybe five? He wasn't sure, but each day would have been sheer hell. Willoughby knew two things for sure—his family loved him and they would be going through enormous amounts of emotional strife, something they had experienced too much of in the two years since his father had died. James Baxter had ruined them financially before he opted out, forcing the move to Oregon. What was left of the estate was tied up in litigation with the family of the unfortunate mother and daughter that he took out with him. It had been a mess and the family had suffered.

There was one more thing Willoughby was aware of—he hadn't helped. In fact, as he sat there with his thoughts simmering in the fiery coals of his bonfire, he realized just what a jerk he had been. His mother and sister had suffered just as much as he had but managed to move along on the road to recovery, but not him. He had wallowed in self-pity now for two years. His mom had been right in what she said when they had argued the day of the incident with Eddie Anderson. It was time for him to grow up and move on.

A chunk of firewood that had burned down fell into the coals and sent a shower of sparks into the night sky. It was dark. Willoughby had lost track of time and darkness had descended upon him as he had sat lost in reflection of his family.

He stood up and scanned the tree line that was just barely visible in what light the fire put out. Seeing nothing amiss, he added several large chunks of driftwood to the fire and soon had it roaring brightly. As the flames attacked the fresh fuel, Willoughby was suddenly aware of how tired he was. It had been a busy day and it would be easy to curl up against the rock in the warmth of the fire and get some much deserved sleep, but that was exactly what he feared.

He tried pacing back and forth between the fire and the river but that grew old quickly. Alternating between sitting on his flat rock and standing up helped for a while. Every time he felt his head start to nod, he changed postures. The more he thought about not falling asleep the harder it became to stay awake.

Willoughby was sitting on his rock, staring into the fire. He had been battling the sleep demon now for a couple of hours. He nodded once, twice, and as his chin hit his chest on the third nod, he shook his head and looked past the fire to the forest; glowing yellow eyes stared back at him from just inside the trees. His company had arrived.

Jumping immediately to his feet, his thoughts went first to his fire. He grabbed several pieces of driftwood and heaped them on. The coals were hot and the fire sprung to life with its infusion of dry wood. The eyes glowed brighter as the fire crackled with new energy.

Strangely enough, though his heart was doing a good job of pounding, Willoughby wasn't afraid. The wolves kept their distance, back far enough inside the trees that their bodies were undistinguishable, but once again a larger set of eyes grabbed his attention. They glared with an intensity that outshone the others. This was the leader; Willoughby knew that in his heart and his mind. This was the dangerous one; the one who would come for him.

Keeping his eyes focused on the intruders, Willoughby bent slowly to his pack and slipped the shield over his left forearm. Immediately he wished he had taken the time to adjust the straps. It hung loose and dangly over his arm.

Shit, he cursed to himself, wondering why he hadn't tried the thing on when he had the chance. But he wasn't sure how much good the shield was going to do anyway, they weren't going to come at him with swords or spears. He thought about drawing the sword but decided against it. For the time being they weren't coming any closer. Instead, he hefted one of the hardwood spears he had stuck in the ground.

"Well come on you stinking shit bags. What are you waiting for?" he screamed in defiance, but got nothing in response. The eyes sat motionless just inside the dark of the trees, just as they had the night before. It actually irritated him that they didn't come closer.

It was a fifteen-minute stalemate before Willoughby got his wish. The large set of eyes to the far left started to move and gradually the shape behind the bright orbs slowly emerged out of the trees, coming to the bank's edge.

Willoughby's fire threw off enough light that he could see the wolf fairly clearly. The mottled gray and white snout he remembered—it was the she-wolf. The one who had spoken the threats last night. The ears were sharp and pointed, upright and leaning slightly forward, listening intently. The long white snout lifted and sniffed the air, at the same time showing an ivory glimpse of sharp canines. The she-wolf stayed on top of the bank, just visible in the flickering light of the bonfire; watching, listening, and smelling. Willoughby gripped his spear tightly and watched back.

These damn wolves were big. Much bigger than he thought they should have been. He had thought that last night as the she-wolf came into view. Mega Wolves or something like that. A cold fist settled itself in the pit of Willoughby's stomach, squeezing out the first vestiges of fear. If these things were all as big as the she-wolf he was going to be in trouble. But before he had time to think about getting really scared another set of eyes broke from the dark into the light, and this one didn't stop at the edge of the bank.

A jet black form bounded down the slope and with one healthy leap covered half the distance between it and Willoughby's fire. It planted all four feet in an abrupt stop and crouched low as if ready to take one more leap towards the boy. Its yellow eyes glared at him across the fire, lips pulled back completely with a fang-exposing snarl. Only the fire and fifteen feet of sand and gravel separated the wolf from Willoughby. That was close enough for him.

"Giitttt!" he screamed as he took one step towards the wolf, cocking the spear back over his shoulder and then releasing it in one quick, fluid motion that surprised even him. He had thrown many sticks and rocks in his time as a kid, but never with a real intent to hurt anyone or anything. But something deep inside the teen had taken over with unpredictable speed and strength just like it had when he had clocked Eddie Anderson with his backpack. Adrenalin mixed with fear and frustration propelled the homemade weapon right over the top of the fire with deadly accuracy.

His challenging yell startled the big animal and it started to make a half turn in an attempt to change course. In doing so, the wolf exposed its right side completely and the spear buried itself in the soft of its underbelly just in front of its hindquarters.

Willoughby had heard a dog scream in similar fashion after it had been hit by a car, but the close proximity of the animal increased the intensity tenfold as a screeching howl of agony pierced the night. It snarled and yipped in a black whirl of fur as it spun around trying to bite the four feet of wooden nastiness that protruded from its belly, for a brief moment forgetting the perpetrator of its pain.

It was more time than the boy needed. No sooner had the spear left his hand and the yell his lips, he reached over his shoulder and pulled the sword free from its scabbard. It felt as if he had done it thousands of times before and it sang with a pleasing metallic ring. There was no thought process at work with this sudden rush of aggression; something had burst inside of the boy, something immensely bigger than when he had attacked the bully Eddie. He skirted the fire in an instant and came at the screaming and twisting wolf with the shield in front of him on his left arm and the sword drawn back in a striking position with his right. The animal was down on its back legs but whirled instinctively to meet the new threat.

Its huge head and foaming jaws crashed into the shield and stopped the boy's momentum with its sheer size and weight advantage. But instead of trying to use his strength to match the collision, Willoughby allowed the arm and shield to turn with the impact, much like a matador with his cape. The massive wolf brushed past Willoughby and as it did, the boy pivoted his own body and brought the sword crashing down in an arc across the back of its neck.

There was a sickening *"thunnkk"* as the blade sliced through thick hair and skin deep into the animal's flesh. The weapon was jerked violently out of Willoughby's hand as the animal toppled over onto its side in a heap. The wolf pawed feebly at the sand and gravel a couple of times as a thick gurgle of bloody foam and air escaped from its open mouth before it shuddered violently one time and then grew still.

Willoughby was too shocked to move. The shield slid off his arm and clattered to the rocks. His hand and arm, suffering from the impact with the wolf's head, was too numb to retain a grip.

Things had happened so quickly. The animal lay at his feet, blood leaked from its mouth and around the sword protruding from the shaggy neck, congealing in gooey, red puddles mixing with the sand. Still not fully comprehending what had just transpired, Willoughby reached down and grabbed the sword grip. Placing his right foot upon the wolf's body, he gave the weapon a tug. It took more than a little effort to wrench the blade free; it had sunk into the animal's shaggy neck well over half way through and as it came loose, Willoughby could feel the bones of the spinal column scraping at the steel. The blow had nearly severed the big animal's neck.

With both hands he held the blade up into the night, the light of the fire behind him illuminating its perverse beauty. Strands of hair and bits of flesh clung stubbornly to the surface as a crimson trail of death dripped slowly down the shining metal, past the grip and down onto his hands, but he didn't care. Willoughby was hypnotized by the sight of it. He had killed, it had felt good, and now he knew how. It had been the sword.

"Aaauuugghhhh!" His scream ripped through the night with a primal intensity that echoed up and down the river canyon before tapering into nothingness, replaced by the gentle sound of the flowing water and the crack and snap of the fire.

But the hypnotic spell was broken rudely by an answering voice that slapped Willoughby back into the reality of the moment—he had forgotten the rest of the wolf pack.

Still atop the riverbank where they had first come out of the trees, the she-wolf plopped down on her haunches and lifted her long snout, sending a mournful howl echoing through the night sky. When she stopped, more dark shapes slowly began to emerge from the veil of trees and align themselves next to her. The pack was showing itself.

The beasts were various shades of gray and black, and though slightly smaller than the she-wolf, still impressive. Several smaller animals, Willoughby figured these were the young, kept back closer to the tree line. But the last one to emerge from the trees was in such sharp contrast to the others that it was startling. It was larger than the she-wolf but apart from its size, what set it apart was its color. The wolf was silver-white and glowed in the edge of darkness with its luminescence. It brushed past the rest of the pack and plopped down on its haunches next to the she-wolf.

The animals made no attempt to come down off the bank and close the distance between themselves and the boy. Instead, they did as the she-wolf had done, squatted on their haunches, lifted their snouts high to the night and together filled the darkness with a chorus of mournful howls. It was obvious to Willoughby that this was a song of death for the wolf he had just killed.

He remained motionless with his sword still held out in front of him, transfixed by the sight and sound. The howls broke off and tapered away into the stillness of the night, once more leaving only the gentle sound of the river and the crackling of the fire. The wolves stared down towards the boy, the fire, and their fallen comrade. Willoughby stared back.

Out of the depth of the trees, one last set of yellow eyes began to slowly move towards the other wolves and the light. The forms of the others faded into blurred obscurity as Willoughby stood hypnotized by the sight emerging from the darkness. He sucked his breath in with an audible hiss as the form materialized into the light of the campfire, revealing the monster behind the eyes.

For a monster it was. This was the beast belonging to the paw print that Willoughby had found in the silt. It was half again as big as the other wolves, and he thought they were larger than they should have been. The wolf's thick coat was jet black except for a star-shaped patch on its chest, the same strange, white-silver color alluding to a possible relationship with the animal to its left. The long, powerful legs supported an enormous body that culminated with massive front shoulders atop of which sat the beast's mighty head. There were two things that Willoughby was sure of as the wolves held their ground and stared down at him; the first, that he was in a standoff with what was surely the king of all wolves; the second was that if this beast came after him, he wouldn't stand much of a chance.

It was the sword that once again was Willoughby's calm refuge in the threatening storm. It seemed to sense the increase in danger arrayed in front of him and sent a surge of calming power through its hilt and down into his arms. He could feel the electric tingle as the energy channeled through his body, dispelling his fear.

It had exactly the opposite effect on the wolves. The pack appeared to sense the same energy emanating from the weapon. The wolves surrounding the massive black beast and his she-wolf leaped to their feet and began pawing the ground and sniffing the air in a highly agitated state.

This seemed to irritate the big wolf who spun quickly and with a throaty growl nipped one of the lesser wolves, sending it yipping in pain back into the safety of the trees. The others quickly took note and backed away. As it turned back to face Willoughby the giant beast snarled in displeasure, pulling its lips back and displaying the biggest and nastiest set of fangs he had ever seen. A deep voice growled its way across the gravel bar separating them and spoke.

"You have killed one of my pack with your magic, man pup, and while it may frighten the rest of them it will not be enough to keep me from killing you."

With its last word the wolf sprung, covering most of the forty feet from the bank to the fire in one huge leap. It landed with a spray of gravel and sand only a few feet from where Willoughby had stood, but the boy had reacted nearly as quickly, putting the fire back between him and the now looming leader of the wolf pack.

The fire crackled and sent sparks high into the night as Willoughby gripped the handle of the sword tightly, waiting for the wolf to leap the fire, waiting for a grim and grisly death by the terrible teeth. But the wolf didn't jump.

The huge beast lowered its shaggy head and sniffed at the wolf Willoughby had killed, nudging the dead animal's head with its muzzle and giving her forehead a tender lick before returning his steely gaze to Willoughby.

"This one was impatient and too young to know better. She sought to please me by killing you. I will miss her." He sniffed the air, his nostrils flaring wide as he tilted his huge head to one side and then the other.

"There is a strange smell about you pup, one I do not recognize. You are not like the others of your ilk who venture into my kingdom."

Willoughby didn't want to speak. It was crazy enough knowing he hadn't dreamed of this the night before and he was afraid if he talked back to this animal he would be so far gone on the road to insanity he could never hope to return. But then again, the wolf was talking to him; it would be rude not to talk back.

"I just want to get home. I went over a waterfall a couple of days ago and ended up in a cave underneath it." The words were hard to get out, he was now officially crazy.

"I...I found a passage and followed it out. That is how I came to be on the mountain last night when your pack first saw me." He could hear the deep rumble of the big wolf's breathing over the sounds of the river and the fire.

"I am sorry about her." Willoughby nodded at the dead female. "She came after me and I was just defending myself."

The beast looked down at the female and then back at Willoughby. *"She was not aware of your power and should have heeded my warning. It has been a long time since we have encountered a human with magic, other than the witch."* He lifted his snout again and took another long sniff.

"My mate told me she could smell the magic about you. It was something she had encountered long ago and the memory frightened her. But I sense that you and the magic are not quite one together. In fact, I do not believe you even know how to use it, do you pup?"

Willoughby gripped the sword even tighter. He had a gut feeling the wolf was talking about the sword. It had to be, there was no other explanation for the way it made him act and feel when he held it. The wolf seemed to sense his thought pattern.

"*Yes, it is the weapon I am taking about. It does not belong to you.*"

Shit, Willoughby cursed to himself. Not only could the frigging thing talk but it could read his thoughts as well. He made sure the point of the sword was pointing directly at the nose of the wolf.

"It's mine. The man who used to own it is dead. I found it and it is mine."

"*Yours or not, it matters little to me. You may be able to kill a stupid female with it, but it will not help you.*" The beast cocked its great head slightly to one side and then, strangely enough, seemed to smile. "*You have no idea who I am do you?*"

Willoughby was wavering. He could feel the sword channeling more energy through the pommel, trying to infuse him with enough strength to carry on. But his mental state was going south fast. The craziness was overwhelming. To go through everything that he had over the last several days and then to just find out he was totally fucking crazy and talking to an enormous wolf that looked like something out of *The Lord of The Rings* was all too much.

"I don't know who or what you are. Right now I don't know where I am. Maybe I'm dreaming all of this and will wake up in my bed. I don't know. I don't know."

There was a long pause before the wolf spoke again. "*My name is Fenrir, and I am King of the Wolves. Men call this forest Darkwood and fear it greatly. It is my kingdom and I suffer no human intrusion. Few come here unless they are lost or stupid, and most never leave. The mice and rats gnaw their bones.*"

Fenrir? Darkwood? What the fuck is this shit? Willoughby could feel his sanity slipping away. The conversation was pushing him over the edge, but he had a feeling that it might just be the thing that would keep him alive; at least for now. It occurred to him that when Fenrir, or whatever, was done talking, that this wolf was going to kill him. As crazy as it was, it was making sense to try and carry this little discussion out further.

"I...I'm sorry but I have never heard of you or Darkwood. Have you ever heard of Spirit Falls?"

"*It is not a name I am familiar with, but then I am not in the habit of paying much attention to human speech. The witch might know of this place of which you speak but she is not here and I do not think I will give you the opportunity to ask her. I have little use for your kind and I grow tired of trifling with you.*"

Willoughby tensed as he sensed a new and much more powerful surge of energy from the sword. The feeling that things were coming to a head was strong and the weapon realized it. He wasn't sure what made him prepare but as he watched the huge specimen across the fire from him he detected a tensing of the animal's legs. There was just enough time to brace himself.

With a snarl, the animal leaped the fire. It happened so fast that Willoughby had only time enough to focus on the white star that marked the beast's chest. His scream mixed with the guttural growls of the wolf as he thrust the tip of the sword towards the target, feeling the impact, he pushed forward with every ounce of strength he could muster. The last thing Willoughby remembered was the gaping mouth heading straight for his face, saliva dripping from black and pink gums framing the nastiest set of teeth he had ever seen.

CHAPTER TWENTY

DAEMON RHUE AWOKE FROM HIS DREAM IN A fit of panic, throwing the thick coverlet off himself and swinging his legs to a sitting position on the bed all in one motion. He was sweating though the room was far from warm, even with a fair amount of coals still alive in the brazier. It had happened again, much stronger than any of the previous ones, yet this time it had left him with a vision, a very important vision.

Slipping his feet into his slippers, he wrapped a robe around himself. The embers in the fire told him that it was still several hours before daylight, but the importance of what he had seen and felt in his dream could not wait. Steyr was going to be very annoyed at being roused at this hour but it gave him little concern. This was not just a small twitch or belch in the hidden magic of the earth that he had felt; this was a full-blown collision of two powerful sources coming together violently. It was coming at a time when he could ill afford to have a slip up in his plan. While he had no clue as to who or what, he now had an idea as to the source—the witch's lair: Darkwood.

Taking a long sliver of cedar from a box near the fire, he touched it to a hot coal. The dry wood caught immediately and he used its flame to light an oil lamp. It crossed his mind to wake his servant from the room below and have him fetch the physician but he thought better of it. He was fully awake now and the cold night air would do him some good. This incident needed some thought.

It took him several minutes to travel the hundreds of steps that it took to reach the bottom of his tower. His position as the king's council would have allowed him to have any of the more elaborate and comfortable quarters within the castle, save for the king's own, but Daemon Rhue had many enemies and the single set of narrow stairs within the tower were easy to defend. There were devices in place to foil any who sought to ascend in stealth and there were sections of stairs that could be dropped out from under any invaders. It would seem to the unknowing that it would be a mistake for him if he were to use the hidden levers to collapse the stairs, leaving him trapped in his lofty aerie, but he had solved that problem long ago. He had installed a rope system by which he could let himself down the walls of his tower. Not a method for the faint of heart but he needed something. Daemon Rhue was anything but stupid.

As he came out of the tower into the inner ward of the castle, he was challenged by a guard who, surprisingly enough wasn't asleep at his post. "Halt," the startled guard challenged as Daemon Rhue came into the light of the torch mounted on the ward wall. But there weren't many within the castle as easily recognizable as the first council to the king. The guard drew his halberd back from the challenge position and slapped his left hand across his chest and bowed his head. "I beg your pardon, Lord Rhue, I didn't…"

"Don't apologize for doing your job, you idiot," growled Rhue as he waved the soldier off and proceeded towards the great ramp at the north end of the inner ward leading down into the underbelly of the castle. His encounter with the guard had been witnessed by others whose duty called for them to be alert at this early hour and a fearful warning had scurried down into the warren of passages ahead. It would be pure misery for any unfortunate guard caught unaware at his post by the most feared man in Artura. Everyone on duty snapped to attention as the man strode purposefully by.

While it wasn't necessary for him to come down into the subterranean workings of the castle, Daemon Rhue had made it a point early on in his time as an inhabitant here to learn every nook and cranny of this massive and sprawling complex. It was attention to even the smallest detail that made it no problem to navigate the dimly lit tunnels.

338

When he reached the door that marked Steyr's room he grabbed an empty bucket from the floor and banged hard. "Wake yourself, you miserable whoreson! NOW!" He banged again.

There were groans and a rustling of bedcovers emanating from inside as Steyr recognized the voice of his master. It didn't take long for the door to swing open revealing a pasty white face squinting into the torchlight of the tunnel.

"My Lord Rhue. Is everything all right?"

"No, everything isn't all right, you fool," Daemon Rhue answered testily as he pushed past the fat physician. "Do you think I would come down into this filthy rat hole if things were all right? Get some light in here."

Steyr quickly lit an oil lamp, illuminating rolls of pale skin flopping around his stubby, flaccid penis. As he did, a lumpy form in the bed groaned in protest at being wakened.

"Get whatever that is out of this room immediately, Steyr. We have important matters to discuss. And your nakedness may be of interest to your bedmate but it disgusts me. Put something on."

"Yes, my Lord," the physician stammered as he hurried over to the bed and grabbed a robe draped over a chair. "Come quickly now." He prodded the form still concealed by the bed's filthy coverlet. When he received no response, he flipped the cover off, grabbed an arm dangling over the edge of the bed and pulled. Daemon Rhue watched in disgust as a young man, around the age of sixteen or so, tumbled onto the floor with a grunt at the fat physician's feet. He wasn't entirely naked but the flimsy female undergarments he was wearing did little to cover him.

Steyr pulled the groggy boy to his feet, shoved a handful of clothes into his belly, and pushed him out the door.

"I beg your pardon my Lord, you should have sent your servant to me and I would have…"

"Shut your mouth, Steyr. You are lucky I tolerate your excesses, but mind you, beware the day you are no longer useful to me. Prepare us one of your concoctions; there is much to be done today and we will need our senses to be sword-edge sharp."

Steyr moved quickly to the small table with the lamp and pulled out a chair for his master. While Rhue seated himself, Steyr fetched a small box and a flat piece of slate off a shelf and sat across from his Lordship. Daemon Rhue talked as the fat physician fumbled with a thin blade and powder vials.

"You were probably too busy buggering your pretty little plaything to have sensed the aura of magic that emanated from the witch's forest?"

"Darkwood?" Steyr looked up from his work in surprise. "Surely Mogga was…"

"It wasn't the witch, you idiot," Rhue interrupted testily. "Do you think I would concern myself with the dabbling of that hag? This was something else; something that needs to be sought out and dealt with."

"Master, there are natural sources of magic within Darkwood, and if it was strong enough for you to sense it here, then Mogga will be aware of it and respond. Please Sire, ease your mind and trust her to deal with it." He pushed the piece of slate across the table. A finger length of sparkling yellow-white powder lay next to the snorting tube.

"She had better. But I want to know what she finds. There were two powerful sources of magic confronting each other and that is not good." Daemon Rhue picked up the tube, bent his head to the slate, and took half the proffered powder. "Aauughh." He brought his head up and winced as the bite of the drug assailed his sinuses with its potent attack. But he shook his head once and bent to the remaining task, repeating the process. He pushed the slate back across the table. "I want you to communicate with the witch and there is no time for subtleness here," he sniffed, still battling the initial shock of the drug. "I want the source of that magic found."

"I will send the fastest bird I have, Master," Steyr answered as he worked more of the drug into fine powder with the blade. "It will still take most of the day. Forgive me if I remind you that if we could work on the mind link with Mogga, we could save much time."

"And I will remind you that Lord Taul has forbidden anything of the sort, Steyr. Besides, until you can improve the process, it takes too much out of me. We will have to rely on other methods. While you are sending the message to the witch, send one to Silas and Sa'mel as well. They will still be in Bargtown making sure things are in order there. Have them alert their network to be on the lookout for the perpetrators." He leaned across the table and pointed a long bony finger at the physician who was now just recovering from his first dose of the drug. "I do not think you realize what this could mean to our plans, Steyr, if we have an unaccounted source of magic on the loose. We have taken great care to eliminate such a possibility and to have it surface now could upset everything, especially since we don't know who is using it."

"I understand, Sire. I will send the messages immediately. Will we wait until we can discern this source before we continue?"

"No. That is exactly what I don't want to do. If there is a problem out there, we will deal with it after we have initiated the rest of the plan. In fact, we are going to do just the opposite." Daemon Rhue stood up from the table, folded his arms, and glared down at the fat physician. "At the council session this morning the king will inform the ministers of the succession plan. Life, as the good folk of Artura know it, changes today. Destiny awaits us, Steyr. Succeed and we will be rewarded beyond our wildest dreams. Fail, well, if we fail, we had better hope the Arturans kill us first because Lord Taul will not be merciful. Are you prepared?"

Steyr rose slowly from the table. The power of the drugs coursing through his system coupled with anticipation at the news his master had imparted to him caused his fat body to tremble and his eyes to bulge nearly out of his hairless head. "Sire, I am ready. All elements of the plan have been in place for some time now and have just been awaiting your command."

"Good." With amazing speed, Rhue's arms shot out and he grabbed the front of Steyr's robe, jerking him forward across the table, the drug box and tools clattering to the floor. Daemon Rhue bent down and pushed his face to within inches of the fat man's. "Impart this message to your people, Steyr," he hissed. "There will be rewards aplenty for those who do their jobs today, but any man who hesitates in his duty will suffer greatly, for I will force him to watch as I hurt his family in the most unpleasant of ways before he also suffers a slow death. Make this perfectly clear to them. They must be ruthless and show no mercy. Do you understand?"

Sweat ran in rivulets down the fat man's forehead and dripped to the table as he stammered his reply. "Y-y-y-yes my Lord Rhue. We will not fail you."

Daemon Rhue relaxed his grip on the man's robe and allowed Steyr to straighten up from the table. When he released his hands, he patted him on his shoulders and broke into a smile. "I have faith in you, Steyr, and at the end of the day you will be standing at my side, the second most powerful man in Artura." He patted the fat man's shoulders again in a fatherly fashion. "And don't forget that certain part of your reward that I promised."

A grin broke across Steyr's dirty, sweat-tracked face and the fear in his eyes was replaced by maniacal gleam. "Thank you, my Lord. You will see. For that alone I will not allow failure."

Castle Daine's great hall hummed with activity as Arturans prepared for a rare major council meeting. Servants and messengers ran to and fro seeing to the needs of the ministers who huddled in small groups, engaging in hushed conversation as they speculated the meaning behind the emergency session that had been called only hours earlier. All plans and activities for the day had been canceled as every single minister and sub-minister had received a summons.

Though it was still early fall, the hall was drafty and cold in spite of the three great fireplaces that had been kindled early in the morning by the hearth tenders. There were two fireplaces flanking the east and west walls and one directly behind the king's dais at the north end of the great hall. Most of the groups of ministers clustered close to the fires in an attempt to stay as comfortable as possible until they were called to their seats. Once seated and away from the hearths, the cold would set back in soon enough. During the winter months, a long council session could be quite a miserable affair. When King Broderic Daine the First had the hall built two hundred years earlier, he had ordered it just so.

"The ministers will assemble here to conduct business and their comfort is the least of my concerns. They will not dally with trifling matters when ice forms on their backsides."

At the far south end of the hall, off to the side of the great set of double doors that were the main entrance to the hall, two men conversed out of earshot. "It is no longer just a suspicion of what will happen today, Cedric," the older of the two said. A slightly stooped man, Horace Montel, was showing many signs that he was losing the battle with age. His hair was totally white where he had any, and brown age marks blotched his worn face. Leaning heavily on a stout wooden staff, he had to bend his head upward at an angle to look the younger man in the face. But in spite of his obvious advanced age, his voice still had firmness and strength to it. "I have it confirmed from a source very close to the Elders and do not doubt the truth of what I have heard. It has been expected for some time and today is the day. You must leave immediately. You will not be able to do so after the announcement has been made. Stick to the plan and trust no one other than those on the list. We do not know who is aligned with whom and I fear many have been blackmailed or bought into this coup."

"But Father, I cannot let you stay behind to face that bastard alone." The concern was obvious in the younger man's voice as he bent close in an effort to keep others from noticing. "Leave with me now and together we will find a way to bring justice to those who plot treason against the king."

"You have not been listening to what I have said about the state of Edmond's mind," countered the elder Montel. "You have not noticed the change in him as I have over the last couple of years. Too many of us have been blind to the fact that Rhue and that fiend Steyr have managed to gain complete control over the king's decision-making. We have all been blind not to see what has happened right before our eyes."

Cedric Montel straightened himself up as he took in the magnitude of his father's words. He was tall and handsome, standing well above the average Arturan's height. His chiseled face still retained its youthful countenance as he had abstained from the recent fashion trend of young Arturan men to grow facial hair. His long, brown locks were tied neatly with a leather thong at the base of his neck. Force of habit caused him to rest his right hand at his hip where his sword would normally have been. His position as a member of the Home Guard would have allowed him to wear his sword in the castle but he also held a sub-minister position in the council, and council members were forbidden to wear any sort of weapon to a council meeting, a rule instituted by Daemon Rhue supposedly by the king's request years ago.

As he straightened up, he looked over his father's head and saw two dark robed figures across the great room, standing at the top of the stairs leading to the raised dais. They had obviously been staring at the Montels as they quickly turned their heads away as Cedric met their gaze.

"We are being watched by Rhue and the physician," he whispered as he bent his head back down. "They looked away as soon as I saw them but it was clear that they are taking note of us."

"Rhue has been spying on me for some time, Cedric. I found out and have been able to ensure that I give him no reason to arrest me on some trumped up charge. He knows full that I will lead the opposition to his takeover. Unfortunately he has also been aware that I have been spying on him and he has managed to keep secret the method he will use to gain power. We have long underestimated his cunning. My fear is that he has contrived a plan that will seem perfectly legal and under the auspices of the king, so any opposition will look like we are the ones who seek to thwart Edward's will. We are the ones who will be deemed guilty of treason."

"But Father, surely Edmond would never accuse you of such a thing. You have devoted your entire service to King and country."

The old man shook his head sadly. "The man who sits at the throne is not the same man I have stood beside for over forty years, son. His mind has been poisoned. That is the very reason you must not get caught up in what happens in this hall today. Do not fear, there are others who will stand beside me. You must get out and seek those who can help. Be out of the castle and preferably out of the city. Do you have the pouch?"

"Yes, Father. I have not let it out of my sight since you gave it to me. My horse is packed and at the ready."

"Good. Inside you will find some things to help you. Do not open it until you are safely away. Besides the list, there is a letter that will explain some other things that I have not been free to mention. Once you are away, I will not be able to assist you, Cedric. If things go badly, you will be accused in absentia of plotting against the king. You will have a price on your head and become a wanted man. You must go now before the council begins. If you have not noticed already, there are more guards in and around the hall than usual. If they question why a sub-minister is attempting to leave before the council starts, tell them you have to retrieve some documents for me that are important to the session. Blame it on the senility of your old father. Once out of the castle, do not dally."

Cedric could sense the urgency in his father's voice. "Father, I…"

"Do not show emotion," hissed Montel as a warning. "Rhue and Steyr are not the only ones watching us. Do not make this an appearance of a good-bye or it will rouse suspicion. I am going to leave you now and make conversation with some of the other ministers. Work your way slowly out of here."

There was an air of finality to the older man's last statement. He patted his son on the shoulder as any father would at the end of a normal conversation but as he brushed by the younger man he whispered, "I love you, son."

Cedric watched his father's stooped frame as it disappeared into the midst of a group of ministers gathered around one of the fireplaces. He wheeled and made for the great doors of the hall, stopping to chat idly with a couple of other young sub-ministers to maintain an appearance of normality. When he thought he had spent an adequate amount of time he excused himself and passed nonchalantly through the doorway into the outer hall. As expected, a group of guards were stationed at the exit to the outer ward but instead of trying to slip by them he quickly formulated another plan as he recognized the officer in command.

"Ahh, Captain Einer. Good to see you in charge here. I need your permission to leave the hall. My dolt of a father has left some documents at home that he needs to present to Lord Rhue. The first council will be extremely unhappy if he does not have them before the session starts."

The captain nodded in greeting. "Cedric. My orders are to let no one out after the session has started." It was the reply the younger Montel had expected.

"I understand Captain. Exactly why I have to hurry. The session will begin shortly and if I don't retrieve those documents from my father's quarters quickly we will all suffer the first council's wrath."

He had placed a lot of emphasis on saying "we." He held his arms out in a show of mock helplessness.

"My father is getting so senile I am amazed that Lord Rhue has not had him replaced. If I leave now I will be back before the herald calls council to order."

The captain hesitated for a moment as if perplexed by the situation. The idea that Daemon Rhue would be angry at all who had anything to do with not getting expected documents seemed to sway him.

"Well, since the order said that no one is to leave after the council session starts I guess it will be permissible. I will say that I warned you if you do not make it back in time." Irritated, he motioned to the guards behind him. "Let him pass."

"Thank you, Captain," Cedric Montel answered. The guards stepped aside and the young man hurried past and down the steps of the great hall, looking very much the part of one needing to hurry along his errand and make it back in time. A pang of regret swept over him as he contemplated the consequences of his actions. With that lie, he had just signed his own death warrant if he was to be caught. His father's fate and that of the rest of his family hung heavily on him as he scurried across the outer keep of the great castle to the stable where his horse waited.

A half hour later a lone rider galloped unchallenged from the upper tradesmen's gate, no one paying much mind on the busy afternoon. The rider rode hunched forward over the neck of his bay mare. He did not look back.

CHAPTER TWENTY-ONE

T HE HERALD NODDED TO THE PAIR OF TRUM-
peters at the top of the steps on each side of the dais. The three-
note call to order blasted through the cavernous hall, immediately
silencing all conversation and grabbing the attention of all ministers. They shuffled quickly to the plain wooden benches forming a
semicircle in front of the raised dais. When they were all seated and
quiet had descended on the gathering, the herald stepped forward.

"This special council session is now brought to order. All rise
for the king."

The group rose as one with all eyes focused on the entryway to
the left of the fireplace at the back of the room. Audible gasps filled
the cavernous hall as the king entered, as many ministers failed to
hide their shock at the sight they beheld.

Flanked by a large servant on each side, who were literally
holding him up by the armpits, a frail and bent form shuffled
slowly towards the gilded chair in the center of the dais. While his
feet moved, they were barely touching the ground as the servants
propelled him forward. His gray beard was scraggly and unkempt,
his crown cocked drunkenly to one side of his head, looking far
too large. Hollow, sunken eyes, barely noticeable under eyebrows
desperately in need of trimming, looked rheumy and dead. The
servants walked the king to the front of his throne and lowered
him gently into his seat. His head hung limply to his chest, drool
dribbled from his lips into his beard and he never made eye contact
with the crowd arrayed in front of him.

While everyone in the audience was fully aware that King

Edmond had been sick for close to a year, they were stunned at how rapidly the man had deteriorated. He had turned sixty just before he had taken ill and had been in robust health for his birthday celebration, singing, drinking, and dancing until the wee hours of the morning. They now stared in quiet horror at the emaciated form slumped before them. The mighty King of Artura looked to be one step from death's door.

Directly behind the tottering king came his physician. Steyr had donned a bright red robe for the event, his pale, bald head stuck from its fold like the head of a nasty pimple ready to burst. The fact that he followed the king and was present at the session at all spoke to the dire state of the monarch's health. Since his attendance was not formally recognized at a council session, a chair had been hastily placed for him at the back of the dais near the fireplace.

Behind Steyr somberly walked the five blue-robed members of the elder council. Formally, these men, all old veterans of Arturan politics, were the last in line to give comment on the king's decisions. While the final say on any matter rested solely with the king, the five elders were allowed to give voice to the opinion of the rest of the assembly and presided over debates in sessions that preceded any major policy decision. They were picked by the vote of all the other ministers and could be replaced only by death or when old age rendered them incapable of performing their duties.

As the five stoic council members took their designated places in front of the chairs directly behind the king, all other eyes remained focused on the entranceway, looking for the man that everyone understood was behind this unprecedented council session.

Daemon Rhue was not a man to let an opportunity to highlight his importance be wasted. He had purposefully waited for a time lag; the herald would not announce for the members to be seated until all were in the great hall. When he was sufficiently sure that all eyes would be on him, he strode purposefully through the entryway.

In another break with Arturan political tradition, the position Daemon Rhue held had never existed at any other time in the history of the country. He had persuaded the king five years ago to bestow the title of First Council to him. What exactly that meant in terms of power and position in relation to the Elder council and the regular assembly no one was quite certain, and no one dared ask. But every person in the great hall was acutely cognizant of one thing—in the ten years since the war with Torbek had officially been declared over, the man with the most power in the kingdom, second only to its monarch, was Daemon Rhue.

After the first council had crossed the dais and stood in front of his chair, the herald ordered the assembly to be seated. Rhue's position was just to the right and only slightly behind the king's throne, another subtle message to the gathering.

As the crowd waited in anticipation, one of the five Elders stood up and marched to the front of the dais to the left of the throne. Although seventy years old, he was still the youngest of the group and maintained a strong speaking voice. Unrolling a large scroll, he began to address the gathering.

"Greetings to all gathered ministers and sub-ministers from his Royal Majesty Edmond, King of Artura. I, Bernard Thrain, who sits at the table of the elder council in the fifth chair, address this special session. I do so with the king's blessing and approval from the elders." He paused to let the effect of the preamble settle on the crowd.

From his seat on the end of a bench in the front row of the assembly, Horace Montel watched intently. He had caught the omission of Daemon Rhue's name from the end of the preamble. A brief flicker of hope that this might be a harbinger of good things to come was snuffed out by a more likely scenario; Montel was more than sure the first council had dictated every word on that document, leaving his name off meant only that he was trying to distance himself in the eyes of the ministers from its contents. One good look at the king was enough to convince Montel that most likely Edmond had no part in the drafting. If the king had been healthy enough to dictate any such document it would not have been needed in the first place. Bernard Thrain cleared his throat and continued.

"This document, to be recorded in the official written histories of Artura, was dictated to Arnis Poe, masterscribe, by the king. Witnesses to the dictation were elder council members Shamus Troy, Enis Beckworth, and myself. Also as witness, General Dayen Holt, current commander of all Arturan home forces in the absence of General Artemis Thoryl. Also present as witness, Steyr, personal physician to the king. Their signatures verify the contents of this document to be truthful and unaltered. So be it recorded in the written histories." Thrain paused and motioned for a servant to bring him water. The crowd remained absolutely silent.

Horace Montel's mind was working feverously. Again, it wasn't as much as who had been present as who had not. Daemon Rhue had covered his tracks very carefully by being absent from the dictation and few could argue against the way it was done considering the poor health of the king. But the list of those present answered one of the questions which the minister had been struggling with recently; it clearly revealed which of those with close access to the king had been coerced, bribed, or threatened into joining Daemon Rhue.

Two of the elders he had long suspected of being bought off. The third name surprised him and he was extremely disappointed because it meant that if the elders had to make decisions for the king, the council would be stacked in Rhue's favor three to two. The fact that the general had been present only confirmed what he had suspected for quite a while; Holt was power hungry and his alliance would most likely be rewarded with complete control over the army once the loyal Artemis Thoryl was out of the way. With him in control of the Home Guard, it meant trouble for those outside of the conspiracy who could now count on no help from the military.

Thrain addressed the gathering again, bringing as much power to his voice as possible. "The word of the king is law. Listen and heed the word of the king." He turned again to the scroll as his words echoed through the hall.

"I, Edmond Daine, King of Artura, crowned in rightful succession after the death of my father Edmond the First, say to this council and to all citizens of Artura. My health is failing, and with it my ability to govern as I should." Thrain paused and the gathering waited. Horace Montel held his breath.

"I herewith declare myself no longer fit to wear the crown."

The audience erupted. While Thrain may not have meant for there to be a pause at this point in his reading of the scroll, it was inevitable as the ministers broke their silence, rising to their feet and voicing protest in a cacophony of verbal shock over what they had just heard.

Bernard Thrain tried to shout over the crowd as the other members of the elder council stood and added their voices in an attempt to quiet the assembly, but they could not be heard over the fervor the announcement had created. It was the herald who finally restored order as he signaled the trumpeters to sound their horns. The horns blared until the ministers quieted. All through the uproar Daemon Rhue never reacted, sitting stoically in his chair; the king sat with his head on his chest and drooled.

When the pandemonium had settled enough so he could be heard, Thrain continued reading from the scroll. "The laws covering ascension to the throne of Artura are clear. Since I chose not to take another wife after the death seven years ago of my beloved Mara, the crown will fall to my only heir, my daughter Alicia."

Another outburst from the ministers; while the succession was proper and in accordance with Arturan law, King Edmond had just handed rule of the country to a fourteen-year-old girl.

Horace Montel showed no outward sign of discontent or acceptance of the information. Instead he chose to sit quietly with his hands on his lap watching, as his brethren reacted excitedly to both parts of the king's message. He thought their display irritating and out of place. While stunning in its content, if they had taken a brief bit of time to think about it, they would have seen that everything so far had been in strict compliance with Arturan law; if the king no longer was able to lead the country, the throne would fall to his daughter. The fact that she was barely able to run a brush through her hair without aid was a moot point that could also be dealt with inside the parameters of the law. Montel knew there was more to come and made eye contact with certain other ministers in the group who were also aware of the situation. There was really nothing for them to get so excited about…yet.

Another blast of the horns restored order. Thrain continued. "Arturan Law commands that if the heir to the throne has yet to come of age, an interim entity will rule in their stead until said requirement is met. During the period of transition, the heir is to be instructed in the methodology of proper rule. The tutoring of the heir to be will be carried out by the elder council, whose mandate will be to ensure that when she is old enough to bear the full burden of the crown she will be properly prepared to do so."

Now we are getting there, Montel spoke to himself. Everything up to this point had been in order. That the elders would be responsible for the heir's tutorage until the heir became of age was exactly what the protocol of succession called for, but it also demanded that while they were teaching the heir all that was needed to be a good ruler, they would also act as the "interim entity" the law referred to. Law clearly stated the elders would govern the country by committee until Alicia Daine reached eighteen years of age.

Thrain paused and allowed the crowd time to contemplate the content of the message. Excited and heated conversations within the assembly filled the drafty hall. Most of the council had become so involved discussing the issues with their brethren they did not notice that all the exits from the hall were now covered by armed guards. It did not escape the attention of Horace Montel.

A blast from the trumpets restored order. Thrain started again as the assembly turned its attention once again to the front of the dais. "My foremost duty as King has always been to protect and serve the good people of Artura and it grieves me that my health forces this abdication. I realize full well that my daughter is not yet ready to assume leadership, but I believe that in the four years leading to her eighteenth birthday, the elder council will prepare her with the knowledge, skill, and compassion necessary to become a strong and fair queen."

Thrain paused again. This was an emotionally charged statement; the king had indeed for the most part governed well and fair. He was a beloved monarch and it pained those who knew him to see he had sunk to such a wretched state. Thrain continued. "It is in the hands of the elder council that the trust of the nation is being placed. By their guidance and wisdom they will ensure your future queen becomes a fit leader who will govern with honor, dignity, and fairness. But the task will demand their full attention and complete dedication."

The hall became deathly silent. The assembly was finally beginning to understand that this was all leading to something unprecedented.

Here it comes, Montel again whispered to himself. If the task of teaching Alicia Daine to become queen required the full attention and complete dedication of the elders, who would run the country while they were doing so? The fact that Thrain had emphasized the words "full attention" and "complete dedication" might have slipped by most in the gathering but it hadn't escaped Horace Montel. Thrain droned on.

"The importance of allowing the Elders to devote their time to this critical task has created a unique situation not found at any time in the history of this great country. It requires a difficult decision and it is one I do not make lightly. Until my heir Alicia reaches her eighteenth birthday, rule of Artura will be placed solely in the hands of my first council—Daemon Rhue."

Bernard Thrain rolled the scroll up quickly as the impact of the statement buried itself within the shocked minds of the crowd. "That is the word of the king. The word of the king is Law."

The assembly exploded into chaos as ministers jumped to their feet and began shouting, men jumped onto the benches and demanded the right to speak, others futilely called for calm. The horns began to add their bleating tones to the bedlam as the herald tried to reestablish order to the hall. The five elders were all on their feet adding to the din but more than anything appeared to be arguing amongst themselves. From his vantage point on the floor of the hall, it seemed to Horace Montel that the announcement may have been a complete surprise to at least two of them. Daemon Rhue sat passively with folded arms, a trace of a smirk on his face. The king drooled onto his chest.

It was the sound of hobnail boots on the stone floor and the clink of cold steel that finally grabbed the assembly's attention. Two columns of soldiers stomped in cadence through the doors at the end of the hall. The force split once inside and the columns proceeded to line the walls flanking the ministers. Once the walls were lined on both sides, the remainder of the columns swung together in front of the doors. The assembly was now completely blocked in on three sides. At a harsh command from Captain Jacob Einer, they all raised their halberds and slammed the butts onto the stone floor in unison. The echo rolled through the cavernous hall as the bewildered ministers looked at each other helplessly as the weight of the situation overcame their anger and bravado. The intent was clear—order would be restored to the hall one way or another.

Daemon Rhue motioned to the elders to return to their seats and the rest of the ministers followed suit. It appeared that the man at the center of the storm was ready to break his silence. Standing, he walked slowly and purposefully to the king's throne and placed his hand on the shoulder of the frail figure. King Edmond drooled onto his chest.

While Daemon Rhue appeared to be cool and collected as he calmly scanned the faces of the ministers, inside was a different story. The powerful stimulant Steyr had prepared for him not more than an hour ago was reaching maximum effect; it had been the second dosage in a day that had started in the darkness of the early morn deep under the castle in the physician's lair. Even without the drug, the first council's intensity level would have been mountain high, but with Steyr's concoction magnifying tenfold every element of the man's psyche, the apex had been reached. Daemon Rhue was a volcano ready to explode. He had waited a decade for this moment—all the planning, the tiniest details carefully thought out, the agony suffered at the hands of Master Taul when setbacks had occurred—and there had been many. The guise of cooperation and sincerity he had been forced to wear in order to fool the people he despised, the intrigues and subplots painstakingly nurtured into fruition. Everything had ripened into a bountiful harvest—the time was now—and Daemon Rhue was ready to reap all he had sown.

"Gentlemen of the assembly." His words reverberated powerfully through the great hall. The ministers turned their full attention to the man at the top of the dais. When Rhue was sure of their undivided attention, he continued.

"I stand before you today humbled and indeed as saddened by the king's announcement as you were. The man who has guided this country like a captain steering his vessel through a great storm, has begrudgingly come to terms with the wretched illness which wracks his body and robs his mind of the wisdom and compassion with which he has led this nation for so many years. Those of us who have had the honor and privilege of close counsel with his majesty over the last few months as he has wrestled with this scourge, know only too well the agony the man has endured. Indeed, had he been any less of a man than what he is, he would not have persevered. It is his greatness and love of his country, which has driven him to make the choice he has laid before you."

Horace Montel sat and listened intently to the subtle nuances of the first council's words, knowing full well what the man was attempting to do. Rhue was clever and had the upper hand at the moment. With three-fifths of the elder council in his grasp and General Holt as well, he had the power to seize control forcibly. But such a violent move would only serve to grab the attention of the man who would be the biggest obstacle in the way of any effort to control Artura—Artemis Thoryl. It was a devious yet brilliant plan and the old minister inwardly cursed his own obliviousness to all that had been going on over the last several years. The fact that the loyal general and a large part of the Arturan army were a thousand miles away at this critical juncture had been another well-thought-out element of the first council's scheme. Rhue's patronizing of the assembly was nothing more than sugarcoating the vile bitterness of a power grab. There would be no need of violence; under the pretense of handing the throne to his fourteen-year-old daughter, the feeble and unwitting king had served a bloodless coup to the Torbekian. Bile rose in Horace Montel's throat as the bitter truth was laid bare—anyone who thought Daemon Rhue would actually give rule of the country to its rightful heir in four years was a complete idiot.

Horace Montel sighed deeply. He was getting old and had intended on retiring in a year or two to his villa on the river above the city with his wife; there to while away the rest of his days tending to a small garden and fishing with his grandchildren. But he could never live in peace and contentment knowing the country and king he loved and served so faithfully had been betrayed and handed over to a man from a foreign land which Artura had been at war with for decades. He was glad he had insisted Cedric get out of the city; the plan they had formulated might be too little too late but it was all they could do under the circumstances. Montel's only regret was that he hadn't been able to tell his son all of the things he had wanted to say before he left. He had a sinking feeling he would not get another chance to do so.

Daemon Rhue continued pouring on the sugar...

"I am humbled that the man, whom I have come to think of as my own father, would trust me to guide this great nation through the transition period until his beloved daughter is capable of taking her rightful place as queen. I realize that there may be those of you who will question why King Edmond has altered the succession process, but I assure you—"

It was time. Horace Montel stood up and with the strongest voice he could muster, cut the first council off in mid-sentence.

"Excuse the interruption Lord Rhue but I address the elder council. It is my right as a minister in this assembly to be heard, but since it seems that I cannot petition my king directly to speak I must do so of the elders."

Shamus Troy, senior member of the Elders started to rise from his seat to answer but was stopped short by a curt gesture from

Daemon Rhue. An uncomfortable silence settled over the great hall as the first council slowly turned his steely gaze to the old minister.

"By all means, Minister Montel, I will excuse your interruption. I am sure you did not mean to be so…rude." There was a glint in Rhue's eyes and a smirk on his face as he stared down towards the old man. Horace Montel countered the Torbekian's smirk with a hard glare of his own while the rest of the ministers in the hall fidgeted in their seats. There was a long, unpleasant pause before Daemon Rhue continued, but this time there was no effort to hide his contempt. His words were sharp and cut through the hall. "But I warn you, and all of the members of this assembly," his cold glare swept over the men seated in front of him, "this is not a regular assembly session. The king did not call for a debate on this issue."

But Horace Montel had steeled himself not to be intimidated. "So is my request to be heard denied?" The old minister swept his arm towards the row of chairs behind the king's throne and his voice raised a notch in its intensity. "What say you? Have the elders lost their voices as has the king?"

His words were a direct challenge to Daemon Rhue and the atmosphere within the cold hall was thick with the anticipation of the oncoming clash.

"Stop." This time Elder Troy rose and spoke before the first council could cut him off. He motioned towards the physician to come forward and pointed to the king.

"Have we forgotten that his Majesty is ill? We will let Minister Montel be heard but the king is suffering and must be returned to his quarters. All stand for the king." All in attendance immediately got to their feet and all eyes in the hall looked to where the form of the once proud Edmond sagged like a pathetic scarecrow. He had not moved once since the meeting had started and not even the harsh blare of the trumpets had sparked as much as a raised eyebrow. His head lolled to the side, held up only by the heavy crown which had come to rest against the edge of the throne. Spittle and snot bubbles matted the gray beard and mustache with sticky wetness. It was a stark realization for many of the ministers as they watched Steyr direct the king's attendants to move the helpless monarch; the man who had just so recently issued such an important dictation about the ascension of his daughter to the throne didn't even know who or where he was. The assembly watched in respectful silence as the servants ushered the sagging king to his feet and out of the hall.

Once the king was gone, Elder Troy, instead of returning to his seat and allowing Daemon Rhue to continue, walked to the front of the dais. His move elicited a venomous scowl from the first council. Horace Montel noticed the interaction with acute interest; it seemed Elder Troy was at least attempting to hold onto some measure of control.

"While Lord Rhue is correct in his assertion that there is no legal protocol allowing for debate on this issue, it is my desire, and I will assert, within my authority as the senior member of the elder council, not to ignore the wishes of the assembly and allow them to speak their voice. It is indeed one of the cornerstones of Arturan history, that while decisions are made for this country by its rightful monarch, there has never been a king or queen that has not allowed the assembly council ministers to be heard."

He turned towards Daemon Rhue and nodded to the other members of the Elder council. "This edict by the king delves into unprecedented territory, and while I myself was present at the dictation made by his Lordship and do not dispute the word of the king, I must, as a loyal subject, citizen, and elected representative, petition the rest of the Elder council and Lord Rhue, to allow the members of the assembly to speak."

Horace Montel watched intently at Daemon Rhue's reaction to the words of Elder Troy. He was sure that the first council had not intended for there to be any sort of glitch in his plan but he had underestimated the loyalty of the old councilman. But while he was mildly surprised and buoyed by the reluctance of the senior Elder to allow Daemon Rhue an unfettered and obstacle-free path to total power, he was concerned by what past history said of those who got in the Torbekian's way; they had a tendency to become dead very soon. The Elder may have just signed his death warrant. "Indeed, Elder Troy." The scowl on the first council's face had been replaced by a gratuitous smile.

"It was not my intention to disallow any sort of comment on the king's decision. I merely sought to remind the assembly that we had heard the word of the king and that the word of the king is law. To comment on the decision is allowed, but to disagree with said decision to the point of openly forming opposition to the king's decree borders on treason." He placed a heavy emphasis on the last word, and its echo, along with its unveiled threat, reverberated throughout the great hall. "Minister Montel. You may continue."

Horace Montel gave the first council a curt nod. The assembly's gaze centered on the respected minister as he began to speak. "Gentlemen. It is unprecedented in the history of this country that a man not born Arturan would assume leadership, even in an interim position. The protocol of ascension has always been clear during those rare times it has been used. The elder council must assume leadership of the country until the heir is ready to take the crown. We are told that the king has dictated this decision, yet before us today we see a man who cannot hold his head up or even speak."

The old minister had been looking at the assembly as he stated his case, but as he paused, he turned and looked Daemon Rhue squarely in the eyes, the animosity between the two men palpable. "Are we to believe that this is the same man who has just handed control over our beloved country to a Torbekian?"

Most of the assembly leaped to their feet, shouts of support for the minister mixing with shouts of protest against the king's decree. As he took in the scene, Montel made quick note of those who remained seated and voiced no protest; these would be the men whom Daemon Rhue had already coerced or bought into his fold. It would be good to note for future reference who could and could not be counted on.

"QUIET!" The eyes of Daemon Rhue burned with fire and contempt as he glared at Horace Montel. "You seem to forget minister, that Torbek and Artura have been at peace for over ten years, yet you speak to me like I am your enemy. I would remind you, and this assembly, that I became a legal citizen of this country four years ago in a ceremony presided over by the king himself. Do you deny my rights as a citizen?" Horace Montel was ready to meet the challenge.

"I do not deny your rights as a citizen, First Council, but I do challenge your right to sit as Artura's ruler. The elder council is required to perform those duties until the time the heir becomes of age. Arturan law clearly states this and I do not believe the elders nor this assembly, should allow the king, given his current and obvious mental state, to bypass protocol and change the law." Shouts of agreement rose from the assembly.

Daemon Rhue coldly eyed the crowd as many added their voice in support of Horace Montel. A quick glance at the scribes assured him that they were doing the job he had laid out for them before the assembly had gathered, documenting the names of those who showed even the slightest opposition. There would be time enough after the storm settled to deal with those gentlemen. Right now he needed to diffuse the situation without resorting to spilling blood. While he had no reservations about killing anyone, he did not want this to develop into any sort of civil war. The old fool Montel and others like him had a lot of support outside the walls of the castle and while there was no doubt as to the outcome of any type of civil disobedience, to go down such a violent path would anger Master Taul greatly. Money and resources would be wasted in great amounts if the spark of revolt were allowed to kindle and his master would hold him responsible. But he needed to do something quickly; the voices of protest were getting stronger and the prospect of having to use force growing closer.

But Daemon Rhue was as smart as he was ruthless. He shifted tack again; there was still one card he had yet to play. "Ministers, calm yourselves and allow me to speak." The hall quieted. "I see many of you agree with Minister Montel that the decision allowing myself to rule this country until Alicia Daine comes of age should be made by the elder council. Is that what you believe?"

The hall erupted with shouts and cries of agreement in answer to his question. Exactly what he had planned. A bone had been thrown for the dogs to chew. Daemon Rhue had them exactly where he wanted them.

"Very well. I can see that it would be futile to try and thwart the wishes of this honorable assembly and indeed, I would be remiss in my duties as a citizen if I were to ignore the voices of our elected ministers. It is therefore my intention to do exactly as you demand."

The sudden change in direction caught the gathering completely off guard and while most began to smugly congratulate themselves on what seemed to be an apparent victory over the first council, Horace Montel wasn't fooled. Rhue had something up his sleeve.

"If it is your desire that the elder council be your voice and make decisions accordingly, do you agree that theirs will be the final word and that you will abide by their decision?" Daemon Rhue challenged the crowd.

The shouts of agreement were loud and strong, this was what they had demanded after all. Very few caught on to the fact that they had played right into the hands of the first council.

"Very well. We shall let the elders decide who will sit in rule until the heir comes of age." Daemon Rhue turned and addressed the blue robed elders sitting behind the empty throne.

"Gentlemen, the ministers have demanded that you be given the power of decision, and have given their solemn word that they will abide by your vote. You must choose to follow the king's edict and grant me the power to rule, or you must choose to rule the country yourselves and defy his wishes. There are five of you. When the elder council was formed long ago it was decreed that its content be of an odd number so there could be no split decisions. We will start with the lowest seniority member. Elder Thrain, what is your vote?"

The assembly grew stone quiet and the members of the elder council fidgeted nervously. No one had foreseen this coming. Daemon Rhue had lulled the gathering into thinking they were getting just exactly what they had wanted and now the Elders were being thrust to the forefront and forced to make a momentous decision. No longer could they hide.

Daemon Rhue raised his voice. He had things going in the right direction but did not want to give any of the flustered elders time to do any serious thinking. "Elder Thrain, what is your vote? The assembly waits."

Bernard Thrain looked around helplessly. He knew which way he had to choose; he just wanted it to look like he had no other option. "I…I vote to follow the wishes of the king." He had intended on stopping there but felt his decision needed a little clarifying. "The word of the king is law," he blurted.

Daemon Rhue nodded his head. He expected nothing less from this one. Thrain's weakness was drink and young girls and for a man of seventy years it took a large supply of Steyr's concoctions to help him perform with such young and unwilling partners. A vote in the wrong direction and his only source of drugs and forced playthings would dry up, leaving him for what he really was—a limp and flaccid old puppet. Bernard Thrain and his vices had been in the first council's pocket for years.

"Elder Bolk. What say you?"

Quinton Bolk was a different story. The man's loyalty to his country was without question. He had been a thorn in Daemon Rhue's side for quite some time and was in line for elimination. That he wasn't in the best of health had kept that plan from going forward. Rhue had hoped that old age would catch up with Bolk and he could be replaced with someone already in his grasp, but the old bugger just kept hanging on. The elder's voice was weak and raspy.

"It is the elder council's duty to govern until the heir comes of age. The histories have recorded it as such. To allow another to rule is not possible."

Rhue nodded grimly. That had gone as expected. He made a mental note to make sure Quinton Bolk didn't hang around much longer.

"Elder Beckworth. We await your choice."

This was just an exercise for show. Enis Beckworth had been hoping to retire but dice and cards had eliminated the possibility of that happening. Unless a benefactor in need of a favor was to surreptitiously eliminate the gambling debts Beckworth had racked up, his retirement was nothing more than an unreachable dream. Fortunately, that benefactor was standing in front of him and waiting for the right answer. His golden retirement plan was there for the taking—all he had to do was make the right choice. He didn't need much time.

"I would agree with Elder Thrain. It is not for us to debate whether the king be of sound mind or not. With my own ears I heard the words he spoke. I make my choice for Lord Rhue."

The first council nodded as the balance swung his way. "Elder Cain?"

Petr Cain was another loyalist in need of elimination but was a tough nut to crack. Although in his mid-seventies, he was unlike Quinton Bolk and in very good health. That he was of sound mind and body wouldn't have been such an issue for Daemon Rhue if he could have found some dirt to dig up on the elder council member. But Petr Cain seemed to be untouchable. The man simply had no vices. Married for over fifty years to the same woman and there was no incident which could ever be found where he had even looked at another woman with prurient desires. His wife and he had also been childless so there were no family members with which to use against him. No drink, no drugs, no gambling, no perverted desires. The first council knew the way the man's vote would go and cursed himself for not dealing with him sooner. He made another mental note; the man's health may be good, but accidents could happen and Elder Cain needed to have an accident.

The old man stood up. Instead of facing the crowd, he locked eyes with Daemon Rhue. In his defiance, there was no masking the contempt he held for the first council and it rang loud and clear in his voice.

"First, let me say that I am surprised Lord Rhue has called on the elders for their vote, since it is fact he allowed only select members of the council to witness the king's dictation."

Horace Montel smiled grimly at the verbal dagger his old friend had just threw at the Torbekian, but it also made him instantly fearful for Petr Cain's life. He could see the dark hatred burning in the countenance of Daemon Rhue as the elder continued.

"I was minister in the court of Edmond's father and witnessed the crown pass to the son. I have served this king for thirty years and it grieves me deeply to say that the man I saw sitting on the throne today is incapable of rendering a decision that has such monumental impact on this country and its people."

Stop there my friend. You have made your choice; please stop there. Horace Montel tried to catch Petr Cain's eye with a slight hand gesture but the elder was wound tight and unflinching in his confrontation with Daemon Rhue.

"I am not afraid to expound on what Minister Montel had to say Lord Rhue, and it is, I would be willing to wager, foremost on the minds of the majority in this venerable hall. Every man here grew up knowing your home country as his mortal enemy. The bitter taste of war lingers long in the mouths of those who remember the atrocities ordered by your true master, Kenric Taul." Petr Cain turned to the assembly. "Minister Eaton. Will you stand please?"

A tall, slender man, his arms folded snugly into his brown robe, got to his feet and faced the dais erect and proud though his gray hair and worn face spoke of his advanced years. He nodded to Petr Cain. Daemon Rhue boiled but Cain returned the nod and continued.

"All here can remember when Hale Eaton led the first peace delegation to Sectos, the capital city of Torbek, to meet with Supreme Overlord Kenric Taul. Minister Eaton handed him a peace proposition written by King Edmond himself. What answer did you get after Lord Taul read the document, Hale?"

Hale Eaton slowly raised his arms high, allowing the folds of the robe to slip away and expose the leather braces and straps holding the two shiny hooks now serving as his hands in place.

"Lord Taul himself cut off my hands and fed them to his dogs. That was the answer I took back to King Edmond."

Voices in the assembly began to rise in the passion of anger as the minister sat back down. The soldiers lining the halls fidgeted in their places as the atmosphere hung thick with tension.

"SILENCE!" Daemon Rhue looked ready to explode. His words hissed with fire as he spit them out. "It seems you have made your choice elder, though I hardly see the reasoning behind opening old wounds that should have healed long ago. Elder Troy? Yours is the final and deciding vote. We will hear you now."

Shamus Troy was as uncomfortable as he had ever been. He had long relished his position as the occupant of the first chair at the table of the elder council and found the comfort and special treatment afforded to the position preferable to what he would receive if he was to retire. Since nothing but total infirmity and an age-addled brain could force him from the council if he didn't want to go, he was perfectly content to spend his twilight years dealing with the issues placed before the elders. His loyalty to king and country had never been questioned and though he knew in his heart no Arturan king in his right frame of mind would hand over rule of the country to an outsider, there was one thing that was going to keep him from standing in Daemon Rhue's way—his granddaughter.

Her name was Serah and she had absolutely been the shining light in his heart for twenty years and she loved her grandpapa as much as he loved her. Six agonizing months ago, while she rode the magnificent horse he had presented to her on her eighteenth birthday along the river below the city, she had purportedly been kidnapped by river pirates. Elder Troy had hired a small army of hunters and trackers to find her and bring her home but she had disappeared completely. For five and a half weeks he had anguished over her kidnapping but there had been no word of her fate—until two weeks ago. Daemon Rhue had somehow managed to get a clue to her whereabouts, and while he warned the old man the chances of getting his granddaughter back alive were slim, he promised to do everything in his power to try.

Shamus Troy was as grateful as a heartbroken grandfather could be and vowed on the spot to be forever in the first council's debt if such a miracle could be brought about. His most fervent wish was answered and two days ago he had been gloriously reunited with his Serah, unharmed and unsoiled. There was only one way Shamus Troy's vote could go. He stood up and solemnly faced his countrymen. He would have to make this look good. He cleared his throat for effect.

"No man knows the histories of this nation better than I, and nowhere has it ever been written that a man not born Arturan could rule this country other than by force of arms. It was as unthinkable as the idea of peace with Torbek was ten years ago. But yet peace was achieved. Not one of you can deny the prosperity that has been awarded us since the ink dried on the treaty our beloved Edmond forged in his wisdom a decade ago. The wars we fought were terrible for those on both sides, yet our soldiers now stand side by side as allies. I agree with Lord Rhue that wounds healed ought not to be reopened, and so too, I believe it is time to add a new chapter to the history of this great nation. Let it show that we honor the wisdom of our king. I was present at the dictation made by King Edmond. While his body betrayed him, I believe his mind was sound when he issued his decision. There was no other voice but his which spoke the words laid down by the scribe. I heard the word of the king. The word of the king is law."

It was done. The eloquence of the old man's words pleasantly surprised Daemon Rhue. While there had been no doubt as to the way the man would vote, it was more than he had hoped for. The assembly had pledged to follow the will of the elders and any who now voiced opposition to the king's edict could be branded officially as disloyal. It was time to finish this.

"Ministers of the assembly. You have heard the vote of the elder council. It is time to put this bickering behind us and get on with the king's wishes. The elders will immediately begin the task of instructing Princess Alicia in all she needs for her to rule as your rightful queen. With their wisdom and guidance she will become the ruler her father would want her to be. A proclamation detailing the events of today's assembly will be issued and the word spread to the four corners of Artura and to all our allies. Let it be known herewith that the will of King Edmond has been done. May his tormented mind and body be at peace for the rest of his days."

The assembly was dead silent as the echo of the First Council's words faded through the great hall. Horace Montel stood numb and deflated as he wrestled with the events which had just taken place. Daemon Rhue had cunningly twisted the assembly's opposition against them and had known exactly the outcome of a vote. It would be futile now to speak out and would more than likely mean his arrest. He needed time to think this through, he was not alone and made eye contact with those as stunned as he. *Not here. Not now,* his eyes warned.

The trumpets blared and the guards slammed the butts of their halberds hard against the cold stone floor. The harsh sound reverberated throughout the great hall with the cruel and brutal echo of a new reality and the history of Artura changed forever. The herald barked out his command.

"This assembly is now adjourned. All rise for first council Daemon Rhue. Interim Ruler of Artura."

Interim Daemon Rhue had to work to keep from laughing at the herald's use of the word even though he himself had made sure that was the term to be used. It wouldn't be long before the fools in this wretched country learned that there would be no such thing as "interim."

Chapter Twenty-Two

H ORACE MONTEL TRIED TO AVOID THE LIGHT
emanating from the smoky oil lamps spaced evenly along the
wide street serving as Tiernon's main business district. The tavern
he was looking for was a small, dank hole of a place called The Ale
Bucket. It was located on a seedy side street running at a right angle
to the one he traveled and which ended at a rotted, unused pier by
the waterfront. He could have traveled the back streets to get there
and stayed out of the light but once off the main street, a man took
his life into his own hands when he traveled alone.

The fog helped, not that there were a whole lot of folk out and
about at this time of the night. There were still patrons at the better,
well lit taverns and inns, but the shops had closed and locked their
doors. This street was well patrolled by soldiers who chased the
riff raff, pickpockets, and prostitutes back to the side streets and
alleys. On this main thoroughfare, the well-heeled businessmen
maintained their shops, inns, and taverns and paid good silver to
keep it clean and safe. While he was dressed well enough not to be
confused as a miscreant out looking for trouble or something to
steal, Horace Montel sought to avoid direct contact with the patrols.
He kept his head down and his cloak pulled tight about his neck.

Finally reaching the side street he sought, he turned and plunged
into the foggy dark. He kept to the middle of the street, away from
the dark alleys reeking of rotted garbage, urine, and feces and was
glad it wasn't far to his destination. A single oil lamp hung over a
crudely painted sign. The Ale Bucket was barely readable but someone had recently applied fresh paint to the drawing of the bucket

itself. Dim light shone through small windows flanking the door and he could hear gruff voices and a woman's high-pitched squeal of laughter coming from within. Just as he grabbed the handle of the door, it burst open, nearly knocking him to the ground as a lurching couple spilled out into the street.

"Watch yourself, sweetie," a drunken prostitute and her customer laughed as he just managed to step out of their way. She was holding a half-full bottle of cheap brandy in one hand and the other was trying to keep her would-be lover from falling over. He had one arm draped over her bare shoulder and his head was lying on her oversized breasts that were nearly bursting from the stained fabric of her dress. From his appearance and smell, Horace Montel could tell he was a fisherman, and had evidently not changed or bathed since he got off the boat.

"My, my, my, ain't we a fine dressed man-about-town tonight?" the prostitute drawled as she stopped and gave Montel the once-over. Her rotted teeth, what few she had, were stained with tobacco juice, and she spit a mouthful towards the stinking gutter.

"Give me a few minutes to drain Charlie's little codfish dry, honey, and I'll come back for you. You be a mite long in years, but if you got a ha' piece o' silver I bet I can make that ol' pecker of yours stand up like it was fifteen again."

Montel didn't answer as fisherman Charlie pulled his head out of the pale cleavage his face had been buried in. "Hey," he slurred, glaring at the older man, "bugger off, Mr. Fancypants. My coin be good as yers n' Betty here be done bought and paid for, ain't you, my sweet?"

Montel ignored the two drunks as they stumbled down the street, laughing and giggling into the dark. Shaking his head in disgust, he stepped into the tavern.

The establishment was typical of the seedy back-street alehouses found this close to the waterfront. A rough plank serving bar ran along one side of the room with a doorless opening at the far end leading to the kitchen and barrel room. Several plain tables lined the opposite wall and a fireplace crackled at the end of the room next to a decrepit staircase leading to the upper level. Only five patrons lounged about the establishment on this night. Two men and another drunken woman sat at one table paying him no mind, as one of the men cupped an exposed breast and sloppily traded kisses with the prostitute, while the other pawed under her uplifted dress. Two rough-looking men huddled over their ale mugs and glanced at him warily as Montel stepped up to the bar. A fat, bald man in a grimy apron came in from the kitchen wiping his hands on an equally dirty towel.

"I can quench your thirst with a pint o' ale sir, but there's no' much for supper left."

Montel shook his head. "Neither for me good man, but I do look for some friends." As he spoke, he tapped a silver piece onto the top of the bar three times before pushing it across to the barkeep; it was a prearranged signal. The man nodded and winked as he snatched it up and tipped his head towards the staircase.

"Last room on the left at the end o' the hall."

Montel nodded. Once away from the main room the stairs were dark and the hall at the top not much better as it was lit by only one oil lamp. The place had a dank and sour urine smell to it. Obviously some of the patrons of the tavern's rooms were either too drunk or too lazy to make their way to the outhouse in the alley. His stomach roiled in protest. When he got to the room, he knocked three times, paused, and knocked twice more. A peek hole cover slid open and an eye greeted him. Seconds later a bolt rattled and the door swung in.

"Horace. Glad to see you could make it." The man who opened the door was Hale Eaton.

"Hale." He returned the greeting and stepped into the small room. Eaton took a quick glance down the dim hall towards the stairs. Satisfied the newcomer had not been followed, he shut and bolted the door.

A small bed was shoved against one wall, a nightstand, water pitcher, and basin next to it. A long, narrow table with six chairs around it used up nearly all the room's remaining space. It was obvious by the size of the table in such a small room that it was often used as a clandestine meeting place. A single garret window looked out into the back alley. Around the table, lit by a single lamp, sat three men.

Besides Hale Eaton, the other men present were Derric Lynn, a small, mousy fellow of fifty, also a member of the Arturan assembly. Lynn was a high-ranking minister in the finance and taxation department and kept a close eye on the nation's treasury. He had been at the special assembly earlier in the day.

Sitting to Lynn's left was a large brute of a young man. Montel recognized him from somewhere but couldn't place the name, but quickly noticed he was well armed with a battle sword strapped in harness across his back and two knives stuck in his belt.

"You remember my son-in-law, Lando Berk, don't you, Horace?" Lynn asked. Berk stuck out a huge, meaty paw.

"Minister Montel," the younger man nodded as the two shook. "I know your son, Cedric. We have trained together on the practice field often. He is a good man to have on your side in a fight."

"Ah yes, Lando. That is where I recognized you from. But I must say I am a bit confused. Were you not with General Thoryl?"

"It's a long story, sir. Let us just say I am here on orders."

Montel nodded. "I understand completely. But nonetheless, I am glad to see you. I fear we may have need of more young men like you before this thing is over."

The third man at the table was one who Montel knew well but was also very surprised to see. A young man in his twenties, he was a couple of inches taller than Lando Berk but lacked the bear-like girth. He had shed his cloak and his sleeveless tunic showed tanned and well-muscled arms. His black hair was shoulder length and tied at the neck in a tail with a leather braid. His dark beard and mustache were well trimmed and as he reached across the table to shake hands, Montel noticed the tattoo of a dagger running from the inside crook of the young man's elbow to his wrist. A quick glance showed a matching one on his other arm.

"Kellen! By thunder and lightning! It is a pleasant surprise to see you here. How is your father?"

"The last I saw of him he was well, thank you sir. He sends his greetings."

Hale Eaton sat himself down at the table and thumped his two metal hooks down on its worn surface. "It was a surprise to me as well to see the lads here Horace. I would have told you this morning but I did not have a chance to get you alone before the assembly. The presence here in the city of these two is known to only a few and as you well know, their lives would be in danger if it were to be otherwise."

"I look forward to hearing the story behind their visit," said Montel as he seated himself. "I would wager a gold piece that their presence is not by chance or wont of some home leave from their duties."

"Unfortunately time will not allow us the luxury of swapping stories," Hale Eaton said. "I believe these two will be highly interested in all we have to say. They have been kept under wraps here since they arrived in the city as we could not take the chance of having them seen. Have you heard about Bolk?"

Montel shook his head grimly. "No. I was wondering why he was not here. What has happened, Hale?"

"Rhue has placed Quinton under house arrest. I sent a man to contact him but he couldn't get within two hundred feet of his house for the guards. I fear for him but there is nothing we can do."

"That is bad news. I was counting on him to help sway some of the ministers. This may frighten them into doing nothing. What about Petr Cain?"

"He respectfully declined our invitation," Derric Lynn said. "He said he needed to think on the matter though I believe in time he will not be able to stomach what has happened. For now, none of the other ministers have been sought out, but there are some outside the assembly I believe we can count on. I have contacts in the business sector that have long feared Rhue's rise to power. While for many it is more about their possible financial loss than their patriotism, they are still willing to help, and we will need all we can muster.

The problem as I see it is, what exactly are we going to need help in doing? We have no plan."

"You must have had something in mind, Horace," Hale Eaton replied. "You sent Cedric away for a reason."

"Yes I did, but it was not as much to carry out a plan as it was to keep him away from the assembly. He has a hot temper and hates Rhue more than anyone. I feared he would do something rash so I sent him with a list of contacts; people we know and trust outside the castle and the city. The news of the king's abdication will travel fast and it will get their attention but we need to come together as a group. We all know the rest of the country is on the verge of descending into anarchy in response to the heavy taxes and new laws Rhue has persuaded the king to implement, especially the ones that seek to restrict and segregate the minorities. That and the fact he has disbanded much of the army and closed most of the garrisons over the last year can send this country into chaos."

"And he let the army go without the pensions promised," Derric Lynn interjected. "So now we have thousands of former soldiers wandering the countryside. There is already an upsurge of bandit activity anywhere away from the cities, and without armed escorts, it is unsafe to travel."

"We have been blind to the cunning of Daemon Rhue for too long my friends," Horace Montel said. "This is all part of his plan to weaken the country. The people are overtaxed, out of work, personal freedoms are limited, and so the stew of dissent begins to boil. He coerces the king to disband the army so there is no rule to thwart revolt. Soldiers without jobs and without pensions and idle men with no money and with time on their hands are trouble. And as Derric says, they grow desperate and many will turn to banditry, adding to the fear and discontent of the people. So who do folk turn to for protection and security? The warlords. Men like Tyson Barg who have the money to hire displaced and disgruntled soldiers. They will again become powerful and will soon fight amongst each other for control of land, trade, and wealth, further weakening the nation. When we can no longer work together as a united country,

Rhue and his master Taul will step in, and unlike before, they will have little trouble taking control."

The mood around the table was somber as the rest of the group contemplated the minister's words. Kellen Thoryl, who had been quiet but listening intently, finally spoke.

"Gentlemen, if you will allow me? It appears my father was right. He sent Captain Berk and me here to assess the situation. He has long wondered why the support asked for time and time again has not been forthcoming. Replacement troops promised but never sent, supply requisitions ignored. Our "allies" regulating us to little more than patrol duty; chasing an enemy who knows every trick of survival in the most forsaken land you have ever seen. Indeed, we have questioned why the rulers of Dazor and Torbek deem it necessary to persecute these hardy folk and try to drive them from a land nobody else wants. None of what we do has made much sense but as our part of the tri-pact alliance, we follow the orders of General Ortair. And you know my father; his loyalty to King Edmond is beyond question, so he has faithfully done his best."

Hale Eaton spoke up. "I have filled Kellen and Lando in on the situation with the king's health and Rhue's part in this as much as I know, Horace. They will want to send a message to the general as soon as they can."

Horace Montel sighed. "What will happen then, Hale? The general will undoubtedly get the official news of the king's abdication soon enough. The communiqué he will receive will demand that he continue to follow orders just as before. So what is he to do? Anything Artemis Thoryl does that goes against his orders will be considered an act of treason and punishable by death." He stood up from the table and walked over to the garret window and leaned heavily on its sill. "We find ourselves standing at crossroads gentlemen. For us, meeting like this could be considered an act of treason. We are one wrong move away from the dungeon and the gallows."

"But we have to do something, Horace," Derric Lynn said. "To allow a Torbekian to rule this country is an abomination and cannot be allowed."

"I agree, Derric, but you saw the vote. Our own elder council has decided against us. Quinton spoke out and look where it has gotten him. So what is Artemis to do when he gets the news? We know what he will think of the matter but he is still loyal to the king. Does he disobey orders and bring the army home? We are on the verge of civil war here if this thing goes south on us and that will play right into Rhue's hands I am afraid."

The room grew deathly quiet as the men contemplated the power of the minister's words. Hale Eaton finally broke the silence and asked, "What do you suggest we do, Horace?"

The old man turned back to the table. "My council, gentlemen, is to do nothing for the moment, that is overtly in opposition to the decision made today by the elders. We are not in a position to gain anything by doing so and would just be arrested and put out of the way. Let the situation play out for now. If we are careful and make no open gestures of revolt we can gain time, and time is needed to think this through. We go about our business as usual but discreetly sound out our brethren. Find those we can count on and those who will stand in our way. We need to look outside the city; I have started that process with Cedric and will wait to hear from those I asked him to contact. You must all do the same. Send feelers through your network of friends, business contacts, any whom we can trust."

Derric Lynn replied, "There will be many who will join us, Horace. People are fed up with the abuses heaped upon them over the last couple of years as you have said. We should be able to find support everywhere."

"Yes, I agree, but to all of you I must say again, this is dangerous ground upon which we tread. Rhue will use the slightest excuse to eliminate any who dare to step in his way. His spies are everywhere as we well know and he will be looking for anything to use against us. Our families are in danger as well. Make the mistake of confiding in the wrong person and you jeopardize us all. Kellen, are you and Lando going to return to your father as soon as possible? If so, I will prepare a letter to him and seek his guidance."

The young man shook his head. "My father has ordered the two of us to stay here and learn as much as we can. Tanner Bryne has already returned to let my father know some of what has transpired."

"Good." Eaton nodded. "Your father and the disposition of the army are going to be critical elements in this. Rhue has stripped our military bare here at home. The only true operable force left is the Home Guard, and we know how much good that will be to us with that lackey Holt in charge."

"What about the warlords, sir? Surely men like Tyson Barg and Edo Talmedge will not stand for having to serve a Torbekian," Lando Berk questioned.

The elder Montel shook his head. "You would think that to be the case but it might be too late to count on any type of support from them. Rhue is far too smart to ignore their power and influence. It is far more likely that he has already bought their cooperation or has a plan to deal with them should they cause a problem. They are hard to figure; it was their support for King Edmond that helped force the Torbekians to sign the peace treaty ten years ago. If it hadn't been for the bargain he worked so hard getting them to agree to, we would still be fighting. For their part, they have bided by their promises."

Hale Eaton snorted in disgust and slammed his hooks hard upon the table. "Thieves, bullies, and cutthroats! Men like Tyson Barg and Edo Talmedge think of nothing more than filling their vaults with more gold and silver, and naught a piece of it come by honestly. They can't be trusted. They will tack their sails which way the wind blows most favorable."

"Truth that be for the most part friend Hale," agreed Derric Lynn. "Yet one cannot overlook them if you seek to control Artura. King Edmond was smart enough to realize that when he forged the deal bringing them into the war. They have money, arms, and the men to use them. Their spy networks are as good and as deep as anyone's, mostly because they don't trust each other."

"I find I must agree with Derric on that, Hale," Montel added. "We must reach out to them discreetly and see if there may be an opportunity. As distasteful as it might be, we cannot afford to ignore them. In the end, they will not remain neutral; we will fight with them or against them."

"We will need to be well funded for this endeavor," continued Derric Lynn. "Loyalty to one's country is a noble thing but money will open doors that might remain closed to us otherwise, though bankers and businessmen will be hesitant to fund open rebellion. But I think many of them are already of the conclusion that Rhue will find a way to empty their pockets regardless. There are also foreign interests who fear the notion of a Torbekian sitting on the Arturan throne. My many years of work in finance and commerce have allowed me to gather quite a large variety of associates, many who owe me favors. It is time to call those favors due."

Horace Montel looked about the table into each man's eyes. "So there is our plan my friends, such as it may be. It will be slow but we have no other choice. All the favorable cards are in the hand of Daemon Rhue. Hopefully, if we give him no reason to suspect us, we will have time to stack the deck before the next hand is dealt."

The men eyed each other; there was a resolute grimness about the table as they all wrestled with the realization they had started down a path from which there was no return. As Horace Montel looked in the face of each, it gave him a glimmer, albeit a small one, of hope. It would be men like these who would carry the fate of the nation on their shoulders, but as proud as he was, his heart was heavy with the weight of what they were facing.

"We plan insurrection gentlemen, to put it bluntly. Bloodshed will be guaranteed and much of it spilled by our countrymen fighting each other. It saddens me greatly to think that we have come so far as a nation and yet stand at the brink of throwing it all away; it is a heavy price to pay for our negligence. But with all this talk of who might stand with us or against us we are forgetting one very important part of what is happening here."

The men looked around the table at each other with puzzled expressions. "What are we forgetting Horace?" Hale Eaton questioned.

"Gentlemen, we have gathered for two reasons," the elder Montel answered. "One, we know that King Edmond is no longer fit to rule this country. Two, we know that we will not stand aside and allow a Torbekian to sit on the throne in his stead. Are we all in agreement to that?" Four heads nodded in unison.

"What we are forgetting is that the solution to both of those issues lies in a fourteen-year-old girl who has no idea at all of what confronts her. The rightful ruler of Artura is Alicia Daine and to think Daemon Rhue will ever allow her to sit on the throne is absurd. Her life is in danger and it is our solemn duty to protect her at all costs."

The men looked around the table at each other and then back to Horace Montel. They had indeed forgotten the pretty, blonde teenager who was more interested in pampering her cats than paying any attention to the fact that she might one day rule a country.

"What are we going to do about her, Horace?" Eaton asked. "She doesn't have a clue."

"Of that I am sure, Hale. She is an immature, spoiled brat who giggles constantly in the most annoying way, and even if the elders started now, they would be lucky if she was prepared to lead the country in four years. But regardless, she is the rightful heir to the throne and it is our duty to shield her from Rhue. I do not know what he has planned, but I am sure that handing this country over to her in four years is not what he has in mind."

"We don't know what Rhue's next move is, Horace."

"No, we don't, Derric, but I am of the feeling he will take things slow and try to make it appear that he has every intention of fulfilling the king's wishes. He will use subterfuge and coercion as he has all along to strengthen his position. I believe that Alicia is safe for now. He will go through the motions of having the elders prepare her to rule, keeping her and them out of his way. We must be vigilant and start gathering support against him. But we must be careful, our every move will be watched and none of us will be able to do much if we are rotting in the dungeon awaiting execution on charges of treason and sedition. Agreed?"

The men nodded their heads and Eaton continued. "Good. We will get together again soon. Use only secure means of communication and be wary with whom you speak. Kellen, you and Lando must stay out of sight. Use your skill to observe but remember, there are many who will recognize you if spotted. Disguise and guile will be valuable tools for the both of you. We will not be able to help if either of you are caught."

"We understand, Minister. We will be careful," Kellen answered for the two of them.

"Good." Hale Eaton looked one more time deep into the eyes of each man. "Stay safe, my friends. It is a dangerous path we tread. We will leave five minutes apart to avoid suspicion. Stay to the back streets."

Montel stood up from the table and the other men followed suit. He put his right hand out to the center. Each in turn placed theirs upon his, the cold hard hook of Hale Eaton's right hand adding a foreboding grimness to the process. "For king and country, gentlemen."

"For king and country," they replied in unison.

Daemon Rhue warmed himself by the fire blazing in the hearth as a serving girl nervously set a large table with wine, cheese, and fruit, hurrying to do so, as she was deathly afraid of the first council. She kept her head bowed and took care not to drop or spill anything.

They were in one of the more lavishly furnished rooms of the castle. The great table and matching chairs about which the servant girl bustled were of dark mahogany and were intricately carved with figures of animals and huntsmen. Set in the room's lone outside facing wall were enormous windows stretching from floor to ceiling, allowing as much of the sun to warm the room as possible on those cold days, of which there were many in this part of Artura. Under these windows comfortable couches beckoned the weary to rest and take in the light. Three huge tapestries adorned the remaining walls, each a detailed scene of the country itself—a seascape with an old castle perched high on the edge of a precipitous cliff, majestic towering mountains on another, and on the third, an image of Castle Daine and the city of Tiernon overlooking the great River Tier. Giant woven rugs of intricate patterns covered nearly every single foot of the stone floor, adding warmth to the room not found in most of the castle. It was a room fit for the entertainment of friends and dignitaries.

But Rhue's mind was not on the girl, the drink, the food, or the splendor of the room. At the moment, he was very pleased with himself and might have even overlooked a mishap by a clumsy young wench had she been careless. Today had been a success and he had managed to pull it off without shedding any blood but he was sure plenty of that would come. The lack of pushback from the assembly had actually been a disappointment, causing him to waste a very prepared plan and which might have made his job easier by eliminating a few dissenters at the point of a sword, but still he was content. All in all, it had been a good day and most important, Master Taul would be pleased.

As the serving girl left, a steward stepped into the room. "Lord Rhue. Members of the elder council and General Holt, here as you requested, sir."

"Send them in," Rhue replied without turning away from the comfort of the fire. "And steward, tell the guard we are not to be disturbed in any way. Is that understood?"

"Yes, your Lordship." The man bowed low and left the room. Moments later, four men entered. Rhue finally turned from the fire.

"Gentlemen, welcome," he greeted cordially and waved his arm towards the table. "Please help yourself to some refreshment. It has been a long day and while I am sorry for dragging you away from the comforts of your homes at this late hour, there are pressing matters requiring our attention. I am sure you all understand?"

While all of the men had grumbled as they were summoned from the warmth and comfort of their individual abodes, none of them dared mention this to Daemon Rhue. Instead, they took the opportunity to help themselves to the table prepared for them.

While they had all partaken of their own suppers previously, they could not ignore the quality of what had been set out. None was eager to refuse the hospitality of the man who now held absolute power. They were not, after all, stupid men.

"Your Lordship. The wine is excellent."

"Why thank you, Elder Thrain." Daemon Rhue nodded amiably. His mood had changed considerably since the assembly earlier in the day. He had gotten what he wanted, had been challenged, though not to the extent he had planned, and had smoothly transitioned the balance of power. For once the enigmatic first council was actually in a good mood.

"It is a special and, I might add, a very rare vintage coming from one of the better wine producing regions south of Sectos. Do the rest of you concur with Elder Thrain's assessment?"

There were nods and grunts of agreement as wine goblets were emptied and refilled. Their displeasure at having been summoned away from their homes at such a late hour had evaporated with the taste of what was truly a treat. While they were all members of what was considered upper class in Arturan society, wines such as the one they were partaking of were expensive enough that even the well-to-do would not likely keep a bottle in their cellar. Add this to the fact that the first council seemed to be in a genuine good mood, the anxiety of being called for a meeting at such a late hour was quickly washed away with each gulp of the fine spirits. Daemon Rhue smiled.

"I am pleased that I have selected a vintage that agrees with all of you. It will be arranged for several bottles to be delivered to each of your homes. Please try the cheese. It is also a rare delicacy and complements the wine." There were acknowledgements and grunts of appreciation from around the table as the men wasted no time in heeding the suggestion of their gracious host.

"Now my good men, to business. I know you are all wondering why I called you at this late hour and I do appreciate the fact that you were able to attend. There are things weighing heavily on my mind and you are just the men who can ease some of that which troubles me."

Elder council member Shamus Troy paused the goblet that was heading for his lips. "I thought you would be pleased with the outcome of the assembly today Lord Rhue."

"Oh, no! Please don't misunderstand me, Elder Troy. The session went well enough. It was indeed a momentous occasion, and although the circumstances of what transpired today are grievous to us all we can say that the king's wishes were carried out. But along that line lays the thing which troubles me and I would pose this question to you all. What would be the intent of those few who sought to deny the explicit wishes of their sovereign, including two members of your own council?"

The four men paused as one in their eating and drinking. There was an uncomfortable silence until Shamus Troy spoke.

"Your Lordship, surely you understand that today's events are unprecedented in our long history. While we have all known for some time that the king's health was deteriorating, I think it was a shock to many who realized for the first time how close to death he actually is. There were dissenters yes, but now, as the reality of the situation sets in, these men will come to see that the decisions made today will be of the best interest for the country."

Daemon Rhue nodded but the smile had left his face. "I appreciate your candor Elder Troy, and also your efforts to play peacemaker here, but let us not sugarcoat the events and try to cover the truth of what transpired today in the Great Hall. Those members of the assembly, and your brethren on the elder council, who chose to ignore the wishes of their rightful king, are guilty of seditious thoughts—treason by a simpler name."

The good mood had been broken and the wine and cheese had lost some of its taste. Rhue continued. "Hard words to swallow even with a draught of fine wine, I see. But the fact is this, there is a conspiracy underway, the goal of which I am sure is to thwart that which occurred today."

Shamus Troy set his wine goblet down on the table. "You have proof of this my Lord?"

"Proof enough to be concerned, Elder Troy. General Holt, will you please tell the council members what you have found so far?"

The general clumsily swallowed the large piece of cheese he had been chewing, quickly washing it down with a swig of wine. "Yes, your Lordship. Today, just before the assembly call to order, there was an exchange between two of the ministers. One of those ministers left the assembly, even though all were ordered explicitly to attend. He managed to leave the hall with an excuse that was found to be a lie; he left the castle, and then appears to have left the city. It also seems there was a clandestine meeting held earlier this evening attended by at least three of the assembly members. We were unable to discern the exact location of this meeting or who may have been present."

"And the names of these ministers, General Holt?" asked Bernard Thrain.

The general looked towards Daemon Rhue before answering. The first council nodded his head. "The minister who left the assembly under false pretenses today was Cedric Montel. The man he met with just before he left was his father Horace. It is also believed that Ministers Montel, Eaton, and Lynn were amongst those who met tonight somewhere near the old docks."

Enis Beckworth spoke up. "But just meeting at any time of the night or anywhere in the city violates no law, my Lord Rhue. Those men were perfectly within their rights to do so."

"They may be within their rights to meet but it is the content of that meeting which concerns me, Elder Beckworth. If I believe there is reason to think they are planning treasonous activity then it is my duty as the legitimate, albeit interim, sovereign of this nation to act accordingly. Is it not?"

Beckworth was a weak man and not up to challenging a personality such as Daemon Rhue, and the tone of the new ruler of Artura made it clear he would tolerate nothing less than total agreement.

"It is your right and duty my Lord," came the mumbled answer.

"Thank you, Elder, for your support." Daemon Rhue made no effort to hide the sarcasm in his voice. "As to the matter of Cedric

Montel, I have ordered General Holt to issue a warrant for his arrest. Leaving the assembly when all ministers were ordered to attend was an unlawful act, was it not, Elders?" The three men nodded their heads in agreement.

Rhue continued. "Very well, then. I have also ordered Elder Bolk to be put under house arrest for his contemptuous and inflammatory comments at today's assembly. His place at the Council table is forfeit until I decide on further action."

"But Lord Rhue," Shamus Troy stammered, "the elder council cannot function when there is a chance of a split decision. Its makeup must be of an odd number."

"I understand fully Elder, and I have no intention of thwarting the intent of Arturan law. That is why I am also relieving Petr Cain of his place at the Council table. Now the elder council totals three, you have the odd number needed to function."

An uncomfortable silence permeated the room as the Elders looked helplessly at each other. But Daemon Rhue wasn't finished and his voice took on a menacing tone.

"But you need not concern yourselves with trivial matters like the makeup of your precious council. You will not be required to function as you have in the past. Getting the princess ready for her ascension to the throne is your mandate from the king and you will concentrate wholly on fulfilling that mandate. I do not require you to guide me on matters of state. It was your decision that fulfilled the king's wishes and granted me whole and unfettered rule of this country until the princess reaches eighteen and I will do so without any interference. Dissent will not be tolerated. Is that understood?"

It was a direct challenge but one the Elders were totally unprepared to act against. They had indeed, by their vote at the morning's assembly, handed complete control over the country to Daemon Rhue and he had just rendered them completely powerless. The castration of the Arturan elder council had been completed by one sharp slice of Daemon Rhue's cunning. The three meekly answered together.

"Yes, your Lordship."

"Good. General Holt, you have arranged for the news of today's events to go out through official channels?"

"Yes, Lord Rhue. The dispatch riders will leave at dawn and ships bearing the news will leave the docks at the same time."

"Excellent. Most of the city is already aware of it thanks to the assembly, I am sure. You know your orders concerning the handling of any dissent amongst the people?"

General Holt nodded enthusiastically. He was one Arturan fully pleased with the way events had transpired. "Patrols will be out in force and no gatherings larger than a few people will be allowed to form. A network of infiltrators will be listening for any seditious talk. Those guilty of such will be arrested immediately and taken to the dungeons."

"Good. It may also be necessary to make an example of some of them General, especially if there are a large number of people watching. Busted heads and broken limbs can be a much better deterrent than just watching someone carted off in chains. Have your men erect some pillories and a new gallows in the town square. That will get their attention."

Rhue addressed the elders again. "You can still be of a great service to your country, gentlemen. I am now ruler of this nation and retribution for any who doubt it will be swift and sure. The people respect you and will listen to your counsel. Dissuade them of any wild notions, for their lot has already been decided. They will walk this ground in abeyance to the rule of law or they and their families will be buried under it." He turned away from the table and walked to the fireplace. "The hour is late. You are dismissed."

"Yes, Lord Rhue," the men replied in unison and quickly exited the room, leaving the first council alone in front of the fireplace. After allowing adequate time after they left, he finally spoke.

"You may come out now, Steyr." From behind one of the huge tapestries on the wall the fat physician emerged.

"Quite a convenient little spy hole I must say, my Lord, especially with the passage coming out under the stairs to the king's attendant's rooms," Steyr said as he walked over and filled himself a glass of wine.

"Yes it is. The castle is full of them and I am sure I have not found them all. A good reminder that while they serve us well, there always may be the chance that someone else may be using one of these to counter us. We must be mindful of that possibility at all times."

"Of course, my Lord. Have you decided what to do with Montel and his pack of traitors?"

Daemon Rhue shook his head as he continued to stare into the fire. "You heard the reaction from Troy, did you not? The old fool is worried any move against them will mean trouble from their supporters, and there are many, but I will not worry about them too much for the moment. General Holt has his orders; from here forward they won't be able to use a garderobe without us knowing it. But it troubles me that they were able to get together tonight right under our noses."

He spun quickly and glowered at the physician who was just getting ready to stuff a thick piece of bread slathered with rich fish roe into his mouth.

"That should not have happened Steyr."

"I am sorry, your Lordship," the fat man answered, hastily dropping the food back onto the serving tray. "There were men assigned the task of following them. I assumed—"

"You assumed?" Daemon screamed as he hurled the wine goblet he had been holding at the physician. Steyr was able to turn at the last second as the goblet bounced off his shoulder, spraying him with red wine.

"We have a treasonous plot at work against us yet you sit back dabbling with one of your young playmates and assume that people are doing their jobs? I needed evidence of rebellion. I wanted to catch Montel and his cronies together."

Steyr was in a deep bow with his head down and his hands clasped in front of him. He was too worried about the extent of his master's wrath to bother trying to clean the wine from him. It dripped off his bald head and spattered the ornate carpet like blood from a head wound. He wailed like an eight-year-old child about to get a bad spanking. "Please, Lord Rhue. I will attend to the matter myself. I beg of you to let me make amends. I will catch these seditious traitors and deliver them to you for justice."

"Quit groveling you miserable fool and clean that wine up. I have every intention of allowing you the chance to redeem yourself."

Steyr look up meekly and started to wipe the dripping wine from his head with the sleeve of his robe. "Yes, your Lordship. I will not fail you again."

"You had better not. There are two tasks that are going to be critical, Steyr, and failure to do either will make you the most miserable person in this miserable country. I want evidence of Montel and his bastard son Cedric's treasonous activities and I want it soon. There are still many things that need to happen before I have this stinking place totally under my boot heel and I can't afford to waste time dealing with that rabble. The other thing which causes me concern is that source of magic which came from Darkwood. Contact your witch and have her find it. That is far more troublesome than the threat of insurrection from a few aging ministers. Do you understand?"

The physician's bald head bobbed up and down. "Yes, Lord Rhue. Yes."

"Very well. Just one more thing, Steyr. It is still necessary to make this charade look plausible, at least for a while. We will go through the motions of having the Elders prepare the darling little princess for rule. This will appease the populace and keep the ministers and others off my back. If the spoiled little bitch was to come to harm while this is happening it would upset our plans and this I cannot allow. You will not touch her until I give you leave. If you dare disobey me I will cut off your hands, stick them up your fat ass and then cut off your miserable little prick and stuff it in your mouth before I hang you. Is that understood?"

Steyr bowed low and bobbed his head. He understood all too well and his balls shriveled instinctively into the deep folds of his fat as a bloody vision of the possibility flashed through his head.

But it also steeled his resolve. There was no prize anywhere in the world that could take the place of that which he had sought for so long. It was the main reason he had sold his soul to Daemon Rhue many years ago. He had watched the princess as she grew, her lovely blonde hair bouncing as she ran chasing her cats and playing about the castle. Every time he lay with one of his little pretties, either male or female, he had visions of her. Yes, he would go to the ends of the earth to get his master what he wanted. She would someday be his to do with as he absolutely pleased. Daemon Rhue had promised.

CHAPTER TWENTY-THREE

WILLOUGHBY WAS BEING SMOTHERED. HIS chest and lungs felt like someone had driven a truck on top of him and parked it there. He labored for every breath and he was entering panic mode as he fought for air. It was like his sick dream. Every time he got sick and ran a fever, he had the same dream where he was being smothered by a giant pillow, except this was no pillow.

He wiggled his body in an effort to get out from under whatever it was that had him pinned, but the rocks jammed painfully into his back. He tried pushing the big dark thing off the top of him but it was too heavy. His hands gripped thick, coarse fur as he grunted and shoved, trying to get a little of the pressure off his chest so he could breathe. The hairy pillow stunk and he could feel a warm, wet stickiness on his hands as he tried desperately to move out from under it.

The wolf. Fenrir. It came back to him in a rush. The Wolf King had jumped across the fire at him. The last thing he remembered was holding his sword out in front with both hands and bracing for impact; the impact he thought was going to kill him. But he wasn't dead, and the thing on top of him felt like it was.

Willoughby pushed hard and continued to wiggle his body back and forth, ignoring the rocks as they dug into him in a hundred places. The need to breathe was far more important than rocks digging into his back. But as he squirmed, he felt movement—the massive animal lying on top of him was stirring.

The big body shuddered and Willoughby could feel its labored breathing. Slowly the wolf tried to raise itself on its front legs, relieving some of the pressure from the boy's chest, but it couldn't get all the way up and Willoughby could now see why—the sword was still imbedded in the great animal's chest.

Frantically he attempted to slip out from underneath the wolf while he had the opportunity but just as he was about to squirm free, a massive paw and foreleg slammed down onto his chest and held him. The wolf brought his great head up and poised it right over Willoughby's; blood and saliva dripped onto the boy's face. He could hear the harsh and shallow rattling of the animal's chest as it struggled to force air into lungs restricted by a foot and a half of steel. Bloody red snot bubbles popped from the huge nostrils as Fenrir struggled to speak.

"The magic in the weapon is strong, pup. Much stronger than I gave it credit for. It is the reason you still live, but you must learn to control it if you want to survive. Its former owner must have been a worthy man indeed to wield such magic. Do him justice and make yourself worthy of the gift he has bestowed upon you."

The mighty wolf took a rasping breath and with a heave rolled over and off Willoughby. The boy scrambled to his feet and was just about to take off running when he stopped. Fenrir wasn't going anywhere.

He lay on his side, the sword sticking out from his chest between the forelegs. Willoughby's aim had been true, or it was just that he was mighty lucky; the point of the blade had driven straight into the white star on the wolf's chest.

The urge to run was strong but the wolf didn't look threatening anymore. He scanned the bank for the rest of the pack, but they were nowhere to be seen. The young female wolf he had killed lay on the other side of the fire, which had now died down to nothing but coals. The first light of the new day was just starting to break through the gloom of the forest, giving testimony that he had evidently been knocked out for quite some time.

Fenrir was still breathing, but barely, the chest rising ever so slowly. Willoughby could hear the air suck in from around the wound. When the beast exhaled, it sounded like someone blowing bubbles through a straw in a soda, but the bubbles were a foamy red mess. The great wolf lay dying slowly and even though it had meant to kill him, Willoughby felt a deep pang of regret.

Fenrir's eyes slowly opened; they no longer glowed with the vibrant red and yellow as they had when the boy had first seen them. The fire within was fading fast.

"Come closer," the wolf spoke in a labored whisper, its lips barely moving.

Willoughby hesitated. He wasn't really afraid of the beast anymore, but was still cautious.

"Come closer," Fenrir whispered again.

This time Willoughby complied with the wolf's command. He knelt down and leaned forward on his hands to get closer to the huge head. The words came slow and forced, he could barely make them out.

"I have not much time left alive, pup, but I have lived long and free and have no regrets. I fought hard to become King of the Wolves and had to fight many times to keep my place. My many victories made me too sure of myself and I now pay for my carelessness but I take solace in the fact that it was not you alone that has bested me. I can hold my head up when I meet my ancestors knowing I was overcome by strong magic and not just by a human pup still wet behind the ears. The magic that killed me was in your hands, though I think you are not aware of its potential. As the victor, you can take my magic when I am gone; it is yours by right of combat."

The words rattled off into nothingness. Willoughby thought for a moment the beast was dead but a slight rise in Fenrir's chest told him that there was still a small amount of life left.

"But I don't know how to take your magic," he leaned in close and whispered to the dying wolf. "Tell me how."

For a while there was no response and Willoughby thought he was too late. But after a long pause, Fenrir spoke again.

"My fangs, pup. The source of my magic lies in my fangs. Pull them and wear them close to your heart. If you can find the way to tap their power, they will be a talisman to be reckoned with. Add their

magic to that of the sword and you would become a mighty warrior indeed. They will also protect you from my kin; the pack will never harm you as long as you wear them."

Willoughby rocked back on his heels. "Pull out your teeth! I can't do that."

There was a long, liquid sounding gurgle in response; the snot bubbles popped. *"You drive the blade of a sword deep into my chest yet you cannot pull my fangs? You are a mystery, pup."*

"You were right. It was the sword. I just held it and it seemed to do the rest. I am sorry."

Willoughby watched as the life slowly seeped from the great beast. Fenrir's muzzle lay in the sand and gravel, a puddle of foamy blood had formed around his mouth and nostrils, the lips were curled back and the canine teeth were exposed. They were huge. Of what Willoughby could see, the ivories were nearly four inches long.

Are they really magic? He thought silently as he watched the great wolf slowly die. In response, the eyes slowly opened again.

"Take them, boy," Fenrir rasped. *"The witch will, if you do not. She and I have had a truce for many years, but she is cunning and evil and seeks power in any form. She will sense your magic and come after you. Take the fangs and leave this forest as quickly as you can. Follow the river and it will lead you to your kind. You must..."*

Fenrir took one last, wheezing breath, let it out slowly, and lay still. The eyes closed one last time. The King of the Wolves was dead.

Willoughby stared at the great black form lying lifeless in front of him and started to rock gently back and forth. He was having trouble putting his thoughts together. He knew he should do something, but his mind was in overload and was shutting itself down for protection. The sound of the river added an ambient hypnotic effect as Willoughby's state of cognizance went into pause mode. He just stared and rocked.

The trance was a complete one, so much so that when it shattered abruptly he never so much as twitched. When the sound registered, he never stopped rocking, he just slowly opened his eyes. Things started to regain focus; the wolf's massive and very dead body, the fire with the un-burnt ends of limbs he had piled on hours ago pointing like fingers to its smoldering center. Just beyond that, the body of the she-wolf he had killed, its head lolling at a right angle to its neck, showing the force of Willoughby's sword strike. The rest of the gravel bar leading up to the vertical riverbank, and now, there on top of the bank, Fenrir's pack had returned.

They were sitting much as Willoughby was, back on their haunches. They looked straight at the boy and he stared back, still rocking gently. The wolves raised their heads to the sky in unison and broke into a mournful chorus, the different notes of each animal blending in weird harmony with the omnipresent sound of the river. The howls would taper off into nothingness and then, on cue, let loose again. Willoughby just stared, rocked, and listened. He wasn't afraid because he knew exactly what it was—a death symphony for their king. They weren't going to rip him to pieces, though at this point he would have just sat there and welcomed it, he was that spent. Their song was praise and sadness, respect and mourning. Willoughby just rocked and listened, tears flowing freely down his blood-splattered face.

But the symphony ended abruptly. The big she-wolf, mate of the dead king and the one who had led the pack to Willoughby, got to her feet and the others followed suit. With one last look towards the boy and her fallen mate, she turned and trotted off into the forest; all followed her but one. The one having the identical coloring as the giant lying in front of Willoughby, stared down from the bank. The two youngsters, one human and one wolf, locked eyes. The animal spoke to the boy with his mind. *"I see you."*

Willoughby never broke from the young wolf's gaze—his mind answered. *I see you.*

The young wolf dipped its head in acknowledgement, spun, and vanished into the shadow of the wood.

Willoughby didn't move for a long time. When he finally forced himself from the clutches of his mental trance, he slowly and painfully struggled to his feet. His upper body ached terribly and his legs were numb from his squatting position. He winced with the feeling of a million tiny needles attacking his legs as the blood flowed back into the restricted vessels.

His face and chest were caked with dirt, blood, and saliva that had hardened to an uncomfortable crust. Forcing his still semi-numb legs to move, he stiffly hobbled to the river. He sunk to his knees, cupped his grimy hands, and bent to the water. The relief was instantaneous as the cold water loosened and gently washed away the slimy residue of Fenrir's death and the trails his own tears had left.

Willoughby washed as much as he could off his face and hands but decided against spending the time trying to get the stuff off his sweatshirt. He had snapped out of his trance and finally started to focus, forcing a promise out of himself not to try and make any type of sense of the things that had transpired. He was sure it would drive him over the edge that he was already dangerously close to.

The need to leave was driving Willoughby now. Fenrir's words of warning concerning a witch were spooking him into action. He wanted out of this forest.

When he had his belongings packed, he turned his attention to the sword. It lay still buried between the forelegs in the great wolf's chest. Reaching down, he grabbed the sword grip with his right hand and tugged; it didn't budge. He sat down directly in front of the animal, pushing the huge forelegs and head to the side as best he could. With his feet planted against the bloody chest, he gripped the pommel with both hands. By pushing with his legs and pulling with his entire upper body, the sword finally slid free from its fleshy embrace. Using Fenrir's fur, he wiped as much of the blood, hair, and shreds of meat off the blade as he could. He would clean it better later on, but for now it would have to do. It was when he was wiping the sword the last time that he noticed the fangs.

They are his magic—his totem. Take them. Willoughby shook his head. It was Jake's voice as plain as if the big man had been standing right next to him. But he didn't know if he could do it. You didn't just reach down and pull the things out like they were stuck in jello. While he certainly was no expert in dentistry, he was pretty sure those over-sized chompers were attached in a very secure way.

But something besides Jake's voice told him he had to. It had been the wolf's last wish—his command, more like it. They were his by right of combat as bizarre and uncivilized as it seemed. It still made no sense, but there was a feeling deep inside the teen's psyche that this primitive and morbid act was an acceptable thing to do under the circumstances. There wasn't much of anything making sense right at the moment but Fenrir had told him he would find his own kind if he followed the river. While Willoughby harbored no inclination that he might find Spirit Falls, anyplace, or anyone would be better than where he was and the wolf's advice was the best thing he had.

He lay sword aside and took out his pocket knife. He shuddered as he thought of the task ahead of him but he wanted to get on the move again. He had had enough of this place.

It took him a long time and it was messy. Rolling the huge head around to where he could get at the mouth, he pulled the lips back and began cutting the gums as deep as he could between the fangs and the rest of the wolf's teeth. But there was not much soft tissue; they were going to have to be broken free from the bone of the jaw by force. He gripped each of the fangs and started pushing and pulling. He sat on the wolf's head, with his body weight holding it down so he was able to gain leverage as he pushed on one fang and pulled on the other. With an actual "pop" the first one broke free, and with a few more rocking tugs, it came out of the jawbone. The other soon followed. The nasty job was done. After rinsing them free of blood and saliva, he held them up.

In total, the things were nearly five inches in length and curved just slightly. Willoughby shuddered as another gory thought came into his head—how many humans had these teeth ripped apart? But it didn't matter; he had done it. He held in his hands the power of the King of the Wolves. Like Jake had said, this was the animal's totem, his symbol. When he got the chance, he would fasten them into a necklace and hang them around his neck. Close to the heart. That is what Fenrir had told him, close to the heart.

For the time being, he slipped them into the pockets of his jeans. They poked him a bit and were uncomfortable with their size but he didn't want to let them get too far from him.

When he had geared up and his pack was secure, he looked once more on the body of the great wolf. It was sad in a strange way, even though the beast had meant to kill and eat him. He felt he needed to say something.

"I am sorry, Fenrir. I don't know why or how any of this is happening. I have never killed anything bigger than a bug in my whole life. To kill you and the female was never my intention. I have done as you said and have your fangs. I will keep them close by my heart. I don't have any idea on how to access whatever power they might have, but maybe I'll figure it out. I have a bad feeling I am going to need all the help I can get."

The sun was well up and the cold of the morning had for the most part gone. Except for a few clouds, it had the appearance of being a good day. From what he could figure by the direction the sun had come up, Willoughby thought the river flowed pretty much towards the west. He had decided he would stick to the trail as long as it kept close to the river, venturing deeper into the woods was not going to happen if he could help it. He scanned the campsite one last time; it had been an amazing night and would make a helluva story if he ever made it out of his predicament alive. But that was a big "if."

Willoughby jerked one of the spears out of the sand where he had planted his defensive picket yesterday; he couldn't see the sense in leaving them all. A lot of time had been spent working them into usable weapons and he was positive there would be ample opportunities to use one again. But another idea clicked in his head and he threw the spear he had just picked up to the side; it wasn't the one he wanted. He walked over to the body of the young female wolf; the spear he had stuck deep into the soft belly was lying underneath her. She wasn't anywhere close to the size of Fenrir and Willoughby was able to work it out from under her with no problem. The last foot of the weapon was still wet with the female's dark blood, but he didn't bother to wipe it off. In a carnal and raw way, this made the most sense. This was a spear that had killed.

Once back on the trail, Willoughby was pleased to see that for the most part it stayed near the river. He traveled at an easy pace, while wanting to put distance between him and his nightmare. He was pretty tired and beat to shit. With everything that had happened in the last however many days since he went over the falls, he was damned near a walking bruise with a scab on it. He hadn't eaten since the fish the day before and his clothes were again in need of a rinsing. Fenrir's blood and fluids had soaked the front of his sweatshirt dried to a hard crust. He would never get the stain out but at least it could be used as evidence as to some of what he had been through.

Uncomfortable as it was, Willoughby kept moving, resolving to toughen himself to his situation. At an easy walk, stopping at intervals for rest and water, he could manage the aches, pains, and the empty stomach. He was also resigned to the fact that another campsite would be needed. He had still seen nothing that might give him hope of finding people and he would stop early enough in the afternoon to find a good site to spend the night. Another fish would be a nice way to end the day, so he would give himself time enough to try his fishing technique again.

The forest bothered him the most. Omnipresent and foreboding, it loomed menacingly and Willoughby could sense a presence hidden deep inside. It was more than just being made of living and growing things, more than the sense of the place being incredibly old. It was an ancient forest, that was what the environmentalists who came out of places like Eugene would call it, and there was something that permeated the shadows of the dark wood. In the hardwood corridor flanking the river channel it wasn't so noticeable, but it was something he had felt the first day when passing through the forest as he made his way to the river. There was a presence somewhere out there amongst the trunks of the giant trees, in the deep recesses where the mushrooms and toadstools shied from the light. It swirled with the fog in and around the ferns, into the hollows and crevices formed by the sprawling root networks of the towering conifers. Willoughby didn't have a name to place on his fear—he just knew that it was evil.

But he continued on. Walking had actually warmed and loosened his sore muscles and if it wasn't for the fact he was so friggin' hungry it would have been an enjoyable hike. He had company too, small birds flittering out of his way, squirrels chattering their annoyance as he passed. Ducks and geese resting in the calmer backwaters of the river and once, when he rounded a bend, he surprised a herd of strange-looking deer catching a mid-morning drink on the opposite side of the river. They were nice to see, but they also made him start thinking again about his situation. Willoughby had seen a lot of deer and elk around Spirit Falls and most everyone had a rack of horns or a head mount somewhere. On the north side of the barn at his grandma's place was a whole wall of antlers, evidence of the Baxter family's hunting prowess. Jake kept close track of a large herd of elk that frequented the south pasture, making sure that poachers or hunters that chose to ignore the 'NO HUNTING' signs kept away. The big Indian still hunted and venison and elk steak often graced the dinner table at the ranch.

But what puzzled Willoughby as the herd bounded back into the safety of the deep wood once they spotted him was that they did not look like any of the animals he had seen. They definitely weren't blacktail, the most common of deer species inhabiting the western side of the Cascade Mountains. They were closer in size to elk but Roosevelt elk had a color pattern to them that was easily recognizable—dark brown hair above the front shoulders around the head and neck, a light tan torso and then a distinctive yellow-tan rump patch. The animals Willoughby saw had shaggy, reddish brown hair and appeared to be females and youngsters since there were no antlers to be seen. But he had definitely never seen anything in Oregon or California that had looked like that. Add another item to the ever-growing list of things that made no sense.

But while they may have been different than any of the elk and deer he was familiar with, it didn't take much effort for the boy to imagine a skillet full of backstrap and onions sizzling away on a fire. The thought of food was starting to override everything else and he was going to have to address it somehow.

Frustration was starting to mount; he could feel it building as he walked along. It always happened this way, whether dealing with jerks and other issues at school, dealing with his mom when she became upset with him, or just those times when remembering his dad triggered anger and resentment. Willoughby had a tendency to let bad things pile up inside of him, one right on top of another. He could feel the build-up of things but try as he might, he could not rid himself of them and when they got to a certain point—BOOM! Maximum overload and a whole lot of trouble. Just like what happened when he dropped Eddie Anderson.

"Your son has serious anger issues, Mrs. Baxter," the strange little therapist his mom forced him to go to before the move from San Diego had said to them. "He retains things inside, small things that most people cope with as they come up, but your son allows them to fester and stay locked up. More things get added that he doesn't want to deal with and soon you have a stew of nasty ingredients on a burner turned on high. Sooner or later they boil over."

What a fucking joke that guy turned out to be! Three hundred dollars a session! For what? The guy had Willoughby more messed up than ever.

"When things start to overwhelm you and build up inside, just find your happy place and focus on nothing but that," he had told Willoughby.

Okay, Willoughby thought to himself as he walked the trail. Here he was stuck in a strange place, with animals that could talk, and that were also trying to kill him. There had been nothing but two energy bars and a fish to eat for a long fucking time, yet Mr. Way Too Expensive Therapist would tell him to find his "happy place" and focus on it. A happy place—he didn't think he had much chance of finding one of those in the real near future.

Willoughby stopped to give his legs a break. By his recollection, he had been walking for several hours and they were starting to protest. Since he had left his campsite, he had kept to the game trail, which for the most part followed the river. He had crossed several intersecting paths, some just leading down to the river, and others leading back into the depth of the forest. Scanning the ground as he walked, he looked for any hint of human presence. A cigarette butt, gum wrapper, anything. But there was nothing but animal tracks and animal poop. Mostly deer or elk, whatever the things were. Twice he had seen wolf tracks but he didn't think they were fresh. A happy place for him to focus on right now would be a Budweiser can.

It was fortunate the game trail he was traveling on was one frequented by larger animals; they had the brush beat back so the going was fairly easy. It kept to the hardwood corridor which, for the most part, extended from the river bank about a hundred feet. At times, when the terrain demanded, it dipped into the edge of the forest, but he was thankful that the animals seemed to prefer to stay out of the dark depths of the woods just as much as he did.

While Willoughby couldn't see the river all of the time, he had been noticing a change in the landscape as he walked. While the trail stuck to a fair or moderate grade, the river channel had been dropping considerably. Although he couldn't see it, he could hear the change as the flow of the water funneling into the narrower channel turned into surging whitewater. The sound of an easy flow over rocks, sand, and gravel was now a thunderous cacophony through a deep canyon.

Willoughby came to a point where the trail made a sharp turn to the left. To his dismay, it seemed to be heading deeper into the forest. Ahead of him, he could see an opening through the trees. Hoping for the possibility that he might get a better look at where he would be heading, he decided to venture through the opening and take a look. When he broke out of the trees, he sucked in his breath at the magnificent panorama spreading out before him.

"Holy shit!" he exclaimed as he gazed at the view. A rocky promontory jutted out over the river gorge and the point where he was standing was easily a couple of hundred feet above the river.

What had been a serene and easy flowing stream was now a raging white torrent slamming through a narrow, rock-walled canyon. The spray from the churning whitewater hung like fog over the canyon. On the far side of the gorge the forest rose again, thick and foreboding. He was stunned as he followed its steady rise, up and up until the trees gave way to talus slopes similar to the ones he had traversed after his exit from the cave. The slopes gradually became white with snow and still they climbed. Higher and higher the peaks rose until they ended in jagged fingers thrust far into the sky. It was a mountain range such as Willoughby had never seen and it extended to the horizon. For the first time since he had come off the mountain and out of the cave, Willoughby was getting a good look at the landscape he now found himself in, and it certainly wasn't anything he had ever seen before.

He may have been a newcomer to the State of Oregon, but he had seen the Cascades enough in person and in pictures to know what he was looking at, and this wasn't them. The sheer scope of the mountain range made him dizzy. The shape of the peaks reminded him a lot of Mount Thielson, a jagged peak in the southern part of the state popular with hikers and rock climbers. Jake had a large framed picture of it hanging on the wall of his trailer and had actually been to the top of it. One of the more recognizable peaks in the state, it jutted out in a tall spire, like the rest of the earth had just fallen away from it. But what Willoughby was looking at was Mount Thielson multiplied ten times over, peak after jagged peak, like teeth on a saw, stretching away until he couldn't see any more. Up and down the river, the sight he beheld was the same; a mountain range such as he had never seen rising up and laughing at his smallness.

Willoughby was overcome by a sudden wave of nauseous vertigo, and it was fortunate that he wasn't any closer to the precipitous edge of the gorge than what he was. He plopped down on a flat rock and stuck his head between his knees. While it was a physical wave of dizziness that had caused his sudden affliction, there was a deeper element to his state, the same one he had been wrestling with since emerging from the cave. Seeing the mountains had pretty much been the straw that blew down the fucking house, or whatever the saying was supposed to be. It didn't matter, it all led to the same conclusion; there was no logical explanation for it, but it seemed that Spirit Falls and home were nothing more than a bad joke.

It took him a few deep breaths to finally settle himself down, and when he did, he shrugged off the pack and let it fall to the ground. Willoughby was battling the urge to break down and cry, but something much more dark and sinister was starting to wedge itself into the cracks of his consciousness. It suddenly occurred to him that there was a way to stop all the torment he was going through—a very simple way. Maybe it was because he found himself on top of a two-hundred-foot cliff with the river raging through a rock-lined canyon below that the idea had come up now and not before.

Confusion, fear, stress. The pain and trauma his body had suffered. All of his plagues could be forgotten with two quick steps. Willoughby raised his head and looked at the distance between the rock on which he was sitting and the edge of the gorge.

Do it, an inner voiced urged, *do it.*

Willoughby wanted to answer no, he didn't necessarily want to do as the voice demanded; the thought of being smashed on the rocks below wasn't really the happy place he was trying to focus on. But the reasons for complying were strong ones; it would be a simple way to end the turmoil racking his mind and body. Who could blame him? It would be like father like son. People said his dad had taken the coward's way out. Was he a coward like his dad? Could he take the same way out?

Oddly enough, an answer came to his troubled questions. As a distraught Willoughby sat there with his head resting between his legs, contemplating on whether or not to end his life, a strange "clucking" sound came from the trail behind him, interrupting his suicidal train of thought. Slowly he turned to look.

Twenty feet away, sitting on the jagged stump of a tree that had broken off years earlier, sat a bird slightly smaller than the average chicken. It had feathers that were different shades of brown with white streaks showing in between and a darker brown ring of ruffled feathers circled its neck. It sat there eyeing Willoughby with curiosity. As it watched the boy, it kept bobbing its head, each time making the "clucking" noise.

A hint of recognition flashed through Willoughby's brain, driving out the dark cancer of thought that had crept in. Similar birds lived along the edge of the Baxter ranch where the pasture line met the timber. A grouse. That was what was staring so intently at Willoughby. He was certain of it. And there was one more thing he was certain of, as he had the opportunity to find out one Sunday afternoon when he visited Jake's trailer.

"C'mon in," Jake had answered to Willoughby's rap on the trailer door. As he stepped in, a delicious aroma assailed the boy's nose as he found Jake busy in the small kitchen.

"Wow! That chicken really smells good!" Willoughby commented as he plopped down at the kitchen table.

"Shit, boy, don't you know nuthin'?" Jake chided as he flipped a crusty, golden piece of meat over in the frying pan. "This is the only thing that would rival your grandma's fried chicken."

"What is it?" Willoughby asked as he poked his head over the frying pan to get a closer look. "Looks like chicken."

"You could call it a Timber Chicken, I guess," Jake replied as he forked pieces onto a plate. "It's a Ruffed Grouse."

He sat a plate down at the small table and nodded for Willoughby to sit. "Try that on for size, son."

The boy picked up a leg and blew on it to cool it off. He pulled a small piece of the skin off and popped it into his mouth. It was still quite hot but the crispy morsel was absolutely delicious. With relish he tore into the rest of the leg.

"Good stuff, huh?" Jake asked as he tore into his own leg. "A mite smaller than a chicken and maybe a bit tougher since it's a wild bird, but that ain't nuthin' to complain about. Really need a couple of 'em to make up a good Sunday dinner but if you use the drippins to make up some gravy to go on top of some mashed spuds, there ain't much better 'n that."

Willoughby nodded in agreement as he had his mouth full of

the savory bird. There was just a hint of wildness to it and the texture was a little tougher than a chicken like Jake had said but the flavor couldn't be argued with.

"Gotta be careful when you shoot 'em," Jake continued. "Lots of people use a shotgun. I suppose that's okay if you're sportin' and want to get 'em on the fly. Don't care much for a shootin' 'em that way myself. End up with a bird full of lead shot you usually find with your teeth. But ol' Ruff'll just sit there like a dumb ass and let you pop 'im in the head with a 22. Don't ruin no meat that a way."

Willoughby's mouth watered and his stomach rumbled at the prospect that was, just like Jake had said, sittin' there like a dumb ass.

Carefully he turned away from the bird, nonchalantly trying to act like he wasn't aware it was there. Working his hand down to the flap of the pack he popped one of the plastic snaps open. *Damn,* he thought to himself as he felt inside for the wrist rocket. He had forgotten about the cooking pot and other stuff of Bob's he had added to the pack in the cave, and he was afraid of making any kind of clanking or rattling noise which might cause the bird to fly off. But just as he thought he would have to move the metal pot, his hand found the smooth, plastic grip of the slingshot. Carefully he eased it out of the pack. He set the weapon at his feet and listened—a satisfying cluck verified the bird was still there. His ball bearings were in one of the side pouches and fortunately on the side he needed them to be. Ever so carefully he extracted the tin box and eased the lid open, taking out one of the marble-sized bearings. Laying the box in the dirt at his feet, he fit the slingshot into his right hand and over his forearm, slipping the ball bearing into the leather pocket. He was ready.

Another "cluck" told him the bird was still there but now he was faced with a dilemma. He didn't want to have to shoot from a sitting position but would the bird fly if he tried to stand? Willoughby decided he had to chance standing up. The bird didn't seem too spooked by the way it had acted so far and if he moved slow enough it might just work.

Willoughby visualized his target—twenty feet, left side of the trail, three feet on top of the stump. Taking a deep breath, he slowly started to rise. *Easy,* he cautioned himself. As he rose, he pulled back the rubber tubing of the slingshot. The bird clucked.

Ever since Jake had given him the slingshot, Willoughby had found himself to be pretty efficient with the weapon when shooting cans set on a fencepost. But killing anything with it had so far eluded him. He had come close to whacking the big barn rats once or twice but they were smart and only exposed themselves when he was empty handed. Crows were even smarter yet and it was a waste of ammo to shoot at them.

Jake had been explicit when it came to what Willoughby could shoot at. It was one of the things he had to do to earn the 22 that the big Indian had promised, providing that his mother would eventually give the okay for him to have it.

"Be a responsible hunter. That's the first step," Jake had explained. "No shooting robins, squirrels, or chipmunks. Go after the pests. Show me that you can be responsible and we'll think about the 22."

Willoughby had never violated Jake's trust by shooting at helpless creatures which never caused any harm. There were plenty of varmints about that needed shooting but he still had never killed anything. But now he desperately needed his luck to change.

As he turned, he lined the leather pocket containing the steel missile into the center of the 'Y' of the slingshot. The grouse came into view and bobbed its head once more in curiosity. Willoughby let loose. The rubber tube snapped and feathers flew. In the next instant his target was thrashing violently in the trail.

"Yeahhh!" Willoughby screamed as he bolted for the flopping bird, afraid it might just be wounded and still able to fly off into the trees. But there was no need to hurry. When he got to the bird it had already stopped moving. His shot had been true and the ball bearing had struck right at the junction of the body and head; the grouse's neck had been broken instantly. It was a clean kill.

Willoughby was ecstatic as he held the bird up by one foot. Once he figured out how to clean it he would have a great meal and the prospect completely erased the morbid notion that had crossed his mind no more than a couple of minutes ago. As he returned to his pack, he felt disgusted with himself for even having the thought.

As hungry as he was, he decided against getting a fire going and cooking the grouse immediately. There was still more daylight left and he wanted to cover more ground before stopping to camp. Willoughby didn't like the spot he was in, it being much too close to the edge of the gorge and too much of a reminder of what he had just been contemplating. Though he was outrageously hungry, he would find a more suitable location.

Tying the grouse to one of the ties of the backpack, Willoughby loaded up and took one last look at the breathtaking vista. The river raged its way down the spectacular gorge, the dark, haunting countenance of the forest stretching away and climbing the slopes of the mountains before bowing to the most incredible peaks he had ever seen. It would have made a great picture postcard, but as beautiful and awe inspiring as it was, it was nothing more than torment and frustration. He had come a long way and had been through experiences that would make a great tale but cold reality kept slapping him in the face like a wet towel—Spirit Falls and his family felt farther away than they ever had.

Chapter Twenty-Four

WILLOUGHBY COULDN'T DECIDE WHICH WAS giving him the most grief—his legs, which had just about given in on him; his feet, which had developed some painful blisters; or his stomach, loudly demanding that it be attended to.

He had gone far enough. The river was too far down in the depths of the canyon to get to but he had come across a small stream running clean and clear from the forest before dropping over the edge of the gorge in a series of stair step falls to the river. It would have to do but it certainly was not a spot that thrilled Willoughby. Since the river had dropped into the gorge, the hardwoods had petered out and the trail traveled through the dark confines of the forest. Like it or not, he was going to have to spend the night in the unwelcome gloominess.

There was no real way to tell what time it was, but Willoughby guessed he had traveled for at least three or four more hours since he had killed the bird. He thought he had plenty of light left in which to prepare a camp and give him enough time to tend to his clothes and himself. The dried blood of Fenrir still covered both.

He decided to make his camp along the stream away from the gorge far enough that an unfortunate case of sleepwalking or blundering about in the dark taking a leak wouldn't put him over the edge, and he found the perfect spot a couple of hundred feet up the stream. A cluster of five giant cedars formed a semi-circle facing the gorge with the stream running next to them. It was the perfect backdrop for a camp and, as tired as he was, he set to work.

Fire was his first task. Pulling some large rocks from the creek bank, he formed a fire ring with a large flat stone to set his cooking pot on. There was plenty of deadfall close by and dry enough to suit perfectly and it wasn't long before the fire was burning nicely, chasing away much of the gloom from his campsite.

The next task was getting some of the nastiness washed from his sweatshirt. It and his jeans had taken the brunt of his fight with the wolf and were crusted with blood and dirt. He had cleaned his clothes before the encounter with the wolf pack and was thankful he didn't have to repeat the whole process over again. He chose to let the jeans ride, deciding that taking care of his sweatshirt would be work enough for the night. He peeled it off and squatted next to the creek to begin rinsing but was interrupted by an alarm going off in his head—*Think about where you're at, dumbass. There may be a lot of other things in this forest besides wolves that might like to kill you.*

Willoughby was learning the art of survival fast and it forced him to think differently here, wherever here was. Walking over to his backpack, he untied Bob's weapon harness and strapped it to his back. The cool of the leather seemed to ease the soreness of his battered torso, it felt like a part of his body. The weapon seemed to hum ever so slightly. It was the one phenomenon that didn't make him unsettled and frustrated. As unlikely the discovery of Bob and his equipment had been, even more so was the fact that the equipment seemed to have been made precisely for Willoughby.

It made him wonder even more as to just who "Bob" was. The sword had saved Willoughby's life. It defied logic but somehow he and the weapon had bonded—if that was the right term—and with that bond came a connection to the spirit of the person who had died in the cave, waiting for ever so many years. As he stood there, a fourteen-year-old wimp of a teenager, lost in a place where he shouldn't be and only hours past the time when he had actually entertained the thought of ending his own life, a new sense of empowerment came over him. Willoughby made up his mind he was going to survive this thing.

With the sword snug in its harness and his homemade spear within easy reach, he settled to the task of rinsing and wringing out his sweatshirt. Though he worked extra hard to get as much of the blood out as he could, Willoughby finally had to concede it was going to be a hopeless task. The stains were dark and deep and it appeared they were going to be constant reminders of his encounter with the Wolf King. When he had rinsed and wrung as much of the cold water out as possible he turned to place the sweatshirt near the fire to dry only to realize that he had forgotten to construct any kind of drying rack.

"Shit," Willoughby cursed. Good hardwood saplings were needed to build a rack and there were nothing but large conifers close at hand. Digging his hatchet out of the pack, he headed back down the creek to where it intersected the game trail and quickly spied what he was looking for, next to the drop off into the gorge, a clump of hardwood saplings. Finding several to his liking Willoughby bent down and was just about ready to start chopping when he felt a strange buzzing sensation against his back—the sword was sending him a warning.

He froze in a crouching position, clutching the hatchet tightly in his hand, wishing he had hold of the sword instead. The hair stood up on the back of his neck—someone or something was behind him.

"Drop the ax, stand up slow, and make no quick movements or they will be your last."

It was ironic but the fact that a human was standing behind him was actually a relief to Willoughby, who at first feared the return of the wolf pack. But that small bit of relief was tempered by the threatening tone of the person's voice—a vision of a deranged redneck with a shotgun pointed at his back flashed through his mind. Willoughby complied with the orders and let his hatchet drop to the ground.

"Do not turn until I tell you and keep your hands out in front. Make the slightest move towards the ax or the sword and you will be dead before you can touch them," the voice threatened. Willoughby rose slowly until he was standing. "Now, turn to me slowly."

The image of a redneck, grinning a toothless smile while hold-

410

ing a twelve gauge wasn't quite what Willoughby got when he turned to meet the person behind him. Shotgun, no, but he was staring at the dark tip of an arrow looking every bit as deadly as the bore of a gun. Twenty feet away stood a tall, blond-haired boy a couple of years older than himself, dressed in rough looking buckskin trousers tucked into a pair of crude boots. On a belt around his waist hung a short sword and a knife and across the back of a dirty white and homespun shirt rode a leather quiver full of arrows. The wooden bow he had drawn was nearly as tall as Willoughby and the boy's deadly and dark eyes stared intently down the shaft of the arrow pointed right at his chest. A wave of nausea settled into the pit of Willoughby's stomach: he had no doubt about the outcome should the newcomer loose the arrow.

"Hey now," Willoughby started gently, trying to remain calm, at least on the outside. "Relax, will you? I'm not a threat. You can ease off on that arrow. I won't move a muscle. I promise."

The eyes behind the feathered end of the arrow didn't blink. The muscles on the boy's bare arms stood out like cords on a thick rope, clearly showing the power it took to draw the heavy bow. But they remained flexed and showed no sign of relaxing.

Willoughby tried again. "Please. I'm not going to move until you tell me to. Just don't let that thing slip."

This time his plea seemed to work. The arms relaxed slowly and the tension came off the bow. The boy dropped the tip of the arrow slightly but still maintained his shooting grip.

"I can still put this arrow through your throat before you could reach either of your weapons," the newcomer warned.

"I believe that," Willoughby answered, relaxing just a touch. Now that the arrow was no longer threatening to sever his windpipe, he needed desperately to get this guy to talk to him. He wasn't sure what he was dealing with but the fact that it was a human was a start in the right direction, or at least he hoped it was.

"I am actually glad to see somebody. I was beginning to think I was the only person around here."

The newcomer eyed Willoughby carefully, seemingly taking a

particular interest in his clothes. "What are you doing here?" he finally asked.

Willoughby sensed the ice starting to break and a whirlwind of questions he wanted to ask the stranger were whipping through his head. This just might be his chance to finally get some answers.

"That's kind of a long story but if you would like to come up to my camp I can tell it to you. I was in the process of cutting some branches to make a rack to dry my sweatshirt. I had to rinse it off in the creek. Would you mind if I finished cutting these branches?"

The boy hesitated, obviously still considering him to be somewhat of a threat, but finally nodded his head in the direction of Willoughby's hatchet. "Cut your branches and I will accompany you to your camp."

"Thanks." Willoughby turned around slowly and proceeded to cut and trim the three saplings needed for his drying rack, fully cognizant of the fact that the stranger watched his every move. When he was done and turned back around, he was relieved to see the boy had un-nocked his arrow. He motioned for Willoughby to lead the way.

They followed the creek the short way to the big cedars and Willoughby's makeshift camp. The stranger approached with caution and surveyed the area carefully as if to make certain there was no one else about. Willoughby, trying to act as calm as he could, went about hammering the legs of his rack into the ground with the head of his hatchet and then placed the cross piece in the forks. He spread out his sweatshirt on the rack and steam immediately started to rise from the wet, cold fabric as the heat of the fire quickly began to do its work. The newcomer stood silently, leaning against the longbow and watching as Willoughby finished his task.

"Supper?" The stranger nodded towards the stiff grouse Willoughby had laid on a flat rock by the edge of the creek.

"Yeah, it is." Willoughby had momentarily forgotten his overwhelming hunger and his intended meal. "I don't have anything else to go with it but you are welcome to share it with me."

The stranger eyed Willoughby with unbridled curiosity. "I

was a fly's whisker away from killing you and yet you offer me the hospitality of your camp and to share your meal. I would be an ungrateful lout indeed if I did not accept your offer. My name is Bryan." He stuck out his hand.

A flood of relief rolled over Willoughby. He was just as curious about his new acquaintance. He stepped over to shake his hand but the boy gripped his forearm instead. Willoughby did the same and quickly noted the strength in the boy's arms, putting some extra power in his own grip without acting like he was trying too hard.

"My name is Willo..." he cut the sentence short. "My name is Will."

"Will." Bryan shook the smaller boy's arm heartily. "A stout name."

Willoughby couldn't help but notice the manner in which the boy spoke. It had a funny clipped sound to it, like something he had heard in a movie somewhere.

"I have my kit stashed down the trail from where we met" Bryan said. "I will fetch it and have something to add to yon bird if you wish."

"Great!" Willoughby nodded enthusiastically. It would be nice to have anything to go with the grouse. But there was something he was forgetting. "Uh...I don't know exactly how to get that thing ready to cook. You know, all the feathers n' guts and stuff. I've never fixed one before."

Bryan gave him a funny look and shrugged. He leaned the bow against one of the big cedars, walked over and knelt down beside the rock where the bird lay. Pulling a deadly looking knife from the sheath at his side, he pulled one of the wings out wide and on its underside, where the soft downy feathers were, he used his finger to find the spot where the meat of the wing ended. With the tip of the knife, he carefully sliced through the soft feathers and skin to the bird's body. When he had repeated the technique on the other wing, he did the same to the underside of each leg. One cut from the bird's asshole along its stomach to the neck completed the operation.

Willoughby watched the procedure intently. Grasping the bird's legs in one hand, Bryan held it upside down. With the other hand he grabbed the tail feathers and slowly but firmly began to pull downward. With a slurping sound, the skin and feathers easily peeled away from the meat. When he reached the head, he severed the neck. Bryan laid the body of the grouse on the rock and pulled four of the bigger tail feathers out from the remaining skin before flipping the rest into the water where it disappeared quickly with the current.

"Not the best for fletching but they'll do." He said, laying the feathers aside. Willoughby had no idea what fletching meant.

Bryan snapped the bird's claws from the legs and tossed them into the stream. With one quick slice in the lower end of the body cavity, he had the bird gutted in not more than half a minute and flipped the entrails into the water. Grinning, he tossed the bird to Willoughby, who promptly let the slick, skinless carcass slip through his hands and land in the dirt and duff.

Bryan laughed easily. "If you will rinse our supper clean friend Will, and get some water boiling in the kettle I will gather my belongings and return shortly." Grabbing his bow, he disappeared down the trail.

Willoughby unfastened his weapons harness and slipped out of it, laying it next to his pack. Picking up the carcass and rinsing the dirt from the outside and the blood from the inside, he was amazed at how it had slipped from the skin and feathers so easily. After checking his drying clothes, he rinsed and filled the cook pot half full of water, setting it on the flat rock where it would get plenty of heat.

As Willoughby worked, he thought about the lanky young stranger who had so abruptly entered his already screwed up situation. After all the time searching and hoping to find someone it had nearly been a disaster. There were plenty of questions to ask, and though he was feeling much better, his anxiety level was still in the red. His newfound friend was either some sort of strange survivalist freak, eschewing the store-bought comforts of life, or he had just stepped out of a Robin Hood book.

414

Willoughby squatted down and pushed the kettle closer to the heat. When he stood up and turned, Bryan was standing just behind him. "Fuck!" Willoughby exclaimed. "You scared the livin' shit out of me."

"Twice now I have been able to slip behind you, Will," he said, taking off his pack and laying his weapons aside. "In this wood that will get you killed—or worse."

"Worse than dead?" Willoughby asked as Bryan rummaged through his pack.

"Certainly worse," the older boy answered, displaying three shriveled potatoes, an even rougher looking onion, and five carrots, which seemed to be the best of the lot. "But we will talk after we have filled our bellies. I managed to dig these out of a garden near an abandoned farm three days ago. They do not look so, but fare quite well when cooked up. Your bird will do them nicely. Shall I?"

"Be my guest," Willoughby nodded. He hadn't thought much about how to cook the bird but had a feeling that his new friend did. He tended to his drying sweatshirt while Bryan cleaned and sliced the meager vegetables into the kettle. He halved the grouse and dropped it in on top of them.

"It will take a while but the wait will be worth it my friend. Sit and we shall talk."

Bryan slid the short sword he wore at his side free from its scabbard, laid it carefully down on one of the large cedar roots that extended like octopus legs out from the giant trees and placed his knife next to it. Rummaging around in his pack, he pulled out a leather bag tied with a rawhide cord and extracted a palm sized stone and a small, stoppered clay jug. He sat down on one of the roots and began working the blade of the sword with the stone.

"You aren't going to tend to your weapons?" he questioned Willoughby. "Grandfather says that when you make camp you tend to your horses first, which we don't have, then to your weapons, then to your stomach."

"Oh yeah, sure," Willoughby answered like it was something he did every day. He wasn't about to be outdone by his new friend. He remembered the whetstones he had found with Bob's things. After fishing his own pouch from his pack, he sat down and pulled his sword free. The steel rang with a clear metallic ping. Bryan stopped sharpening his sword in mid stroke and sucked in his breath with an audible hiss as Willoughby's weapon revealed itself.

"That is quite a weapon you have there, Will." He was clearly impressed, but as he went back to working his stone across his own blade, he dropped a bombshell.

"But it does not belong to you."

A surprised Willoughby raised his head to find Bryan staring intently at him, waiting for a response. He decided the truth was the best option. "No. You're right. I found it along with a bunch of other stuff in a cave back up on the mountain. The person it belonged to is dead, killed in a cave-in. He's been dead for a long time."

Bryan nodded at the explanation and returned to his work. "His name was Gaelron."

Willoughby was surprised again. Now he was getting somewhere. "You knew him?"

"I met him once many years ago when I was but a lad of six. He came to my grandparent's house and stayed with us. If you will look at the blade just under the hand guard you will see runes etched into the metal. The shield has the same marks. I do not read runes well but I recognize them as Gaelron's."

Willoughby looked at the spot and could see the strange markings. Bryan continued. "I was afraid of him at first because of what he was and hid from him, but he always knew I was watching. No matter where I was hiding, he would turn and wink at me."

"Afraid of what he was?" Willoughby asked.

"Gaelron was gnoman."

"A No-Man?"

"Yes," Bryan answered as he stopped with the whetstone and began polishing his blade with an oily-looking cloth. When he saw Willoughby's perplexed expression he expounded on his statement. "Half Gnome, half human. Gnoman."

Confusion was something Willoughby was getting very accustomed to since he had rolled out of the cave on the mountain-side. Bryan's explanation was fitting right in with everything else. "Gnomes? You mean like the little pointy hat guys people use to decorate their lawns?"

Now it was Bryan's turn to express confusion.

"Never mind." Willoughby didn't want the conversation to get off track. There were other things he needed to find out from his new friend. There was one question he was desperate for an answer to, although he was frightened as to what that answer might be. But he had to ask. "Bryan, have you ever heard of a place called Spirit Falls?"

His friend hesitated for a moment but then shook his head. "I am not well traveled Will but I know of no place which bears the name. The village nearest my home is Lightwood."

Willoughby's heart sank. It was not a total surprise; he had been halfway expecting something of the sort but it was still disappoint-ing. He couldn't hide the look on his face and Bryan noticed.

"Is that your home, then?" he asked.

But Willoughby just sat with the sword in his lap and stared into the fire. Home. It and his family had never seemed farther away than they did right at this moment and he was getting ready to cry; something he did not want to do in front of his new friend. For a long while the two boys sat there not saying anything. The only sound came from the crackling of the fire. Finally Bryan broke the uncomfortable silence they had lapsed into.

"Will, you are not from here," Bryan started as he laid his sword down and picked up a short piece of cedar that lay on the ground. With his knife, he began to shape the stick.

"You are dressed strangely, clothes I have never seen the like of." He pointed with the tip of his knife towards Willoughby's sneakers. "Your speech is different, though that could be explainable. Artura is a country full of folk who hail from different places."

The one word fell like another sledgehammer blow on Wil-loughby, breaking him out of the depressive trance that he had been in. Gnomes and Gnomen...now he learned he was in a place he had never heard of.

He looked at Bryan. "Artura?"

The single word question must have spoken volumes to his friend, that, and the expression on Willoughby's face.

"Will, I think you have a story to tell. I don't know if I can help you or not, but I will listen and we will see what can be done. You must trust me."

Willoughby nodded. He needed to talk about it. His whole focus on the last couple of days since he had stumbled out of the cave was to find help. Under normal circumstances he should have been elated, but normal was a word that did not fit here.

"I was just going for a hike…" With the fire crackling and the stew boiling, Willoughby launched into his story. Without going into too much detail about his home or town he did tell Bryan about Jake. What the big man had told him about the waterfall and its sacred connection to the Indian tribes Willoughby had a feeling was important. The waterfall and his situation were directly related, of that he had no doubt.

True to his word, Bryan listened carefully, stirring the pot every now and then as the grouse and vegetables simmered their way towards supper. The camp was filled with the savory aroma and Willoughby's stomach gurgled in anticipation as he went on with his story. Bryan tended the stew and never interrupted until Willoughby came to the part about his fight with Fenrir.

He stopped stirring and looked at Willoughby with shock and surprise on his face. "You killed the great wolf?"

Willoughby nodded and then remembered the teeth. He stood up and fished them out of his jeans pocket, holding the grisly trophies out for his friend to see. "Before he died, he told me to take them. He said it was the source of his magic and that they were mine by right of combat. But he told me I must figure out for myself how to draw their magic. Does that sound crazy to you?"

Bryan stared in awe at the fangs his friend held in his palm but leaned away as Willoughby held them out to him. "I have heard stories of the great wolf and his pack. They are one of the reasons folk do not venture this deep into the forest."

He looked at Willoughby with newfound respect. "You are more than you seem, Will. It is said that many have tried and failed to slay the King of the Wolves. You have done what many great warriors could not."

"I don't think I had much to do with it, Bryan. Look at me. Do I look like a warrior to you?"

Bryan knelt and stirred the pot. "My grandfather was a soldier for most his life. I have heard others tell of his bravery and he is as skilled in the art of weaponry as any man. But he told me once that the size of a warrior means nothing and those who think to gain an advantage by dismissing one because of his small stature often end up dead."

"Well, I ain't a warrior, Bryan," Willoughby said as he held Gaelron's sword out in front of him. "I was lucky I was able to kill Fenrir and I think this weapon had a lot to do with that. Ever since I picked it up I could feel some force, something in it that made it special. When I hold it, I seem to know what to do."

"Grandfather spoke highly of Gaelron, Will. He said he was a warrior whose stature belied his courage and his heart. Not much bigger than you as I remember. Grandmother and he had a special connection and they talked often and long while he stayed with us. She said Gaelron was a seeker."

"A seeker? A seeker of what?"

"Magic. Earth magic. She said he devoted his life to finding those secrets which the earth holds close and parts with reluctantly. His heritage made him an outcast and Grandmother said he felt more comfortable alone in the wild than he did around others. He seemed fond of my grandparents but after he left us, we never saw him again. They will be saddened to learn his fate."

Bryan's information about Bob, well, now it was Gaelron, explained some things to Willoughby. "That must be why his stuff seems to fit me so well. It's almost like it was made for me. As far as the magic thing goes, you gotta understand something, Bryan. Where I come from, there's no such thing as magic, talking wolves, gnomes, or gnomen. But after what I've been through, I think I'm becoming a believer. Gaelron's sword has magic; I can feel it. If I was home, they'd lock me away for being crazy, but I ain't home. I'm here and I don't think home is anywhere close."

Bryan stirred the stew. "Your story is a strange one, Will. It is one I think my grandparents should hear. Maybe they can help. If you would travel with me, I will take you there. You will be welcomed."

Willoughby was relieved. He knew he was a long way away from his family and he welcomed his new friend's offer. "I think that is what I would like to do, Bryan. I don't have much choice. I have something else of Gaelron's I would like to show you. Maybe you can tell me what it is. It was in his hand when I found him."

He dug through the pack and brought out the pouch. He extracted the crystal shard and held it up for Bryan to see. The six-inch crystal seemed to gleam in the last rays of daylight that wormed their way through the forest.

Bryan carefully took the crystal from Willoughby's hand, held it up, and examined it. "By thunder, Will! Grandmother told me of these but I have never seen one."

"Well? What is it?" Willoughby asked.

"It is a lightstone." Bryan stood and walked over to a rock that still had a small piece of sunshine warming its surface. Gently he laid the crystal onto the rock. It began to glow the moment it came into contact with the sunlight.

"Expose it to the sun and it will give you the same amount of light it takes in when darkness comes. Gaelron must have been using it instead of a torch to light his way in the cave."

Willoughby watched amazed as the crystal shimmered, absorbing the meager influx of light that remained of the day.

"Grandmother says that crystals hold all sorts of earth magic. They were one of the things Gaelron sought. It seems he has left you another great gift, Will."

Willoughby picked up the crystal. It was slightly warm to his touch. Out of curiosity, he walked over to where the roots of one of the cedars exposed a fox-sized hole leading under the tree. He thrust the shard into the dark and watch in amazement as the hole lit up with light. It wasn't manufactured light like he was familiar with, light from a bulb or a flashlight, but a natural brightness, just like the sun illuminating the hole. The boys watched as the light shone briefly before fading out. Just about the same amount of time it had been exposed to the sun.

"Wow!" was the only thing Willoughby could think of to say as he put the crystal safely back into the pouch. He was feeling a pretty heavy tinge of guilt as he thought about the man, or gnoman's, body under a ton of rock in a dark hole far up on the mountain.

"I made a promise back in the cave, Bryan. If I ever get my situation figured out, I have to go back there and bring Bob…I mean Gaelron, out and give him a proper burial. It's the least I could do since I took all his stuff."

Bryan nodded his head in agreement. "It is the noble thing, Will. But Gaelron's weapons and his belongings are yours by right of discovery. The fact that you and he were of the same size is no mere chance. Things happen because they are meant to happen. If we get the opportunity, we will come back and give Gaelron the respect he deserves. Grandfather would agree. It would be a dangerous quest but it is still the right thing to do."

"Dangerous because of the wolves?" Willoughby questioned.

"The wolves are not the only things in this wood we must be wary of, Will. While they are deadly, there are creatures here even more evil. In fact, we are in danger as we speak for daring to spend the night this far in. I do not usually venture here but I was looking for a certain type of rare mushroom that can only be found in the darkest places of this forest. I was getting ready to turn back when I came upon you."

Willoughby was thinking, remembering something Fenrir had said before he died. "When the Wolf King was dying, Bryan, when he told me to take his teeth, he said the witch would come for me if I didn't get out of the forest."

"Aye, Will. That is one we must be wary of. This is her wood, or she likes to think. Mogga's heart is black and it is said she is in league with many of the other evil things who live in this place. We are not safe here."

"Mogga? Is that her name? Fenrir said he and the witch had a truce but she would come for his magic when she learns of his death. His magic, his power, they're in his teeth. I have his teeth. That means she's going to come after me."

Bryan stirred the pot, deep in thought. "It does no good to panic now, Will. We are too close to darkness to try and get farther down the trail. Traveling this wood at night is death in itself. We must stay where we are and keep the fire high. Mogga is a creature of darkness and does not like the light. We will leave early on the morrow and if we travel hard, can clear the wood. She will not venture out of it."

But Willoughby wasn't convinced. "But if she does come tonight? Then what?"

Bryan shrugged. "We have our weapons and our wits. We will just have to remain alert and see what happens. If she learns I am here, she may choose to leave us in peace, though that is something we cannot count on. Fenrir was a wolf of great power. She will be angry that her ally is gone and will be even angrier when she finds the source of his power is gone also."

"What do you mean when she learns you are here? Is she afraid of you?"

Bryan shook his head. "No, she certainly does not fear me and we are in her realm. But if she harms me, she will have to deal with Grandmother. It may be enough to make her think before she acts. It is not a lot to hope for, but it is all we may have."

Willoughby wasn't too sure what Bryan was trying to tell him and had to ask. "Why would she have to worry about your grand-mother, Bryan?"

"I guess I need to explain about my grandmother, Will. You will need to know if you get the opportunity to meet her. Her name is Mattie and she is the best healer around. It is for her that I search plants and other wild things she uses for potions and medicines. She devotes her life to doing good for those who are suffering no matter who or what they are." Bryan looked up from the pot he was stirring. "But as good as her heart is she is also very powerful and can be very dangerous. You see Will, my grandmother is also a witch, and she is Mogga's sister."

CHAPTER TWENTY-FIVE

THE AROMA DRIFTING FROM THE KETTLE Bryan was stirring was driving Willoughby's stomach crazy, but what his friend just told him made him momentarily forget the gnawing hunger. "Your grandma is a witch?"

Bryan nodded. "There are good and bad witches, Will. Grandmother uses her skill to relieve the suffering of people, of which there is a great abundance in this time. Mogga is a dark, evil witch."

Good witches, bad witches. Willoughby had heard that somewhere before—a movie maybe. "I take it they don't care much for each other?"

"Grandmother speaks little of it." Bryan shrugged. "They are sisters but other than that, they keep their distance. But I once overheard a conversation where she was telling Grandfather she believed Mogga was practicing some ancient dark arts thought to be long forgotten. They both agreed that if such was true, Mogga was going to have to be stopped. Forever."

Willoughby shook his head as he pondered what he was hearing. "I gotta tell you Bryan, none of this stuff makes any sense to me. I know it's happening, but this stuff only exists in the movies where I come from."

It was Bryan's turn to shrug. "I do not know what a movie is, Will. But you are here and if you want to survive, you must believe. You have been through much already but are still in great danger. My grandparents are wise and may be able to help you, but it will take us several days to reach home and I do not believe my presence will be enough to stop Mogga from coming after you. You killed her wolf and now carry his magic. She will neither forgive nor forget."

"Great," Willoughby grunted as he worked the whetstone over the edge of his sword, just more to worry about. He decided to change the subject. "So you live with your grandparents? What happened to your mom and dad?"

"My mother died giving birth to me." Bryan stared into the fire. Willoughby could tell it was something he wasn't used to talking about. "I have never been told much of my father. Grandfather said only that he was much older than my mother and their union was one which never should have happened. I do not ask, for it makes my grandfather very angry when he speaks of it. Just before I was born, my grandparents and my mother left the city of Tiernon where they lived and moved to the farm where my grandmother was born. There I came into the world and my mother left it."

He grew quiet and Willoughby never pressed him for more, but after a pause Bryan started again. "Grandmother was happy to leave the city and return to the country where she could tend to her remedies and help the good folk. Grandfather was a soldier most of his life, but now he works as a smith making and fixing tools. We live a quiet life and they have raised and taught me well. I love them very much." He turned and sat on a root across from Willoughby, taking up his sword and whetstone again. "You spoke some of your mother and sister Will. What of your father?"

Normally this was where Willoughby would retreat into his shell and give his therapist, or whoever else was trying to get him to talk about his issues, the cold shoulder. But this strange place he found himself in, this strange youth whom he had known for only a couple of hours, he had a feeling that they were now the new norm for him. His life, his family, his home, all seemed so far away. For the first time since his father died, he actually wanted to talk about it.

"My dad died a couple of years ago. He was a pro football player, a pretty good one, but he got hurt and couldn't play anymore. It was hard for him, not being able to do what he loved so much. My mom never said much about it but other people told me he got addicted to painkillers because of his injuries. The newspapers said that he was high on drugs and alcohol when he had the car wreck."

Willoughby was staring into the fire as he talked, not noticing the look of confusion on Bryan's face, but he was on a roll and rattled on as tears welled up in his eyes.

"One article said there was speculation by the San Diego Police that he might have committed suicide. Whatever it was, he killed a mother and her six-year-old daughter in the accident as well as himself. Mom tried to make a go of it in San Diego for a while after that but we lost everything in the lawsuit. We finally had to move to Oregon and live on Grandma's farm. My sister and her adjusted pretty well, but things just seemed to get more fucked up for me. I don't fit in there; it was my dad's hometown. He was a big hero jock and people look at me like I'm supposed to be like him. Hell, when he was my age he was six feet four inches tall. I ain't nothin' like him and I think that disappoints everybody."

Willoughby lapsed into silence. The fire crackled and the stew bubbled.

"I am sorry about your father, Will. I do not understand much of what you have told me but I can sense your feelings towards him. You said he was a hero of some sort and that you are nothing like him, but tell me, did he ever kill a wolf such as you have?"

Bryan was being as serious and as compassionate as he could but the moment took a sudden turn when Willoughby quickly realized his new friend truly had no understanding of the majority of what he had just told him. His lapse into self-pity and grief faded as he thought about his friend's statement.

"No, you're right about that, Bryan." He grinned as he wiped the tears from his eyes with the back of his hand. "That is one thing I know for absolute certain he never did."

"There. You see, Will? It is as Grandfather says, it isn't the size of the warrior that makes him, it is the size of his heart."

It made Willoughby feel better but their conversation opened up questions from Bryan. "What is this "foot-ball," Will?"

Willoughby smiled and did his best to explain the game as they sat around the fire and waited for their supper. He knew the game, but really had never played much. He had given it a try, but after a

426

disastrous attempt in the Pop Warner league, both father and son knew it wasn't going to happen.

"We'll wait until you get bigger, son," his dad consoled as they turned in Willoughby's helmet, pads, and uniform. But in his heart, Willoughby knew that it would never be. Though his dad made light of the whole episode, Willoughby had felt his disappointment.

"This foot-ball, Will. It sounds much like fighting in the arena. Such things have been outlawed in Artura but it is said that in Torbek, Supreme Lord Taul loves gladiator games and has himself fought in arena combat. To fight like you say, in armor but not killing each other, sounds like a civilized way to determine a champion."

Willoughby laughed. "That's funny, Bryan. A lot of people in my world call football pretty barbaric and would like to see it disappear, but it's a pretty big thing and you can make a lot of money at it if you are really good. We have holidays that are centered around watching football on TV." But TV was something else Bryan didn't understand and when Willoughby tried to explain it to him things really got confusing.

"But that sounds like magic to me, Will. You say there is no magic where you come from, yet you can see things happening from very long distances? Is there not great magic in that?"

"It ain't magic, Bryan." Willoughby tried to explain but he could see his friend was not convinced. "It's called technology. It took hundreds, even thousands of years to invent some of that stuff." He walked over to his backpack and started rummaging through the pockets. "Let me show you a couple of things."

He brought out two items which he thought could explain the difference between technology and magic. Bryan watched intently as Willoughby sat back down. The first thing he showed his new friend was the lighter.

"Now watch this." He held the lighter in front of him and gave it a flick. The flame jumped immediately to life.

"You bring fire from a colored bauble and yet do not call it magic?" Bryan asked in wonder as Willoughby flicked the lighter again.

"It's technology Bryan. How do you start your fires?"

"I use my flint, striker, and tinder as everyone does, Will."

"Exactly. That is what I am trying to tell you. This isn't any different except it comes in a real small package." He showed his friend the body of the lighter.

"Inside this is a fuel that burns easy when a spark is applied to it." He pointed to the chrome workings on top of the lighter. "Kinda like your tinder. There is a tiny flint here, just like the flint you use except way smaller. When you turn this wheel quick with your thumb, it strikes against the flint and makes a spark like your striker. The spark connects with the fuel that comes out when you press down on that little piece and you have a flame. It's the same thing; it just looks a little different."

He handed the lighter to Bryan, who was a bit reluctant to reach out and take it. "C'mon, try it." Bryan took the lighter carefully, as if afraid it might do something to him. He gave the wheel a weak turn which produced nothing.

"Do it harder and faster," Willoughby urged. This time Bryan got results and the lighter produced a healthy flame. "See? It's not magic. Just more advanced than your flint."

Bryan let up and the flame went out; he struck it again.

"It is a wondrous thing this ticnolicky, Will," he said as he handed the lighter back. "But there are those who would still call it magic. You had better keep it out of sight. What is the other thing you have there?"

Willoughby smiled as he put the lighter away and held out the pocket-sized Maglite. "If you thought the lighter was pretty cool, wait 'til you see how this works." Unscrewing the end of the flashlight, he dropped the two batteries into his hand. He wasn't sure the batteries would be as easy to explain as the workings of the lighter so he fudged a little.

"These things are kinda like the lightstone. They store energy in them like the crystal does when it gets the rays of the sun. Got that so far?" Bryan gave an uncertain nod. Willoughby put the batteries back in.

"See this thing in here?" he asked as he pointed to the bulb. "That's kinda like the wick of a candle except more powerful. When you push this little thing here forward, it releases the energy stuff and it goes into the bulb, er, the wicky thing."

He flipped the switch and grinned at Bryan's reaction as the small but powerful light lit up the darkening camp.

"Just like the lightstone, huh?" Willoughby asked.

Bryan held the light and flipped the switch a couple of times. Willoughby knew what he was thinking.

"I know, I know. People still won't understand, so I gotta keep it outta sight." He took the light back and packed it away with his lighter. "The trouble with the light is that the batteries will go weak and eventually lose their energy. When that happens unless you replace them, the thing is worthless. Not as good as the lightstones in that respect. So ya see? Amazing, but not magic. The place I come from is full of this kinda stuff."

Bryan shook his head. "It must be a great and wondrous place with the...the ticnolicky, Will."

"Technology. Well, to tell you the truth Bryan, we have a lot of amazing stuff but that don't make it so great. It can get kinda fucked, really. People just wanting to have more money and more stuff, and if you have something there is someone around the corner that wants to take it from you. It can be pretty mean and nasty at times and a lot of technology is the kind used to kill people—a lot of people. Put it in the hands of the wrong guys and you have a war. Seems like there is always a war."

"Then our two worlds are not all that different, Will. Artura is a place where we have not known much peace for as long as I can remember. Our soldiers fight a war in the wastelands of Torbek. There are robbing and murdering bandit gangs roaming the country now that our soldiers are away. We are overtaxed and folk barely have enough to eat. Pirates roam the coastline and if traders do not pay a protection fee, their goods are stolen and their ships burned and sunk. Grandfather says we are slipping back to dark times and our king and his first council are making it happen."

"You guys have a king?" Willoughby asked.

Bryan nodded. "His name is Edmond and I remember when people spoke of him with great respect. I do not know much of what goes on in the court of the king, but Grandfather has a lot to say and most of it is not good. He says Edmond was once a great and brave leader and led Artura to victory over Torbek, a country we had been at war with for half a hundred years. When the war finally ended ten years ago, things seemed to go well for the nation. There was peace and the king garrisoned troops throughout the land to protect the people and the trade routes. The king's fleet was able to keep the pirates at bay and people began to prosper. But all that is gone now."

"What happened?" Willoughby queried.

"After we entered into the peace treaty with Torbek, a man came to the king's court at Tiernon, our capital city. Grandfather calls that the blackest day in Arturan history. His name is Daemon Rhue."

Willoughby couldn't help but notice the way Bryan spat the name out like it tasted bad in his mouth. "Wow, even sounds like a bad guy."

"Not just bad Will, he is evil. The misery which has fallen on this land comes from his hands."

"So why does the king put up with that shit if the guy is so bad, Bryan? If the guy is king and all powerful or whatever, why don't he take this dude down?"

"It is a complicated matter, Will," Bryan answered as he stirred. The aroma coming from the pot was sending Willoughby's stomach into triple flips.

"My grandparents have tried to explain the situation during my study lessons. It still doesn't make much sense to me but what I know is that after King Edmond and Artemis Thoryl defeated the Torbekian army in a terrible battle on the plains of Ansrak, Kenric Taul sued for peace. He sent Rhue and a delegation to meet with the king in Tiernon. It was a momentous occasion; a treaty was signed and everyone celebrated—the war was over. But instead of returning home, Daemon Rhue stayed on at Castle Daine to officially serve as the Torbekian Ambassador to Artura. Grandfather said that from that moment on, Rhue started to exert his influence on King Edmond. Of late it is said the king has slipped into a great sickness, and the weaker he grows, the more power he bestows on Lord Rhue. Grandfather says the first council is now the one making the decisions which are hurting the people. It was he who has increased taxes and abandoned the garrisons."

"Wow," Willoughby grunted. "Sounds like somebody seriously needs to take this guy out."

"If you mean kill him, yes. That is what needs to happen, but take care you do not speak such words if you are around anyone, Will. Daemon Rhue has spies throughout the land and people who are loose with their tongues and speak against the first council are arrested quickly and never heard from again."

Willoughby thought about that one for a while. His mind was still having trouble grabbing hold of logic with all that had happened. Part of him didn't want to accept the fact he found himself in a place a million light years away from what he thought of as reality. But the other part of him knew the tall, blond-haired kid stirring their dinner was his key to survival. It was ironic in the sense that it hadn't been too many moments before he found his new friend that he had been close to stepping off the edge of the gorge and ending it all. He shuddered as his mind drifted back to that moment, just a step away from taking the coward's way out.

Suicide. Was that the way his dad ended his torment? His mother never uttered the word when they spoke of his father, which was rarely. Willoughby and his sister had been shielded from the ugliness which surrounded the liability case brought by the husband and father of the two people James Baxter had obliterated when his Cadillac Escalade t-boned the minivan at an intersection in the San Diego suburb of Spring Valley. The police report said the Caddy had been traveling nearly eighty in a thirty mile an hour zone. A blood alcohol level of .26 and a significant amount of the pain killer oxycontin in his system, the autopsy report had stated. Not much of a defense against that one.

The lawsuit had also targeted the watering hole his dad had been a loyal patron of. The End Zone was a favorite hangout for washed up or retired pro athletes in the San Diego area and the fact that it was only three blocks from the scene of the accident amazed the testifying officers. One of them stated that for someone to get going that fast, given the weight of traffic on that street at one o'clock on a Saturday afternoon, he must have had a death wish. The comment was stricken from court documents but the officer had repeated it to the local news stations covering the hearing. The suicide angle of the incident was never proven but it made for spectacular headlines in the gossip rags. James Baxter's fall from the top had been well documented and though Jennifer Baxter had tried hard to protect her two children, they had hopelessly been trapped in the quagmire of negativity that eventually drove them from San Diego. Drove them to Oregon and a place called Spirit Falls.

"Will...Will!" Bryan's voice snapped him out of the trance. He was looking at Willoughby with concern.

"You were lost in your thoughts, Will. I thought you might be pleased to know that supper is at last ready. Are you ready to eat?"

"Wow, sorry Bryan," Willoughby apologized. He had gotten lost in his thoughts but the one thing that could override anything right now was food, and the stew smelled absolutely delicious. "Am I ever!"

Bryan pulled two small wooden bowls and a large wooden spoon from his pack. He pulled the kettle away from the fire and began spooning broth, vegetables, and meat into each.

"Grandfather makes things like this to sell. We take in a small amount for such and Grandmother brings in a little for her medicines. It is not much but we raise and grow most of our food. Game and fish are plentiful if you have the skill to find them."

Willoughby was impressed. "Sounds like you live like folks in our country did a couple hundred years ago. Before technology. You live off the land and make what you need. My friend Jake would be impressed."

Bryan shrugged. "We live as we must, Will. It is a good life but of late it has become more difficult with the increase in tax levies. Rhue has issued taxes on everything. His collectors visit frequently and are none too pleasant when they do. Many folk are suffering but to protest or refuse is to invite even more grief. Men who can't pay are pressed into labor gangs and disappear, leaving their wives and children to suffer on without them. Grandfather says when folk are pushed too far they will fight back eventually."

He passed Willoughby a bowl of steaming stew. "Sorry I have no bread to offer."

Willoughby took the proffered bowl with both hands and gingerly sipped the hot broth. Hunger was something else he never had to deal with his entire life, yet since he had gone over the falls it had been his constant companion. It had been over twenty-four hours since he had eaten his trout and he was hungry. Never again would he look at food and take it for granted.

The two boys ate in silence. The simple stew, concocted of a gamey wild bird and a few withered remnants of a late summer vegetable crop, was as satisfying as anything Willoughby had ever tasted. There was enough left in the pot for each boy to have another half bowl. Every grouse bone was picked clean and every drop of broth found its way home.

"Twas good!" Willoughby said as they rinsed the pot and bowls in the creek.

"It was good, Will. I hadn't realized it had been so long since my last meal," Bryan agreed. "I ventured much farther into the wood than planned, though I am glad for it. Had I not, I would never have found you."

"I am glad you did, too," Willoughby replied as the boys settled back comfortably around the crackling fire. A warm afterglow folded its arms round Willoughby. While he was no closer to home and family, it was the first time he had been truly able to relax. A full stomach, warm fire, and new friend were a heady elixir for the myriad of torments he had been through. "Are your grandma and grandpa going to be worried about you?"

Bryan shrugged. "They have taught me to take care of myself and Grandmother has a special gift knowing when I need assistance or not. I broke an ankle once two days out from home. I splinted it up and had just finished whittling myself a crutch when out of nowhere Grandfather appeared. He said he had just settled in for supper when she looked up from her pots and said 'Quint'—that's my grandfather's name—'the boy has got himself in trouble. You'd best go find him.'"

"It sounds like she's a special person."

"Well, she is that, but I think it is more because she is a witch. Some folk are afraid of my grandmother, yet when anyone is in need, she is the first they call for. She is a healer for both folk and animals. There are more children alive in our village today because of her skill as a mid-wife, yet there are folk who bolt their doors, shutter their windows, and hang spell charms over their hearth when she goes by. I do not understand people."

It made sense to Willoughby, though he didn't want to say as much to his friend. Bryan was talking about his grandmother being a witch like it was an everyday thing.

"Maybe it's because of her sister and not so much because of who she is," Willoughby ventured.

Bryan nodded as he poked the fire with a stick. Sparks rose into the darkness with a fiery resolve before fading into oblivion. "There is truth to what you say, Will. Mogga is like a shadow hanging over everyone's shoulder. Our village is close to the forest and though she keeps away from us, her presence is felt. When a hunter goes missing folk blame her or the wolves. What they do not realize is that Grandmother is the one who holds Mogga in check."

It sounded strange to Willoughby, but then again, he was settling into the notion that this was a world where everything he knew to be real was now as foreign as magic, talking wolves, and witches were.

"So you said before that you don't normally come this far into the forest. How come you did this time?" he asked his friend.

"I gather the things Grandmother uses to make her powders

434

and potions. She has taught me what to look for. She said the things which grow in this forest are stronger in their potency than similar ones growing elsewhere. There is a willow that grows here along the banks of small creeks. Its bark, when cured and pounded fine, produces a powder that deadens pain. Willows that grow outside the forest produce the same, but their powers are greatly diminished. There is something about this wood that makes things different."

"I can totally agree with that," Willoughby added. "Ever since I came in here things have been strange."

"My grandparents are going to be unhappy when they learn I have ventured in so deep. They have always warned me against doing so. But there are things Grandmother needs that can be found nowhere else. I just wanted to get them for her."

"Well, I sure am glad you did. Like you said, you wouldn't have found me if you hadn't," Willoughby added. "I know what you mean about not doing exactly what you are told sometimes. If I had listened to my friend Jake and stayed away from the top of the waterfall, I wouldn't be here now. He said the Indians believed the waterfall was a spiritual place where strange things happen. I guess he was right."

"We will tell my grandparents your story, Will. They will help you if they can. They will also be interested in hearing of Gaelron's fate." Bryan let his words trail off into the night. There was something else on his mind. "Will, if they cannot help you, well, you will be welcome to stay with us. You would have a home and at least be safe."

Willoughby gave him a smile. It wasn't what he truly wanted to hear, but it did make him feel better. "I appreciate it, Bryan. I was having a pretty rough time with this whole thing until you came along. Knowing that I can at least have a place to stay does make it better."

Bryan beamed a huge smile back at him. "Good then. It is nearly a day's travel to the abandoned cottage where I cached the rest of my belongings and the things I gathered for Grandmother. We need to get some sleep and break camp early. Let us gather enough wood for the night's fire and then make our beds."

After bringing in more wood and banking the fire, Willoughby spread Gaelron's canvas poncho onto the ground next to one of the exposed cedar roots. Bryan did the same with a thick cloak he produced from his pack. With their backs to the roots and facing the fire they would be warm enough. With full bellies and the adventures of a long day behind them, it didn't take long before both boys drifted off into a deep and welcome slumber.

WILLOUGHBY WOKE FROM HIS THANKFULLY DREAMLESS SLEEP because of two pressing issues. The first was a golf ball sized rock under the poncho jamming uncomfortably into his side, and the second was he had to pee something fierce.

Painfully he rolled over and pushed himself to his knees, acutely feeling every one of the numerous bruises and bumps acquired over the last few days. Fishing under his poncho, he found and eliminated the culprit rock. The fire needed wood but it would wait until he took the pressure off his bladder.

Willoughby stumbled to his feet and slipped into his sneakers, which had dried nicely near the fire, and made his way past the last of the giant cedars surrounding their camp. Just beyond the edge of what little light the dying fire provided he dropped his jeans, seeing no need to fumble with cold fingers trying to get his dick out through his zipper. The night air had a definite chill to it and his warm urine gave off a cloud of steam as it arched into the air. Willoughby grunted with relief as his full bladder emptied, but just as he was about ready to shake himself, he froze. Ahead of him in the dark shadows, a fog-like cloud snaked its way along the ground towards him.

Slowly the fog cloud slithered around the giant tree trunks, a disembodied patch of lightness against the dark of the wood. Mesmerized, Willoughby couldn't take his eyes from it as it drifted lazily towards him. Deep inside his mind, a fire alarm of a warning clanged away but he paid it no attention—he was hypnotized by the creeping apparition.

When it was no more than a few feet from where he stood, the cloud began a slow, swirling, upward spiral. Round and round it went until the tip of it was the same height as Willoughby. It stopped rising but swirled faster and faster; thickening as it spiraled, taking shape. Suddenly, in an instant, the cloud disappeared. Stunned, Willoughby gazed in stoned wonder at the incredible sight which remained.

Standing within arm's reach was absolutely the most beautiful girl he had ever laid eyes on. She might have been near his age, maybe older; he didn't know and didn't care. She was wearing nothing more than a very short and sheer nightie that made its seductive way over the swell of her hips, barely covering her crotch.

Willoughby's eyes wandered caressingly over every inch of her stunning beauty. Frequent visits to his sister's Victoria Secret catalogs never came close to what he was staring at. Every slight curve of her body stood out, the swell of her pert breasts with their dark, hard nipples pressing tight against the flimsy fabric. His gaze traveled hungrily down the taught stomach to the gentle rise of her pubic area, the dark triangle lay teasingly just under the edge of her flimsy shift. He had never seen anything so intoxicating. His previous encounters with naked female bodies had been confined to cold, glossy pages of porn magazines or covert trips to internet sites, but they were nothing compared to what he was experiencing. The desire to touch, to taste, was reaching critical overload. His eyes drifted on past her hips. Her pale, smooth legs were long and her feet were bare, partially buried in the moist duff of the forest floor.

A giggle immediately snapped his attention upward. Willoughby had been so entranced with her body that he had paid no attention to her face.

She smiled at him. An intoxicating smile that pushed the night back. Her full, pink-red lips pulled back slightly, revealing dazzling white teeth. A beautiful, perfectly shaped nose was flanked by dark, sparkling eyes. Her jet-black hair hung unkempt in a wildly inviting sort of way over her shoulder to the exposed swell of her breasts.

Her smile warmed him, driving the night chill away. The piercing dark eyes locked onto his and as much as he desired to let his gaze roam back over her body, he couldn't break away. She spoke to him.

"You are a beautiful boy but not quite what I expected." Her soft voice floated around him with a soothing gentleness, breaking down his defense mechanisms. Willoughby reached deep into the control center of his mind and flipped off the warning bell. There was no harm here. She spoke again. "You are a strange one. Do you have a name?"

"Will…Willoughby." The words blurted out. She commanded and he spoke. There was no need to lie to her about his name.

"Greetings Will Willoughby." The voice enveloped him like jetted water in a hot tub, warm and caressing. "You and your sleeping friend trespass in my forest. I would know where you come from and what brings you here?"

Something deep inside tugged at him. A barely perceptible warning of something not quite right. Confused, he hesitated.

"Come now my charming boy." Her words stroked him gently like a verbal hand job. "You have no need to fear. I have come to help you. Do you not find me pretty enough?"

"No…no," Willoughby stammered. "You are the most beautiful thing I have ever seen." He felt stupid saying it but it was the truth. He could not hide what he was feeling; he had to tell her.

"Yesss. You do think I am beautiful, don't you?" She teasingly ran her hands up her sides and cupped her breasts, squeezing gently. Her fingers found her taught nipples and pinched them as she let out a moan of pleasure. As his eyes agonizingly followed every movement of her hands, she slid them down over her taut stomach and her round hips to the edge of the gown. Ever so slowly she started to slide the fabric up. Just as she exposed the tiny patch of soft dark hair crowning the top of her pouting lips she dropped the hem back down, denying him. Willoughby could only groan his displeasure as she hid her treasures.

"First you must tell me things I need to know," her voice teased. "I think you will because I can see your desire to have me is strong."

She dropped her eyes to his crotch. Willoughby had felt his reaction since she had materialized from the fog but as he looked down at himself the extent of her effect on him was firmly obvious. His jeans and underwear were still bunched halfway down his legs and his erection poked itself out from under his sweatshirt.

Sheer embarrassment was enough to break the spell. The only females ever to have seen him naked had been his mother and his sister but never in the state he was in now. As he turned his back to her, hurriedly jerking his jeans up, it struck him that he had never been so…so…big before.

She was still smiling when he turned back to face her. The spell had been broken, but just temporarily. Seeing her, the wanton desire flooded over him again.

"You hide it from me but I know your desire," she teased. "Tell me what I want to know and I will give you everything you lust for. You are a stranger and not from this land. From where and how do you come here, Will Willoughby?"

"I…I don't know," Willoughby blurted. He desperately wanted to tell her everything, the need to touch her, to have her, was overwhelming. For that he would do or say anything.

"I went over the waterfall and ended up in a cave. When I came out, I was here. I don't know where I am."

She looked deep into his eyes, penetrating, gripping him with her gaze. "I see you speak the truth. That is well for you because I do not tolerate being lied to."

She sniffed the air like a dog smelling a treat. "You have the taint of magic about you, Will Willoughby. From whence does it come? Tell me now."

He was still trapped by her piercing eyes but the warning coming from inside was at it again, faint, but still there. There was a hint of cold edge to her voice as she demanded an answer. But he had to tell her, the desire for her was there, as hard as ever. She was his—all he had to do was tell her.

"The magic comes from…things. Not from me."

"What things, my darling?" she coaxed softly, the edge in her voice masked once again. "Tell me of them and then you will have what you want. You will have what you so desperately need."

As she spoke those last words, she dropped her eyes back down to his crotch. She wasn't touching him but he could feel her caress on his iron hard boner straining against the fabric of his jeans. Gently she stroked him. There was no denying her any longer. Willoughby was ready to explode.

"It's the sword. The sword and the wolf's teeth," he blurted out.

She stepped back and hissed. The stroking stopped and her lovely smile vanished.

"You? You are the one who killed my wolf? That cannot be! Do not lie to me, boy!"

"I'm not lying," Willoughby pleaded. The fear that she wouldn't believe him was more than he could stand. "I didn't mean to kill Fenrir. It was the sword. I was holding it and it just seemed to do the rest. He told me to take his teeth as he was dying and I just did it. They are in my pocket."

The soothing demeanor and smile snapped back in an instant. Her voice calmed him again.

"So young, yet such a warrior to have slain Fenrir, mighty King of the Wolves. You are more than you seem, my dear boy. Much more." She held out her arms and her bodily charms beckoned, inviting him in.

"Come to me, Will Willoughby. Come and touch me."

He could feel himself throbbing inside his Levi's. He was going to explode. He wanted her and she was inviting—all he had to do was step forward and take it. His legs felt like lead as he tried to move towards her. It was like a dream where you're trying to fight and can't move your arms or legs. That was what he was experiencing.

"Come to me," she enticed. "I have seen your manhood. Come and take me like the man you are."

Willoughby pulled hard at his legs. Bells and whistled screamed in alarm as he willed himself forward. One step was all he needed. He could almost touch her. With a grunt and heave he made the last step and she circled her arms around him, grabbing his butt cheeks and pulling him the rest of the way in. There was fire in his crotch as he ground hard against her. He buried his face in her neck and breathed deep, but her smell surprised him. A deep, musty aroma assailed his nose, like old dirt. He had imagined an exotic, perfumed fragrance but as much as it surprised him, he still breathed deep, sucking it in, this was her smell, this was what he wanted. He pushed his throbbing hardness forward and she ground her crotch back against him.

"Give it to me, Will Willoughby," her hot breath whispered as she bit hard on his ear lobe. "You are mine now—give yourself to me."

Willoughby closed his eyes and his world exploded.

No sooner had he released himself when his ecstasy turned to agony. There was a voice shouting his name from what seemed to Willoughby to be a long ways away. When the first shout was heard, the girl hissed and bit down hard on his earlobe. Willoughby screamed in pain as he felt a piece of his ear come away in her teeth. As he struggled to push himself away from her, his head started to clear and the shouts became more intense—it was Bryan.

"Fight her, Will! Fight her! It is Mogga! It is the witch!"

Willoughby jerked himself hard backwards, trying to break away from the agonizing embrace but she had grabbed hold of his sweatshirt and he wasn't able to free himself. Her strength was enormous as he slipped to his knees trying to escape her grip.

"She has cast a spell on me, Will!" Bryan screamed. "I cannot move! You must fight her!"

Willoughby was jerked violently back to his feet and he came face to face with his captor, but the beauty he had so erotically entwined his body with moments before had disappeared, and he found himself staring at the ugliest old woman he had ever seen. Her face was wrinkled and sagging, covered with open sores and hairy moles. The delicate, perfect nose had been replaced by a swollen orb that protruded over a toothless mouth with festering black gums. She was nearly bald with only wisps of white scraggly hair poking out in all directions. The delicate and sexually arousing shift she had been wearing had turned into a filthy gunny-sack-looking rag.

Willoughby struggled to no avail against the witch's vice-like grip. She had him firmly grasped in one enormously strong hand while the other pointed palm out directly at Bryan, who was no more than five feet away. Standing there with a fiery brand in one hand and his sword in the other, he was pulling his legs like they were trapped in quicksand. Again, he screamed at his friend as he struggled.

"Fight her, Will! Fight her!"

But Willoughby couldn't. He tried to grab at her with his hands but she just shook him side to side like a rag doll.

"You trespass in my wood and slay my beast. I will have you and your magic, brat," she hissed at Willoughby. She looked back at Bryan, struggling helplessly against the spell she held him in.

"I smell my sister's stench on you, boy. But she is not here to protect you is she? I will make you both suffer beyond belief for your intrusion."

Willoughby didn't know what to do. It was obvious he could not make her release the hold she had on him. She was ten times stronger than he was. But she still only had one hand holding onto his sweatshirt. She couldn't use the other because that was the one holding Bryan in check. His hands were free. But what could he do? Every time he tried to grab hold of her, she flung him around like he was nothing. She could break his neck by jerking him back and forth so hard. But there was one thing he hadn't tried. The teeth of Fenrir were still in his pocket.

"They have great power," the Great Wolf had told Willoughby as he lay dying, "but you must find the strength to use them."

It was his only chance. He quit struggling against the witch and slipped his right hand into his pocket. But he didn't even have to figure out how to use them. The instant he closed his hand firmly around the canines, an electric jolt shot up his arm and out through his body.

442

Mogga must have felt it immediately for she let out a scream of pain and anger that pierced the dark of the forest with its intensity. With incredible strength, she flung Willoughby away from her and he landed with a vicious thud against a tree, knocking most of the wind out of him. But the effort it took to do so must have taken everything out of her, because when she did it, it released the spell she had on Bryan. The instant he felt her power relax, he let out a scream to match hers and charged forward.

Bryan met Mogga just as she turned from throwing Willoughby. He swung his sword at her filthy neck with a strike that would have surely severed her head had he connected but she ducked under the blow just in time. But Bryan had a weapon in both hands and as she slipped under the blade, he drove the burning pitch torch square into her hideous face.

There was a sickening sizzle as the end of the fiery limb took out Mogga's left eye and her scream of pain again pierced the darkness. But before Bryan could attack again, she flung up both arms and with a sweeping motion he was thrown a good ten feet, tumbling head over heels to the ground. The impact stunned him for a moment, but he fought to his feet with sheer determination as he realized what the witch intended. He was too far away to do anything and could only scream a warning out to his friend.

"Watch out, Will! She has a blade!"

Willoughby had regained his feet after Mogga had thrown him against the tree, but was still bent over struggling to catch his breath. He heard Bryan's scream of warning and looked up just in time to see Mogga charging him, a black mass of smoldering pitch and sloughing skin where her left eye used to be. Something shiny flashed in her right hand. Willoughby was still too dazed to react; the best he could manage was to hold the wolf's teeth weakly out in front of him and hope for the best, but Mogga flung out her left arm, knocking his to the side. Willoughby felt the power of the teeth surge as the two limbs made contact. Mogga grunted with the shock as the magic slammed into her again, but it wasn't enough. She drove the knife deep into Willoughby's side.

"Noooo!" Bryan screamed as he charged across the ground with his sword raised high. But the witch was quicker and threw up her hands. In a flash of smoke and fire, she was gone.

Bryan threw down his sword and knelt beside Willoughby, who had dropped to his knees.

"Bryan..." he gasped weakly as both boys looked down to the handle of Mogga's knife sticking out from Willoughby's sweatshirt, the gray of the fabric already turning dark with his blood. He looked into the face of his new friend and reached out with both hands grabbing the front of Bryan's shirt. He pulled him close. Bryan tried to speak.

"Will...I...I..."

Willoughby was looking directly into his eyes but Bryan's face started to fade in and out. He was slipping away fast.

"Bryan," he coughed. Something nasty tasting was in his mouth. He gasped again, struggling to finish. The words slipped out in a pathetic whimper. "Bryan, pl...pl...please don't let me die."

Bryan was saying something to him but Willoughby could hear nothing over the incredible roar in his head, like a freight train bearing down close. But it didn't matter that he couldn't hear his friend; nothing mattered anymore. Willoughby let go and slid into the darkness.

CHAPTER TWENTY-SIX

WILLOUGHBY REMEMBERED LITTLE AND dreamed a lot but the dreams were varied and confusing. In one dream, his grandma wiped his brow and tried to get him to swallow some of her soup. At least he thought it was his grandma, but she called him Will. Grandma Rose never called him anything but Willoughby.

He thought he remembered lying on his back, but moving at the same time. Had that been a dream? No, he didn't think so. He had opened his eyes and saw trees and sunlight overhead as he bounced hard. The bouncing caused him a great deal of pain, especially in his side. It was on fire.

People were talking, talking about him. One of them was Jake, or so he thought. Jake was a big man. There was a big man towering over him; it must be Jake. He didn't know anyone bigger than Jake.

Willoughby drifted in and out of sleep. At times he burned with fever, so hot he wanted to cry. Then he was cold. The shivering would start and not stop for a long time. Someone held his head and poured a bitter tasting liquid down his throat. He struggled, wanting to spit it out, but they wouldn't let him. After they made him drink the nasty stuff, he would sleep and dream again. One dream in particular, over and over. It was a wonderful dream and then a horrible dream all in one. There was a girl, the most beautiful thing he had ever seen. Dreaming of her made him hard. He throbbed as he thought about her. She would take off her clothes and make him come to her. He lay naked on top of her, touching, tasting her beauty. But when he would start to make love to her, he would look

into her face and suddenly be looking at the most hideous and horrifying woman he had ever seen. He would try to get away from her
but she would hold onto him. She was powerfully strong, forcing
him to have sex. Her rotted teeth and foul breath made him want
to puke. He belonged to her, she would tell him. Someone else was
yelling at him when he was with her, yelling at him to fight back.
But he couldn't fight back. It was the greatest dream and the worst
nightmare all in one. The worst part of it was the pain in his side

when it was over. A deep burning pain that made him moan and cry out in his sleep; he just wanted the pain to go away.

Willoughby dreamed of ravens, waterfalls, caves, and wolves, none which made any sense. But then there were things he didn't dream about. His family. Confusion reigned in his fitful sleep—why couldn't he think about his family? Why did they seem so far away? He dreamed and slept for a long time.

"Will…Will." Someone was shaking him gently but he didn't want to open his eyes. The bed was soft and the covers warm, but it wasn't his bed at Grandma's house. He just wanted to sleep more.

"Will…Will…Wake up." More shaking.

Willoughby opened his eyes. At first he wasn't sure who the person sitting next to him on the bed was. He blinked a few times and struggled with recognition, but then it came to him. He remembered. "Bryan?" he asked in a weak voice.

"Will, my friend. It is me." Bryan smiled at him and took his hand, holding it firmly in his. "You had us very worried. We were afraid we were going to lose you."

Willoughby attempted to sit up so he could see where he was, but as soon as he moved, a stabbing hot pain deep in his side brought that notion to an agonizing abrupt halt. Bryan gently pushed him back down.

"You still can't move too much, Will. You will break open the stitches. Just lie back and rest, I will fetch my grandparents. They have been very anxious and will be pleased to hear you have at last woken." Bryan got up from the bed and was gone.

The pain in his side was still intense; an unpleasant reminder to do as Bryan warned and not to move much, but by turning his head a little from side to side he could see where he was. His surroundings were unfamiliar.

He was in a small bedroom with simple furnishings. Besides the bed, there was a small wooden table and chair against one wall. On the table was a plain brown water pitcher and matching cup. A nightstand next to the bed held a vase with flowers in it and a half-used candle in a holder. The flowers gave off a pleasant and soothing aroma which filled the room. There was a window in one wall, but no glass. Two wooden shutters flanked the opening. Willoughby could hear birds singing and chickens clucking. Fresh air swirled in with a slight breeze and he could see the sun shining outside. Inside, below the window, sat his Mossy Oak camouflaged backpack, right next to a crude one that looked homemade. Something about the old pack rang a bell but he couldn't focus on why. They were connected to the items hanging from a hook near the door. There was a leather harness of some sort, and in the harness was a sword in a scabbard. Next to that hung a small round shield and in it, Willoughby could see the outline of a bird with its wings spread, fashioned out of brass rivets. Leaning in the corner was a crude spear with a sharp whittled point, the end of the spear stained a dark, reddish brown. Strange things, connected somehow to him, but he couldn't remember why.

Things he didn't see confused him even more so. There was no TV, no computer, no alarm clock, no light fixtures, no wall sockets. But as it was, he didn't have much time to think about the meaning behind the lack of such things.

"Well, awake at last," a powerful voice boomed, causing a startled Willoughby to turn towards the door too quickly. The fire in his side made him grunt with pain. The doorway was completely taken up by a huge man with shoulders nearly touching both sides. Willoughby barely got a chance to look at his face before the hulking giant was shoved the rest of the way into the room. A small woman with gray hair pinned into a bun on top of her head pushed her way past.

"Quint, you old fool," she said, shaking her tiny fist in the huge man's face. "Don't you come barging into the room like a witless artox scaring the poor lad. Don't you have any sense?"

"Sorry, Mattie." The big man grinned sheepishly. "Just wanted to make the boy feel at home."

The woman was plainly attired in a simple white cotton dress that reached nearly to the floor. Colorful but simple embroidery adorned the collar and short sleeves and a simple embroidered belt was tied in a bow at her waist. She was about his grandma's age and her mannerisms reminded Willoughby instantly of her. She sat down on the bed beside him, one gentle hand taking his and one reaching out to feel his forehead.

"You'll have to excuse the big fellow Will, I know he startled you but you have to watch moving about so. Break those stitches in your side open and we'll have to start over again. My name is Mattie and this is my husband Quint. We are Bryan's grandfolk if you haven't already figured that out."

The big man waved slightly and broke out into a big grin. His gray beard hung nearly to the middle of a massive chest covered by a thick leather apron. While he wasn't quite as tall as Jake, he was an imposing figure nonetheless. His arms were thick as small trees and his shoulders broad and square. Shoulder-length hair, gray as his beard, was tied back out of his face with a braided leather thong. Willoughby thought he looked like a Viking.

"Pleasure to make your acquaintance, lad." Quint smiled easily. "Bryan has told us of your adventures. We are glad we didn't lose you."

The little woman motioned the big man out the door with a flick of her hand. "Time enough for small talk later, Quint. Please see if Bryan has that soup ready. The boy needs to regain some strength before we pester him."

Quint grinned and gave him a wink before he ducked through the door. Willoughby liked him immediately.

Mattie's hand was cool and pleasant on Willoughby's forehead. "How are you feeling son?" she asked gently.

"Better now" he answered.

"Good," she said, patting his forehead one last time before getting up from the bed.

"I will get you some chicken soup and bread fresh out of the oven. After you have eaten, we must clean your wound and change your bandages. Can you sit up?"

Willoughby nodded though he knew it was going to hurt. She helped him rise up and propped a thick pillow behind him to support his back. He couldn't hide the wince as stabs of pain shot through him. Mattie noticed. She poured a cup of water from the pitcher and helped him with a long drink. The cool water tasted so good.

"It's going to take some time, that one is. Like I said, you must take care not to push things too quickly. Tear the stitches or get the wound infected again and we lose ground."

Willoughby handed the empty cup back to her. "How long have I been here?"

"Quint and Bryan brought you in four days ago," she answered as she refilled his cup. "It was two days prior to that when Mogga stuck the blade into you."

Six days. Things were starting to come back to him. Counting the days before he met Bryan, he had been gone from home for nearly a week and a half.

"Drink some more water Will; you need it," Mattie urged as she handed back the cup. He drained it.

"Your body shut itself down to protect against the infection. I could only get you to take small sips of water and broth while the fever raged. Now that you are drinking and going to start eating solid food, you will soon need to use the outhouse. The trips back and forth will not be easy."

An outhouse? He didn't say it outloud. An embarrassing thought crossed his mind that he might have messed himself while he had been out. If so, it would have been this woman who would have cleaned him.

"Thank you, Mattie," Willoughby said red-faced. "You remind me a lot of my grandma."

"Well you are quite welcome, Will. I take it as a great compliment that you compare me to your grandmother. I am sure she is a wonderful woman." She sat back down on the edge of the bed and took his hand once again. Her voice was calming.

"I know your story, Will. Bryan told me and you talked a lot in your sleep as you fought the fever but I do not think it as strange as you might think. There are many things hard to explain in this world. If Quint and I can help you, we will. If not? Well, then you are welcome to live with us. Bryan has found a good friend."

"Thanks again," Willoughby answered. Things were flooding back to him now, but in disorganized bits and pieces. The waterfall, the cave, finding the sword. Talking wolves and witches and a knife plunging into his side. His family. Counting the days he had been here he had been missing for nearly two weeks. He came close to tears thinking about what they must be going through but didn't want to cry in front of Mattie. He tried to change the subject but immediately wished he hadn't.

"Is Mogga really...I mean are you...well, never mind." He was instantly sorry he had opened his mouth.

Mattie squeezed his hand gently. "It is all right, Will. You mean to ask if Mogga is indeed my sister? You have as much right to know as anyone; she did try to kill you after all. Yes, she is my sister and yes, I am a witch also, though I prefer to think the manner in which we practice our craft different enough to avoid mistaking one for the other. Mogga and I went our separate ways when we were barely ten years old and we have spoken to each other only a few times since. Usually it was her threatening me and me warning her to stay away from my family. She uses her craft for evil and I use mine for good. It is as simple as black and white, day or night. But while I do not practice dark arts, I know enough of it to counter some of what it can do. Your wound did not heal as others because the knife Mogga used was tainted with a rare poison. I knew something was amiss when you failed to respond to my regular treatments. That is why the fever took so long to break, and that is why we nearly lost you before I was able to figure out what she had used. I have some tricks of my own and countered her poison, though none too soon."

"How did I get here Mattie?" Willoughby asked. He couldn't remember that either.

"Well, it was Bryan mostly. After Mogga stuck you with the blade, he knew it was going to be serious. He did what he could to stabilize the wound, rigged a litter of saplings, and was able to get you on it and drag it to the abandoned cottage. It took him nearly two days to get you there. He brewed some white willow bark into a tea and that helped fight the fever. You were burning up and infection had already set in."

"Bryan dragged the litter all the way here with me on it?"

"No, not quite, Will." Mattie wiped his brow with a cool, damp cloth. "I knew something was wrong. I sensed the magic passing between you and Mogga. I sent Quint out as soon as I felt the tremor. It is something most folk who can wield magic can do, though the distance varies according to their capabilities. Quint was able to catch up with you and Bryan at the cottage. They brought you the rest of the way on horseback. You were nearly gone by the time they got you here." She gave his hand a sincere squeeze and smiled. "But it was time enough. We did not lose you."

Willoughby returned her smile. "I owe you all for saving my life."

"Well, I must thank you, Will. My grandson is a very special lad and from what he says, you saved him as much as he did you. For that Quint and I will be eternally in your debt."

Willoughby protested. "But I didn't do anything. Mogga had me and it was Bryan who came just in time."

Mattie just smiled and shook her head. "You do not give yourself enough credit, Will. You had the strength and cunning to channel the magic of the Great Wolf. Bryan told me how it happened. She had him trapped in a spell but you were able to draw power from the teeth at just the right moment. Had you not, Mogga would have taken you as her captive—and killed my grandson."

"I didn't know if it would work. Fenrir said I must learn how to use it on my own. But somehow it just happened." Willoughby was starting to remember. But talking about the teeth brought about a moment of panic—they were gone!

"I must have lost the teeth!"

Mattie smiled, reached into the pocket of her dress, and drew out the great canines. A hole had been drilled into the root part of both teeth and threaded onto a leather thong.

"Lean your head forward, gently," she cautioned. Willoughby

452

complied and she slipped the leather round his neck, tied it, and then tucked the teeth under his shirt.

"Bryan made sure you did not lose them. Quint put them on the leather. Keep them close to you always, Will. I knew the great wolf Fenrir and his magic was incredibly strong. For you to have bested him is a story for the ages. Though I believe you had some help with that, didn't you?"

Willoughby knew exactly what she was talking about. "You know about the sword, don't you?"

Mattie nodded. "Gaelron was a dear friend and Quint and I were deeply saddened to learn his fate. We long wondered what became of him but he was a wanderer. He felt more comfortable being alone than he did around folk. It seems fate led your paths to cross."

Her last sentence set Willoughby to remembering. "It's funny, Mattie. My friend back at home, Jake, he kinda said the same thing. He said there are things in a person's life that don't happen by chance. It's destiny. He believes we are guided by spirits who lead you one way or the other."

"Well, I believe your friend Jake is a wise man. But there is something I must say to you, Will." Mattie's tone became much more serious. "I was going to wait until you were stronger but since we are speaking of such things I will mention it now. Magic is not something that everyone has the ability to use. On the contrary, most folk don't. For one such as yourself to be able to wield both the magic Gaelron willed into the sword and that within Fenrir's teeth is truly remarkable and I have not heard of such a thing for a long time. While there is much magic to be found within this world only few can use it. Why that is I know not, but I do know it can be both a blessing and a curse. Some folk will shun you if they realize you can wield magic; it will frighten them. Others will come after you because of it. I told you I could sense the magic being summoned? Well others can feel it too; that is what drew Mogga to search for you. But be warned, we are not the only ones who will have sensed the channeling."

"But who...I don't know anyone here except you, Bryan, and

Quint."

Mattie patted his head in typical grandma fashion. "Not to worry about it now young Will. The four of us will talk more when you have regained some of your strength. I have pushed you too far as it is. Soup and rest are what you need and you can enjoy both without fear. You are safe here." She looked towards the door. "It's about time!"

"Sorry, Mattie," Quint apologized as held the door open. Bryan followed close behind.

"Chicken soup and fresh bread, Will," Bryan beamed as he set a tray with short legs down on the bed in front of Willoughby. On it sat a wooden bowl of steaming soup and two pieces of warm, crusty, thick-sliced bread covered with melting yellow butter.

"Grandmother makes the best of both, though I would say our grouse stew would give it a challenge."

"Thank you Bryan and Quint but the lad does not need company right now. He still is in my care so out, both of you." The diminutive Mattie pushed the men towards the door. Size mattered not and it was quite clear who ruled the roost here.

"We will talk later, Will," Bryan yelled over his shoulder.

Willoughby polished off the soup and the bread in short order. It was delicious and he was ready for more but Mattie told him he would have to go slow. She took the tray from him.

"Now comes the hard part, Will. I must change the dressing on your wound. I will try not to cause you much discomfort but it must be done."

She was gentle as she took back the bedcovers and carefully helped Willoughby turn onto his side with the wound up. As she lifted up the cotton nightshirt he was dressed in he became embarrassingly aware that he had no underwear on.

"Your backside is of no interest to me, Will," Mattie chuckled easily as she removed the old dressing, "but the wound is, and I am pleased to say that it appears to be healing nicely. We should have you up and about in no time."

After she cleaned and redressed the wound, she took a small

ceramic vial from a pocket in her dress.

"You must take a swallow of this. It will help you sleep and keep the infection at bay."

She got him a cup of water and Willoughby did as he was told, chasing the bitter medicine with a long drink. He laid his head back onto the pillow. His stomach was full and he could feel the power of the drug Mattie had given him already starting to work. For the first he could remember in a long time, Willoughby felt comfortable. He felt safe. He felt drowsy. He started to nod off.

"Thank you Mattie, for everything," he whispered sleepily as she started to leave the room.

"You are welcome, Will Baxter." She paused at the door and gave him a reassuring smile. "And thank you."

MORE DREAMS. WILLOUGHBY SAW MOGGA'S FACE OVER AND OVER, morphing from the sensuous, beautiful young girl to the hideous witch she was. But there was someone else in the background, a dark, foreboding presence he could feel but not see. A man was looking for him, an evil man that meant to do him harm. Fear drove Willoughby. He tried to run but with every step he took, he slipped back two. Panicked, he kept looking over his shoulder but saw only an unrecognizable dark figure gaining on him. Harder and harder he struggled, only to lose more ground. Closer and closer he came until Willoughby could sense the man reaching for him. But in an instant the nightmare disappeared, replaced by a different vision, Mattie's gentle, smiling face looking down at him. *"Rest easy, Will, rest easy. Bad dreams will not harm you here."*

The rest of his sleep was deep and restful after the nightmare had been chased away. He woke to the sound of someone humming a sweet song and when he opened his eyes, Mattie was at the windowsill. The shutters were open and sunshine flooded the room. Willoughby could hear voices and the hammering of metal on metal outside. Mattie had both hands open and resting on the sill where no less than a dozen small, colorful birds hopped over her palms and fingers, helping themselves to a mound of dried breadcrumbs.

Next to Mattie sat a great long-haired black cat, which eyed the birds carefully, but they paid the feline no mind and hopped about as if he wasn't there. Willoughby watched as she sang softly to the birds. They in turn would flit from her hand or sill to her shoulder, chirping in harmony. Never once did the cat attempt to bother them.

"Good morning, Will," Mattie said without turning towards him. The birds continued their chorus and breakfast.

"I trust your sleep was better though I must apologize for your bad dreams. I should have placed a protective ward around you earlier but I did not think them strong enough to find you here. It was a mistake I will not make again."

Willoughby knew instantly what she was talking about; she knew of his nightmare. "Who was it, Mattie? He was looking for me."

She gently flipped the rest of the breadcrumbs out the window and the birds followed. Wiping her hands on her apron, she turned back to him. The big cat jumped from the sill onto the bed next to Willoughby with a plop and sniffed him with curiosity.

"Carefully, you furball monstrosity," she admonished the cat. "Our guest is recovering from his wound and does not need you bouncing around on his bed."

The cat eyed Willoughby with suspicion and then looked back at Mattie. She gave him a little nod and he promptly curled up into a big hairy ball next to the boy.

"Will, this great beast is Lord Fuggs. While his manners are crude and he often looks as if he would like to attack, he is relatively harmless unless you are a mouse or rat. When we do not have guests, he usually sleeps on your bed. He does not mind sharing, though. But if it bothers you, I will ask him not to."

The big cat popped one sleepy eye open and fixed it on Willoughby, as if waiting for a response. Willoughby held his hand out cautiously and the cat rubbed his head against it and allowed him to scratch behind his ears.

"Pleased to meet you, Lord Fuggs. Thank you for letting me use your bed and I would be more than happy to share it with you."

After talking to wolves, carrying on a conversation with a cat made perfect sense to Willoughby. The big cat promptly started to purr and closed his eyes.

"There." Mattie smiled. "I knew the two of you would become friends, and his Lordship here does not make friends easily, I assure you of that."

She sat down and felt Willoughby's forehead. "In answer to your question of who was looking for you in your dream Will, I do not know. Whoever was searching was a long way away. It was not focused so I think they were just casting a net in hopes with luck they might find you."

"I don't understand, Mattie. Who would want to find me and why? How could they know anything about me?" Willoughby was confused.

"They sense the magic, Will. It is as I told you. The use of magic is perceptible by others who also have the power to wield. My sense tells me it is not you, so much as the magic they seek. I have warded Gaelron's sword and the wolf's teeth. My own magic is already shielded. I believe I was quick enough not to allow them to get any sense of exactly where you might be, but we must remain wary. But let us worry no longer about such things. A beautiful day has come and chased the night shadows away and your breakfast is here."

As if she was choreographing the whole thing, the door opened and a smiling Bryan entered the bedroom with another tray. There was a big steaming bowl of something that looked to Willoughby like oatmeal sprinkled with black berries. A small pitcher of milk and a clay jar of honey flanked the delicious smelling cereal. More of Mattie's wonderful bread and butter also graced the tray.

Mattie and Bryan left Willoughby to eat. He attacked his breakfast as if it was his last, devouring every bite of the appetizing repast set before him. He figured if his appetite had anything to do with his recovery he was well on his way.

After breakfast came a task much tougher than he had anticipated; he had to go to the bathroom. It was embarrassing that he could not walk on his own and the production made out of what should have been a simple private task was almost comical. Mattie had told him of the outhouse. The only ones Willoughby had ever used were in rustic campgrounds and picnic areas and he had always been a bit leery of them.

At first, when he informed Mattie of his need to go, she wanted Quint to carry him but Willoughby was adamant they allow him to make it on his own, so with Bryan's assistance, it was decided to let him try. Just out the back door next to his room was a flat-stone path at the end of which was his intended destination; a quaint little outhouse made with sawn cedar boards and a cedar shingled roof.

Arranged in the hallway before you stepped out the door were several pairs of fleece-lined slippers. Bryan helped him slip a pair onto his bare feet before they went out.

It might have well been a mile away for the effort it took Willoughby to get there, and he came close to having a major accident when his bowels figured out they were getting close to relief. He was weak from having been in bed for so long and with every step, an electric shock of pain jolted from his wound. But they made it. As the door shut, Willoughby was able to get the nightshirt he was wearing up around his waist just in time.

It was always amazing to Willoughby how a simple act such as relieving the pressure on one's bowels could change a person's outlook so much for the better. While there were no *Home and Garden* or *Field and Stream* magazines to help him relax like there were in the bathrooms at Grandma Rose's house, it was actually much more pleasant than he thought it would be. There were clumps of dried weed-looking things hanging on the walls that gave out a very pleasing and relaxing aroma covering up the obvious odor he had anticipated.

Sitting on the wooden platform next to him was a woven basket full of wide brown leaves with blood red veins of color shot through them. He picked up one and fingered it. The texture was surprisingly soft yet the leaf was resilient and didn't tear as easily as he thought it might. Willoughby had thought they were part of the aroma masking effort until he noticed the lack of the thing he was going to need very shortly—toilet paper. It should not have been a surprise to him given everything he had seen so far. He had taken a giant step back in time and things he had always taken for granted were not to be found. He almost panicked until he realized what the basket of soft leaves was there for, and when he finished, he found they worked quite well.

After Willoughby was finished he found Bryan sitting on a bench near the path waiting for him. Instead of going right back to his bedroom the two boys sat for a while. The sunshine and fresh air felt wonderful, though it wasn't overly warm. Bryan had anticipated it and had a thick robe ready for him. It was the first chance Willoughby had to look around since he had arrived.

He was immediately struck by how tidy everything was and it reminded him of how Jake and Grandma Rose kept the area around the Baxter farmhouse. The little house where Bryan and his grandparents lived was mortared stone about halfway up and then framed with rough-hewn wooden timbers to the roofline. The roof was covered with thin tiled slate and a tall stone chimney dominated the center of the house. While there were plenty of windows with their shutters open wide to the sun, Willoughby could not help but notice there was no glass anywhere.

Next to the bench where the boys sat, a well tended garden thrived with produce even though fall was settling in, just like it had been at home. Orange pumpkins and bright yellow squash splashed the garden with color. Just beyond the garden, a split rail fence marked the boundary of an orchard where apple and pear trees stood with their heavy laden branches ready to shed their fall fruit. Between the garden and the house was a large mound of dirt. A stone lined path led at an angle into the ground below the mound to a thick wooden door.

"What is that?" Willoughby asked.

"It is the cold cellar," Bryan answered. When he saw the perplexed look on his friend's face he continued, "Don't you use a cold cellar to store food?"

Willoughby understood now and was going to tell Bryan about

freezers and refrigerators and frequent trips to the grocery store but thought better of it. Instead he just shook his head. "We use different methods to keep our food. They kinda work the same way I guess."

As the boys sat, Willoughby asked Bryan a lot of questions. He was enjoying the opportunity to be outside and wanted to make the best of it. Bryan explained how fruits and vegetables they didn't use fresh in the summer and fall went into the cold cellar, where they kept quite well for most of the winter. He pointed out the smokehouse where they smoked and cured meat and sausages, which were also stored in the cold cellar. There was a cider house where apples and pears were pressed into juice for drink and to make the vinegar which Mattie used to pickle fruits and vegetables. Everything went into the cellar.

A funny-looking little house sat atop a pole just behind the cold cellar. Bryan called it a dovecote. It was where Mattie kept her pigeons. She used the trained birds to deliver and receive messages from places. The house was high on the pole to protect the sleeping birds from prowling predators which might be searching for a midnight snack.

Across the dirt lane from the house were the blacksmith shop and barn where Bryan spent a lot of his time caring for the family's horses and small herd of livestock and helping his grandpa Quint at the forge. Willoughby just sat and listened as Bryan explained the workings of the farm and imagined that this had been the way things were at his grandma's before the advent of electricity and other technology. When he had tumbled over the falls and woke up in the cave, he had not only found himself in a different land, but a different time as well.

Mattie broke off the boy's outdoor interlude. She wanted Willoughby back in bed, much to his displeasure. He was enjoying being outside in the sun but followed her orders without protest. After watching the interactions between his three hosts he was convinced Mattie was top dog here and he wasn't about to get on her bad side. As Bryan helped him back to his room, he knew she was also right about the healing process. His strength was low and the short trip to the outhouse had weakened him considerably.

Two days later was a different story. Mattie marveled at how quickly Willoughby's wound had healed. When he told her it was because she was such a good caregiver, she thanked him but hinted at something else. "I believe you have an advantage most folk do not have, Will."

He didn't know what she meant and asked her to explain. "It is the magic. Its effect on the possessor is as varied as the ways in which one can use it. Magic can suck the life from you and leave you old before your time or it can give your body an energy and vitality to do amazing things, such as heal terrible wounds quickly. From what I see of the way you have healed, I would say you possess the latter, Will."

Willoughby hadn't thought much about magic in the last couple of days. Fenrir's teeth were secure about his neck and he hadn't touched the sword, but he couldn't deny he was feeling better. Mattie even allowed him to help around the farm with small chores. As fall took hold there was much to be done and he threw himself into the tasks Mattie gave him to do. Not only did he want to repay these folk for all they had done for him but it helped keep his mind from thinking about his own family. He could make it work while busy with other tasks but when night dropped its veil over the little farm and he settled into his bed Willoughby could not keep his mind from the painfull thoughts of those he had left behind. And in the dark of his room no one could see him cry.

On a pleasant afternoon as Willoughby was helping Mattie around the house, he noticed a small shelf in a corner next to the large fireplace. There, surrounded by fresh flowers, was a portrait of a stunning young woman not much older than himself. Whoever had painted the picture had captured her sheer beauty in the finest detail. Sparkling eyes, and blonde hair that looked as if the sun were shining through it. When Willoughby looked at the portrait he swore the girl looked back, captivating him with the intensity of her dark eyes and the warmth of her smile. As Mattie came back from the cold cellar carrying an armload of clay pickling jars, he asked her about the painting.

"Is that your daughter?" he asked softly.

Mattie stopped and looked at the picture with sad eyes. "Yes, Will. That is Brianna, Bryan's mother. She was the light of our life, Quint and I. Bryan has spoken of her?"

Willoughby nodded, almost sorry he asked, for the pain in Mattie's face was obvious as she gazed wistfully at the portrait.

"Bryan and I talked a little about our mothers around the campfire the day we met. He didn't say too much other than she died giving birth to him."

Mattie forced a tired smile onto her worn face and motioned to the kitchen table. "Sit, Will. Let me put these jars away and I will get us some tea and tell you about her."

Willoughby sat down at the big table in Mattie's warm kitchen as she prepared the two of them mugs of hot tea. The day was autumn cool but since it wasn't raining, the shutters were open, letting fresh air and sunlight fill the room. The sounds of Bryan and Quint working in the smithy drifted in on the breeze.

""We will celebrate Bryan's sixteenth birthing day coming up in a couple of months," Mattie started as she sat a steaming mug of hot, honey-sweetened tea in front of Willoughby. His grandma was a tea drinker and his sister liked it but he had never cared for it much. Soda had always been his drink of choice, much to Grandma Rose's displeasure, but there was no such thing here and he had become very fond of Mattie's tea, especially when flavored with just the right amount of honey. He wrapped his hands around the warm mug and sipped slowly as Mattie continued.

"A bittersweet occasion because it is also the day of Brianna's death. That which brings joy to our hearts also carries with it the pain of our loss. Folk said Quint and I were too old to be parents. You see, we did not meet until late in our lives. He had been married before but his wife was barren. Still they loved each other nonetheless and it was a terrible blow to him when she died of the black sickness. Quint never looked at another woman for years after she passed. Always a soldier, he labored in the great castle at Tiernon as a weapons master. He threw himself into the work of training young men for battle and there was none better than he.

"It was in the time of the last great war with Torbek that I found myself in the city. There had been terrible battles and a call went out across the country for healers to come and help tend the wounded and I felt it my duty as a loyal citizen and healer to answer the need. A great hospital was set up on the outskirts of Tiernon and so I went to work there. Oh Will, it was a dark and terrible time. So much misery and mutilation inflicted on so many young men..."

Mattie's voice drifted and Willoughby watched as she stared out the open window, her mind wandering back to a different place and time. After a quiet moment she started again.

"I had worked at hospital for a month when I began to notice this very large and handsome man who came often in the evenings to visit the wounded men. He was very caring and his visits cheered many who had nothing to be happy about. Nearly every other day he came faithfully regardless of weather. One evening after he had gone I asked one of the young men he visited who he was and he told me about him."

"His name is Quint and he was our weapons trainer," the lad said. "He comes here because he knows many of us and treats us all like we are his sons."

"I thought it a high compliment indeed coming from a young man so terribly disfigured but I could see the truth of his praise in the faces of the wounded as this man visited. Truly they loved the man and he loved them. But as I watched this bear of a man I could see the pain in his eyes as he sought to comfort young men who would never again be whole. Oh, and he tried to hide it he did, but my eyes saw through it. How he suffered for them.

"Then one day I saw him in the ward wandering and looking like a lost child. I asked if he needed help and he told me he was looking for a young patient with bright red hair.

"They call him Red," Quint said.

"Immediately my heart sank, for the fellow he was speaking of had passed in the night and had been taken out for burial. When I told him the young man was gone he took it very hard. To see such a man with tears in his eyes, it touched my heart so. I think I fell in love with him at that very moment. He was so upset I asked if he would like to walk with me in the garden because I had always found it to be a place of comfort amongst such suffering and misery. From that moment on we saw each other every day and four months later we were married."

She paused and stirred her tea. The sound of laughter drifted in from the smithy where her two men, Quint and Bryan, shared a joke. Willoughby could see her eyes brighten as she listened.

"Ah, but you asked about our Brianna." She smiled across her cup at him. "I stayed with Quint even though I was a country girl and longed for my home. I did not like the city but Quint bought a small cottage for us up the river a bit from Tiernon. We would rise early in the morning and he would walk me to hospital where he would visit the wounded before going on to the castle. Each night he would be there to walk me home. Even though there was a war going on and we were surrounded by death and suffering we were happy.

"Our beloved daughter came to us a year later. She was a surprise for both of us but a wondrous and welcome one. It was late in life to start a family but we both had so much love to give and our Brianna was such a beautiful and happy child. Her laugh could bring sunshine to a cloudy day. As she grew, she became as smart as she was beautiful and wanted to learn about everything. We would go for walks in the forest near the dwarves' quarry looking for medicinal plants and she would question everything she saw. 'Why did birds sing and how did they fly? Why were the foxes red and the ravens black? Why was there a sun, a moon, and stars?' She wanted to know about everything. Traders and craftsmen would stop by our cottage to barter and she would beg them for stories of faraway places. They would bring her books and oh, how Brianna loved books! Quint and I taught her everything we could and still she wanted to learn more. Such a child she was."

Mattie paused and stared deep into her mug. Willoughby

noticed a change on her face, like a shadow passing. When she started talking again there was a bitter tinge to her voice she did not try to hide.

"Her thirst for knowledge was her downfall and the beginning of our curse. The three of us lived for fifteen years in our happy world, oblivious to the tribulations of war going on round us. Quint had thought of retiring but the king valued his skills and would not release him from duty so he still went to the castle every day. Brianna, her curiosity never satisfied, started to question us about the castle and the city. Quint and I tried to answer as best we could without arousing her interest too much. We were very protective and sought to shield her from the filth and vileness that breed when masses of people live together.

"But alas, we could not stop her from hearing folk talk and one day a trader told her of the school in the castle that was open to the children of those who worked in the king's specialty services. Brianna demanded she be allowed to go and try as we might, Quint and I could not dissuade her. She made us feel guilty that we knew of the school and had conspired to keep her out of it and in the end we gave in. She started going with her father each day as he went to the castle and it was heartbreaking for me. For fifteen years she had always been by my side and I had to let her go. I let her go to the castle where that beast came into her life."

Mattie stood up suddenly from the table, grabbed their mugs and began refilling them with hot tea. The change in her demeanor was sudden and frightening. Willoughby had never intended to bring up her buried demons.

"Mattie you don't have to tell me any more if you don't want to. I understand."

Mattie shook her head as she added honey to their tea. "Thank you Will, for your concern, but I will be all right," she said as she sat back down. "The wound to my heart has had many years to scar. Sometimes it is necessary to release the bitterness one builds up over the years.

"He was a much older man, powerful and wealthy and he

became smitten with her. The fact he was married made no difference and his wife being a sickly sort and confined to her bedroom made it easy. Quint saw the way he looked at Brianna and became concerned, but the man was smart and did not hesitate to use his power and influence to get what he wanted. When Quint started to get in the way, he had him transferred to the field where he could not interfere. This man was totally infatuated with Brianna and there was nothing we could do. Quint, being the ultimate soldier, did as he was ordered." She paused and stirred her tea as the memories stirred her emotions.

"Your daughter didn't love this man did she, Mattie?" Willoughby asked.

"Brianna was naive about such things, Will. Maybe that was our fault; we had sheltered her so much. She was influenced by who he was, his wealth and his power. I don't think she even understood what that kind of love was. He knew she had a thirst for knowledge and he preyed upon that, using it as an excuse to spend time with her. He showed her the castle and its secrets, the city and the docks. He showed her the great library and being the kind of girl she was, she loved it all. As her mother, I tried to warn her but the blindness of youth got in my way. Brianna became angry and wondered how I could be so cruel to think such a thing. He was her friend and mentor, or so she thought.

"We had never argued before, Will, and it was devastating to me. I started to question myself and my motives. I began to think maybe Quint and I were wrong and that it was nothing more than a childless man letting his fatherly instincts take over. With Quint away I had no choice but to trust the man's intentions were harmless." Mattie stopped talking and stared blankly. A long moment of uncomfortable silence passed before she resumed.

"I remember the day so well, one of the first beautiful days of spring. The kind you welcome so much after the long gray gloom of winter. I had resolved not to continue arguing with Brianna and prayed my instincts were wrong and things seemed to get better between us. We took breakfast together and I helped fix her hair.

466

We made plans to walk in the woods after supper and enjoy the last brightness of the day and then I walked her to the gates of the castle and kissed her goodbye. Brianna was always so happy and excited about going to school. She told me she loved me and skipped off through the gate. Such a beautiful girl she was."

Mattie dabbed at her eyes with her sleeve. Willoughby desperately wanted her to stop; he had a feeling what was coming next was going to upset both of them. He started to speak but with a wave of her hand she cut him off and continued.

"I spent the day in the city and when I came home that evening I expected to find her bustling about the kitchen getting supper ready, singing, and happy as always, ready to tell me of all the wonderful things she had learned that day at school. But I found the cottage dark and cold, no fire in the hearth. I could hear her sobbing in her room and I went to her."

Mattie wrapped her hands round her tea mug and stared into it. The bitterness and anger in her voice seeped out like pus from an infected wound.

"The only lesson she had learned that day was one of vileness and treachery. The monster told her of an ancient book he had found in the library and wanted to show it to her. But when he got her alone in one of the back rooms he began talking of love and things that confused her. He put a necklace of rare jewels and worth a small fortune around her neck and tried to kiss her. When Brianna pushed him away, he became furious and accused her of teasing and leading him on. She tried to leave but he wouldn't let her and in the end he was too strong. He raped her, Will. That monster raped my innocent daughter."

Mattie swayed and Willoughby thought she was going to fall over but she caught herself just as he was jumping up to go to her aid.

"I am all right, Will," she said, composing herself. "Thank you, but do not be concerned. Sometimes the anger overwhelms me when I think about what that man did to Brianna."

"Didn't you have him arrested for what he did?" a perplexed

and distraught Willoughby asked. The whole story was far more upsetting than he had bargained for and Mattie's raw emotions affected him.

She shook her head. "You do not understand, Will. Things may be different where you are from but this man was too powerful for anyone to accuse him of wrongdoing. I went to the castle to confront him and was thrown out.

"My poor Brianna was never the same after that day. She never returned to school and the happiness drained from her like water from an overturned bucket. My shining star was replaced by a lifeless shell that only went through the motions of living. The man made no effort to contact us and we secluded ourselves in our little sanctuary, keeping away from everyone and waiting for Quint to return. But I feared for us all because I knew Quint would try to kill the man when he found out what happened. Then I began to notice the signs in Brianna—she was with child.

"At first I wanted to put an end to it, my anger was so strong. It would have been so simple, the right mixture blended with her morning tea. She would never have known. But my desire to erase any traces of that evil beast was overcome with the knowledge that this innocent unborn child was part of my daughter, part of Quint and myself. The same blood runs through all of us. I could not do it. When I look at my grandson now and think back to that time I feel shame for what I thought."

Mattie turned to Willoughby and he was relieved she seemed to have regained her composure. Her bright smile had returned.

"Would you walk with me Will? There is something I would like to show you. The way is not long and it will do us both some good I think."

Willoughby was ready; Mattie's story had depressed him and he needed a break. The day outside was as pleasant as it had been for some time, the coolness of autumn not yet harsh enough for extra clothes. He was comfortable enough wearing outgrown hand-me-downs of Bryan's, the thickness of the cotton cloth soft and warm. They had decided to stash his old clothes out of fear they would raise the eyebrows of any visitor who might happen by.

Mattie led Willoughby past the garden and into the orchard. A well-manicured trail began just past the last of the fruit trees and led off into the woods. Mattie grabbed two firm, yellow-green apples from the low hanging branches and tossed one to Willoughby. They munched the sweet fruit while following the path that wandered gently to the top of a small knoll crowned with a rock outcrop. When they got to the top, Willoughby found himself in front of a mossy stone semi-circle forming a natural fence surrounding a patch of lush green grass. A single hardwood tree, its leaves bright with the brilliant red hues of autumn, grew within the stone circle. As they paused and look back down the hill, Willoughby could see the farm below. It was a beautiful spot.

Mattie took him by the hand and they entered the semi-circle. "The grass here never grows too high and never turns brown," she said in a soft voice, barely above a whisper. Willoughby could sense the peace and calmness. It was a place of solitude and quiet reflection. This was a sanctuary.

A single flat stone rested at the top of the patch of green grass, surrounded by a stunning array of flowers blooming magnificently even so late in the growing season. Mattie knelt by the stone and brushed its surface gently. Willoughby edged close where he could see the face of the marker nestled in its bed of floral brilliance. A single name was chiseled into the hard smooth granite, "BRI-ANNA."

Mattie knelt quietly for a minute or so with her head bowed, as Willoughby remained silent, fearing to interrupt the moment. She stood up and brushed her face with her sleeve, but not before Willoughby caught the shine of a tear glimmering in the corner of her eye.

"Sit with me, Will, and I will finish the story of my beloved daughter." She led him to a natural bench in the stone wall facing Brianna's grave.

"We hid ourselves in our little cottage by the river while Quint was far away at war fulfilling his duties. We managed to exchange a few letters but I did not mention the truth of the situation to him. The stress for him would have been unbearable.

"When Brianna was in her seventh month a man from the castle came to see us. It surprised me. It was the first time anyone had contacted us since that horrible day and I was caught off guard. Brianna answered the door and the first thing the man noticed was the swell of her belly under her dress. By the shocked look on his face, I think her condition was a big surprise. He stated he was an official from the castle and had a message for us. Quint was being discharged from his duties and would be returning home within the month. The man gave us a small bag of coin, saying it was Quint's pension. Forty years of loyal service and he is dismissed like a common kitchen boy.

"But I recognized the man from what little time I had been in the castle. He was a friend of the man who had assaulted my daughter. As he was leaving he asked to talk with me in private. I walked him to the gate but before he started to speak I told him I knew who he was and demanded to know the true meaning of why he had come."

Mattie stared at Brianna's grave, remembering. "His answer chilled me to my marrow. The sneer on his face and the contempt for Brianna and myself was unhidden in his voice. He stated the last time his employer had encountered Brianna she had been delusional and mentally unstable and had threatened him.

"Oh Will, how I so wanted to kill that man! I had the power to do it. I could feel the rage manifesting itself but as I told you before, I use my magic for good and do not delve into the dark side. But I could summon such if I wanted to, and it was all I could do to stop myself from constricting the man's windpipe and watch him suffer a slow and horrible death.

"But I did not. I had the well-being of my family and my coming grandchild to think of. The man informed me that when Quint returned we would be expected to leave at once, never to return to this part of Artura. It was an ultimatum and not a request. We were being banished. I was too stunned to speak. Not only was there no justice for the evil inflicted upon my daughter, he was using his power to force us to leave. We were a potential problem and he was taking steps to eliminate us."

Mattie sighed heavily. Willoughby was afraid she was going to cry and he knew he would cry with her if she did. He never paid much attention to the news at home but you couldn't help but be aware of attention-grabbing headlines and the media blitz when a powerful man, usually a politician or such, got caught in a scandal involving a younger woman. The story usually involved an elaborate attempt at a cover-up but when the media got hold of it, more often than not it meant the fall of the man involved. But whoever the man was who violated Mattie's daughter, it was clear from her story that he was above the law. Maybe Willoughby didn't understand the rules of this place he had unwittingly found himself in but one thing was clear—they weren't the same as they were at home.

Mattie went on with her story. "I thought he was done but he had another dagger to strike with. He said there was the matter of a very valuable necklace belonging to his employer my Brianna had openly coveted. It was thought she had stolen it. He was now accusing my daughter of being a thief. The man was far closer to death than he realized but I held myself in check. I was thankful Quint was gone. He would not have been able to stay his hand. I told the man I had no knowledge of any such necklace and we would be leaving as soon as my husband returned. He got on his horse but before he rode off he had one last comment. I remember his chilling words and the way he said them so clearly, even after all these years."

"You will leave as soon as your husband returns. The next time I ride this way if I find you here I will have you all arrested and slapped in irons. Your family will disappear from the face of this earth. Do you understand?"

"I could not speak; the cruel unjustness of it all overwhelmed me. I just nodded my head and he rode off."

"What happened when Quint came home?" Willoughby asked. He knew Bryan's grandpa to be a mild mannered man yet underneath that huge amiable exterior Willoughby believed was a sleeping volcano of power and skill that you wouldn't want to be in front of when it was unleashed.

"As you would expect Quint wanted to kill them both, but I had prepared for that. I used my powers for something I was not proud of but I felt it necessary to protect my family. I slipped a potion into his tea that made him passive and susceptible to my suggestions. When I told him of the grave danger Brianna, our grandchild, and all of us were in he was able to see beyond his anger. We left that very day.

"We traveled here but the journey was trying for our poor Brianna. She was late in term and should not have been on the road in her condition. Winter had set in and we fought the wet, cold, and mud for many weeks. When we arrived we found this place had been neglected for years and was not fit for a hog to live in but we had no choice. We sought to make Brianna as comfortable as possible but the ordeal had been too much. Though it was still a month early, she went into labor just after we arrived."

Willoughby could see the strain on Mattie's face.

"You must understand, Will," she went on. "I am as skilled a healer as you will find in this land. I have delivered many a child and had never lost a baby or its mother. But when it came time to save my own daughter, my efforts failed. I tried everything I knew but Brianna was too fragile to take the strain of the journey and the delivery of a child. I was able to save Bryan but not her."

The tears were flowing freely now, streaking down Mattie's worn face and Willoughby was crying right along with her, his sleeve becoming wet as he sought to stem the torrent.

"I think part of it was that Brianna just gave up. She was never the same after what had been done to her. Her world that had been so bright and full of wonder and joy had been soiled and dirtied with a single moment of a powerful man's uncontrollable lust. I knew she was fading fast so I laid her new baby boy into her arms, she kissed his forehead and said she wanted to call him Bryan, after a hero in her favorite book. Then she looked at Quint and me.

"'Take him, Momma,' she whispered. 'You and Poppa must raise him as your own and he will be the better for it. Tell him always that I loved him.'

"I took the boy from her arms and laid him in the cradle Quint had made for him. When I turned back our Brianna was gone."

Willoughby was bawling like a baby. The raw, emotional power and gut wrenching misery of Mattie's story had been too much. She was crying unabashedly as well and they hugged each other close. This woman, who reminded him so much of his own grandma, had saved his life and shared a personal story of unthinkable grief. He felt a kinship with her as the two hugged and sobbed next to Brianna's grave.

"So you know the rest, Will," she continued after they had composed themselves. "Quint and I chose this spot as her final resting place. It is the kind she would have loved if she had been able to see it for herself. We raised Bryan as we would have our own son. He is our life now and has been for sixteen years."

Willoughby smiled at her. "I am glad you raised Bryan to be the person he is, Mattie. Had he been anyone else I don't think I would be here today."

She returned his smile and as she hugged him, a low flying bird zoomed by, barely over their heads. Mattie looked up quickly, shielding her eyes with her hand against the low lying sun as she followed the pigeon in its flight.

She stood up quickly. "We must go back to the house, Will. That is one of my birds. One whose return I did not expect so soon. The news it carries must be important."

They left the hilltop in a hurry, leaving the peace and solitude of Brianna's resting place behind them.

CHAPTER TWENTY-SEVEN

AFTER COMING DOWN FROM THE HILL MATTIE went immediately to the dovecote to tend to her bird while Willoughby returned to the house. He had been on his feet more than any other time since his injury and its effect was telling. He was tired and the wound in his side, though it had healed nicely under Mattie's talented hands, was throbbing with burning intensity. She had left him a small dose of painkiller on the nightstand next to his bed just for such a time and he swallowed the bitter liquid, chasing it down with a cool drink of water. He lay down on his bed fully clothed and was immediately joined by Lord Fuggs who curled up next to him. But Willoughby didn't mind the company and the two drifted quickly off into the bliss of a late afternoon nap.

He woke to a wonderful aroma drifting from Mattie's kitchen. He hadn't eaten since breakfast and his stomach was growling in displeasure. Lord Fuggs, annoyed by the jostling of the bed as Willoughby got up, yawned, stretched, and gave his nap partner an irritating look before going right back to sleep. He had no intention of ending his nap quite yet.

"Ah, Will," Mattie greeted as he entered the kitchen. "I hope your nap was restful. Fetch Bryan and Quint for me please and the lot of you wash up for supper."

Willoughby stumbled out onto the front porch and stopped by the washbasin, pouring in some cold water from the pitcher. The sedative Mattie had used to ease the pain and discomfort of his wound left him feeling groggy when he woke so he splashed the invigorating cold water onto his face and cleared his cobwebs.

Bryan and Quint had been in the smith shop nearly all day working on some sort of contraption. Willoughby was always a bit apprehensive about going into the smithy and preferred to watch from the door. It was dark, stuffy, extremely hot regardless of the weather, and busy, especially with a hulk-like Quint wielding his tongs and hammer and jumping back and forth between the forge and the huge anvil where he did his shaping. Bryan fed fuel to the forge and manned the bellows. Willoughby, though fascinated by the place, was comfortable watching from a distance. A guy could get run over in there in a heartbeat.

Quint made and fixed all kinds of things from farm tools of all sorts to pots, pans, and smaller kitchen implements. His talent brought lots of people out to the farm and at the moment he and Bryan were working on something called a yoke and crosstree assembly. When asked, Quint said it was for a wain, a very large wain. Willoughby nodded, but had absolutely no idea what a wain was. It was Bryan who came to his rescue and explained.

"This is for a wagon, Will. A large one we call a wain. Grandfather is an excellent wainwright, amongst his other talents. The wains are used for hauling things and are pulled by huge beasts called artox. It is the way most goods and merchandise are transported. How do you move things where you come from?"

Willoughby thought for a moment. Trucks, planes, and trains would have been a normal answer but he didn't want to have to spend half a day trying to explain them.

"We use something similar. We call it a truck." Better to keep it simple. He informed the two men supper was waiting and Mattie wanted them to wash up.

Mattie had prepared a fresh venison roast, boiled potatoes, peas, and of course, a fresh, round loaf of bread. Her fare was simple but wonderfully good. Willoughby had never been a huge eater but you didn't have much say sitting at Mattie's table, and she never had to prompt Quint and Bryan to eat. It was astonishing how much the two could put away but she always had a concern for Willoughby. But his appetite was returning as he grew stronger and he was making her happy by eating more.

Mattie bustled about the kitchen while the men sat at the table and ate, so similar to the way Grandma Rose did things. Their kitchens were their domains and if you thought you were going to get up and get your own second helping or put your dishes away you were brought up short. This was their place—you were a guest and were treated as such.

After a meal that had Willoughby ready to explode, Mattie served them each a piece of her spiced honey cake. Topped with a spoonful of fresh cream mixed with more honey, it was a dessert hard to turn down no matter how full you were. Quint was the only one who accepted a second piece of cake.

"Mattie, that was a fine meal, though I have had better. If you keep improving your cooking, I might keep you around for a bit longer," he said, winking at the boys.

"You had better keep me around, you old fool. You are uglier than the backside of an artox and smell worse. There is no other woman in Artura who would put up with the likes of you," she shot back.

Bryan and Willoughby smiled at each other. Mattie and Quint's banter was always light-hearted; no newcomer could watch their interaction and not come away with the knowledge the two truly loved each other.

Mattie sat down at the table with her mug of tea. "We have important matters to discuss my boys," she said. Her tone was serious and the look on her face matched it.

"What is it Mattie?" Quint asked as he pushed his plate away.

"Two matters," she started. "One is an issue we have chosen to ignore of late and for that I offer our guest an apology. We have welcomed him as an addition to our home and perhaps our delight in having him here has blinded us to the fact young Will has a family. A mother, sister, and grandmother who love him very much and agonize over their loss every day."

Willoughby kept his head down. He didn't like being the center of supper time conversation. Mattie continued on. "So the question arises as to what we should do, or maybe better said, what we can do about it?"

"I, too, apologize Master Will," Quint spoke. "It has been a pleasure having you here and I know I speak for Bryan as well. We owe you a debt of gratitude and have been remiss in not repaying that debt."

Willoughby's cheeks flushed red with embarrassment. He had always thought Bryan did more saving than he had but he couldn't convince these good people of that. He had gotten pretty comfortable here and was so grateful just having a home and family to be around he was guilty of not thinking about what his own family was going through.

"What do think we should do, Will?" It was Bryan who spoke this time.

The three looked across the table to Willoughby who was pushing a few crumbs of honey cake around with his fork. "I...I don't know what to do." Willoughby stumbled for an answer. " I am grateful for just being here. You have been very kind to me and I think had it not been for all of you, I would be lying dead out in that wood somewhere, or worse."

"We could go back to the cave on the mountain if that is where you would like to start, Will," Quint said. "Judging from what you have told us about your journey, I believe we could get there in maybe four days normal travel on horse. The wood is dangerous as we all know and the mountains past it are vast and uncharted for the most part, but we should be able to find the spot where you slew Fenrir and start our search for the cave there. I know Mattie would agree when I say we would also like to retrieve the body of Gaelron, if possible. He was a good friend and deserves more than an unmarked pile of stone under a mountain."

Mattie nodded in agreement. "Is that where you would like to go, Will? Do you think retracing your route could lead you back to your family?"

Willoughby stared into his plate. He had thought about it somewhat and felt terribly guilty for what he knew his family was going through. Had he paid attention to Jake the whole thing would never have happened. But it did no good to fret about that at this point. He was here now and these people were offering to disrupt their lives and put themselves in danger to help him. But he had some serious reservations.

"I guess I haven't thought about it as much as I should have. The trouble is, to be as honest with you as I can be, I don't know if I could get back once we found the cave. I crawled such a long way and there were a whole bunch of side passages. I wouldn't know which one to take going back. The other thing is, and maybe this is the biggest one of all, if I ever did get back to the cave under the waterfall I don't think I would be able to get out that way."

The memory of being pulled under the water by the powerful force was something he did not want to revisit. "I think I was lucky going in not to have drowned. I don't see how I could fight against that current and get back out."

The table grew quiet as they contemplated the dilemma. But Willoughby had something to add. He had been through more than could ever be imagined but he knew his survival so far had been mostly a matter of luck—he had to tell these people the truth. He hated being a bawl baby but the friggin' tears were about ready to flow again.

"I…I miss my family a lot. I know they're going through a lot of suffering not knowing where I am, or if I'm dead or alive. But I guess I need to tell you all, I can't go back under that waterfall. I would rather face a pack of wolves again before I had to try that. It scares me more than anything."

Mattie reached out and placed her hand over his and squeezed. "We understand, Will. There may be other options for us to get you some help, but it will take time and that time will not be kind to your family. I know what it is to lose someone you love and would not wish such grief on anyone. They will hold your memory close to their hearts and cling to the smallest fragment of hope that someday you will return."

"What else do you suggest we do for the boy, Mattie?" Quint

asked.

"There are those who may know something of the sort of thing young Will has been through," Mattie answered. "There is much in this world that cannot be explained but if you seek the wisest of the wise, and tell them of that for which you search, you will then know if there is hope or not. I could ask those in my sisterhood, though I do not believe they would know any more than I. But we must be very careful. Asking too many questions could bring Will to the attention of the wrong folk. He has brought notice to himself by the use of magic, though he did not intend to do so. It could be a very large problem for us all. From here on I would advise you, Will, to keep the magic in check—use it only when all other means have failed. While it will serve you well against your foes, it will also bring unwanted eyes upon you."

Willoughby nodded in affirmation to Mattie's warning. He had a feeling the dream the other night was exactly what Mattie was talking about. Someone was already looking for him.

"So if you do not think your sisterhood can help, Mattie, who do we turn to?" Quint questioned.

"There is another whose guidance we might seek," Mattie answered. "If there is one who could wear the mantle 'Wisest of the Wise' it would be him. Though asking him may be much easier said than done. I could not tell you at the moment where this man might be."

"Who is that, Mattie?" Quint asked with a puzzled look on his face.

"It is Theron I speak of, Quint."

"Theron!" Quint's voice boomed in surprise. Willoughby was certain the dishes in the cupboards rattled. "But Mattie, Theron has been dead for years."

Mattie shook her head. "That is the story for the common folk, Quint, but I have long suspected he survived the attack on his keep. Theron was not one to be taken easily. If he is alive, as I believe, he may be the only one who knows of an answer to young Will's problem."

Quint shook his head. "But if he is alive Mattie, and I for one am not sure of that, how is he supposed to help? Are we to think a man who has not been heard of for the last ten years is all of a sudden going to come out from under a rock and offer to assist?" The sarcasm laden doubt in the big man's tone was not lost on the rest of them. Willoughby and Bryan exchanged glances.

"No Quint, I do not believe he is going to come out from under a rock but, contrary to what is in that thick head of yours, I have good reason to believe Theron alive. There was just never cause to bring the subject up until today." Mattie got up from the table and started to clear the dishes, but she wasn't done talking.

"Aside from the debate about Theron, there is the other issue which has been brought to my attention. Much has happened in Tiernon over the last few days; a momentous turn of events that will have this country in flames if something is not done. It may well be another reason to seek the advice of Theron. Will's unfortunate situation has been overshadowed by one that has impact on us all. King Edmond is dead."

Quint looked like he had been hit with one of his own blacksmith hammers. He wanted to speak but the words wouldn't come; he gave Mattie a perplexed look. It was Bryan who finally spoke.

"Why should that affect us Grandmother? The king has been sick for a long time and his passing expected, and I thought you and grandfather hated King Edmond."

Quint and Mattie exchanged furtive glances which Willoughby caught out of the corner of his eye. He had a feeling some covert communication had just passed between the two.

"Disliking the man and wishing him dead are two different things, Bryan," Mattie started. "We have our own reasons for our displeasure with Edmond but it does not affect our loyalty. For the most part, he was a fair and just ruler who cared for his people but his passing and aftermath leave Artura in a compromising situation. It seems that before he died, Edmond appointed First Council Rhue to rule in his stead while the elders spend their time preparing the king's young daughter Alicia for the crown. It is a total breach of the protocol of ascension."

Quint was fuming. "His illness must have made Edmond insane. The elders or the assembly would not have stood by and allowed that Torbekian dog to seize control. It is unheard of."

Mattie continued, "There was intense dissent from the ministers as you would imagine Quint, but it appears the elder council was allowed to vote on the issue and the assembly agreed to accept their decision. The vote was three to two in favor of following the king's wishes and allowing Rhue to rule until Alicia turns eighteen. As much as the notion would turn any loyal Arturan's stomach it seems the transfer of power was legal. My source said he believes this takeover was planned and also believes Rhue has no intention of ever letting the princess rule."

"But Grandmother, the council surely will see that the princess gets on the throne won't they? It's the law."

"Politics is a dirty, vile game when power is the prize, Bryan," Mattie answered. "Blackmail, bribery, and even murder are its tools and Daemon Rhue plays as well as anyone. That the majority of the council has been bought off should come as no surprise. My source tells me the elements needed for this coup were in place and many loyal Arturans who sought to stand against this abomination are already under arrest or dead. So now it is just a matter of time. Whether he takes it outright and declares himself ruler or plays this charade out for a while makes no difference. Lord Taul and his lackey Rhue have brought about what decades of war could not—they rule Artura."

Mattie sat back down at the table and the four brooded over their after supper tea in silence. Though he understood little of what they were talking about, Willoughby could tell it was a serious matter. He wasn't sure if he could think of a situation at home that mirrored exactly what was going on here, but he followed world news enough to know it rang familiar—power and politics.

"Rebellion and bloodshed," Quint spoke softly as he stirred his tea. Worry lines bunched round the big man's bushy gray eyebrows. "That is what will come of this, especially with the one person who would have stood in the way of this coup being out of the country."

"Do you not think that was by design, Quint?" Mattie asked. "We are dealing with a clever and cunning man here. Having Artemis Thoryl and the army out of the way had to have been a key component in Rhue's plan."

"But General Thoryl will bring the army home and put an end to this, won't he Grandfather?" Bryan excitedly interjected. "Especially when he hears Daemon Rhue has murdered the king."

"Careful now, Bryan," Quint admonished his grandson. "If words such as those were overheard by the wrong person you could be arrested or worse. It was well known by all Edmond had been very sick for quite some time. I did not hear your grandmother say murder was involved in Edmond's passing."

"Listen and heed your grandfather's words, Bryan," Mattie added. "While it is likely there is more to the king's death than meets the eye it would be unwise to speak openly of what many others undoubtedly believe. Even this far away from Tiernon and Castle Daine the ears of those loyal to Rhue will be listening. He will have to react quickly to any hint of rebellion lest it gain momentum. When he moves against those who dare oppose him it will be harsh and without mercy."

"So what are we to do, Mattie?" Quint asked. "For any of us to sit by and allow a Torbekian interloper to usurp the throne of Artura would be unthinkable and cowardly. It is our duty to stop it or to die in the attempt." He slammed his meaty fist down upon the table, causing unsuspecting tea mugs to jump and splatter their contents.

"There is no reason to declare war on my kitchen table and its army of cups and spoons, you overgrown fool," Mattie chided as she grabbed a rag and began to clean up, though not before taking a playful swipe at Quint's head. He caught her tiny hand in his huge paw and gently kissed it.

"Sorry." The big man grinned sheepishly.

"What does this mean for us, Grandmother?" Bryan asked.

"For now it means we go about business as usual and for you two lads not to worry yourselves. There are livestock and evening

482

chores to tend so off with you, and mind those stitches, Will. If all goes well, we will remove them in a day or so."

There was never a need for Mattie to have to ask Willoughby twice to do anything since he had regained enough strength to start helping around the farm. It made him feel guilty to think about how aggravated his mother would get when she had to keep after him to do even the simplest things. He had promised himself more than once to do better when he got home—if he got home.

As the boys excused themselves from the table, Quint got up to follow, but Mattie stopped him short. She watched as Willoughby and Bryan disappeared into the barn and then closed the door.

"Sit with me a spell my husband. We must talk." She sat down and reached across the table with both hands. Quint wrapped his massive calloused paws around them and squeezed gently. He stared deep into her eyes.

"We knew this day would come Mattie, but now that it has, I don't know what to do. After all these years trying to lead a normal life. I hate to say it but, I am afraid."

"I know, Quint. We were both so content here away from all of the business of the court to have thought much about it, and we were guilty of nothing more than being overprotective grandparents. But now the situation has changed and we can no longer sit by and not recognize Bryan's heritage. We have to act."

"So what are we to do, Mattie, stand up and announce to the world the true heir to the throne of Artura is not Alicia Daine but a bastard son of the king who we have kept hidden from view for the last sixteen years?" Quint stood up from the table and walked to the kitchen fireplace and stared hard into the coals. "I have been a fool, Mattie, to think we could hide here and let the world pass us by. But who is going to believe us if we bring this secret to light? And if we do, how can we keep Rhue from coming after us? He will not allow Bryan or any of us to live once he finds out. I was not able to protect Brianna from the wiles of Edmond and I will not be able to protect my family from this. I will have failed again."

Mattie got up and walked over to where Quint stared worriedly into the glowing dregs of the fire. She put her tiny arm around his massive waist and squeezed him gently to her.

"You are too hard on yourself, my husband. It was not your fault our beautiful and innocent daughter ran afoul of the sordid weakness in Edmond. But fate took her from us and left our grandson instead and we have raised him to be a fine young man. But no longer can we deny who he is. It is not only us we must think about. Artura is on the brink of disaster if Rhue is allowed to hold forth as ruler. We will become no more than slaves to the Torbekian empire."

"But who will believe us, Mattie, if we bring Bryan forth to claim the throne? Do we just stride into the great hall at Castle Daine and say, 'Here is the rightful King of Artura'?"

"No Quint, but we must act. You forget there are those who know of the affair and its outcome. And there is the matter of the letter."

"The letter? I thought you destroyed that. Are you saying it still exists?"

"I did not tell you at the time, Quint, because your rage at Edmond was so great I feared you would go after him. I did not burn the letter as I told you and for that lie I am sorry. Please forgive me. I kept it and the gold Edmond sent with it. It has been hidden away for all these years with the necklace he gave Brianna, but it may be the very thing which will prove to those who must know that Bryan is truly Edmond's son."

Quint pulled himself from Mattie's arm, sat down on the hearth and buried his face in his huge hands. "I should have killed him, Mattie. I should have killed Edmond for what he did."

Mattie knelt in front of him and pulled his hands from his face. "And what would that have done for us, Quint? For Brianna, Bryan, and myself? He was King. You would have been dead and who knows what would have happened to us. But such was not our destiny. After hiding Bryan away for all of these years, fate has led us to this point and the stakes have been raised. Nothing less than the future of our country is at hand and we must proceed carefully."

Quint raised his head and looked deep into her eyes. "What

about Bryan, Mattie? Do we tell him? And what of young Will? He has been thrown into this mess not of his own choosing."

Mattie stood up. "I believe the answer may be the same for both, Quint. We cannot do this thing alone. We must seek out those who can help."

"You are still talking of Theron, Mattie. Do you really believe he was not killed? It was General Holt himself who declared him dead in the raid."

"I knew him better than anyone, Quint. I heard what everyone said but in my heart I never believed Theron killed, though I will admit after so many years even I began to doubt. But a year ago a strange bird flew into my dovecote. It was not one of mine or a courier bird from any of my contacts. There was a message attached and when I removed it the bird flew away."

"What was the message, Mattie?"

"A riddle. There was no mark of the writer and it wasn't even addressed to me, just a simple riddle. *'When things grow dark, turn to a place that is dead. From the ashes within, you may find an old friend instead.'*"

"That was it?" Quint asked. "That was all it said?"

"Nothing more. Quint, I believe it was a message from Theron. Like I said, I knew him well and it was just the type of thing he would do. The man was not one to underestimate. To let everyone think he was dead for all of these years would be to his advantage. If he is alive, as I believe, then he will be aware of what has been going on. He was always one step ahead of everyone else and his control of magic was unsurpassed, though he was not one to make it known. That is why Rhue went after him, I am sure. Theron was an obstacle and he would never have allowed Rhue to get as far as he has. If we can find Theron, he will be able to counsel us on what to do. Though I never told him of Brianna's situation, he would have been aware of it. After all, in that time he was the second most powerful man in Artura."

Quint shook his head. "But it was a mantle Theron did not want to wear, Mattie. He made no bones about his disgust with the deceit and intrigue of politics in Edmond's court. He was very vocal about it and that started the rift between the two. When the Torbekian arrived, the wedge between Edmond and Theron had already been driven deep and Rhue just hammered it home."

"I remember well, Quint. It was one of the things I hated about life around the castle. It was why I chose not to live there and the very reason we tried to keep Brianna away. Not that it did us much good in the end. She got trapped in the filth without even realizing she was knee deep in it."

"Edmond was furious when Theron disobeyed him and left," Quint continued, trying to avoid getting caught up in the bitter remembrance of his beloved daughter. "His warnings to the king about the inclinations of Rhue and his master Taul were prophetic."

Mattie moved from the hearth where she and Quint had been having their conversation and opened the door to the porch. The voices and laughter of Bryan and Will tending to the chores drifted across the yard. When she was sure they weren't about to suddenly reappear, she shut the door and turned back to Quint.

"The wheels of fate are turning fast dear husband and I must tell you it frightens me to no end that Bryan must play such a huge part in this. We are both getting old and will not be able to protect him by ourselves once the matter of his heritage comes forth. Those allied against us will be many and strong but there will also be those who will help. Revolution and civil war are inevitable if Rhue is allowed to continue and I do not doubt the true patriots not cowed by his power are already plotting to move against him."

Quint sighed heavily. Doubt creased his worn face. "So getting help means we try to find a man who everyone believes is dead. Everyone but you, that is. Where should we start looking, Mattie?"

"The answer lies in the riddle, Quint, and if you would use that thick head of yours for something other than a hat rack you might find it an easy one to decipher. A place that looks dead? A friend rising from the ashes? Theron is still at the ruins of his keep, or somewhere close by."

"His keep!" Quint's voiced boomed and Mattie quickly brought her finger to her lips.

"Hush yourself," she chided in irritation. "Must you bellow like a bull artox in the rut? There is no need to announce it to the world, and there are two boys outside with questions we do not want to answer quite yet."

"Sorry, Mattie," Quint whispered as he tried to curb his surprise. "But Theron's keep is impossible to get to except by sea and we have no means of accomplishing that. The tip of the Dragon's Spine is beyond the trade routes and no right-thinking captain would charter his ship into those waters for any amount of money; it would be a suicide voyage."

"I know that Quint, but there is a land route to Theron's keep. How do you think he found the place to begin with?"

But the big man was not convinced. "Mattie, Theron may have traveled the length of the Spine to get there but inaccessibility was the very reason he chose it. The weather alone on that miserable peninsula would keep sane men from traveling there, let alone dealing with the mountains."

"Men, maybe yes, Quint, but not dwarves," Mattie responded. "They are the ones who helped Theron restore the keep and they did not travel there by sea. You know as well as I that no dwarf would set foot on the deck of a ship voluntarily. We find one who knows the route and go by land."

"We?" Quint's bushy eyebrows raised in question. "I was thinking that if indeed someone need find Theron—a man we do not know for sure is even alive—it would be me, not we."

"Well there you go again," Mattie shot back. "Thinking instead of listening. None of us can stay here and do any good, Quint. It will be a dangerous journey and the wrong time of the year to undertake it, but we have no choice. We all need each other."

"Mattie, please," Quint pleaded. "Let me try to find Theron and if he is still alive I will bring him here. When I explain it to him, he will understand and come. You stay here with the boys and expand your contacts. We will need to bring all who oppose Rhue together. How can we do that if we are all running around the most forsaken part of Artura chasing a ghost?"

"You have a good point, Quint, but I have given much thought to this. It has a lot to do with young Will. He is not safe here. Someone is searching for him and I was lucky enough to feel the probe and get a ward in place before they found what they were looking for, but I will not be able to ward him forever. He is a unique person and the fact that he has the innate ability to use different forms of magic without instruction is astonishing, but it will be his downfall if we do not protect him. I shudder to think what would happen to the poor boy should he fall into the wrong hands, and we owe it to the lad not to let such a thing happen. I must train him to control the magic. While I deal with that, you and Bryan must teach him to protect himself. You can obviously see such basic skills were evidently not necessary in the world from which he comes. We all owe it to Will to teach him to fight and survive. I do not think fate led Bryan to him for nothing, Quint. He has a role to play in what lies ahead—I stake my life on it."

Quint was about ready to say something when Mattie cocked her head and held her hand up.

"Someone is coming. Single horse and riding hard." Just as she finished her sentence, the kitchen door flung open and Willoughby appeared.

"Excuse me Mattie and Quint, but Bryan says to tell you a rider is coming down the lane."

Mattie pulled Willoughby into the house. "Thank you, Will. Quint and Bryan will see to the rider but you must stay here with me until we find out who this is."

The farm of Mattie and Quint was off the main road with a long dirt lane connecting the two. When Quint got into the yard in front of the house, Bryan was watching the approach of the rider, a little more than halfway down the lane.

"Who do you think it is, Grandfather?"

"Use your skills, Bryan." Quint was never one to let a learning opportunity slip by. "The horse is larger and more visible than the man. Your eyes are good, tell me of the horse."

"A bay mare," Bryan answered after a hard look. "A big one. She isn't lathered so the journey has not been long, maybe from the village. The rider leans hard over her neck and is wearing a green cloak; you can see it trailing in the wind. It is Pel Marin."

"Good eyes, Bryan! Good eyes. It is Pel."

The two waited in the yard as the horse and rider pulled up in a cloud of red dust.

"Pel!" Quint's voice bellowed out a greeting. "It is good to see you but your haste says this is not just a social call."

Pel Marin, a tall, lean man with hard, dark features and a thick black beard peppered with gray, agilely slipped off the saddle of the big horse, slapping some of the road dust off before offering his hand in greeting.

"Master Quint and Bryan. Good to see the both of you."

"See to Bonnie, lad. She'll be needing some water." Quint nodded towards Bryan who took the reins and led the horse to the water trough.

"The village isn't far away Pel, yet you ride hard. Is it wolves or bandits?"

"Let the man get the dust out of his throat, Quint. The horse isn't the only one who has need."

Mattie had come up behind Quint bearing a mug of cold tea. Willoughby followed.

"Pel," she greeted as he took the mug from her, "you must excuse my overgrown husband's lack of hospitality."

"Mattie." The man nodded in return as he took the mug and drained it in one long draught. He handed it back to her, giving Willoughby a quick once over as he did.

"Sera and the children are well, I hope?" Mattie questioned as she took the mug. "Little Mattie is all right? Not in need of a healer?"

Pel shook his head. "No Mattie, but thank you for asking. They are all well and Sera sends her greetings. Ben and Tristan grow like weeds and it is all we can do to keep them from trampling little Mattie. She is just learning to walk and is into everything thanks to you." He grinned. "But 'tis neither wolves nor bandits; I bear news."

Pel pulled a roll of parchment from the folds of his cloak and handed it to Mattie. With the hulking form of Quint hovering over her shoulder, the two read its contents. After they finished they exchanged a quick glance. Willoughby, standing to the side and watching, was sure another unspoken communiqué had just passed between them. Mattie rolled up the parchment and handed it back.

"When are you going to be the bearer of good news, Pel?" she questioned.

"Sorry, Mattie," he apologized, knowing she was not truly holding it against him. "When there is good news you will be the first I seek. What do you think of this?"

There was a simmering furrow in Quint's brow. "The first part comes as no surprise, may he rest in peace. We all knew the king has been standing at death's door for some time now, but how can it be that he declared Daemon Rhue ruler until the princess comes of age? A Torbekian!"

Willoughby thought it strange Quint was acting surprised at news he had already heard, but Mattie gave him a quick look that told him to keep quiet. The two men went on talking.

"Everyone in the village what heard the news be of the same mind, Quint," Pel answered. "Myself, I smell trouble and a lot of it. Folk been suffering for a long time now and to have this added to the king's passing will come to no good. We have had enough. What kind of man adds an announcement raising taxes with the news of the death of the king? Shows what respect Rhue has for our plight. Like you said Quint, the man has no right to rule this country. What in the name of all that is good was the elder council thinking when they allowed this to happen?"

"You know the answer as well as I, Pel," Quint responded. "Rhue has the elders bought and paid for, at least enough of them to secure the vote. The real question is how many folk actually believe Rhue will ever allow the princess to take the crown."

"Careful, Quint," Pel warned. "I know your resentment and it is mine as well. But you must take care of what you speak, especially in the village. Rhue's spies are everywhere and they will report any dissension."

"He is right, my husband," Mattie added. "We do not want to bring attention to ourselves by running afoul of Rhue and his henchmen. Their time for reckoning will come, but for now we must suffer this travesty."

"I haven't told you all of it, Mattie," Pel continued. "Along with the increase in taxes there has been a new collector appointed for this area. The job has been given to Denton Prout and his sons."

"Prout!" Mattie and Quint spit out the name simultaneously like it was a burning ember in their mouths. They looked at each other with faces mirroring their disbelief.

"Surely that cannot be the truth, Pel?" Quint spoke first. "Prout and his sons?"

"Aye, Quint, 'tis true." The man nodded. "Had a time believing it myself but the postings went up in town just this morn'. They are the official agents for the region, reporting to the king's representative in Bargtown. They are taking census and counting assets. That is one reason I am riding today, warning folk to hide their valuables."

"Prout and his sons are the laziest, no-good, thieving bunch of thugs this side of Tiernon," Mattie spat. "Having them as tax collectors is akin to putting the crows in charge of the corn bin."

"Be that as it may, Mattie," Pel continued, "but they have the power and the old tax and asset rolls to work from. Thom Pratt has already been arrested because he tried to hide his milk cow. They are looking for everything of value a man and his family might have. Bad enough ol' Thom got pinched, but they beat him bad and ransacked his house to boot—all of it legal."

Pel tipped his head towards Willoughby, who was intently listening to the conversation just a few feet away. "And don't forget the census. Any new additions and the tax will go up."

Mattie looked at Willoughby. "Reckon we can't hide that, can we?" She motioned and he came and stood beside her. Mattie laid a hand on his shoulder and gave it a firm squeeze. Willoughby did not miss the message.

"You'll have to pardon us, Pel, for not introducing the newest member of our family. This is Will Baxter, the grandson of one of Quint's old friends in the army. Both his parents are dead and we have taken him in."

Pel tipped his head towards Willoughby and extended his hand. The two locked their forearms in the traditional greeting.

"Sorry you lost your parents son, but a lad such as yourself could naught do better than to land in with these good folk. 'Tis a pleasure to meet you, Will Baxter."

The man's grip was firm and his smile genuine but Willoughby was glad he never asked any questions. The what and wherefore of his circumstances were something Mattie obviously did not want to share with anyone.

"We've a bit of supper left Pel, if you will. Cold, but I can warm it for you," Mattie offered.

"Thanks, Mattie, but I've more stops to make before dark. 'Tis a sad time indeed when good honest folk have to hide what little they've left." Pel took the reins from Bryan and mounted his horse.

"Thank you, Bryan. Mayhap you, Quint, and Will can come by some day soon and help the boys and I do some hog hunting. That big boar is back and raising a ruckus in Sera's garden."

"We'll be sure to do that, Pel. Tell Tristan and Ben hello."

Pel nodded his head. "Mattie, you and Quint know better than anyone else that there is trouble coming hard and fast. But folk depend on you and it would do no good for either or both of you to be locked up afore it gets here. When it comes to this tax thing, just remember, Prout has the law on his side."

Quint reached his huge paw out and the two shook. "We will heed your warning, my friend. Though the inclination to throttle that miserable fat ass will be hard to resist, we have our boys to think about. Stay safe, but ride hard and warn as many folk as you can."

"And you take care of your family," Mattie shouted as Pel wheeled the big bay and started down the lane.

The four of them stood silent and watched until Pel turned hard onto the main road, Bonnie's massive hooves throwing up clouds of red dust.

"What is all of this about, Mattie?" Willoughby asked as they watched Pel disappear. She pulled him to her side and did the same with Bryan. Quint stood behind and encircled them all within his massive arms.

"It's about a storm of trouble coming hard at us, young Will. A storm that I fear will sweep this land with a whirlwind of fire and death before it passes."

Chapter Twenty-Eight

L IFE IN THE GREAT CITY OF TIERNON HAD come to a standstill. The docks lay quiet, save the creaking and thumping of ships tied to piers, and the shrieking of gulls overhead which cared not for the administrations of men. The streets were empty and even the drinking houses and brothels had been ordered closed for the day. The proclamation read that after the funeral and procession to the Cave of Kings, there would be a day of mourning. It had also come with a warning; anyone caught doing anything else would be severely punished. Daemon Rhue would tolerate nothing less.

The body of Edmond Daine, thirty-fourth King of Artura, lay in state in the great hall for two days, in strict accordance with Arturan law. For the most part, he had been a good king; fair, just, and hard when he needed to be. He had brought the country together in a time of war and had, at long last, been the deliverer of peace. Bernard Thrain, the senior member of the Arturan Elder Council of Five, had called him such in his eulogy, The Great Peacemaker.

For two days, the common folk who lived in the city or near it were allowed into the great hall to pay their respects. The body lay on a great slab of rock surrounded by fresh cut flowers changed twice a day; more to mask the inevitable odor of death than anything else. The attendants warned that firing the great fireplaces in the hall to chase away the fall chill would hasten the decay but Daemon Rhue had ordered the fires built anyway.

"If folk take offense to the stink of death they will not be wont to linger" had been his reasoning.

Dignitaries and notables, those who could make it to the city in time, came and went. Those too far away to attend sent birds to the dovecotes with notes of condolences and pledges of fealty to the young future queen. Rhue had demanded that Alicia Daine, as grieved as a fourteen-year-old girl could be after losing a doting father, meet with all dignitaries and notables, allowing them to pay their respects personally.

"If she wants to be queen, then she need act like one," he had warned Bernard Thrain. "This will be a learning experience for her, so see to it she does her part." Rather than out of any pretext of grief or respect for the dead king, Daemon Rhue wanted people, especially those with power and money, to think all was going well.

The funeral procession began within Castle Daine's inner keep. The bier of the king, borne by select members of the palace guard, followed his favorite warhorse, a big black destrier named Longstride. The aging animal was led by a mere stable boy, totally out of place in a funeral procession for a king, but the only one the huge horse would allow to touch him. The attendants had managed to scrape the dung and muck from the stables off the boy and get him dressed in the appropriate clothes; better that than have the warhorse stomp someone else to death.

Longstride was resplendent in full war regalia, his polished, black mail chest and head protector gleaming in the sun. Strapped to one side of his riderless saddle was the king's war shield, to the other, his great sword. Unadorned and plain, they had served their bearer with honor. The scars, nicks, dents, and gashes giving mute testimony that Edmond had been a warrior king, fighting beside his men instead of cowering behind them. Some argued they had been too plain and unfashionable to accompany a king to his grave, but loyal friends of Edmond demanded they be included. He had ridden towards death countless times armed with these weapons and in death should not be discounted because they weren't bejeweled and fancy.

The great sword was said to have been forged by one of Edmond's closest friends when they had been young men fighting behind the banner of the king's father, Edmond the First. The future sovereign had used it to slay the renegade troll Maxon as the monster prepared to deliver a killing blow to the unhorsed king in the first war against Torbek. Bloodied and wounded, a young Edmond had charged the monster on foot and hacked off the huge arm in which the troll brandished his mighty war club, befouled with the blood, brains, and flesh of no less than three score of Artura's best, before plunging the sword deep into the monster's unarmored belly. History's record stated, and verified by eyewitness accounts, that the troll still did not fall, but pulled the sword out of his belly and stood there laughing. The monster licked the blade clean of his own blood and entrails before tossing it back to the feet of Edmond who crouched protectively over the prostrate form of his fallen father.

"Tha's a good blade," Maxon had grunted as blood flecked spittle foamed from his distorted mouth. Only then did he fall over and die.

After the battle, King Edmond had never wielded any other weapon in battle and had proclaimed the weapon's maker, a close friend named Quint Ironhand, one of the finest metal smiths in the entire land. No one was quite sure what had become of Edmond's friend and forger of his favorite sword. It was rumored a falling out between the two caused Quint Ironhand to leave the king's service.

It was a good story and Arturans held great respect for the great broadsword. But Daemon Rhue cared not a speck for stories. If it meant that people would be kept happy by allowing the king to take the weapons with him to his grave, that was all right with him. The man was dead and that was what was important.

The procession was a long one. Following the dead king came Alicia Daine dressed in mourning attire, her pretty face covered with a black lace veil. The distraught young girl was now not only fatherless, but kinless entirely. As the last surviving Daine, and heir to the throne, it was her job to follow the bier, on foot, on her own and unattended. Following her came the Elder Council of Five who, by the supposed good will of First Council Rhue, were allowed the help of attendants. With their age, such a walk unaided might kill one or two of them. But it was more to maintain a good appearance than sympathy for the old councilmen which led the Torbekian to allow aides to accompany the elders. Behind the elders walked a solemn Daemon Rhue, wearing a plain black robe. Most of those lining the funeral procession route would have said the notorious first council had dressed in appropriate mourning garb, and dutiful in paying the proper respect to the dead king. But the few who knew him were aware this was no less than what the man wore every day.

Flanking Rhue marched a smartly dressed honor guard comprised of fifty of the biggest and toughest swordsmen the castle could muster. It made for good politics to call them the King's Honor Guard but they were there, situated between the crowd and the first council, to do nothing more than protect Rhue. He was taking no chances, assassination attempts by disgruntled loyalists who thought he had blatantly overstepped his power and position were possible at any time with the crowds and cover offered by a funeral procession. More than a few heads were cracked when innocent townsfolk, trying to get a better view of the king's bier, got too close.

Behind the first council and his guard strode General Dayen Holt, decked out in sparkling military finery, not one to let an opportunity to shine pass him by. "A strutting peacock" was what Daemon Rhue called him. This place in line would normally have been reserved for the commander of all Arturan military forces, General Artemis Thoryl, currently indisposed in the wasteland between Torbek and Dazor. Available military officers according to rank came next; the fact Edmond had been a wartime king for most of his reign had not been lost on the planners of the funeral procession. Trailing those, in no particular order and jostling for position, came prominent ministers and council members, wealthy businessmen, and their wives. Representatives of the warlord houses, those close enough to attend, followed. Daemon Rhue took note that not a single warlord themselves bothered to make the journey. Not that it mattered, but it would serve as useful information if the loyalty of the warlord houses to the Daines came into question.

Noticeably absent from the funeral procession, and one that did bother Daemon Rhue, was that of the king's personal physician, Steyr. The man had sent a hastily scribbled note to the first council, briefly hinting at a matter of high importance requiring immediate attention. This was the kind of thing that irritated Rhue and would bring his wrath severely down upon the fat physician if said matter turned out to be less than described.

The procession was long and grew in size as it coursed through the three gates of Castle Daine and wound down the cliff road into the city of Tiernon. Once the procession cleared the two great towers at the bottom they were on the Street of Trade, a long, wide, and well-kept boulevard running directly from the castle gate to the docks.

This was where the great city of Tiernon conducted the majority of business, legal business anyway. Two way traffic was strictly enforced on this street and stalls and shops crammed into every available space on both sides. Well lit, constantly protected by armed patrols, and governed by strictly enforced laws regarding waste and trash, it was a buyer and seller's paradise. It was said if you couldn't find it to buy on the Street of Trade it didn't exist. It was the heart and pride of the city. All other streets ran at right angles to it. Alehouses, inns, and brothels were required by law to conduct their business off the main street and the quality of the establishments was directly relative to their proximity. The farther away from the Street of Trade, the seedier and nastier the town became.

But today the shops were locked and shuttered; no ale being poured nor wine bottles uncorked. Those who normally would be buying, selling, or drinking instead lined the broad street to pay final homage to the man they called king. The townsfolk stood several rows deep while others viewed from rooftops and windows. Gossip and small talk hushed as the ironshod hooves of Longstride clopped on the pavestone surface of the street, announcing that the procession was growing near. Leather creaked and wood groaned as the bearers struggled under the weight of the king's bier. Alicia Daine kept her head down, denying the common folk a glimpse of her face.

Some folk wept openly, Edmond had been a good ruler on the whole; others just shrugged as the procession passed. Kings came and kings went but for the dirt poor and downtrodden it mattered little who sat upon the throne. Their lot in life was meager at best and the passing of a king, good or bad, would not change such. Many businessmen and traders, while dutifully standing in the crowd watching the procession, were just counting hours until they could re-open their shops and start making money off the swell of folk in the city for the event. When the procession got to the dock area marking the end of the Street of Trade, the funeral procession came to a halt. The honor guard fanned out along the pier and kept onlookers from stepping onto it. The stable boy peeled off with Longstride, this was as far as he and the horse would go. The king's sword and shield were removed and placed upon the bier.

Alongside the pier, a sleek, two-mast war galley bounced easily against the wooden dock riding the gentle river swell. Her long, stout oars, twenty-five to a side, stood straight at attention along her trim, black hull, the smell of fresh paint mixing with the sour tang of rotten fish and mud flats. It was upon this ship that a small entourage would accompany the body of the king to his final resting spot in the Cave of the Kings upriver from the city.

The Black Manta, a name she bore proudly, was on loan from the fleet of Edo Talmedge, the warlord chief who held power in Ansrak, the port city at the mouth of the river three hundred miles downstream from Tiernon. While Talmedge was known as a rebel, he had always paid homage to King Edmond and had used his fleet to hold the Mandalin pirates, under hire by the Torbekian ruler Kenric Taul, at bay when it was crucial the Arturan army not be hamstrung by attack from the sea. For his loyalty, Talmedge had gained a free hand dealing with the massive volumes of trade coming by ship through Ansrak on the way to Tiernon. The Black Manta was Talmedge's flagship and he had sent her as a show of respect to carry the body of the king on his final voyage.

The captain of the Manta met the procession as they came

onto the dock. He was of slight stature but his appearance was as frightening as the man was small. His head and face were shaven slick, devoid of hair other than his eyebrows. His ear lobes had been pierced, pulled, and stretched until they were several inches long and the holes filled with round globes of polished amethyst crystal and a thick ring of silver hung from his nose. He bowed low to Alicia Daine, then to the members of the Elder Council of Five and finally gave a slight and condescending one to Daemon Rhue. The order and nature of the homage was not lost on the first council.

"My condolences Princess, on the loss of your father. My name is O'san Batu, captain of this ship. I send word from the king's servant, friend, and ally, Edo Talmedge. The Black Manta, pride of the Ansrak fleet and personal vessel of Lord Talmedge himself is honored to carry the king's body to his tomb. My Lord is grief stricken that he could not attend personally but is confident the princess understands nothing less than the safety of the Arturan coastline is at stake. As we speak, my Lord is commanding the Swordfish, sister ship of the Manta, chasing pirates."

Daemon Rhue was irritated at the effrontery of the diminutive captain and made himself a mental note to deal with Edo Talmedge as soon as he had things under control. The man had too much power and was not afraid to openly flaunt it. He would hang the corpse of Talmedge and his ugly little captain from the masts of his precious warships. But his anger was quickly replaced by surprise as Alicia Daine answered the captain in a calm, yet surprisingly strong voice.

"My father would be honored as I am Captain Batu. Tell Lord Talmedge I would be pleased if he and I were able to discuss matters of import to both of us in the future after we have adjusted to the loss of my beloved father. I have much to learn from the elder council but I believe for one to be a proper ruler one must understand the true nature of what goes on in the country. Castle Daine and Tiernon are great of themselves but still just a small portion of this nation."

Those on the dock, including the Elder council members,

listened in shocked wonder as the slight sprig of a girl, who had barely uttered a whimper since the death of her father, spoke out. Captain Batu's eyes widened and he broke into a grin, showing a full set of solid gold teeth. He bowed low.

"Well said, Princess. I will deliver your message and convey my own opinion to Lord Talmedge that the daughter of Edmond Daine be a very beautiful and capable young lady."

When he lifted his head, his dark eyes caught the baleful glare of Daemon Rhue, but if O'san Batu was concerned he had just made a deadly enemy it didn't show as he barked orders for his crew to relieve those carrying the bier of the king.

The first council had been shocked Alicia Daine had found a voice and he would have to see her newfound confidence didn't go too far. His notion of having her act like a future queen only went so far and a small amount he could tolerate, but if the little bitch started to really try and act like one it could be a problem for him, and Daemon Rhue didn't like problems.

A special raised platform had been installed on deck in the center of the ship and the crew laid the king's bier upon it. A covered chair had been brought for the princess to sit on next to her father for the hour-long voyage upriver but the rest of those who would be making the trip were offered nothing but a spot to stand next to the stern rail behind the ship's wheel.

"You will excuse the lack of comfort here m'Lords," Captain Batu offered bluntly, with more than a hint of mockery in his voice. "This be a warship and equipped as such." He had jettisoned the vocal eloquence with which he had addressed Alicia Daine.

"But surely you can't expect us to stand out here without cover and proper accommodations, Captain Batu?" Elder Enis Beckworth wailed. He was already looking pale and seasick even though the ship was barely rocking. The other members of the elder council nodded in agreement, looking as nearly peaked in the gills as Beckworth was. Daemon Rhue glared at the captain and said nothing.

Batu ignored the council and shouted orders for his crew to cast the Black Manta loose. As the ship gracefully slid away from the docks, a toothless sailor, calloused, tanned, and barefoot approached the captain.

"The order for sail, Cap'n?" he gummed a question. "'Tis a favorable wind for the trip upriver."

"No sail," Batu answered his first mate. "Call to oars and have the drummer beat the pace slow. This be a funeral ship for the moment and the king in no hurry to get where he's goin'. Naught but cold stone a waitin' for 'im. Mind you stay course to the center of the river, Turtle. The engineers will be firing the Sisters in salute as the ship passes under the Kingsgate. Wouldn't due for any of our passengers to get a nasty bit o' balefire on them funeral robes now, would it?"

First mate Turtle grinned, his gums stained brown with tobacco juice. "Oars to ready," he bellowed as the ship slid out into the river channel. The River Tier flowed with a slight and bumpy chop and two of the elder council members were already hanging over the rail. Fifty oars dropped as one with an angry wooden thump to a position hovering just above the water.

"Drummer, beat ship ahead slow," Turtle ordered.

The drummer, a ragged lad of no more than twelve or thirteen, squatted on a small raised platform just below the rail of the stern deck in front of the helmsman with his drum between his legs. As the first note thumped out in cadence, the oars shifted ahead in perfect unison, on the second beat they dipped smartly into the water and pulled, lifting in synchronization at the end of the stroke and shifting ahead again with the next beat. The drum thumped, the oars moved, and the ship slid gracefully through the water. The elder council deposited their breakfast over the rail.

Ships of all sizes lay at anchor in the river outside the docks, waiting their turn to unload or take on cargo, a process delayed a full day by the king's funeral. As the Black Manta slipped between them, their crews lined the rail, dipping their flags and doffing their hats in respect. The solemnity of the moment sullied slightly by retching sounds as the elders purged their guts.

The River Tier was deep and wide where the docks jutted out

into her green waters, but upriver past the city, a natural formation changed the landscape dramatically. Five hundred feet of vertical basalt rose from each side of the river like a gate of the gods—The Kingsgate. The same dominating plateau where Castle Daine was situated also commanded the river, the city, and the land around it in all directions. Here the river channel narrowed to less than a quarter of her width.

Atop the plateau on the castle side of the channel rose a great tower, adding another hundred feet onto the height of the cliff. There, squatting silent and menacing, sat the Sisters of Chaos. The Sisters were a matched pair of trebuchets, the mightiest throwing machines in the known world. Each sat atop a turret that could be rotated in a full circle, allowing the throwing arms to cover attack from land as well as up- or downriver. Housed deep in the tower were man-powered gears and mechanisms which raised the counterweights of the throwing machines and rotated the turrets. Weight could be added or taken away depending on where the master engineer wanted to aim his missiles.

Sitting at the ready were various types of projectiles, each weighed carefully and designed with a specific and deadly purpose. Large stones, destined to crush the hulls of oncoming ships; smaller ones, designed to be thrown many at a time, used for destroying oars, rigging, and men. There were razor-sharp metal caltrops which would cut and maim living flesh or slice through sails and cordage.

But deadliest of all was balefire, a highly combustible mixture of crude oil and other flammable ingredients. Dried straw was combined with the mixture, pressed into balls, then placed into the throwing platform and set afire. These fiery balls of death and destruction would wreak havoc on ships or troops as the sticky burning mixture was hard to get off once it made contact. Lining the tower walls next to the Sisters were dozens of smaller throwing machines called ballista, which could darken the sky in an instant with hundreds of arrows.

Deep within the walls of the tower and the tunnels carved out of solid basalt lived a small army of men and dwarves whose only job was to service and fire these deadly weapons. Wedded to the Sisters—such was the mantle worn by those who came into this realm, betrothed to stone, metal, and wood. They took an oath and were required to foreswear marriage and family. They were allowed to patronize brothels and drinking houses on their days off but beyond that, they remained segregated from the daily life of castle and city.

They trained constantly, rotating the huge machines, loading and firing different types of missiles. When they were not doing drills, the upkeep on the wood and metal of the weapons allowed no idleness. Daily target practice kept the crews sharp and disciplined. Distances on the land and river were calculated and marked; the master engineers knowing which projectile could do what based on size and type, angle and counterbalance weight. It was this amazing defensive complex, along with the natural formation upon which it sat, that gave Castle Daine and the city of Tiernon its well-deserved status as one of the most impregnable fortresses anywhere in the known world.

Daemon Rhue looked up at the tower wistfully as the Black Manta sliced gracefully through the green waters and into the shadow of the Kingsgate. He knew the history of those defenses well. He had studied them inside and out for they were the main reason Lord Taul had been forced to do the unthinkable a decade ago and agree to a peace accord with Edmond Daine. No army or fleet could break those defenses from the outside. The rot that would infect the Sisters and bring them down needed to be fermented from within. Cunning, deceit, and trickery would be the only things which would bring the Sisters to their knees.

Rhue's moment of deep thought was interrupted as a shout went up from the crew of the Black Manta.

"The little man honors his dead king with colored balefire, m'Lord Rhue," O'san Batu spoke as he joined the first council along the rail.

Daemon Rhue remained silent as both men watched two bright

balls of fire arching high out over the river from the tower. Special powders added to the balefire mixture produced brilliant blue and green colored flame. The hued fireballs arched over the Manta and splashed harmlessly into the river hundreds of yards behind them. As soon as the two missiles splashed down, two more quickly followed. Like earthbound comets they traced brightly colored trails of red and orange across the sky. Even the elder council had to interrupt their purging activities to watch the sight.

"Tanos Strongbeam is a dwarf, not a man, Captain Batu," Daemon Rhue's voice hissed with irritation. "His balefire is indeed impressive though a waste and the master engineer neglected to inform me such a display would be occurring."

Batu shrugged. "Could be said m'Lord that anything done for the dead is a waste, bein' they ain't able to appreciate it. But for the living it serves a purpose."

"And just what purpose might that be, Captain?"

"Well m'Lord, as I suspect in the case of Master Strongbeam here, it be showin' respect 'n honor 'n shows the high regard in which the deceased was held in life. 'Tis the same reason m'Lord Talmedge offered the use of his favorite and most valuable ship to carry the body of the king. Honor the man 'n show the future queen that respect and loyalty showed one jest might be available ta tha other."

Captain Batu nodded to where Alicia Daine sat beside her dead father's funeral bier. She had poked her head out from under the protective canopy and had watched the balefire display with as much awe and interest as everyone else.

"Just a slip of a girl but seems ta have a good deal of grit in her. Might just make a good queen, eh m'Lord?"

Daemon Rhue turned towards the diminutive Captain. Their eyes met and held fast. The line had been drawn.

"We can only hope such is the case, Captain Batu. The girl is young and enters a world she is ill-prepared to deal with. Our task is to protect and nurture her for the challenge ahead. The change from girl-child to woman is difficult enough without the burden of a heavy crown. History will bear witness as to how Alicia Daine's legacy will read but who can say what the future holds? This is a dire world, fraught with danger and evil, and survival in itself is never guaranteed."

Daemon Rhue paused, holding the gaze of the diminutive captain to see if the true meaning of his words were getting through. "I would ask when you return to Ansrak, that you convey to your Lord Talmedge a message from me as well as the one you deliver for our future queen."

"I am your humble servant m'Lord Rhue. What might that message be?"

"Tell Lord Talmedge, being a man of the sea and sail such as he is, that it would be of critical importance to him to make sure he understands full well which direction the winds blows. Should he miscalculate, the consequences could be grave for his empire, mayhap even fatal."

O'san Batu acknowledged Daemon Rhue's message with a slight tip of his head. "I will deliver m'Lord's message as soon as my ship touches the dock in Ansrak."

Satisfied the irritating little man understood, Daemon Rhue turned away. The Manta was now deep into the narrow cleft between the north and south plateau, the looming granite cliffs blocking out all sunlight and a cold, damp fog had wrapped its gloomy arms about the ship. They traveled in relative quiet for another half hour, only the splash of oars in the water and the occasional cry of canyon dwelling birds breaking the stillness. First mate Turtle, forced by the fog to navigate from the tiny foredeck jutting out over the Manta's ram, finally broke the silence.

"Quay ahead portside, Cap'n," he shouted.

"I see it, Turtle," Captain Batu responded. "Take 'er in."

In the river ahead, just becoming visible through the fog, a single stone pier jutted into the water. A small barge, which had carried workers preparing the tomb and a small honor guard to carry the bier to its final resting spot, was already moored alongside the quay.

The Black Manta was coming into the pier straight on. Though her speed was slow, Daemon Rhue and most of the funeral party were grabbing the rails to brace for impact when it looked like she might ram the stone pier.

Turtle bellowed out orders. "Starboard oars up!" The twenty-five oars on the right snapped into the air as one with a resounding *"thunk."*

"Port oars, turning stroke!" With one hard stroke, the ship swung hard to the left. She would have come around too far if the oars hadn't dipped back into the water at exactly the right moment and pulled a reverse stroke, checking the ship's momentum. The Manta slid gracefully sideways into the mat-covered wooden bumpers lining the stone pier with little more than a begrudging thump. Barefoot sailors leaped to the quay and had the ship secured to the dock before those on board could let out their breath.

"Well done, Turtle." Captain Batu nodded to his first mate. "See to the funeral party." He turned and gave a smirking smile to Daemon Rhue and the elders who were still clutching tight to the rail.

"Lord Rhue, Council, we've arrived at the Cave of Kings. We will wait for your return."

Orders were shouted, the gangplank dropped, the king's bier unloaded and the procession reformed. The attendants waiting at the quay had brought extra cloaks for the princess and the procession members. The temperature inside the sunless river canyon was significantly lower and a biting wind nipped at exposed skin. The stone on the quay was slick with green slime and as the attendants hurried to reform the funeral procession, a misstep by one of the bearers nearly dumped the bier and the body of the king into the river.

"Fools," Daemon Rhue growled as disaster was narrowly avoided, "can't you idiots do anything right? Let us be done with this." The first council was getting tired of the whole process and the cold wind was serving to aggravate his already sour disposition.

The quay jutted into the river about a hundred paces and at the shoreline, a pavestone track led across the gravel bar to the base of the basalt cliffs, disappearing into the dark and sinister maw of a cave opening. Flanking the opening, two massive and hideous statues loomed menacingly.

Mounted on square pedestals of stone half again taller than an average man, each figure was at least forty feet tall, a rendering of a man's skeletal form carved in great detail out of solid rock. They semi-crouched in a defensive posture, stone shield on one skeletal arm and sword raised high in the other. On their heads they wore lopsided crowns and each grinned with a gruesome stone smile.

"What in the name of all that is sane are those monstrosities?" Daemon Rhue muttered as the procession grew closer to the cave.

"The Guardians of the Dead, my Lord Rhue." General Holt had come up behind the first council, pulling his cloak tight about him. His ceremonial military garb was ill suited for the cold and he had been one of the first to grab the extra protection offered by the attendants as the Manta had docked at the quay.

"I take it my Lord has never been to the Cave of Kings?" His voice had a slightly amused ring to it.

The two men stopped and allowed the small entourage to pass by, there no longer being a need to maintain the proper hierarchy positioning that had been necessary as the funeral procession traveled from the castle through the city to the docks. Alicia Daine followed her father stoically and the elders stumbled along with their attendants behind them.

"And what reason might I have had, General, for coming to this dreadful place?" Daemon Rhue demanded irritably, his tone suggesting that Holt might want to keep his amusement in check.

"Why, to honor the long dead rulers of Artura, my Lord," Holt answered. "This has been the burial place for the Daines for hundreds of years. Hugo, the first to call himself king, found this place not long after he started to build the castle. It was said he had a fear of the afterlife and commissioned a warlock and a witch to come up with something to protect him after he was dead and buried. They had these "guardians" built and were said to have performed all kinds of dark rituals and spells over the two, including, it was rumored, human sacrifice. It is rumored the bones of Hugo's personal servants and indeed, his favorite mistress, are buried in the bases."

"Hideous and absurd to say the least," Daemon Rhue spat in disgust. "But given the barbaric nature of your ancestors, Holt, I should say it does not surprise me. In Torbek we build great monuments to our dead rulers instead of hiding them in cold, stinking holes in the ground."

General Holt nodded. Unlike others, he knew which way the wind blew and had no intention of aggravating the first council.

"I agree with you totally Lord Rhue, and in defense of my ancestors, our burial tombs are located south of Tiernon on a hillside where the sun actually shines. The histories say Hugo was an eccentric in many ways, hence his nickname "The Mad Bull." Nonetheless, it was he who started the tradition and it has been followed by every heir since."

The two turned to follow the procession, now moving past the gruesome stone guards and entering the cave.

"Well, it is no concern of mine where these people wish to bury their dead," Rhue hissed as the two moved under the glare of Hugo's protectors.

"If the next Daine in line wishes to plant her bones in this hole as well then I would be happy to accommodate her. And the sooner the better."

The cave floor had been paved with flat stones but the walls had been left in their natural form. Cold, wet stone arched over the procession as they passed into the cave, the way lit by giant pots of burning oil. Shadows thrown by the flickering flames cavorted in macabre dance on the dark walls and ceiling as the group marched deep into the bowels of the cavern.

The procession was traveling agonizingly slow for Daemon Rhue, who had become entirely unhappy with the whole affair. It was one thing to put on a show for dignitaries, notables, and people of wealth and power, but there were none of those here. They were out of the wind but the air in the cave was cool and damp, adding more misery to the first council's irritation. He was also more than apprehensive about what Steyr was up to. That he managed to excuse himself from this charade had not set well with Daemon Rhue, and while he would listen to the excuse, he would enjoy seeing the fat man punished if he found it to be inadequate. Steyr served him well but Rhue believed as his Lord Taul did; those who bent to power needed to be reminded sometimes that they owed everything, even their lives, to those who held it.

The procession came at last to a massive set of stone doors, three times a man's height, two feet thick, and wide enough for twenty stout men to stand shoulder to shoulder. They were now thrown open to accept the body of the king. A crest was carved into the massive lintel at the top of the great doors—under a set of crossed swords, the head of a glaring bull artox, its horns curved up and then out.

The bull was the symbol of the Daines, the family who had held power against many odds for nearly five hundred years. The bones of thirty-three kings and eleven queens lay at rest in their cold stone tombs. Some had enjoyed long and prosperous rules, others were cut short by war, treachery, or sickness. One, King Percy, a dandy who cared more about his wardrobe than his country, ruled for a mere eleven days before being killed in a fit of rage by a jealous male lover. To this eclectic mass of bygone monarchy now came Edmond the Second, forty-fifth in the line of Daines, followed to his final place of rest alongside his ancestors by his young daughter, Alicia, destined in four years to become the forty-sixth.

Once through the stone doors the arrangement of the burial chamber was quite simple. The rulers of this hard land and its hardier folk had never been high on glorification of their positions. As they lived, their homes, castles, and defenses were sturdy, built to last, but simple. In death, they sought nothing more. Each side of the cavern was lined with plain stone burial vaults with naught other than the title of each ruler chiseled across the front. It was hard to distinguish some of the older vaults from the natural stone of the cave; water dripping from the roof had coated them with a hard, mineral laden crust. A new vault, its heavy stone lid resting behind it on a frame of timber, lay at the end of the right hand row.

The procession stopped and the bearers set Edmond's heavy wooden bier onto the floor, its thump echoing eerily through the depths of the cavern, announcing to the dead Daines another of their kin had arrived to take his place amongst them.

The attendants and bearers moved aside and the small group of mourners moved forward. The covering had been pulled back and in the flickering light thrown from the oil pots, the haunting death face of Edmond stared blank and empty at the ceiling. In death, his eyes had sunk back into his skull and the skin had pulled back from the cheekbones. His head lolled crookedly inside the crown he would wear to his grave, his thin wispy tufts of gray hair poking out at all angles. The face of death was a cruel joke for Edmond Daine. A hale, hearty, and vigorous man for most of his life, he now looked more akin to the ghastly guardians at the mouth of the cave.

Alicia Daine knelt next to the king's bier with her head down as Elder Thrain recited a litany of Edmond's accomplishments and accolades. Daemon Rhue stood back from the group, disinterested irritation worming through him like the chill of the damp cave air. Edmond's list of conquests was long, and included victories over Torbek and Supreme Lord Taul. But that they had at last come to this point, putting the old man in his tomb, with his little bitch of a daughter weeping on her knees next to him, was salve to his pride. He had worked hard for this but still there was much more to do. That the princess had started to show some backbone when she had been talking to Captain Batu had not gone unnoticed and was rankling him. He had to fight the urge to be done with her and this whole charade but knew it would not be prudent. There were too many moves in this game yet to be played and Lord Taul would not tolerate a setback.

When Thrain was finished, Alicia Daine rose from her knees and stood on her tiptoes to plant a kiss on her father's dead forehead. The attendants pulled the covering back over the king's face and placed his sword and shield on top of his body. The small group stepped back away from the bier as it was lifted and moved to the tomb. Gently they lowered Edmond Daine's body into the depths of the cold stone vault. The eight attendants who had borne the body from the quay moved to the stone slab and, with great effort, slid the heavy lid into place.

Bernard Thrain cleared his throat, the strain of the day had been trying on the old man and the cold air unhealthy. A hot bath, mulled wine, and a young girl to massage his tired body were still a couple of hours away, but as senior member of the elder council there was one more task required of him. His voice was feeble and labored as he uttered the words that would bring closure to the day.

"Let it be duly recorded in the histories that the burial of Edmond Daine, King of Artura, has been carried out in full accordance with Arturan law." The scribe documenting the entire funeral procession scribbled hastily to catch his words as Thrain continued. "In this hallowed place, his body will rest in eternity with his ancestors. Artura mourns its loss but hails its rightful heir. The king is dead. Long live the queen!"

"Long live the queen!" The words echoed through the gloom of the cavern as the voices of those assembled responded to Elder Thrain's words. All save for one.

CHAPTER TWENTY-NINE

THE CARRIAGE RATTLED TO A STOP ON THE stone of Castle Daine's inner ward as servants rushed to its side with a set of steps. They had been waiting for the return of the funeral party but when they recognized the first council's private carriage driving hard through the gate they scrambled to assist in double time. It had carried Daemon Rhue back to the castle from the docks after the Black Manta had returned from the Cave of the Kings. He had not waited for Alicia Daine or the elder council and the rest of the entourage; he had more than enough of Arturan protocol for the day.

"Find me that pig Steyr and have him meet me in my receiving chamber. Now!" he screamed at the cowering servants as he strode angrily up the steps leading to the great hall. "And for the sake of your miserable hides there had better be a fire going."

"M-m-my Lord Rhue," a terrified servant boy stammered as he ran to catch up to him. "If it please my Lord, physician Steyr is already awaiting your return."

Guards snapped to attention, doors banged open and servants whose presence was not required beat a hasty retreat out of the way as the awareness of Daemon Rhue's foul mood surged ahead of him like a tidal wave. The first council's anger and irritation had nearly boiled over on the return trip from the Cave of Kings and the Black Manta's cocky little captain had added fuel to the fire, fawning over the future queen and inviting her to his private cabin so she might make the rest of the trip downriver in relative comfort while the rest of the party suffered again at the rail. Daemon Rhue fully intended to unleash his pent up frustration upon Steyr, who had wiggled his way out of attending the funeral procession with some sort of lame excuse, but when informed the physician was waiting for him, he choked off some of the anger he had been fully prepared to vent. Something important must be afoot and he would force himself to allow Steyr a chance to explain.

"See to it we are not disturbed," he snapped at the two guards standing in rigid attention at the doors to his private receiving chamber. Steyr arose quickly from a table set with food and drink as Daemon Rhue entered the room. The fat physician had been helping himself to a late meal and washing it down with some of the first council's private wine stock, something that normally would not have been a surprise, but what did surprise Daemon Rhue was that he was not alone.

The other man was standing in front of the fireplace, more content with the radiating heat of the fire than helping himself to the plentiful stocked table as Steyr was. He was small and bent with age, his features indistinguishable for the most part, wrapped up in a thick but well-worn and tattered winter cloak, which might have been because of the cool weather or for the need to keep his identity a secret. He turned slightly as the first council entered the room. His head was the only thing visible from the folds of the garment. Thin wisps of gray hair hung from his wrinkled scalp, bald on top with deep brown age splotches splattered across it. Deep-set eyes were framed by bushy gray brows in sore need of trimming. The only thing fleshy about him was his nose, the bulbous red and blue-veined appendage of a man who had spent too many years looking over the edge of a wineglass. There was a vague hint of something recognizable about the man.

"My Lord Rhue." Steyr jumped up from the table, wiping the grease from his mouth with the sleeve of his robe. "I trust all went well?"

"The king lies in his crypt in that miserable cold cave. I have spent the day putting up with fools and fawners, and the little princess begins play at being ruler. That is how my day has gone, Steyr."

The room was at least comfortably warm and Steyr jumped to fill his Lord a goblet of wine as Daemon Rhue took off his cloak. The stranger never acknowledged the first council at all, either a grave oversight or the actions of a man comfortable in his position. Daemon Rhue was not amused.

"We have important matters to discuss Steyr," Rhue said as he accepted the wine from the physician. He tipped the goblet towards the newcomer who again had his back to them facing the blazing fire in the hearth.

"This interruption had best be important."

"My Lord. Naught but a matter of serious nature would have caused me not to attend today. This man has come to me and swears upon his life he has a story you will be highly interested in. I took it upon myself to ensure there was proof of at least some of what he has to say. I know your Lordship is not a man to have his time wasted by lies and fabrications."

"So what is it that is so important Steyr? And is our guest here lacking a tongue?" Daemon Rhue growled impatiently.

"Oh my tongue is perfectly functional, Lord Rhue," the old man finally spoke as he turned towards the two men standing at the table. "You must forgive me for being distracted by the comforting warmth of your fire. Chill weather is an old man's bane, your Lordship."

Daemon Rhue eyed the newcomer suspiciously. The old man seemed harmless enough, and Steyr would have never consented to the man having an audience with the first council had he not thought his story, whatever it was, would be of interest. Steyr was only too painfully aware of the consequences of wasting Daemon Rhue's time. Assassins could come in many forms but this had n' the look of an attempt on his life. This man wanted something

"You did not come to my private chamber to partake c warmth of my fire old man so if you have something to sa' may want to hear you had better be out with it. My day l long and cold; I grow tired and my irritation grows ac Steyr here can attest as to what forms my irritation c' itself."

The old man nodded his splotched head. "Your man here offered me a glass of wine earlier Lord Rhue, but I was more interested in warming myself after my long journey to the castle. Mayhap if I was able to enjoy that wine now I would tell a tale which I am certain the first council will be most grateful to have heard. Most grateful."

Daemon Rhue tipped his head to Steyr. "Get the man some wine. I think our guest here is anticipating compensation for whatever secret he has brought with him. Is that not correct?"

The man accepted the goblet from Steyr and proceeded to drain it in one hearty pull. When he was finished, he flashed a nearly toothless smile as red wine dribbled down his chin. He wiped it off on the sleeve of his tattered cloak.

"Thank you, my Lord. Your taste in wine is exquisite." He held the empty goblet out towards Steyr. Daemon Rhue motioned the physician to refill it.

The man continued. "It has been a long time since I have had the pleasure of enjoying such a vintage. From the southwest region of Torbek, your Lordship?"

Rhue nodded as Steyr handed the man a full goblet. "Correct in your assumption. I would venture there are not many here within this castle who could make that identification. You appear to have knowledge of such but you did not come here to discuss fine wines?"

The newcomer took the goblet from Steyr and raised it in a gesture of appreciation towards Daemon Rhue.

"Ah, but if only that were the case, my Lord. Once, many years ago, I was able to enjoy the finer things in life. As I was telling your man Steyr here, I may not look like such now but I once held an important position here at Castle Daine. Now I am forced to live piously on a pittance of a pension after all of my years of loyal service to King Edmond. The secret I bring to you today is the kind that can change history. Be it so wrong to ask for a little compensation, as you say, for such information?"

Daemon Rhue now knew where he had seen this man before. t had been early on in the years before he had gained complete access to the court of King Edmond. He had been Lord Taul's peace emissary, making many trips back and forth between Sectos and Tiernon. During his audiences with the king and his elder council this man had always been present, in the background but still there. His irritation had now been replaced by curiosity.

"If your information is valuable as you say, then I assure you good man, you will not go away without getting what you deserve."

The man bowed slightly. "Then if it please my Lord, my name is Thaxton Tabard, and at a time I was one of King Edmond's most trusted friends and confidants. Much like your position sire, except I carried no title. I was at the king's side every single day and knew the man better than his own father and mother. Since Edmond was a young man, I attended to his needs at the castle, laughed with him when he was happy and suffered with him when he was not. There were not many closer to the man than myself."

Rhue eyed Tabard with careful interest. "So close to the king? Such a friend, yet today we buried the man and you were not at his funeral? A close confidant but you have not been seen around here for many years and receive a pension of no more value than that of a common soldier? How is that?"

"Sad to say but you have touched on the truth of the matter, my Lord. I fell out of favor with King Edmond and was forced from his service. He sought to soothe his displeasure by allowing me barely enough pension to feed and clothe myself. All those years of faithful service and I am kicked to the gutter liked a rat."

There was deep bitterness in the old man's voice. Daemon Rhue could feel the resentment and seething anger lying hidden behind his words. Those were the kind of emotions he liked to play on. Often as naught, if you probed and struck the right nerve any man would give up a secret, no matter what its value.

The man drained his cup again and held it out to Steyr. Daemon Rhue nodded his assent. After it was refilled, he continued with his story. "As I was saying, my Lord, at one time I was very close to King Edmond. I knew the man's strengths but I also knew his weakness, and therein may have been the heart of my problem. Getting to the crux of the matter, my good King Edmond was caught in a scandal; one he sought desperately to cover up. It was I who was forced to do the dirty work and try to fix his mess, but he did not approve of the manner in which I sought to lay the incident to rest. We argued frightfully as I warned him of dire consequences if he would not allow me a free hand in dealing with the matter. But Edmond would not listen to reason. I was forced to do his bidding and now the consequences of that action so long ago can be laid at your doorstep, my Lord."

Daemon Rhue and Steyr both listened intently to the man's words. While he had yet to divulge the true nature of his secret they both had the feeling there was something looming behind all this—something big.

"At my doorstep?" the first minister asked. "Something that happened so long ago is of no concern to me."

"Ah, but it should be of concern to you my Lord, a very big concern. You know the rule of Arturan law as it applies to succession by an heir after the death of a rightfully crowned king or queen?"

Daemon Rhue was trying to control his outrage at Tabard's effrontery. "Of course I do, man. We have just been through the matter and the rightful heir, Princess Alicia is being groomed by the elder council to take her proper place as queen when she comes of age. But come now Tabard, you are not here to lecture me on the nuances of Arturan law."

The old man bowed and forced a crooked smile, the smile of a man all too sure of himself.

"No indeed my Lord, but I must tell you that you are wasting your time, for Alicia Daine is not the rightful heir to King Edmond's crown as you would believe." The old man barely spoke above a whisper but the words rattled through the first council's hall like thunder. Daemon Rhue looked at Steyr in shocked anger and got a dumbfounded look in return.

"Do you know anything of this?"

"No, my Lord Rhue, I swear." Steyr saw the look in the first council's eyes and was instantly fearful. "I knew the man to have

518

been in the court of King Edmond as he says but I had no knowledge of this."

Daemon Rhue turned back to the old man, his dark eyes narrowed and his words dripped with venom. "I am going to give you one warning old man; you had better be able to prove this story of yours or I will feed your liver to the kennel dogs. While you are still alive."

The old man bowed again; this time he did not smile. "I understand your surprise my Lord, but I assure you it is the truth. I would dare not come before a man such as yourself with a lie. Please allow me to finish the tale before you judge me, Sire."

"Then by all means finish it."

"As you please, m'Lord. I was many years in the king's service and knew Edmond to be a true Daine at heart and a stalwart man when it came to being faithful to his wife. He partook naught of mistresses or prostitutes and cared deeply for Alena, though she was constantly in poor health. They tried to produce an heir but at the time it seems she was destined to live barren." He stopped to take another long draught from his wine goblet.

"But then a curious thing happened. A young girl came to the castle. It was, and mayhap still, a practice for those who serve the king to be allowed to send their children here for an education. There was a family who lived upriver near the great hospital. The father was a friend of Edmond, a weapons master and also a fine metalsmith. His wife was a healer working at the hospital. They sent their only daughter, who I believe was thirteen or fourteen at the time, to partake of the free education offered. Such a beautiful girl she was, hair the color of sunlight shining on gold, eyes of the deepest blue that sparkled so. Always smiling and happy."

"There are many pretty young girls in the castle." Irritation dripped from the first council's words. "Steyr can attest to that. Get on with your story."

The old man nodded. "Yes, my Lord. It seems the king became infatuated with this girl, though forty years her senior. She was flattered, as any would be, to receive such attention from the most powerful man in Artura, but she was naïve and oblivious to the craven yearnings old men have for young girls. Her father was quick to recognize the situation and sought to bring an end to it but Edmond's lust had been stroked and would not be denied. He finally sent the father away to remove him as an obstacle. The mother tried to keep the girl at home but the poor young thing was enamored with the opportunities offered her at the castle and persuaded her mother to allow her to continue to be schooled. She was, as I said, encumbered by the ignorance of youth.

"I must say, that those of us who saw what was happening tried to dissuade Edmond from his misguided interest in the girl but to no avail. He was crazed as a man in the desert dying of thirst and she was his life-giving water. He started ignoring his kingly duties to spend as much time fawning around her as he could and gave her expensive gifts. He found she was fascinated by books so he started to take her to the great castle library. You could see that he had worked himself to a position where she trusted him, as she would have her own father."

Tabard held his goblet out for more wine. Once again Rhue nodded to Steyr to refill the cup. "Thank you, my Lord. 'Tis an excellent vintage and this old throat becomes parched." He took another long draught and sat the goblet on the table. His eyes dropped and he shook his head, remembering the sordid details.

"In a secluded reading alcove in the library Edmond's lust for the girl finally overcame his common sense. It could not have been at a worse time; a busy morning in the castle, with ministers and councilmen attending to business and servants going to and fro. I was just outside the library speaking with one of the elder council members. Edmond made advances on the girl, she balked, and he took her by force. When the deed was done, she ran from the castle screaming in tears, her torn garments barely covering her. Everyone knew what had happened. Word spread quickly and the queen soon became aware of it. Edmond secluded himself in his private chamber with a jug of wine. Needless to say it was quite a mess."

Daemon Rhue shook his head. "I will never understand this

sense of proper moral conduct you Arturans seem to demand adherence to. The man was king. If he wanted to take the girl, he had every right to her no matter her age. Her parents should have been dutiful subjects and brought her to him and been honored he chose to bestow his royal member upon their daughter."

"True as you say, my Lord but that is not the way of our kings. That is not to say they have all been faithful men and able to withstand the carnal desires of the flesh. But while there have been many mistresses and illicit affairs and such, that sort of behavior was kept quiet and out of sight and the proper folk paid to keep it so. But for all the uproar Edmond caused he may have well raped this young girl in the middle of the Street of Trade in broad daylight."

Tabard took another long draught from his wine goblet. "The situation might have been allowed to fade into nothing had nature not taken a hand. The girl never returned to the castle and eventually Alena forgave the king and allowed him to return to her bed. All seemed well for awhile until rumor came to me the girl was with child. No one had seen the girl or the mother for some time and the father was still away at war so the king bade me to visit and confirm the rumor and I found it to be true."

Daemon Rhue had guessed as much. Though he hadn't heard the whole story it was giving him concern. His Supreme Lord Taul was fairly content with his progress and things were going according to plan. The king was finally dead; the charade with the princess and the elder council was in place. This was not the time for a mistake. He nodded for Tabard to continue. "Go on."

"Yes, my Lord. King Edmond was in deep regret about the whole affair and just wanted the matter forgotten but now the specter of a bastard heir raised its head. The queen was furious because she was still trying to give Edmond a legitimate son or daughter.

"I was called forth to bring the matter to a resolution but found myself caught between the king and the queen as to how this was to be taken care of. Alena, as jealous and vengeful as a wronged wife could be, sought to soothe her rage at the affair by taking it out on the girl. She demanded the baby not be allowed to live and

I for one agreed wholeheartedly. I argued vehemently with him but Edmond was against it. It would have been so easy had he relented. The proper potion mixed in the girl's drink. Her mother, being a healer could have done it. If she had refused, I was prepared to use other, let us say, more forceful ways to ensure the child never came into being. But to this end Edmond was as stubborn as ever. He refused to allow any harm to come to the girl or her family and warned I would be held accountable if it did. He threatened me."

Tabard drained his goblet. The old man was now starting to show the effects of the wine. He held it out again.

"No." Daemon Rhue barked as Steyr reached for the empty goblet. He wanted the rest of the man's story and wanted it without the annoyance of a drunk's countenance. "Finish your story, Tabard, and then we will refill your cup."

The old man bowed slightly. "As my Lord commands. In the end, I secured the father's release from the king's service, they were given a bag of gold, and told never to be seen again. The family disappeared shortly after and that was thought to have been the end of it. Then two years later, and much to everyone's surprise, Queen Alena finally gave Edmond his heir; the Princess Alicia."

"We know that part of the story," Daemon Rhue growled. "What came of the girl and her child?"

"Ah, Lord Rhue," the old man forced a smile but it failed to hide his bitterness. "That is where the story gets interesting. As I said, I fell out of the king's favor for arguing against allowing the child or the family to live. I was eventually dismissed and even Queen Alena turned her back on me. Forced into retirement and given a pension barely enough to put food on the table and buy a jug of cheap wine to soothe an old man's troubles. That is what I got for years of faithful service. As I said Lord Rhue, kicked to the gutter like a rat."

"But I think the rat might have done a bit of snooping as to the what and where of the situation. Is that not correct, Tabard?"

The old man bobbed his head and the crooked smile returned, even more lopsided given the effects of the strong wine. "My Lord is a very wise man. It was some years later. My outrage at the injustice forced upon me never left, but while I yearned for revenge, a man of my meager means had little recourse. But it occurred to me that knowledge, and especially the right kind of knowledge, can be a powerful weapon in itself."

Daemon Rhue had nearly reached the end of his patience. "You are taking up a lot of my time, Tabard. You know what happened to the girl and her child or you would not be here. For your sake you had better finish your story."

The old man's eyes hardened and the crooked smile vanished. Steyr, who was still sampling the food on the table while listening to the story, was impressed by the fact that Tabard seemed not a bit cowed by Lord Rhue. But the old man did not know the first council as he did; when you stood up to Daemon Rhue, the outcome was usually not good.

"I do your Lordship, and what I know is enough to create quite an uproar here, especially at this time. King's blood is king's blood and there is no exception within Arturan law. You laid Edmond to rest today in the Cave of Kings and there are no less than three bastard rulers there to keep him company. Alicia can never become the true ruler of Artura while there is an older sibling still alive."

Daemon Rhue glowered at Steyr who had been slicing cheese with a large knife. This was a disruption to his plan and his anger was starting to boil. His words hissed. "I guess it had not occurred to me that such an abominable situation might present itself. I was not aware you Arturans would stoop so low to allow one not of pureblood to rule. The taint of a bastard would never be allowed to stain the throne of a civilized nation."

"Civilized or not, King's blood is king's blood," Tabard repeated shrugging. "Alicia Daine has a sixteen-year-old sibling that by law must be recognized as Edmond's rightful heir."

Tabard paused; he had started a fire and was now ready to pour oil on it.

"There is one more element of Arturan law you may not be aware of, Lord Rhue. Steyr here can attest to the fact. Heirs to the throne may not rule until they have reached legal age, hence the decree giving control to the elder council until they do. Legal age for females is eighteen but only sixteen for a male. Edmond fathered a son, and bastard though he might be, the boy is now of legal age to rule. The true king of Artura is alive and well. What say you to that, my Lord?"

The first council was seething as he turned his back and walked to the fireplace. There was a long pause of uncomfortable silence as Daemon Rhue stared into the fire, searching for an answer to his dilemma in the fiery depths. It seemed an eternity before he finally turned and walked back to face Thaxton Tabard.

"You seem quite sure of yourself old man. You must know where this boy is and have confirmed he is alive before you came to me with this news? How is it that?"

Tabard nodded with just a hint of a wry smile. Steyr thought the man was exhibiting far too much confidence in his position. Such self-assurance was misguided when dealing with the first council.

"I took it upon myself long ago, Lord Rhue, to find the location of this child and have kept watch best I could, given my meager resources. But I assure you he is alive and well. As I said, knowledge can be power and I gambled a day such as this would come about and this information might be of value to someone."

"Does the boy know who his father is?" Daemon Rhue asked.

Tabard shook his head. "Of that I know not, Lord Rhue. Observations on his whereabouts were never close enough to tell."

"And you, Tabard. Did you ever mention this to anyone else?"

"Not of the lad's whereabouts, sire. But there were others close to the king who knew of this situation."

Daemon Rhue stepped up to within inches of Thaxton Tabard and looked him straight in the eyes, his voice cold and hard. "But there is no proof of this. Who could stand and swear without a doubt the boy is the king's bastard or not? Edmond certainly can't speak for it."

Steyr felt the steel resolve in Daemon Rhue's voice, razor-edge sharp, it could cut deep as any blade. He recognized what the fool

Tabard did not; his master had been pushed beyond his limit. But the old man seemed sure that what he had to offer the first council was going to keep him from harm. A brave notion, but Steyr did not share his confidence. Tabard pressed on with his point.

"I understand what you say Lord Rhue, but it just may be such proof still exists. When I went to the family with the gold and the warning that they were to disappear, Edmond entrusted me with a letter to give to them."

"And of course you being the faithful confidant of the king, you read the contents of this letter?" Daemon Rhue asked, though it was more statement of fact than question.

Tabard maintained his wry smile and shrugged his shoulders. "Guilty as charged, Lord Rhue. I did take it upon myself to read the contents of the letter. It was the king's apology for what had happened and his personal guarantee no harm would befall the family or the child. It was affixed with his seal."

Tabard's eyes were locked tight to Daemon Rhue's. The possibility of a letter not only acknowledging the whole affair, but affixed with the king's personal seal had just made the matter more complicated.

"Where is this boy Tabard?"

"I understand your desire to get to the heart of this delicate situation, Lord Rhue, but first there is the matter of compensation. You see before you an old man wronged for simply doing his duty. I have suffered this injustice for many years and now desire only to live out the rest of my pitiful life with a small degree of comfort. I must say I believe the information to be valuable. Do you not agree?"

"How valuable?" Daemon Rhue's words dripped with poison.

Thaxton Tabard wrung his hands together. His mouth and throat were dry and he felt like he was chewing sand. He longed for another drink of the first council's wine. Meticulously he had gone over this plan time and time again only to waffle indecisively when it came to this critical point. This was where he needed to be strong; he had the information and information was power. But still he hesitated. His future hung in the balance. How much would the man pay for this information? He stole a nervous glance at Steyr and then looked back to the first council. He cleared his dry throat.

"Two hundred pieces of gold, Lord Rhue, and I will tell you where the boy and his family are."

A long uncomfortable silence draped over the room like a wet blanket. Steyr fidgeted while Thaxton Tabard tried to maintain an aura of calm strength. The man bravely tried to hold the first council's gaze, but his tactics did not fool Daemon Rhue and it was all he could do to keep from laughing out loud. Extortion. If Tabard would have had a real understanding of just how important the information was, the old fool could have demanded twenty times the price. Ten years' worth of careful planning, alliances forged, loyalties bought. The King dead. Artemis Thoryl and the army made impotent by time and distance. The condescending humiliation of this miserable charade he had been forced to play, and now so close to success. He had no choice. Thaxton Tabard's demand would have to be met.

Daemon Rhue turned and walked over to a large chest shoved against a wall behind one of the large reclining divans that made up part of the room's furniture. Slipping a key from the pocket of his robe, he unlocked and raised the heavy lid. He knelt in front of the chest for a few moments and rummaged through its contents. Steyr saw Tabard's eyes light up when he heard the jingling of coin. As his master stood up, the physician noticed he did not bother to close and relock the chest.

"Two hundred pieces of gold," Daemon Rhue said as he tossed a leather bag to the old man. The coin jingled as he caught and nearly dropped the heavy pouch.

As Tabard's attention diverted to keeping his reward from spilling onto the floor, Daemon Rhue shot Steyr a venomous look and tipped his head towards the old man. The physician nodded his understanding.

Thaxton Tabard cradled the heavy pouch in his arms like it was a newborn babe. A wine infused smile spread lopsided across his face as he gazed upon his long sought treasure. "I have forgotten what two hundred pieces of gold felt like, your Lordship. It has been a long time."

"Tell me where the boy is old man, now." Daemon Rhue was out of patience.

The old man bowed slightly."On a farm just outside a small village called Lightwood. It lays on the edge of the great forest a week's journey by horse from Bargtown. I know not what the boy is called, but I do know the folk he lives with."

"His mother?"

"No, my Lord. It seems she is dead. But the boy lives with his grandparents Mattie and Quint; they go by the surname Ironhand."

Immediately there came a racking cough from the table. Both Daemon Rhue and Tabard turned quickly. The fat physician had evidently choked on something and was desperately trying to dislodge the offending morsel. He pushed his chair away from the table and bent his head between his legs, forcing deep coughs that sent spasms through his body. Neither of the other men made any move to help, but after a few more gagging coughs, Steyr made a vile retching noise and a wad of saliva-covered and half-chewed cheese made a heavy splat onto the floor. The choking fit stopped. Steyr sat upright, his puffy face red and his eyes watery. He wiped the slime from his hands on his robe.

"By thunder Steyr, you fat pig," Daemon Rhue growled, furious at the interruption. "Try chewing your food next time."

"I beg your pardon, Lord Rhue," Steyr squeaked in a pathetic whisper of a voice, still trying to recover.

Rhue turned back to face Tabard. "You have gotten your gold old man. I would say this would be the end of it. You have given me information and I have paid for it, but there is one part of this bargain that suits me not."

"What might that be, Lord Rhue?" Tabard asked with a puzzled look on his face. "Surely you know the information to be worth the price."

"No, it is not the price that troubles me. You leaving here with the information still in your head does. What will keep you from trying to sell this knowledge to someone else?"

The old man shook his head emphatically. "I assure you Lord Rhue, my lips are sealed. Long have I waited to extract revenge for the wrong done unto me. Now my only wish is to live out the rest of my days in peace and comfort."

Daemon Rhue studied the man intently and then folded his arms and let out a long sigh. "Well, I suppose I must trust you. But allow me just one more question if you will Tabard."

"Yes, my Lord, ask anything."

"Just how many days of peace and comfort will two hundred pieces of gold buy you?"

Thaxton Tabard looked confused for a moment and then started to speak. "Well, my Lo..."

The words choked off with a sudden intake of air and his eyes grew wide in surprise; the bag of gold fell from his hands and dropped with a metallic clunk to the stone floor. He reached his arms behind him as if trying to scratch an itch in the small of his back. His mouth opened to speak but in place of words, red-flecked foam drooled out over his lips. Tabard's body shuddered with a violent spasm and he gurgled out more blood-flecked foam. Daemon Rhue's cold, hard eyes watched without emotion as the old man struggled to cling to his last few moments of life.

"Not many, evidently," he said coldly as Thaxton Tabard shuddered one more time and then fell forward. The first council stepped deftly to the side and out of the way as the old man's body thudded face-first to the floor, landing atop his bag of gold. The knife Steyr had been using to slice cheese was buried in the small of the old man's back, just to the left of his spine. Blood began to seep around the hilt through the fabric of Tabard's tattered cloak.

"I would say the man got what he deserved, my Lord." Steyr grinned maniacally as he gazed down at the prostrate form.

Daemon Rhue nudged the body with his foot. Satisfied that Thaxton Tabard would no longer be troubling him, he shot a questioning look at the physician.

"The old fool got exactly what he deserved but for a moment

I thought you may be incapable of doing the deed. What was that all about?"

"I beg your pardon, Lord Rhue, but the names Tabard spoke caught me by surprise."

Daemon Rhue raised his eyebrows. "You know of these folk?"

"It is the other reason behind my absence from the funeral procession today, my Lord," Steyr started to explain. "I received a bird from Mogga this morning, sire, and the message she sent had quite a story to tell. I had contacted her as you instructed about the flow of magic you felt had been emanating from the forest."

"The witch knows of the source?"

"Indeed she does, my Lord. Not only does she know from whence it came, but she had a confrontation with the user. The outcome left her with injuries which took her a while to recover from."

Daemon Rhue stepped over the body of Thaxton Tabard and poured himself a goblet of wine. A bad day was getting worse.

"You have always bragged about how powerful your witch's magic is, Steyr. Yet now you tell me she came out on the losing end of this confrontation?"

Steyr shrugged his shoulders. "There was an intruder within the forest. This interloper ran into Fenrir and his pack. The intruder's magic was strong enough to kill the Wolf King my Lord; quite an accomplishment in itself. That must have been the first use of magic you felt. Mogga felt it, also. She knew something was amiss because she could sense the wolf's magic but could no longer sense the wolf. The intruder not only killed Fenrir, but acquired the wolf's talisman for his own, my Lord."

Daemon Rhue drained his goblet in one long drought and refilled the cup immediately. "So you are telling me this person not only possesses strong magic of their own, but now has acquired that of the wolf, also?"

Steyr shrugged again. "So it seems, my Lord."

Daemon Rhue stared deep into his wine cup. His face grew dark and his brow knotted with worry. With a sudden scream, he turned and threw the full goblet at Steyr. Red wine showered the face of the stunned physician as the cup narrowly missed his head and smashed against the stonewall, exploding into pieces. Immediately the door banged open and the two guards stationed outside burst into the room with swords drawn.

"Get out you idiots!" Daemon Rhue screamed. "If I want you I will call you!"

The perplexed guards took one quick look at the scene in the room and never uttered a question, nearly tripping over themselves in their hurry to exit.

Daemon Rhue turned to face a terrified Steyr who had stepped back in alarm at his master's fit of rage. "So the news keeps getting better and better. We have a bastard king and now a powerful magician on the loose to deal with. Please tell me how all of this fits together, Steyr?"

The physician was sweating profusely even though the room was not at all warm, the sweat mixing with red wine and running in rivulets down his face before disappearing into the fat folds of his neck. The fat man held out his hands and pleaded.

"Please, my Lord. Mogga went to investigate and she came upon a camp within the forest. It was there she encountered the bearer of the magic. It was just a boy of no more than thirteen or fourteen years old, sire. She was able to lure him away from the camp but when she tried to lay hold of him, his friend interfered. There was a struggle and the boy ended up drawing forth magic from the wolf's talisman. Mogga said he seemed to have trouble controlling it but when he did bring it to bear, she was not able to withstand the attack."

"A boy? Yet your powerful witch was not able to best him? Not very impressive to say the least, Steyr."

"My Lord, Mogga said this boy was very different and the magic he drew forth from Fenrir's talisman very powerful. She also said she could sense another source of magic within the camp but could not tell from whence it came. Had the boy been able to bring both to bear she might not have survived at all, but as it was, she was able to leave him with a present of her own. She stuck him with a poisoned blade. As you know my Lord, Mogga's poisons are strong and with any luck, he is already dead."

Daemon Rhue turned away and walked to the fireplace. "Don't count on it, Steyr. If his magic was that strong, it might have protected him. You say the boy had a friend? What of this person?"

"Ah, that is what ties this together with Tabard's story, Lord Rhue. The other boy in the camp was someone Mogga recognized. She has a sister, a known healer and a witch also, my Lord. This sister lives with her husband in a village not far from the edge of the forest. A village called Lightwood, sire."

"Lightwood? The same village the old man referred to?" Daemon Rhue asked, nodding his head towards the stiffening body of Thaxton Tabard.

"Yes, Lord Rhue. The other boy is the grandson of Mogga's sister. The names of the sister and her husband are Mattie and Quint Ironhand. When Tabard mentioned their names it caught me by surprise."

"Well, well, well," Daemon Rhue muttered as he stared in deep thought at the fire. "The bastard and the source of magic together. Maybe this whole affair has been wrapped up in one neat package for us, Steyr. All we have to do is go get it."

The physician sighed in relief, recognizing a chance to turn away his master's wrath. "I will see to it at once, your Lordship. I can send some men from here or I can find some of our folk in that part of the country to take care of the matter."

Daemon Rhue turned away from the fireplace and walked back to face Steyr, carefully sidestepping the blood oozing from Tabard's body. He shook his head. "I think not."

"My Lord?"

"While having them together will make it easier, this still has to be done with care. We don't want word of this bastard to leak out and I definitely do not want someone who can wield magic roaming the countryside, whether he is but a boy or not. I need a man who can handle all the elements involved. But more so than that, I need a man who knows full well the consequences of failure. That will be you, Steyr. Captain Einer will help with the men, horses, and supplies you will need for the journey. He will accompany you. I have not forgiven him for allowing Cedric Montel to escape us. Make your way to the village. Silas and Sa'mel are in Bargtown working on another matter for me. Send word to them and have them meet you along the way. You can fill them in on the situation. The two of them should be able to deal with the boy and his magic."

"But surely, sire, you can't mean for me to make such a journey," a shocked Steyr stammered. "I am ill-prepared for such an endeavor, and what of my work here?"

"Your work here?" The first council's voice had a hard edge to it. "Your work is to do exactly what I tell you, Steyr. There is nothing more important than this. Do you understand?"

"But Lord Rhue, I…"

Before Steyr could finish his sentence, the first council grabbed the front of the fat man's robe with both hands and shoved him hard backwards onto the table. Trays of food and wine goblets clattered to the floor and the table groaned in protest as Daemon Rhue bent the physician hard over the table and hissed into his face.

"Enough of your whining. You have grown fat and lazy and are good for nothing other than sniffing the crotches of your playthings. I want you out of here before daybreak tomorrow. You will do this as if your life depends upon it for I assure you that it does. Do you understand?"

"Yes, my Lord Rhue," Steyr squeaked a pathetic response, stunned by his master's outburst. "What are my instructions as far as the bastard and the other boy are concerned my Lord?"

"I want you to find them and the grandparents. The one who wields the magic I want brought to me unharmed, do you understand? Unharmed. If he has the power your worthless witch says he does, then I will have it for myself. The twins should be able to counter the boy's magic and bind him."

Steyr nodded. "And the others, my Lord?"

"They are of no use to me. Our plan will go on unaltered once you have completed your task. Go to Lightwood. If you find there are those who know of the situation regarding the bastard, kill them all. Kill the boy, the grandparents, the villagers, whoever, and burn the place to the ground. You need to be heavy-handed, Steyr. Have Einer select men capable of doing the deed. It shouldn't take too many. After all, they are just peasants. Do you understand?"

The physician nodded his head. He understood all too well.

"Yes, my Lord Rhue."

"Good. And one more thing, Steyr."

"Yes, sire?"

Daemon Rhue swept his hand towards the lifeless body of Thaxton Tabard and the strewn contents from the table lying about the floor. "You have made a mess in my receiving chamber. Clean it up before you go."

CHAPTER THIRTY

WILLOUGHBY WAS AWAKENED BY LORD Fuggs' tail swatting him in the face. The cat had been out prowling all night and was ready to spend the better part of the day curled up in a black fuzz ball on Willoughby's bed. Lord Fuggs allowed his roommate to scratch behind his ears for a while before he selected his spot and was soon settled in for his nap, purring his contentment. He raised one eyelid in annoyance as Willoughby flipped his coverlet back and swung his legs out of the bed.

"Sorry, Fuggs," he apologized as he fumbled for his clothes and began to dress. The sounds of Mattie in the kitchen and the smell of sausages frying told Willoughby the day had already begun and that his new family had probably been up for some time going about their chores. He was somewhat embarrassed by the fact he was a late sleeper but they let him set his own clock and seemed not to mind.

They had been busy for the last several days. Mattie and Quint hadn't spoken much of what they were planning but it had instilled a sense of urgency around the farm. Mattie had removed the stitches in Willoughby's side and except for the bright pink scar, the wound had healed nicely. It made him feel better that he was now able to help with some of the more strenuous chores without fear of breaking it open.

He stretched after he had gotten his pants on and was immediately and quite painfully aware of how sore his arm and shoulder muscles were. The healing of his wound had done more than allow Willoughby to help with some of the harder chores around the farm. In the last couple of days, Quint and Bryan had started to teach him how to fight with a number of different weapons, something his body was ill-prepared for.

Cautiously he tried to stretch some of the tension out of his arms and shoulders. Notwithstanding the soreness, Quint's training regime was doing him a lot of good. His muscles had atrophied severely while he was lying in bed recovering from the poisoned wound. At first they had started with simple wooden practice swords, but even those made his arms ache from holding them up and trying to ward off the countless blows Bryan threw at him. But each day Quint changed the swords.

"Hey, this one is heavier than the one yesterday," Willoughby had complained on the second day in the practice yard.

"And you are stronger than you were yesterday," Quint chided as he fixed the padded armor around Willoughby. As untrained as he was, they were worried about Bryan hurting him even though the weapons were only wood. Like the swords, Quint added more to Willoughby's training regime every day, and for someone who didn't even like dodge ball, the activity was brutal. The more he wanted to quit, the harder Quint would press him.

"You must push your body, Will. You are small and a small man must trust his quickness to counter a bigger and stronger foe. Speed depends on your muscles reacting immediately how and when you want them to. React too slow in the heat of battle and you are dead."

Willoughby was still having a hard time wrapping his mind around this whole thing. Not more than a few weeks ago, his concept of hand to hand combat was pushing the right buttons on his Xbox controller and slaying the bad guys in Skyrim. If you weren't skilled or quick enough there, you got another chance. Quint was quick to remind him of a different set of consequences here.

"This is becoming dangerous country Will," the big man told him as he and Bryan took a water break from their training. "Folks who do not understand that oft find themselves in trouble and at the mercy of men who have none. It is a sad state of affairs and I for one wish we could get to the point where a man and his family did not have to worry about such things. But I would be remiss in my duty if I did not give you the tools to protect yourselves."

So continue they did. Sometimes to the point of driving both boys to exhaustion. Quint was indeed a hard taskmaster.

"Stop!" he would yell during their sparring sessions when Bryan managed to connect with what would have been a killing blow, and that was often. "You are dead, Will. You cannot stop moving your feet when you battle a larger man. Remember, use your quickness to keep him guessing as to where you will be. Stay stationary and you lose your edge."

Back and forth across the practice yard, Willoughby and Bryan would battle, stopping when Quint would point out needed improvements in technique. Each morning Willoughby's body would painfully remind him of the intensity of the previous day's lesson. But as he stood there next to his bed and worked some of the soreness out of his arms, Willoughby could swear he was starting to get muscle where he never had any before. He could feel the urgency in Quint's practice sessions. Though it was not mentioned, everything seem to be building towards their journey to find the man Theron. If he kept this up, he would be able to wield Gaelron's sword with no trouble at all.

The thought caused him to glance towards the corner and immediately an alarm inside his head sounded—his sword and shield, pack, and all of his other things were no longer there. He hadn't paid them much mind since he had arrived but seeing them gone sent a shockwave through him. Panicked, he fumbled for the leather cord round his neck, checking to see if the wolf's teeth were still there. His relief was instant when he felt the hard canines inside his nightshirt.

"No need to be alarmed, Will," Mattie said as she suddenly appeared at his door with a bouquet of fresh-cut flowers. "Your belongings are safe. I had Quint hide them. If the Prouts come nosing about as Pel has warned it would not do us good to have them ask questions about such things. The ones they do ask about you will be enough. Do you remember what to say?"

"Yes, Mattie," Willoughby sighed in relief. "I went over the story in my mind as you told me to." They had concocted a slightly more detailed version for Denton Prout than what they had told Pel Marin.

"Good," she said as she arranged the flowers in the vase by his bed. She fluffed the petals gently with her tiny calloused hands and then leaned forward to smell them. "It is such a shame when the weather turns and the flowers no longer bloom. This will be the last of them for the year I am afraid." She turned and looked at Willoughby.

"Can you sense the sword, Will?"

Mattie had been trying to teach him to connect with the magic found in his two talismans. He could feel them all of the time, sort of like an itch he couldn't scratch, but Mattie wanted him to be able to take it further; to actually sense the power within. "It is there, reach out to it," she coaxed.

Willoughby closed his eyes and brought up an image of the sword in his mind. He did as she had told him and tried to imagine his hand, reaching for the hilt of the sword. It was so close. All he had to do was grab it. But just as he was about to feel his hand closing upon the leather grip, the sword seemed to move just out of reach.

"I can't do it, Mattie," he said, opening his eyes and voicing his frustration. "When I concentrate I can almost reach it but then the power of the wolf's teeth seems to interfere and my mind loses the connection to both of them."

Mattie patted him on the shoulder. "The two powers are foreign to each other, Will. I cannot say which is the stronger because they are as day is to night and each has their inherent qualities. The talisman around your neck might hold sway because you wear it close. We should allow you to wear the sword every day as well, but I fear you will not be able to control the combined power of the two and it might set off a reaction that could be felt outside my wards. You must continue to work on the control as I have taught you. Use your mind to reach for the power; force it to come to you. Concentrate and try again."

Willoughby had been trying. They kept him busy every day with exercises of some sort. If it wasn't Mattie coaching on the control of the magic, it was Bryan and Quint instructing him on the use of weapons and self-defense. While they never talked much about their plans, Willoughby could sense the urgency building. He and Bryan had talked about it just yesterday.

While taking a well-earned break from sparring in the yard behind the smithy, Willoughby had broached Bryan about their plans. The bigger boy had just sent him to his knees with a hard blow to his side. The thick padding they made him wear absorbed much of the shock but it still had knocked the wind out of him.

"Sorry, Will," Bryan apologized as he helped the smaller boy to his feet. "You are getting better and I had to use a little more power to get past your defense. Enough for a while."

Bryan helped him out of his protective pads and they helped themselves to a ladle full of cool water from a bucket nearby. Willoughby sat on a bench, leaned back, and closed his eyes. The sound of Quint's heavy hammer shaping iron on his anvil reverberated through the wooden wall. His arms were dead weight and his body ached in a dozen places from Bryan's well-aimed strikes. Willoughby was thankful they had been practicing with swords. Bryan was good with the blade but when it came to fighting staffs, he was really good. Willoughby took a lot of punishment when they trained with the staffs.

As he rested his tired body, leaning his head back and feeling the vibrations from Quint's hammering, he let his mind drift, trying to imagine what he might have been doing a few weeks ago. Trying to coax the PE coach into allowing him to sit out from a dodgeball game? Doing his best to avoid Eddie Anderson in the halls between classes? It hadn't been that long ago but so much had happened; home and the world he had come from seemed like just a dream.

"Do you know anything about where we are going or this Theron guy we are supposed to find?" Willoughby finally asked Bryan.

"Only stories, Will. It is said that he was many things; soldier, statesman, scholar, advisor to the king. My friend Tristan says he was a wizard as well, but Tristan also said he saw a dragon once." Bryan laughed. Willoughby forced himself to chuckle along with him but even a dragon wouldn't have surprised him anymore.

"Grandfather says the two men most responsible for finally bringing about the defeat of Torbek were Artemis Thoryl and Theron Greystone."

"If he was such a great guy, how come the king tried to have him killed?" Willoughby was confused.

Bryan shrugged. "My grandparents have tried to teach me about the way the king's court works. They seem to think it important for some strange reason, though it seems like so much worthless nonsense to me. Power, politics, deceit, and treachery; the more they tell me about it, the more I am convinced how much better off we are as plain woodsmen and farmers. They said Theron became angry when King Edmond started to listen to the advice of Daemon Rhue. The more the king came under the influence of First Council Rhue, the more frustrated Theron became. He and the king had a fierce argument and Theron told Edmond he was leaving, but the king became furious. Theron was placed under arrest and confined to a high tower at Castle Daine. Grandfather says it was Lord Rhue who convinced Edmond to arrest Theron."

Bryan's story sounded like a script for a great movie. Willoughby wanted to hear more. "So Theron must have got away somehow?"

Bryan nodded. "He escaped from the tower but the story about how he did so has many different versions. One of the more common ones is that he sprouted wings and flew from the top of the tower in the middle of the night to a ship waiting for him out in the river."

Willoughby grinned. "I suppose that is the one your friend Tristan likes to tell?"

Bryan laughed. "Yes, that is his favorite, but he is not alone in telling that version of the tale. Many people swear by it. However it happened, Theron got away."

Willoughby shrugged. "It ain't so hard to believe I guess. I've seen a lot of strange shit since I been here so a guy growin' wings don't seem all that farfetched. What about this place he lived, the place we're supposed to look for him? Quint said it's called the Tail of the Dragon?"

"If you could see the maps, Will, you would know why they call it such. It is in the far northwest corner of Artura where the land narrows and pokes far out into the North Sea. It's the tail end of the mountain range called the Guardians. The place where you came out of Gaelron's cave is on their lower slopes. It is the greatest mountain range in the known world and protects the borders of Artura to the north and to the east."

Willoughby remembered coming down the steep slopes after coming out of the cave. He had glimpsed the towering upper reaches of those mountains; massive snow-covered spires of stone and ice. It still made him shiver. It had been his first clue that he was someplace besides close to home. What little he had been able to see of the Guardians dwarfed anything he had ever seen of the Cascades and they were supposedly second only to the Rockies in their magnitude. Bryan had continued with his story.

"At the very end of the Tail, on a high cliff overlooking the sea, there was an old castle. Grandfather said it had been built ages ago as a lighthouse and beacon point for navigators trying to sail around the Tail. That is where Theron fled after he escaped the tower. It is told he took a party of dwarves overland with him and they rebuilt the castle."

"Then the king had him hunted down?" Willoughby questioned.

Bryan shook his head. "Grandfather said Edmond got over his anger with Theron and had chosen to leave him be but that it was Daemon Rhue who finally ordered his death. He sent a general named Dayen Holt with ten ships and five hundred men to do the deed."

"That many to kill just one guy?"

Bryan shrugged. "Grandfather said the first council was deathly afraid of Theron Greystone."

Willoughby was perplexed. The more of the story he heard, the less it seemed that Mattie's plan made much sense. "If this place is so hard to get to and the guy is supposed to be dead, why would we go to all the effort to get there? What if we don't find him?"

"Grandmother would not have us chase a ghost, Will. She thinks Theron is alive and the best chance we have to get you some help."

Bryan had grown suddenly silent. He was still holding the wooden practice sword and was tapping the end of it nervously in the dirt in front of him. Willoughby could tell there was something else on his friend's mind; something that was troubling him. "What are you thinking Bryan? What's wrong?" Willoughby had asked.

Bryan had just kept tapping and shook his head. "I am not sure, Will. I have a funny feeling that there is something important my grandparents are not telling me."

"Will…Will!"

Willoughby jerked his head around, for a moment forgetting where he was. Mattie was standing there looking at him.

"Oh sorry, Mattie. I kind of got sidetracked thinking about something else."

Mattie looked at him with concern. "Is everything all right, Will? You seemed to have been lost in your thoughts. Your wound is not troubling you?"

Willoughby gave her a smile. "I'm okay, Mattie. I was just thinking about something Bryan and I talked about yesterday. I didn't mean to lose concentration on the sword. Sometimes my mind wanders and lets all sorts of things in. It used to get me in trouble at school when I wouldn't pay attention."

Mattie sat down on the bed and patted for Willoughby to sit beside her. Lord Fuggs yawned and stretched as she scratched his head.

"You are worried about things Will; I can see it in your eyes. I know this has been hard on you, and a burden such as yours no young man should have to bear. But I assure you, Bryan, Quint and I will do everything we can to help you, though I know we are no substitutes for your family."

"But Mattie…what if we get all the way out to this Tail of the

Dragon place and we don't find this guy we are looking for? What do we do then?"

Mattie patted his knee. "Then all of us will sit together and think of another plan. The sun will still rise as it always has and life will go on."

Willoughby smiled warmly at her. It amazed him how much Mattie was like his Grandma Rose. When she said things, they just seemed to be right.

"Then I guess we will make this journey and see what we see," said Willoughby.

She patted his leg again. "There you have it, Will Baxter. Now wash up for breakfast and fetch Bryan and Quint. We have a busy day ahead and I need you and Bryan to run an errand for me."

An hour later, after they had eaten a hearty breakfast of sausage and oatcakes with maple honey and butter, Mattie kept them at the table.

"We must finish the chores in the next few days and then we need to be away. I know it is the wrong time of the year for travel of this sort but we have no choice," she said.

"Quint and Bryan will deliver the livestock to the Marins' on the morrow. Will and I can put away the rest of the winter stores and the perishables we cannot use, Quint can also take to Pel's. It will be part of the payment for having his boys look after the place while we are gone."

Bryan spoke up. "How long will we be gone, Grandmother? And what is to become of Lord Fuggs?"

"It will take us at least three or four weeks of hard travel to get to Backwater Cove. It is a small fishing village at the base of the Tail. Would we be fortunate enough to find a boat that would take us up the coastline at least for a ways we might be able to shorten the journey, but that is highly unlikely. The fisher folk do not sail in that direction. What we will need to do is find a guide who knows the Tail and go by foot. As far as Lord Fuggs is concerned, he will be fine here. He can take care of himself and will keep the mice and rats from overrunning the place." She smiled. "I have spoken to him; he understands." There was something special about that cat. When Mattie said she spoke to him and that he understood, Willoughby knew it was exactly what she meant.

Quint shook his head. From what few conversations they had about this upcoming adventure, Willoughby knew he was opposed to it. "We'll not find anyone in Backwater Cove who will be inclined to traverse the Tail," Quint said.

"No," Mattie agreed, "on that point you are right, my husband. The most likely place to find a guide who knows the land past the Cove will be Bargtown. That is where we will head when we leave here."

"Aauuggh!" Quint had been in the process of taking a drink of hot tea and promptly spilled it down his chin and into his thick beard.

"Bargtown?" Quint spit the name out loudly and with such a sour look on his face like it tasted bad. "Well, we won't need to worry about finding a guide to take us up the Tail if we go there."

"Why would that be, Grandfather?" Bryan asked.

"Because we will probably all have our throats cut not long after we get there. Bargtown is nothing but a haven for thieves, murderers, and whor..."

"Quint!" Mattie sharply cut him short. "That will be enough. There is no need to frighten the boys with that sort of talk. I know what kind of place Bargtown is but that is where we will be best served to find a guide. The place will be full of traders and travelers this time of year getting one last run in before winter takes hold. Better yet, there should be dwarves down from the mountains. We should have as much luck finding one in Bargtown who knows the Tail more so than anywhere else. You know we have no other choice, Quint."

Bryan had perked up when he had heard the name Bargtown. "Tristan says Tyson Barg is bigger than a mountain and meaner than a bull artox in the rut," he blurted out.

Mattie cuffed her grandson playfully on the back of the head. "Well there you have it. Straight from the mouth of the world's most renowned traveler and expert on the mating habits of artox."

Bryan grinned sheepishly and gave Willoughby an "Ooops. I should have kept my mouth shut" look.

"Sorry, Grandmother," he apologized.

She smiled and rubbed the back of his head where she had whacked him. "You are forgiven, Bryan, but I remind you once again that just because something comes out of the mouth of Tristan Marin does not make it the absolute truth. That boy can turn a trip to the privy into one of the greatest adventures ever told."

They all had a good laugh but the tone soon again turned serious. "Unfortunately there is truth in what Quint says about Bargtown," Mattie continued. "It can be a dangerous place so we will have to keep our guard up, but I believe that is where we have the best chance to find someone who can lead us up the Dragon's Tail to Theron's keep. But let us not worry about Bargtown until we get there. There is still much to do so while your grandfather and I tend to things here, Bryan, I need you and Will to fetch me some things I need for my kit."

"What do we need to find for you, Grandmother?" Bryan asked.

"I need the two of you to go to the meadow that lies at the east end of the ridge beyond the old watchtower."

"Poppies." Bryan knew the area and there was only one thing Mattie would need from there. "You want us to fetch poppies."

Mattie nodded. "My supplies are low. It took the better part of my kit to heal Will and we cannot travel without a full stock. Search for the pods that are still sealed tight and have not flowered. It is late in the year but you should still be able to find enough."

Quint stood up from the table. "They will need to take Meg if they are to go as far as the old watchtower. I will get her ready. They have to be away soon if they are to get there and back before dark."

An hour later Bryan and Willoughby were well on their way. The trails were few but Bryan had traveled this way before and Meg seemed to know where they were bound. The old mare worked best at one speed, slow, and try as he might Bryan could get no more out of her. For Willoughby that was fine, he was uncomfortable enough on her bareback. His sister loved horses but Willoughby did not share her opinion of them. Grandma Rose had rescued a mustang from a nearby farm whose occupants had been busted for cooking methamphetamine. The horse's name was Striker and it had remained wild and unbroken until Kendall came into the picture. She fell in love immediately with the feisty Mustang and with Jake's help, the two of them had worked Striker into a well-mannered horse. Well-mannered or no, Willoughby steered clear of him.

The boys made easy small talk as they traveled. The trail wound through patches of forest thick with conifers that choked off the sun and then broke into grassy meadows dominated by massive oaks and ash. Several times they spooked herds of the big red deer and had a tense moment when they came face to face with a huge mother bear and her cub using the same path going in the opposite direction. Meg had panicked and nearly dumped both of them but a quick reacting Bryan had been able to steady her. He grabbed his bow and was a breath away from letting an arrow fly when the two bears made a quick exit into the underbrush.

"Man, she was friggin' huge!" Willoughby exclaimed as they waited to make sure the bears were gone. It had been his first bear encounter ever, and he had been impressed, and more than a bit intimidated.

"She's a crag bear," Bryan said as they started back down the trail. "They usually stay to the higher mountains but come down into the valleys to fatten up on berries and apples before the snow sets in. They will usually let you be as long as you don't get between momma and her cub. They are very protective. I am just glad it wasn't a male; they can be unpredictable, besides being much bigger."

"Bigger?" was Willoughby's only comment. He didn't think he wanted to see how much bigger a crag bear could get.

They made a stop at a stream, allowing Meg to drink and doing the same themselves. The water was clear and cold.

"Not much farther, Will," Bryan said as they stretched their legs.

Willoughby's inner thighs ached from having to use his leg muscles to stay on the back of Meg and he was grateful for the break.

"We will ride until the trail starts to climb the ridge. There the path becomes steep, narrow, and full of loose rock. We will have to leave Meg and go the rest of the way on foot. She is getting on in years and we can't risk her making a bad step and coming up lame. Grandmother would skin us if anything happened to her."

An hour later they had reached the bottom of the ridge. The trail had been climbing gradually since they had left the creek and the patches of forest had now given way completely to the oak and ash grasslands. Willoughby could see the ridge as they grew closer, its tail starting abruptly from a small rise and climbing steeply to the top before turning into a long spine with a narrow flat top. A "hogback" was what Jake called them. Just where the ridge flattened off he could see a tall, jagged rock formation jutting up from the edge like a crooked finger pointing to the sky.

They tied Meg in the shade of a gnarly oak that had enough green grass growing under it to keep her occupied until the boys returned. Bryan shouldered a small pack in which Mattie had packed a lunch for them. He would use the pack for the poppies when they found them. Willoughby carried Bryan's bow and quiver and they each had a short sword strapped to their backs. Willoughby had wanted to take Gaelron's sword but Mattie had advised him against it for now.

"You'll be wearing it constantly soon enough," she said. "Better you wear it when I am with you in case it draws unwanted attention." He hadn't argued.

As they started up the ridge, Willoughby could see why they had to leave Meg. It was clear the path had been made by human hands but what had once been a useable trail had now turned into a treacherous walkway that required every step to be a sure one. It cut across the rocky slope in switchbacks and was shored up in many places by mortared stonework but had not been maintained for a very long time. Rock falls had tumbled down and littered the pathway, often forcing the boys to skirt them. In places, the rock slides had taken out the trail completely, leaving dangerous gaps.

"Who made the trail?" Willoughby asked Bryan as they stopped for a break after navigating around a particularly wide section that had tumbled down off the hillside.

"No one is quite sure," Bryan answered as they rested on a flat rock, each taking a long pull off the waterskin.

"It was made to access the tower, obviously, but as to who built it we don't know. Grandfather said Artura has always been at war with someone or amongst ourselves. He thinks the tower was made to watch over the old road that passes just north of here. There are other towers like it. When the new road was built to the south— that's the one that passes through Lightwood—they probably just abandoned the towers."

The boys each took one more pull off the waterskin and resumed their climb. Soon they negotiated the last switchback and broke out onto the top of the ridge.

"Whoa!" Willoughby exclaimed. The view that spread out before them was jaw dropping. The grass-and-scrub-oak-covered butte was high but actually the lesser of many that rose from the bottom lands like molehills in a well-kept lawn. Between the buttes—some of which were long and flat-topped like the one they were on and others were more like small round mountains—small forested valleys and vales nestled against their slopes. In the far distance, Willoughby could see the glimmer of a river snaking its way through the landscape, disappearing behind the buttes and ridges before coming back into sight. But it was the view beyond the hills and valleys that grabbed Willoughby's attention and left him with his mouth agape.

"It is a good day for a look, eh Will?" Bryan said as he followed his friend's gaze. He pointed out a large herd of red deer grazing on grass in the distance. Fluffy white clouds dotted the brilliant blue sky and the air was fresh and clean.

Willoughby didn't say a thing as he stood there taking in the sight. The forest and grassland mix stretched away and it was hard for him to judge distance without any recognizable landmarks. He guessed maybe twenty miles or so but it could have just as well been fifty. But there it was. The forest. Like a great green beast it broke the grasslands and stretched its emerald vastness to the far horizon, only to run headlong into a monster even bigger. The great, gray wall of the stone mountains broke the hold of the forest and disappeared into the clouds.

"That is where you came from, Will," Bryan said softly. He pointed to where the thin line of the river disappeared into the green backdrop of the wood.

"The abandoned farmstead I took you to after Mogga pierced you with her blade lies there. Grandfather and I brought you along the old road home."

Willoughby stared silently. He didn't have much recollection of that time, only bits and pieces of what had seemed to be a terribly bad dream. But he could feel the weight of Fenrir's teeth. They pulled toward the wood, it was home and they could feel its nearness.

"Where do you think Gaelron's cave is, Bryan?" he asked, scanning the horizon where green met gray.

Bryan pointed to a nondescript area above the tree line. "I am not sure Will, but I believe it to be there somewhere. It is hard to tell. The distances are deceiving and it is a long way to the mountains."

Willoughby stared hard. Someday he needed to go back that way. But for now he had to trust Mattie and Quint and he knew their path lay in a different direction. Nonetheless, the feeling was strong; that was the way he came in and maybe that was his only way back, if he could ever get back. But there was something else—a strong sense of something deep in the wood, vitally alive and somehow connected to him. It took him a while before he finally realized what it was.

"I can sense them, Bryan." His friend gave him an uncomprehending look. "The wolves," Willoughby explained. "I can feel the pack; it's the teeth."

"I don't understand the power of magic, Will," Bryan admitted. "Grandmother has it, but those of us who don't can only wonder what it is you feel. She says you are gifted with the ability and that the power in you is strong but uncontrolled. That is another reason she seeks help from Theron. Grandmother says there is no one better who can teach you to control the magic."

"I still don't understand any of it, Bryan," Willoughby admitted, shaking his head. "I never even had a hint of that sort of thing when I was home. The deal about being connected with the sword and the teeth, I have absolutely no idea where that comes from. How can it have anything to do with me?"

Bryan shrugged. "Grandmother says the strength and the ability to use the power in the talismans has to come from inside, Will. I held your wolf's teeth when Grandfather was braiding the leather strap for them. He held them too, and neither of us could feel anything. It is the same with the sword, the magic is there but is useless for any who cannot channel the power from within. It is special, Will. Learn to control and use it and you will be a powerful man."

Willoughby could feel the magic's presence. He couldn't really explain it but it was a tangible thing, almost an electrical energy. It fascinated, and scared him at the same time.

"What if I can't figure out how to use it, Bryan? So far it seems like it controls itself and I have nothing to do with it. Mattie says I have to learn to control it or it will control me."

Bryan smiled and put his hand on his friend's shoulder. "So that is why we leave soon to find Theron, Will. He will help you do what you need to do. Now let us gather Grandmother's plants. We want to be heading back before long."

Willoughby's legs ached from their climb but they were on top of the ridge now and the going was easier. Ahead of them the tall spire of rock he had seen from below jutted abruptly from the ridge, but as they closed the distance he could see what he had first thought to be a rock formation was actually the remains of the old watchtower. Most of the tower itself had long ago fallen in on its base, leaving only the remnants of one wall pointing to the sky like a stone finger with seemingly very little holding it up.

"Who did you say made the tower, Bryan?" Willoughby asked

as they skirted past the piled rubble, keeping a wary eye on the wall towering above them. *Remove the right block or put pressure in the right place and the thing would come down like a bad move in a Jenga game,* Willoughby thought to himself.

"Dwarves most likely," Bryan replied. "They are masters of mortar and stone and still do most of the building when it comes to anything more than a farmstead home. The quarry they used to take the stone from is still visible on the south side of the ridge. Grandfather says most dwarf-built structures will stand for the lifetime of a man and a hundred generations of his kin. This one must be old indeed to be coming down."

Bryan stopped suddenly and pointed in front of him. "There is what we came for, Will. Poppies."

Willoughby knew next to nothing about plants and their uses but he had heard of poppies. Afghanistan was always in the news—you couldn't get away from it—and part of the situation in that volatile country had to do with the opium trade. They had discussed it in geography and history classes both. Willoughby was standing on the edge of a field of wild poppy plants.

The poppies were in various stages of development. The thick green stalks were waist high and drooped heavily either with brightly colored orange and red blooms or white-yellow pods the size of a tennis ball that had yet to open and flower. These were what the boys were looking for.

"The tight pods are the ones Grandmother wants," Bryan explained. He took one in his hand and drawing his knife, made a thin slit down the side of a pod; a thick white, milky-looking substance oozed slowly through the slit. Bryan caught a drop on his knife tip and held it out for Willoughby to see.

"The milk of the poppy. Grandmother milks the pods for their extract and then dries the husks and grinds them fine. She says the poppies that grow here are very potent and make the finest powders and potions."

Willoughby didn't know much about plants and their chemical properties but he knew what his experience had been as far as pain went and knew he was looking at a powerful drug that had helped his recovery, but also one that could be highly addictive. If he was back at home right now he would be looking over his shoulder and waiting for police sirens.

Even though the top of the ridge was covered in plants it was late in the year, and the tight bulbs meeting Mattie's expectations were few and far between as the majority of the pods had already opened and flowered. It took most of the afternoon before Bryan's pack was full. They returned to the ruined tower and ate a late lunch in its shadow. Thick slices of Mattie's crusty bread spread with butter, strong white cheese and, as a special treat, she had wrapped up one of her delicious apple pies. It had suffered a bit from the journey but nonetheless made for a great way to finish off their lunch. They washed their repast down with pulls from the waterskin. Willoughby had just finished a long drink and was handing the bag back to Bryan when a vicious jolt slammed into his chest.

"Aauugggh!" Willoughby screamed as he stood up suddenly. The waterskin tumbled out of his hand to the ground. Willoughby clutched his chest with both hands and collapsed as Bryan quickly jumped up and caught him, preventing him from tumbling and possibly striking his head against the stone blocks.

"Will!" a confused and concerned Bryan shouted as he latched on to his friend. "Will! What is wrong?"

Willoughby slipped from Bryan's grasp and slid to his knees. Struggling for breath that came only in short, raspy gulps, he fought to speak and breathe at the same time. His hands clutched tightly at the front of his shirt where the wolf's fangs lay against his chest just under the fabric.

"B...Br...Bryan," Willoughby finally managed to gasp, "s... something is wrong."

"Will, don't try to speak. Try to get your breath first," Bryan implored. It took several moments but Willoughby was finally able to control his breathing. Bryan managed to get a bit of water down his throat which helped a bit.

"Can you speak now, Will? What happened? What is wrong?"

Willoughby, his face sickly white and eyes wide with shock, looked helplessly at his friend.

"What is it, Will? What is it?" a panicked Bryan pleaded desperately.

"Home, Bryan." Willoughby was finally able to force the words out. "Magic! It was strong. Very strong. Something is terribly wrong at home. Mattie and Quint are in trouble. We have to get back there, now!"

Chapter Thirty-One

Lord Fuggs brushed contentedly against Mattie's legs as she poured him a small saucer of milk laced with thick cream, a treat he did not often get, but Mattie knew she was going to leave her good friend behind for a while and a bit of indulgence wouldn't hurt him.

"I told you why we needed to go" she said as she put the saucer down. A normal cat would have started feasting on the treat immediately but Lord Fuggs looked up at Mattie with his big yellow eyes, the narrow slits of his jet black pupils gleamed back at her. Mattie got down on her knees and leaned forward onto her elbows. She and the cat were eye to eye.

"Yes, it is going to be some time before we are able to return and no, you cannot go with us. Who will keep the mice and rats from our pantry if you do not stay here? We must seek Theron; he is the only one who may be able to help young Will."

The cat blinked several times and tilted his head slightly. "You remember Theron, don't you my friend?" Mattie asked. "It has been many years since he came to visit, and no, I do not believe he perished as so many others do."

Lord Fuggs blinked again, closed his eyes, and pushed his fuzzy head against Mattie's. She closed her eyes and the two stayed forehead to forehead for several moments. Mattie finally pulled away and petted him gently.

"Aye, it will be dangerous my friend and I would be welcome of your company to warn us of danger but the task you are charged with here is an important one. I know you understand." The cat looked at her once more with his piercing eyes and then turned to his treat. The conversation was over.

Mattie and Quint had been working since Bryan and Will had left that morning, taking care of small chores needing to be done before they started their journey. Quint would deliver perishable foodstuffs and livestock to the Marins early the next morning and then the family would be off. Mattie stepped out on the porch from the kitchen and hollered across the yard towards his blacksmith shop.

"Quint! How about a bite to hold you 'til supper?"

The big man stuck his head out the open window of the smithy. "Aye, Mattie, I'll be right in."

She expected nothing less. Her oversized husband and food were never ones to shy from each other's company. She had begun to slice bread, cheese, and apples and was thinking about what to fix for supper when she stopped suddenly. Mattie set the knife down and paused, trying to make sure it wasn't something else, but the feeling manifested itself again. There was something wrong. She could feel it coming from the village. She had just reached the door when she heard the bells start to ring.

Quint was coming across the yard as Mattie stepped out onto the porch. They never spoke but both looked to the south towards Lightwood. The sound of the bells was loud and strong coming across the open fields.

"Wolves?" Mattie finally spoke.

"Not likely," Quint replied, worry lines mapping his worn face. "They wouldna' come raiding stock this time of year. They have been feeding well all summer. They save their thievin' for winter and hard times. Bandits would be more to my guess. See to the house and be ready, Mattie. I'll fetch my weapons." The bells rang on.

Mattie ran back inside the house and began to close the heavy wooden shutters on all of the windows. Once shut and barred with the stout wooden crosspiece they would not open from the outside until they were splintered into kindling, and a man who labored long at that endeavor would leave himself open and vulnerable.

As Mattie hustled about securing the windows, the sense of trouble and foreboding kept getting stronger by the moment. The feeling of something bad coming was as strong as she had ever felt, and her premonitions were never wrong. There was something she had to do to prepare for the worst. She ran to her knitting table and pulled a rough sheet of parchment from a drawer, dipped her writing quill into the inkwell, and began writing furiously. When she was done, she rolled the parchment tightly and ran out the back door to the cold cellar. Once inside the cellar, crammed with a myriad of the foodstuffs needed to see them through the winter, she went to the back wall where a large shelf stood packed with sealed clay containers. Reaching behind a row of pickled pears, she pulled a concealed lever and the lower section of shelving swung easily open, revealing a small crawlway dug into the dirt at the back of the cellar.

Mattie didn't waste time lighting a lamp. While the crawlway was pitch black, she knew what she was looking for and her hands found it quickly enough. Quint had stashed Willoughby's belongings here when they thought Denton Prout was going to come nosing around. She felt for the flap and tucked the parchment roll under one of the tie downs. It wasn't much but it was the best she could hope for. Backing her way out of the crawl space, she pushed the shelf shut and was satisfied when she heard the solid "click" of the latch falling into place.

Quint was on the porch when she got back to the house, his stout longbow and quiver of arrows leaning against the wall. Beside them stood his shield and battle-ax which were nearly as tall as Mattie. His great sword was slung across his back and he had donned a hard leather hauberk. The bells were still ringing.

"Where is your chain mail, Quint? You don't know what's coming," Mattie asked as they kept their eyes glued to the horizon where the village lay.

"By a dragon's ass Mattie, you have been feeding me too damn much. It won't fit anymore."

Mattie was about to answer when suddenly the bells stopped.

The two looked at each other with the same question on their minds; was the stopping of the bells a good thing or a bad thing? The answer came soon enough.

"Mercy, oh mercy, Quint, look!"

He had seen what she was talking about as soon as she said it. On the horizon, over the tree line, two dark columns of smoke snaked their way into the sky. As they watched, the two columns were quickly joined by a third and then a fourth.

"Hell's hounds, Mattie, it looks as if someone has fired the village. I have to go see what has happened." He had grabbed his bow and quiver when Mattie felt something else.

"Hold, Quint," she said, grabbing his thick arm. "A single horse coming fast this way."

It wasn't long before the horse appeared at the end of the lane, kicking up clouds of red dust as it galloped hard towards them.

"It's Bonnie," Quint said, recognizing the big bay, "but it isn't Pel who rides her." It took a few moments before Mattie and Quint were able to identify the riders, for there were two of them who were pushing the horse as hard as she could go down the dirt lane.

"Mercy, Quint! It's Pel's boys, Tristan and Ben!"

The horse thundered into the yard in a cloud of dust. Quint grabbed the reins of the big bay. "Whoa Bonnie, whoa girl," he said, trying to calm the excited mare. The two boys slid down onto the ground. Tristan had a longbow and quiver of arrows across his back and a troubled look on his face. Ben, the younger one, his eyes swollen and face smudged with tear stains, ran to Mattie as she approached and fell into her arms.

"Tristan, the bells," Quint asked the older boy. "What is wrong in the village?"

"I...I don't know exactly what has happened, Quint," Tristan stammered.

"Father, Ben, and I were putting in some wood when we heard the bells ringing. Father was getting ready to go into the village and see to the alarm when Tad Tofter came riding in. He got to the yard and fell off his horse." Tristan had a look of terror on his face and was nearly ready to burst into tears like his younger brother. Quint put his big hands gently on the boy's shoulders.

"Settle yourself, Tristan. You are safe now. Be a strong lad and tell me the rest."

"It was horrible, Quint," Tristan started. "Tad's head was split open and half the side of his face was gone. We did what we could for him but his wounds were bad. He died in Father's arms."

"What did he say, son?" Quint urged the distraught boy gently. "Was Tad able to say anything about what was going on?"

Tristan nodded his head. "Riders. Riders came into the village. They went to Bertie's Ale House and started pushing people around and asking questions. Tad said Bertie's husband Marl told them to leave and one of the strangers pulled out a longsword and killed him right there on the spot. They started tearing the place apart. Tad and some of the men fought back and someone started ringing the bells. Father told Mum to take Little Mattie and hide in the forest and sent me and Ben here to warn you. Father took Tad's horse and rode towards the village."

Quint looked at Mattie. "What do you make of this?"

Mattie had both her arms wrapped tightly around young Ben who still had his head buried in her chest. "It can't be bandits, Quint. There is something else afoot but I know not what it is. Look!" She pointed to the horizon again. More columns of smoke had joined the others.

Tristan stammered again. "Tad said something else before he died, Quint. He said there was a tall man in charge asking questions about you and Mattie and they're not all strangers. Tad said the Prouts rode with them."

Quint cursed and was about to say something when Mattie cut him short. "Riders. A lot of them and coming this way."

Quint grabbed Tristan by both his shoulders and looked him in the eye. "I need you to be strong, son. Go now. Take Ben into the woods. Stay away from here until you know trouble has passed."

But Tristan shook his head vehemently. "No, Quint," he countered, stepping out of the big man's grasp. "I am a good hand with a bow and am man enough not to run at the sign of a fight. You and Mattie cannot stand alone against so many. Let me help."

Quint looked at Mattie who shrugged her shoulders and reluctantly nodded her answer. "There is no time for the boys to get into the woods without being seen."

Quint turned back to Tristan. "Very well, son. Your father would be proud of you. Take Ben, go into the barn and get to the loft. Keep the loft doors shut and stay quiet. If trouble comes, use your bow but do not stay and fight if things go bad. You must take your brother and escape to the woods. Make your way back and find your mother and sister. Do you understand?"

Tristan nodded.

"I'll be brave, too," Ben said as he pulled away from Mattie.

"I know you will, Ben," she said as she hugged him close one last time. "Your father will be proud of both of you. Now get to the barn. We do not have much time."

The boys sprinted away as Quint gave Bonnie a hard slap on the rump. She took off at a gallop across the yard towards the woods. The riders were riding hard down the lane towards them. When Quint was sure Ben and Tristan had reached the barn, he tipped his head towards the house.

"On the porch Mattie. We will stand there."

The big man positioned himself on the porch with Mattie at his side. He stuck several arrows into the wood of the bench next to him. Nocking one of the deadly three-foot shafts to his bow, he stood ready.

"They are not here just to ask questions, Quint," Mattie spoke softly to her husband as the two stood quietly watching the approaching riders, now halfway down the lane. "I think this has something to do with Bryan. Thank the stars he and Will are not here."

Quint nodded solemnly as he watched. "There are too many of them for the two of us Mattie. Tristan may account for a couple but the odds are not good. I count fifteen and some of them ride like soldiers. I see those miserable Prouts. If blades are drawn and arrows fly I will make sure that Denton will not live to try out his new job as tax collector."

"We will give them more than they bargained for my husband. I have some tricks that may surprise. But there are two in the group who can wield magic. I can smell it. The two smaller men in black. Be wary of them."

She reached up and pulled at his arm. When he looked down at her, she whispered softly, "I love you, Quint."

He smiled wearily, bent over, and kissed her. "I love you too, Mattie."

The riders pulled their mounts up directly in front of the porch in a cloud of red dust, spreading out in a line facing the cottage. Mattie and Quint stood silently. Out of the corner of his eye Quint saw the loft door open slightly; Tristan was giving himself some shooting room. As much as he admired the lad's grit, he immediately regretted allowing the boys to stay in the barn.

Though he had long been retired, Quint Ironhand had been a professional soldier, and a very good one, for most of his life. Honed and sharp as ever, his thought process had already begun to ready himself for the coming battle. Scanning the line drawn in front of the house, he mentally plotted his targets according to what he thought their potential might be. The Prouts—only two of them, Denton and one of his hulking sons—he discounted as not being much of a concern at the onset. The old man had a rusty-looking sword strapped to his side but Quint did not believe a man who would not take care of his weapon knew how to use it, so he discounted the older Prout as being of little consequence in the opening phases of the fight. The son, an ugly, pimple faced brute, had nothing but a wooden cudgel slipped into his waistband. Quint thought it was Dylan but he wasn't sure. A bully of a man-child who shied away from a fair fight, he would have to get close to use the club, and Quint had no intention of allowing that to happen.

Two slight men in black were in the center of the line—Torbekians by the look of them, their long robes hiding any weapons they might have. While their physical stature might fool some into looking past them in a fight, Quint had no such inclinations. These were the ones Mattie warned him about, and while he knew she had something up her sleeve, he hoped she would be strong enough to counter the two of them.

Next to the Torbekians, in line to the left, was a pudgy bald man, sweating profusely, and looking terribly uncomfortable. He struggled to maintain control of his horse, appeared to be unarmed, and looked totally out of place. Quint could only wonder as to what purpose this man might serve and counted him out immediately as any kind of a threat.

But that still left ten that were professional soldiers and hard men by the look of them, wearing light chain mail and longswords strapped across their backs. Three carried crossbows with loaded bolts; these would be dangerous in the initial attack when it came, but Quint was quick to spot a flaw in their preparedness, a casual lapse that would cost them dearly. They rested the stocks of the crossbows against their thighs, bolts pointing to the sky; the position of men who were taking their foes for granted. This would cost them precious time before they could bring the weapons to their shoulders, aim and shoot. While Quint was getting on in years, his skills as a bowman were still far better than most men. If Tristan could understand enough to take out one of them it would help, but which would he choose? If they by chance were to take on the same man it would leave at least two free to get off a shot. Quint determined Tristan would probably take the one on the far left. The man was almost straight away from the loft door and would present the boy his best target. One for the boy and two for him—good odds. Once they eliminated the crossbows, things would get interesting.

Quint Ironhand had been in countless situations like this before and was mentally and physically prepared for the sheer brutality of mortal combat. Most of the soldiers facing him were young men and he could see the nervousness in their eyes and the twitching of their hands, sure signs of anxiety. These men would hesitate before closing with him and though the numbers were in their favor, surprise, determination, and ferocity could reduce what appeared

560

to be overwhelming odds, and by choosing the elevated porch on which to make his stand, he had given himself a tactical advantage to boot. For them to get at him with their blades they would have to come up the three steps of the porch or try to scramble up and over the railing. Quint had further reduced the odds by narrowing the field of battle. It was the best he could do, and he hoped for all of their sake it would be enough.

A tall man with a well-trimmed beard, sitting straight in his saddle, spurred his horse slightly ahead of the others. Quint looked him over carefully, taking in the well-kept appearance of his equipment and weapons and the calm of his demeanor. His hands did not shake nor his eyes twitch with nervousness. *This will be the dangerous one,* Quint thought to himself as he waited for the man to speak.

"You are Quint and Mattie Ironhand?" the man demanded.

Quint nodded slightly. "I think you know who we are. It appears you have come here for a reason though what that might be I know not. But my wife and I do not take kindly to armed men on our doorstep so why don't you save yourself some trouble and head on back from whence you came."

"Is that a threat old man?" The tall stranger leaned forward in his saddle and countered Quint's steely gaze with an equal one of his own.

"In case you can't count, you are severely outnumbered and your wife looks as if she would do what? Throw her knitting needles at us?" Several of the men laughed nervously at the man's joke. The forced laughter of men afraid to die.

"Oh, she may not be much to look at, but if she wanted to throw that knitting needle she could pierce your eye and bury its point in your brain before you could spit," Quint answered.

"Watch out for the old woman, Cap'n Einer," Denton Prout spoke up. "She's a witch that one is."

"Shut up, Prout, you idiot," the tall man shouted back. "I'll handle this."

A slight hint of recognition at the name caught Quint's attention. "Einer? Didn't I know you when you were a green recruit in the king's service?"

The man nodded. "My first weapons master you were, and you taught me well. But that was a long time ago."

Mattie had been quiet, concentrating on controlling and readying her talents for when the time came, content to let Quint do the talking and making the men forget about her, but she now spoke up.

"Why would the king's own come this far from Tiernon to bother an old man and woman? And since when do the king's own kill and burn poor village folk?"

"Mind your tongue old woman." The voice came from one of the two Torbekians who spurred his horse up beside Captain Einer's. Both Mattie and Quint could see the two were identical twins. Both wore matching dark robes and their inky black hair and beards were cut and trimmed exactly the same. With small, beady eyes and noses that had a slight hook to them, they looked like a pair of crows.

"In case you haven't heard, Edmond is dead. Rule of this country is now in the hands of First Council Daemon Rhue and we ride on his orders," the other of the small dark men added.

"And just what might those orders be Silas…or be you Sam'el?" Mattie asked. The brows of the two raised in surprise at the mention of their names.

"Oh yes, I know who you are but I don't know which is which. Not that it matters; one pile of Torbekian shit looks and smells just like the other to me and my husband."

Snorts of laughter came from the rest of the line but it was choked off immediately when the black robed men turned to mark the laughers. When the laughter had quieted, they turned their steely dark eyes back towards Mattie.

"You think we don't know what you are, crone?" one of the men hissed. He turned to the tall man on the horse next to him.

"Prout was not wrong, Captain Einer. This woman is a witch and by Lord Rhue's law, she is guilty of a crime against the crown. For that alone her life is forfeit."

562

"This conversation has gone on long enough, Einer," Quint broke in. "I knew you to be a good man and a better soldier once but it seems things have changed much since my years in the king's service were finished. Why have you come here?"

Silas, or maybe it was Sam'el, didn't give the captain a chance to answer Quint's question. "Where are the two boys who live here with you?"

"They are not here at the moment and what business could you have with my two boys?" Mattie challenged.

"I will ask the questions here, witch. Where are the boys?" Sam'el, or was it Silas, growled at Mattie. But before she could answer, hell broke loose.

"Captain Einer!" One of the men on the end of the line stood up in his stirrups and pointed. "Movement behind us in the loft!"

"Kill them!" Captain Einer screamed. Men began to move but some didn't move fast enough. The man on the end of the line had caught movement by Tristan in the door of the loft and had shouted the warning but it served the wrong purpose. Of the three crossbowmen two looked immediately in the direction the man pointed. The one who didn't sprouted a nasty barbed shaft two feet out the back of his head before he could even think about raising his crossbow. The man toppled straight backward off his horse. In the split second it took the rest of the men to realize the fight was on and start to draw their weapons, a fireball exploded in the face of the Torbekian who had been asking the questions, lifting him out of his saddle and dumping him into the dirt of the yard where he lay motionless.

In the blink of an eye, Mattie threw two more fireballs into the line of men and horses. Sparks and fire showered everywhere. Panic more than injury was what she had been looking for and her effort was rewarded. Chaos reigned as horses screamed, reared, and slammed into each other. Men cursed and shouted as they fought to calm the frightened animals.

The two remaining crossbowmen managed to control their mounts but one quickly joined his friend dead on the ground as

Quint's second shaft punched a hole in the light chainmail and ripped through the man's heart.

The battle line was now in complete disarray as men fought to control horses spooked by the fireballs and draw their weapons at the same time. Though untouched and uninjured, the fat, bald man squealed like a wounded pig as his horse reared and took off on a dead run down the lane, the man hanging on for dear life. Mattie had her arm back and another ball of fire in her palm ready to add to the confusion when a powerful blast of air caught her and slammed her back with a vicious thud into the kitchen door. She landed in a limp heap.

"Mattie!" Quint screamed. It had been the other Torbekian who had flung the blast of air at Mattie. Quint already had another arrow nocked and he let fly towards the dark-skinned man. With the short distance between them, he should have been able to shoot a fly off the end of the man's hooked nose but the Torbekian made a slight flip with his hand and the arrow sailed off like it had struck a stone wall. Magic.

"Kill him! Kill him, you idiots!" the man screamed.

"Four of you to the barn!" Captain Einer shouted orders as he struggled to control his horse. "The boys are in the barn! Get them!"

Quint took another quick look at Mattie; she had not stirred. He grabbed another arrow but now had to be concerned with the men who had managed to dismount. Out of the corner of his eye, he caught the third crossbowman leveling his weapon and taking aim. Quint had taken an arrow in battle before and as a rule, a man never saw the bolt that felled him, but the one locked into the crossbow's chamber loomed large and deadly as Quint prepared for the worst. But instead of releasing the bolt, the man jerked upright, staring stupidly at a foot of Tristan's arrow protruding from his chest. As he started to topple from his horse, he dropped the tip of his crossbow and pulled the trigger, shooting his own mount in the back of the neck.

Quint had run out of time for another clear shot with his bow as two men with drawn swords charged the steps. He let the shaft fly without aiming but luck was with him, at least for a brief moment. The result was something he had despised doing in all the battles he had ever fought, but in the heat of conflict a man needed every advantage, especially when the odds were against him. His unguided arrow buried itself deep in the neck of the poor horse of Silas, or Sam'el, whichever had still been mounted. The beast screamed horribly and reared, adding its cries of misery to that of the crossbowman's mount. The Torbekian fought to stay in the saddle but when the screaming horse reared the second time, it toppled over backward, landing in a thrashing heap with the man underneath. Silas and Sam'el were at least for now, out of service.

Quint reached behind his shoulder and swung the five-foot great sword free. As he focused on his attackers coming up the steps, he saw four of the men had reached the barn door. He cursed as he realized Tristan and Ben now had little chance for escape, but the older boy quickly showed he was still a force to be reckoned with as he stepped into the doorway of the loft and shot the last man charging the barn from almost directly above. The man flopped and flailed like a headless chicken in the dirt of the barnyard.

There was little time for Quint to worry about the situation of Tristan and Ben as the first two men reached the porch, but they had not mounted the top step when they met six and a half feet of trained swordsman with five feet of slashing death in his hands.

"Come get some, you bloody whore's sons!" Quint screamed as he slashed downward and met the first soldier's blade in mid stroke. The attacker was no small man but Quint had the power of two normal men and a defensive height advantage to boot. The force of his strike cause the man's sword arm to snap like a piece of dry kindling and fold, causing his own blade to slice into his neck just above his chainmail.

The piteous wails of men screaming as razor-sharp steel cut deep into flesh and bone was something Quint had never become used to in all his years as a soldier. While some could take a spear driving into their guts or a battle-ax severing an arm at the shoulder with a grunt and a curse, Quint knew others, no matter how brave or bold they portrayed themselves to be, who bawled like a two-year-old in a hornet's nest when wounded. The man with the broken arm and his own blade buried in his neck was a screamer, collapsing at the foot of the porch stairs with a high-pitched wail announcing his agony to the world. A red mist sprayed into the air from a severed neck artery.

The second man tried to seize the brief advantage Quint's blow to the other had created. He reached the top of the stairs and slashed at the big man's head, but with countless hours of melee combat training under his belt, Quint was able to turn the man's blow. Strike, parry, counterstrike. A slight flick of his hands and Quint's blade met his attacker's and redirected the strike to the side. As the man's momentum carried him forward and down Quint stomped his leg just above the ankle. The bone snapped with a crack that could be heard above the din of chaos and the man added his scream to his partner's, but only for a brief moment. Blood, bone bits, and brains splattered the porch as Quint's heavy blade split the man's head down to his collarbone.

The odds had narrowed quite a bit since the fray had started but there was no time for taking count, and Quint barely turned in time to block a savage and powerful blow from Captain Einer. As big and as strong as Quint was, the younger man was in his prime and a well-trained swordsman to boot. The blow forced the older man back and down onto one knee in a defensive posture as Einer rained a flurry of strikes down on him. Sparks flew and the blades sang a song of death as they rang with every stroke.

Quint was finally able block one of Einer's strikes and slide his blade down the length of the Captain's until they were crossed at the hand guards. Einer had the height advantage with Quint on one knee but he misjudged the old man's power. It was strength against strength as the two pushed against each other trying to gain the advantage. Slowly Quint was able to force the younger man back until he regained his feet.

With a grunt and a heave Quint's raw strength prevailed; he broke the deadlock and shoved the captain back. Einer would have been fine and still in a position to fight had he not stumbled over the man whose head had been split like an overripe melon. He went down on his back hard, his sword flying from his grasp and off the porch. Quint raised his great sword high with both hands for the killing stroke when a crossbow bolt punched deep into his right side just below his armpit.

Quint grunted in pain and shock as the shaft buried itself nearly to the fletching. His arms dropped and he turned slightly to the right side, trying to see where he had been hit when the second bolt pierced the hard leather of his hauberk just below the first one. His sword clattered out of his hands as he staggered, severely wounded, against the wall of his house.

"Shoot him again, you fools!" Einer screamed to the Prouts as he rolled off the porch and to the ground where he was able to pick up his sword. Denton and his son had been unwilling to join the hand to hand fray but had not passed on the opportunity to snatch up the crossbows. They had waited as Quint and Captain Einer had struggled but when the big man gained the advantage and had thrown Einer down, they had their opening. Even an untrained crossbowman could hit such a big target at such a short distance.

"Quint, into the house!" Mattie grabbed him by the back of his trousers and yanked him as hard as she could towards the kitchen door. Blood streamed down her face from a nasty gash in her scalp but it never slowed her a bit as she pushed him through the open door, where he collapsed in a heap. He hadn't quite fallen far enough into the kitchen for her to get the door shut and she was struggling to lift one of his heavy legs and push it inside when a bolt buried itself into the door jamb just a hair's width from her head. Denton Prout had gotten another shot off and his son was about to let his bolt fly but Mattie was quicker. A ball of fire appeared and flashed from her hand in a heartbeat and caught the younger Prout square between his wide eyes. He screamed as his eyes and face were seared with white hot flame.

"Help me, Quint!" Mattie pleaded as she struggled to get his prostrate form far enough into the house to get the door closed.

With a groan, he managed to roll out of the way. Mattie was able to get the heavy door shut and drop the wooden cross arm into place.

"Quint, oh Quint," Mattie cried softly as she dropped to her knees and cradled the big man's head in her lap. Blood from her wound dripped onto his face. He opened his eyes and managed to give her a weak smile.

"Mattie, you're hurt," he whispered.

"Just banged my head hard on the wall when that weaselly bastard caught me with a spell," she answered as she wiped her blood off of him with a corner of her dress. "I should have been a mite quicker."

Quint winced and groaned as a wave of pain shuddered through him. "You have to get out of here, Mattie. Leave me and get out through the tunnel. Find the boys and get to Theron."

"No, Quint, I can't leave you. We are not done for yet. We gave the bastards a good thrashing and they will have a hard time getting at us through these walls. Mayhap Pel and some of the village folk will ride to us if we can hold out for a while."

Quint groaned and grimaced as pain seared through him. "Get me some of your potion, Mattie; make it strong."

"I will, my husband. Hold on. I have to see what they are up to outside." She gently laid Quint's head down on the floor and moved swiftly to one of the shuttered windows. She pulled back a slat covering an arrow slit and peered through.

"What are they doing?" Quint moaned.

Mattie looked through the crack for a moment and then pulled her head away. There were tears in her eyes. "Mercy, Quint, they have fired the barn! The bastards have fired the barn. Oh, Tristan and Ben!"

Quint cursed loudly and heaved himself up to a sitting position. Sweat poured down his forehead as wave after wave of pain shot through him. "Get me that potion, Mattie! Hurry! I have to get to my feet."

"Quint, you can't," Mattie pleaded. "The more you move, the more those bolts will work to kill you. I have to get them out."

"Mattie, listen to me." Quint gasped for breath. "We are going to be dead anyway if we don't do something quick. Do you think they are going to just go away and leave us be? Get me that potion so I can at least stand on my feet when they come."

Mattie did as Quint asked and fetched a stoppered vial from her medicinal cupboard. The big man drained it in one gulp. The effect of the powerful drug was almost immediate.

"Help me get up, Mattie." With great effort, they managed to get Quint to his feet. He leaned his massive frame against the bolted door and closed his eyes. Blood dripped to the floor from inside his leather hauberk. The powerful painkiller was working but every effort was still excruciating.

"Look to the yard and tell me what they are doing now. Is there any sign of Tristan and Ben?"

Mattie returned to the crack. They could now smell the smoke and feel the heat as the barn became totally engulfed. When she turned back to Quint, she shook her head.

"Mattie," he groaned, "we can only hope they were able to escape to the woods. Tristan is a smart lad. They could have gotten out."

"There are still seven of them out there, Quint," Mattie said. "The Prout bully isn't so tough now. He is still down with Denton tending to him. With any luck my little fireball will have burned his miserable eyes out. I don't think he will be coming for anymore soon. That leaves six. Those Torbekian pigs are on their feet though and they both have magic as strong as mine, Quint."

The heavy wooden kitchen door shuddered with a blow from the outside, quickly followed by another. They were using Quint's battle-ax, trying to chop through.

"Get me something to fight with, Mattie. I was an idiot for not stockpiling some weapons inside. Anything sharp. If they think they can come through the door without paying the price they will be mistaken."

Mattie quickly had an array of kitchen utensils on the table within Quint's reach. There were no longswords or battle-axes but a wicked meat cleaver and an assortment of sharp knives would take their toll on anyone trying to get past the big man even as wounded as he was. Quint nodded and, despite the pain, he cracked a smile. Mattie was holding a pair of knitting needles in her hands.

She gave him a wry smile in return. "They might think you were making a joke but you and I know better don't we?"

"With your magic and those knitting needles I wouldn't bet against you in a fight, Mattie." His big smile quickly was replaced by a grimace of pain.

"Do you think they will try to burn us out, Quint?" Mattie questioned as she went back to her spy hole. The door shuddered with more blows.

"The house will not catch easily, Mattie. Bryan and I didn't work our tails off for nothing hauling the slate from the quarry to put on the roof. The walls and timbers will eventually fire, but not quickly. Mayhap help will come before it does."

Mattie looked at her wounded husband; her face held nothing back. Their eyes met and the message they passed was clear; they were in dire straits and they both knew it.

"What about our boys, Quint? What will become of Bryan and poor Will?"

"They will survive, Mattie. My heart feels it." Quint struggled to speak, as strong as Mattie's medicine was it couldn't help but lose ground against the severity of his wounds. "You left them a message, didn't you?"

Mattie nodded sadly. "I did not have time to explain much. There will be so many questions Bryan will have. It was always our plan to set him down and tell him of his father, Quint. Why did we wait?"

"We did what we thought was right, Mattie, but fate has taken it out of our hands now. We raised him to be a good man. If he ever fulfills his destiny he will be a good king and the heavens know this country will need one to release the grasp Rhue has on it." Quint gasped as a jolt of pain slipped past the effects of Mattie's potion and surged through his body. "I am sorry I will not be here to help him."

Mattie was about to say something when shouts were heard

from their attackers in the yard. She quickly put her eye to the crack to see what was happening. The hammering on the door had stopped.

"Quint! Riders coming from the village. Help is on the way! Hang on my husband." She reached out, grabbed his huge hand in her tiny one and gave him a reassuring smile.

"You will not die if I have anything to do about it."

Quint forced a smile of his own around the pain. "You are a good woman, Mattie. Did I ever tell you that?"

Mattie squeezed his hand. "Not near enough times you big—"

They both felt it at the same time—a palpable change in the air inside the house. Mattie's eyes widened suddenly as she realized what was happening. Desperately she tried to pull her husband towards her.

"Quint! Magic! Away from the door!"

Quint propelled his wounded body towards her as the air sucked from out of the room with a loud hiss. Dishes were pulled from the shelves and the ashes in the fireplace swirled out into a thick sooty cloud around them. Mattie hugged her tiny body tight to the big man's frame as the whole front of the house imploded. In a heartbeat, Mattie and Quint's world evaporated.

CHAPTER THIRTY-TWO

ARTEMIS THORYL PUSHED BACK THE FLAP OF his tent and stepped into the hot embrace of the sun. Even at midmorning the heat had already pushed back any remnants of the early coolness and another hot, dry day was well underway. He had come to know little else during his two years in the parched and barren land men had aptly named The Waste. But this was not just another day like so many he had spent; today his heavy brow knotted with worry.

Around him the camp was a flurry of action as the Arturan army prepared to move towards battle. He had lost track of the number of days of forced march in blistering heat that it had taken his army to get to this point, close enough to the Kasseri Pass they could reach it with one more push. But yesterday they had been stopped short of their goal by the appearance of their Torbekian liaison, Tae Denron, with orders from General Ortair to hold fast, make camp, and wait for further orders.

Artemis Thoryl had been relieved that his troops would be able to rest for whatever lay ahead; the march across this hard and desolate wasteland had taken its toll on men and animals both, but any thought of prolonged recovery had been short-lived. This morning just after breakfast, Denron had returned in great excitement with a new set of orders. The rebel forces under Jenga Batu had, during the early hours before dawn, attacked and overrun the forward positions of the Torbekian army stretched out along the road coming down out of the pass. Denron reported heavy and fierce fighting and the outcome of the battle was in serious jeopardy. A forced march by the Arturans was desperately needed to attack the rebel flank and keep them from being reinforced by more troops coming out of the pass from their mountain strongholds.

Though it was the event he had been hoping for, for over two long years, Artemis Thoryl couldn't ignore the churning anxiety in his stomach. It was not fear of conflict; he was too much an old warhorse to allow that to affect him. It was something more, something intangible he couldn't put a finger to, but he felt it strong nonetheless.

"I don't like this one bit, my friend," he said to the smaller man who had stepped out of the tent and now stood beside him. "What do you think?"

"A coincidence of major proportions I would have to say, General," Bronsen answered as he handed the big man his battle helm. "A man couldn't have planned it this way if he had all the time in the world. We arrive at our last camp before the pass and the rebels pick the very next day to come down from the safety of their mountains and attack. I find it strange but if the Uthans have finally decided to do battle as we have so long hoped, will this not be for our benefit? If we can defeat them decisively there will be no need to continue this charade. We will be free to go home, will we not?"

"That would be logical Bronsen, but since when has logic played any part in what we have done in the time we have been here? And this flies in the face of any military strategy." The general shook his head. "I have to ask myself, why now? For two years we have chased these rebels like a fox chases a rabbit and then the rabbit suddenly decides to turn and fight? Think about it, my friend. Jenga Batu has to know he cannot face the combined weight of both the Arturan and Torbekian forces, and he has to worry about El'nin and the Dazorian army coming at his rear if he has truly come down out of the pass. How many thousands do you think he could have gathered from what you know? Three, four, five at the most? Though we can only field 60 percent of our force, the combined strength of us and the Torbekians will be at least twenty thousand. Add ten thousand Dazorians to that number and Batu has no hope of victory. Does he intend on bringing his army down out of the mountains just to be slaughtered? This makes no sense Bronsen, no sense at all."

The smaller man was buckling a short sword around his waist, but unlike the general, he wore no armor or battle helm at all. Bronsen was well trained in the art of war but speed and agility were his strengths and he would not allow heavy encumbrances to hinder him in the heat of battle.

"A feint sire?" Bronson questioned. "Maybe Batu is using this to draw us in. If he stays within the confines of the pass, we cannot bring our full weight to bear against his force. Calvary will be useless and if he lures us into the canyon his archers positioned in the cliffs could pick us off easily."

Artemis Thoryl nodded. "That thought has crossed my mind my friend, but I cannot believe Batu would think we would allow ourselves to be drawn in like that. He cannot remain engaged with the Torbekians if he knows we will be coming in force to block his route back to the pass. I do not think he would expose himself to being trapped in the open."

Before Bronsen could comment further, a breathless orderly ran up to them. He saluted the general with a slap of his right hand across his chest. "General Thoryl. Commander Rand says the army is assembled and stands ready to march. He awaits your orders, sir."

Artemis Thoryl nodded. "Tell Commander Rand I will be there shortly." When the orderly had turned and gone, he spoke again to Bronsen. "Captain Berne and my son are away?"

"Yes, sire," the smaller man nodded, "but it was just as you thought. I had to make sure Kenner understood it was an order and not a request. He was not a happy man being sent away General. He is, after all, a soldier who takes after his father. To go the other way while his comrades march towards battle was something he did not stomach well."

"I expected nothing less, my friend. But my heart tells me that this battle we march to is the beginning of something, not the end. Men like Captain Berne, Kenner, and Kellen may be the ones who have to pick up the pieces if this goes bad."

"Surely you do not expect to lose this battle, General! In all of my years by your side I have never heard you speak such. Why now?"

Artemis Thoryl sighed and forced a half smile. "You are right again, my friend. I am talking nonsense. Forgive an old fool of a general who has seen one too many battles. Come, our army is waiting and we have a forced march to get to the pass. Let us hope Batu and his Uthans are still looking for a fight."

The two men strode purposefully down the slight rise through a city of tents now sitting empty. On a dusty expanse of flat desert, the Arturan army waited in formation for its leader. In front of the mass the men who would lead them into battle stepped forward to meet their general.

"General." Commander Oren Rand slapped his chest in salute as Artemis Thoryl approached. The seven commanders behind him slapped smart salutes of their own.

"Commanders," the general acknowledged.

"Marching orders, sir?" Oren Rand questioned.

"Send pickets out ahead on the flanks, Commander. Pick two of your best scout patrols and have them ride hard to the pass. Send one along the base of the mountains and have the other circle through the desert and come around from the west. Have them report back as soon as they can. I don't like going into this blind. The foot will go first and the archers will follow. Quick time, but don't march them into the ground. We have a long distance to cover in this blasted heat and I want them to be able to fight when they get there."

Oren Rand nodded. "Yes, sir. And the horse?"

"Both mounted regiments will follow the foot. If there is any sign of trouble before we get to the pass, have them split and flank the column. And I want the water wains to stay close, Oren; I don't want to get separated from our water. Have Quartermaster Kenda hold the rest of the supply train here in camp until we send for it. You have seen to the guard at hospital?"

"Yes, sir," the grizzled veteran nodded. "Some of tha mounted troops who unfortunately find themselves without horses will post tha guard at tha camp and hospital both, General."

He spit out a stream of brown tobacco juice onto the cracked dry earth. "Not that they liked it much. They been waitin' two years for this and to find themselves stuck in camp done got them a bit riled if'n you don't mind me sayin', sir."

Artemis Thoryl smiled. "Well Oren, that is the second time this morning I have heard that. But I guess they wouldn't be soldiers if they didn't find something to complain about." He turned to the rest of the commanders.

"My friends. If this is truly the battle we have been wanting then let us all do our duty as good Arturan soldiers. Let no man shirk his responsibility. Tell your troops that I have the utmost faith in them that they will perform their duty as true Arturans. We must march hard to get there by midafternoon. Our scout patrols should be able to give us an idea what to expect when we get to the pass. We will formulate a more detailed battle plan once we know more. Fight well and live. Now, let's move!"

The eight men lined in front of the general saluted smartly in unison, the echo of hard fists slapping dusty, leather hauberks reverberated across the desert morning. Horns blew, men shouted orders, and horses stomped and snorted in excitement as the Arturan army began its march towards the Kasseri Pass.

Artemis Thoryl watched silently from the rise as the columns of men and horse slowly began to move. His emotions stirred; pride for his men, but tempered with the sincere empathy and compassion he felt when ordering men to go and kill other men. But under those emotions still lay the uneasiness he had felt since the rat-faced Denron had ridden into camp early that morning. Something about this whole thing was not right.

"Your horse, sire."

He turned in surprise as his train of thought was broken. So engrossed in thought he had been, watching his army pass, that he was unaware Bronsen had come up from behind with their mounts.

"Thank you," the general said as he took the reins. His horse was a huge black gelding and the animal gave him an affectionate nudge on his shoulder.

"Whitestar, my friend." The big man scratched the white patch on the horse's long nose for which it had been aptly named. "How are you, this morning?" The animal responded with several vigorous nods of his head and stamps of his foot. "Ah, you know a fight is brewing, don't you, big fellow?"

"I took the liberty of not putting his battle harness on, sire," Bronsen said as he helped the general slip into his sword baldric.

"Right, as usual. You know how he much he hates that. White star has always preferred to fight free."

"Just as his master does," Bronsen chided with a slight air of sarcasm. "Are you sure you won't let me fetch your chain mail, General?"

"I'll be fine, Bronsen. Do you want me to die from heat exhaustion before I even get to the battlefield? And what about yourself? I have never seen you don so much as a helm in all these years."

"But I do not stand and fight like you do, General. Speed and movement take the place of brute strength in my case, and besides, that is not the point. My survival is not as critical as yours and I would be remiss in my duties if I did not at least remind you of such. My horse here likes to fight as her rider does, free and fast."

The big man clapped Bronsen on his shoulder and gave him an affectionate smile. "Well your survival is very critical for me, my friend, and in all these many years you have never been remiss in your duties, Bronsen, and I do not tell you often enough how I appreciate it."

"Nor do you need do so, sire. The fact that the one we have chosen to serve is alive at the end of the day is all the appreciation one of my order needs."

"Survival is the best both of us old soldiers can hope for," Artemis Thoryl replied as he turned and pulled himself into the saddle of Whitestar in one fluid motion. Bronsen followed his lead and nimbly leaped onto the back of the smaller roan.

The two men, one born to lead and the other trained from his youth to make sure the other survived to lead, watched silently for a long moment as the Arturan army, stretched out in columns on the plain in front of them, moved ahead towards harm's way. A great cloud of dust had started to rise as the trumpeters and drummers beat out a quick march tempo. Artemis Thoryl cursed silently at the orders that had kept his army from getting closer to the pass the day before as he would have preferred. It would now take a forced march of several hours to get there and his troops and horses would be fighting the strength sapping heat of the worst part of the day. While the general did not doubt his men's fighting spirit, he knew the energy it would take when they finally closed with the enemy in pitched battle. Not only was his enemy used to this heat, but they had not had day after day of forced marching to get to this point as the Arturans had. Artemis Thoryl did not like going into battle hamstrung. His thoughts were finally interrupted by Bronsen.

"May the fates grant us the good fortune to finish this today and return to our homeland, General. Fight well and live."

Artemis Thoryl nodded grimly. "To our homeland, and whatever we may find if we get back there. Luck ride with you, Bronsen. Fight well and live."

THE BLISTERING SUN WAS RIDING HIGH IN THE CLEAR SKY AS THE Arturan army marched to within sight of the great cleft in the mountains marking the entrance to what the locals called the Kasseri Pass. Great clouds of dust swirled as General Thoryl brought the head of the column to a halt. Off in the distance, through the waves of shimmering heat rising from the barren ground, telling dust clouds gave sign that men and horse of some sort were moving.

"By a whore's ass, it's still too blasted far away to make out anything." Irritated, Oren Rand spat a huge wad of tobacco juice onto the desert floor. "Where in the blazes are those scout parties? They should have been back a long time ago."

Artemis Thoryl shielded his eyes as he scanned the horizon, trying in vain to get a hint of what might be happening. "Have the water wains brought up, Commander Kane," the general ordered, squinting at the sun and then back at the dust on the horizon. "This may be the last chance for the men and horse to drink. Their throats will be dry enough soon, I think."

"Yes, sir." The man wheeled his horse about and set off at a hard gallop towards the back of the column.

"The fact that neither scout patrol has returned does not bode well, Oren. We have to find out what is going on. There is sign of much activity along the road into the pass but we can't move until we find if it is friend or foe."

"Aye, sir. I am as vexed about the scout parties as you. I'll send out another patrol, General." He was about to give orders when a shout from Bronsen cut him short.

"Riders coming hard from the west, General."

All eyes snapped to the direction Bronsen was pointing. Several riders could be seen at the front of the dust column kicked up by the hooves of horses coming at a hard pace.

"Our picket riders, General," Thad Ferrin shouted out. "At least some of them."

"Good eyes, Commander," Artemis Thoryl complimented. "I can see them now. It looks like Torbekians ride with them."

A dozen riders soon thundered out of the shimmering heat to a dusty halt in front of the general and his Commanders. There were four Arturans and eight others who bore the falcon crest of General Jaren Ortair—Commander in Chief of the Torbekian army—across the chests of the white desert robes the Torbekians were fond of wearing.

"General." A young Arturan soldier, his face caked with dry desert dust, nudged his horse ahead, followed closely by one of the Torbekians.

"Sub-General Jalut from General Ortair's staff, sire."

Artemis Thoryl nodded at the sub-general. "Someone get these men some water," he barked out before turning to the newcomer.

"General Jalut. It is good to see you again. What news do you bring us?"

The Torbekian gave a slight and very stiff bow of acknowledgement and cleared his throat for an obviously prepared speech.

"General Thoryl. Jaran Ortair, General of Supreme Overlord Kenric Taul's army and Commander in Chief of all the forces of the Tripartite Alliance sends you this message. The situation here is critical and my Lord Ortair can only wonder why it has taken so long for the Arturan army to arrive on the battlefield?"

"We came as soon as we could muster, General Jalut," Artemis Thoryl answered calmly. The other Arturan commanders winced at the obvious insult that had just been delivered but controlled their emotions, save for Oren Rand who spit a well-aimed stream of brown tobacco juice onto the hooves of the Torbekian's mount. An icy glare stabbed through the desert heat as the two eyed each other in ill concealed contempt. After an awkward moment, the Torbekian continued.

"General Thoryl, the rebel leader, Jenga Batu, launched a surprise attack from the pass in force this morning before the break of day, catching our forward positions off guard. Our outnumbered forces were quickly overwhelmed and slaughtered to the last man. This allowed Batu to attack our main camp without any advance warning. Our camp was overrun and our losses were heavy but we were finally able to halt the attack and form a defensive perimeter along the high ground of the wadi that lies just to the north. For over half a day now we have been repelling repeated attacks. Minister Denron was sent early this morning to bid you haste in coming to our aid. Did you not understand his message concerning the severity of the situation?"

Artemis Thoryl took a deep breath, trying to hold his seething anger in check. Two years his beloved army had wasted away in this forsaken land. Two years they had dealt with a supposed ally who treated them with no more respect than common peasants, even though the Arturans had twice defeated them in war. Two years of pestilence, disease, poor rations, bad water, and the death of hundreds of young Arturans, and now they were being berated for not responding fast enough? The tension was as thick as the hot air that suffocated the land with its smothering heat.

"General Jalut," he calmly spoke, forcing his rage under control, "if the situation is as dire as you say, then you waste precious time. We are here and ready to fight. Do you bring orders from General Ortair?"

The Torbekian nodded curtly and pulled a scroll from beneath his robes. He handed it to the young Arturan scout who passed it to Artemis Thoryl.

A scowl broke quickly onto the General's worn face. He looked up at the Torbekian and then back at the scroll, as if trying to determine whether he had read the note correctly the first time. Finally, he handed the note to Oren Rand. It didn't take long for the old veteran to announce his opinion of the orders to those gathered.

"Tha's a load of artox shit!" He spat angrily as he handed the scroll back. "There be no reason for that. An immediate attack on their flank in force will rout those vermin once and for all."

"Easy, Oren." Artemis Thoryl tried to calm his highly agitated commander.

"Surely you do not question the content of your orders, General Thoryl?" Jalut queried. "Like you said yourself, we cannot waste precious time."

Bronsen caught the look on the face of the man he had served for thirty years, and it was one for a moment he did not recognize. For the first time Artemis Thoryl appeared unsure of himself. Horses stamped and fidgeted in the heat as the gathering awaited his word. For once even Oren Rand was keeping his mouth shut, but the glare he was shooting the Torbekian was death in itself. After what seemed an eternity, General Thoryl spoke.

"What is the estimated strength of the rebel force, General Jalut?"

"We believe there are no less than four thousand attacking our positions now. While we have killed many, reinforcements keep pouring in from the pass. That is why it is imperative that an assault on the road happen as soon as possible. If you were to atta—"

Artemis Thoryl cut him off sharply. "You do not need to explain General Ortair's orders any further. The principle behind his battle plan is sound and we will execute immediately. Ride back and tell him such."

General Jalut nodded and with a flick of his wrist, his horse spun smartly and took off with a gallop with most of his party at his heels, leaving two of his men behind.

"Surely you can't mean to follow those orders General?" Oren Rand challenged gruffly. "That goes against all military doctrine to do such a thing."

"There will be no debate about military strategy, Commander Rand. We have our orders."

The tone of General Thoryl's voice was terse and the gathered did not miss the omission of the old veteran's first name. Artemis Thoryl's instincts had reasserted themselves and he would accept no challenge of the orders he had received, especially in front of the two Torbekians that had remained behind.

"Commanders Ferrin and Hardwyck, you will take your mounted regiments and ride to the mouth of the pass and halt any further attempts by the rebels to reinforce their main body. Commanders Palner and Darwin will take the archers to the north. You will follow General Jalut's men here and they will lead you to the high ground where you will join General Ortair's main force. Commander Kane, prepare the foot in standard battle order. I will lead them across the gap where we will hit the rebels on their flank. The Torbekians will counter attack when we relieve the pressure on their front. Let each man do their duty as good Arturan soldiers. Fight well and live."

In a flurry of movement and dust the commanders broke away and set about following their orders. When the others were away, Oren Rand nudged his horse next to the general's.

"My apology, General. I did not mean to question you in front of the men. I will not do so again."

Artemis Thoryl shook his head and forced a smile on his weary face. "There is no need for an apology my old friend. You simply spoke what my heart was also telling me. Splitting your force is never a good idea unless the situation is carefully considered. But we do not have such a luxury as time, Oren. Ortair's plan should work so let us be about it."

They turned their horses and rode hard back to where the Arturan foot soldiers were arrayed across the desert floor. A quick glance to the east showed that the Arturan mounted force had already crossed a good portion of the distance to the pass. To the north, the archers trotted in neat formation behind the two mounted Torbekian scouts.

Artemis Thoryl stood high in his stirrups and tried to see what lay across the gap of desert they would have to cross to get to the flank of the rebels, but he could still see only dust. He looked down the line of massed troops, fanned to both sides, each commander raised his arm signaling the readiness of his troops. It was time.

"Buglers! Sound quick march, double time!"

The horns blew and the Arturan foot surged ahead as one, starting their march towards battle. The sound of thousands of feet stamping the hardpan rose with the dust they created. Bronsen pulled his little roan up beside Whitestar as the mass of Arturans surged forward across the barren ground.

"I don't understand the blasted dust in front of us, sire," he yelled, trying to get his voice heard over the tramp of the foot soldiers. "The Uthans don't have enough mounted forces that I know of to create such."

"Mayhap a trick of the wind and this forsaken desert, Bronsen," the general replied. "We'll find out soon enough, my friend."

Onward the army surged forward, nearing the line of dust that marked the hidden enemy. But as they came within bowshot, the dust began to dissipate and men could at last be seen. Lined up in ragged formation along the dirt road the rebels waited, waving a varied assortment of weapons. Swords, spears, war clubs, and battle-axes, a few carried crossbows. They screamed in defiance as the disciplined ranks of Arturan foot soldiers surged towards them.

The experienced eyes of Artemis Thoryl darted up and down the line ahead of him, searching for the unexpected. His initial estimate of the rebel force was a thousand at best; not near enough to stop the massed force bearing down on them, but it appeared they were going to try anyway. Behind the ragged line, he was able to discern the source of dust that had so skillfully hid the rebel activity; men were scrambling to untie clumps of dry brush and dead limbs from behind horses. They had run these up and down the dirt road, using this crude method to stir up the huge dust clouds. A ruse to create the appearance of a much larger force. Simple, but effective. He respected their resourcefulness.

The closer the Arturans came, the louder the rebels screamed in challenge. Artemis Thoryl's combat instinct kicked in. He picked his target—a tight knot of Uthans directly in front of him. They jumped around in a crazed frenzy; a few had battle helms and he noted a varied assortment of chain mail and leather hauberks, some had nothing but traditional garb. He narrowed his focus, trying to hold Whitestar in check so they wouldn't reach the enemy line too far in front of his own troops. In the center of the mob a single Uthan stood, calmer than the rest, his battle-ax waiting. He was larger than the norm for the mountain tribes and his dark eyes were fixed on Artemis Thoryl in a deadly stare.

Pressing his knees tight to control Whitestar, the general reached behind his shoulder and swung the heavy great sword free. He would need both hands to wield the weapon but his battle horse was well trained and could sense the slightest variance of pressure from the general's knees that would dictate changes in direction or speed. Horse and man functioned as one. He nudged his mount faster, wanting to hit the line at full speed, not giving his foes a chance to react. Crossbow bolts began to zip past the Arturan front line as the big Uthan ahead tensed for his strike. Artemis Thoryl thought the man was going to swing the heavy ax at him but just as Whitestar reached the Uthan line, he saw the man give a quick glance downward—he was going to strike at the legs of Whitestar and hope to bring them both to the ground.

It was just enough edge to give Thoryl time to send the great horse the slightest signal. Just as the Uthan initiated his strike, the horse leaped. The man screamed as he swung but his ax found nothing but air as Whitestar sailed past. The great sword crashed down on the man's skull, cleaving it to his collarbone in a spray of blood, brains, and gore.

Whitestar landed on a huddle of bodies as the surprised men behind the Uthan went down under the massive horse. None of them managed so much as a passing strike as bones snapped and heads were crushed. Artemis Thoryl swung the great sword from side to side, hacking at limbs and heads and blocking strikes. White star was as much a trained warrior as the man who rode him and used his feet to stomp and kick. Around them the line of Arturans plowed headlong into the waiting rebels; the sound of battle rose to a crescendo as screams of rage and agony mixed in terrible harmony with the sound of steel on steel.

A crossbow bolt cut a deep furrow into Artemis Thoryl's leg, but he kept focused on his task. An open circle had formed around him as the Uthans had become painfully aware that to come anywhere close to the general and his mount was to invite death.

Vicious hand to hand combat raged up and down the line. The Uthans were outnumbered but made up for it with a ferocity and skill that surprised the Arturans. Never before had this evasive enemy stood toe to toe and fought such a battle.

Artemis Thoryl spotted Bronsen desperately fighting off an attempt by three Uthans to pull him from his mount; a bloody gash ran from his shoulder down his right arm. He nudged Whitestar ahead and hacked an arm from the shoulder of a man who was about to stab at Bronsen with a curved sword. Blood spurted and the man screamed; another could only gurgle his death knell as Bronsen's short sword slashed his throat. The third man let go of his hold on Bronsen's horse and bolted.

The Uthans were being pushed back by the sheer weight in numbers of the Arturan regiments. For a brief moment, the general and his steward found themselves in a gap from the fighting. "Are you all right?"

Bronsen nodded his head. "It's just a scratch. General, do you notice anything besides how well these rebels fight? Where are the

Torbekians?"

The words struck the general like a hard slap across his face. He had been so caught up in the heat of battle he had missed the obvious—nowhere on the battle line could he see a single Torbekian soldier.

"There is something wrong here, Bronsen!" he shouted as he scanned the chaotic fray around them. "I smell a trap!"

But before he could speak again the rebel forces broke. They turned almost as if by plan and began running towards a gap between two low-lying ridges. Before Artemis Thoryl could shout a command for his forces to hold, the Arturans, sensing victory, plunged ahead after the fleeing Uthans.

"We've got to stop them, Bronsen!" the general shouted as he spurred Whitestar ahead. They caught up with the rear of the pursuing Arturan forces just as the Uthans plunged in mass into the gap.

"Halt! Halt! I command you!" Artemis Thoryl and Bronsen were both screaming at the top of their lungs, but only those soldiers close to them held up at the commands, the main body surged ahead into the gap behind the fleeing Uthans. The two men charged ahead, nearly running down their own troops in an effort to get to the front of the Arturan line so they could stop their reckless momentum. The two had just reached the front of the gap between the ridges when the sky strangely darkened—the sun partially blotted by the deadly flight of thousands of arrows.

The victory cries of the Arturans turned quickly into screams of agony as arrows cut them down by the hundreds. Before Artemis Thoryl could slow his horse, Whitestar buckled at the knees, tumbling forward and throwing the big man over the top, catapulting him head first onto the rocky ground.

"General!" Bronsen screamed as he brought the roan to a stop. He grimaced as he saw Whitestar struggling to get up, the brave horse was pierced by no less than three arrows, two in his neck and a third half-buried in his rump. Miraculously, neither Bronsen nor the roan had been hit. As he nimbly leaped off the back of his horse and hit the ground running towards his fallen master, Bronsen couldn't help but notice the markings on the shafts of feathered death sticking out of the ground and out of the dying men around them; they were Torbekian arrows.

Just as he reached the unconscious general, the sky darkened again—another flight of arrows. He threw himself over the top of the prostrate man as death rained again down upon them. Bronsen grunted in pain as a deadly barbed shaft buried itself deep into the back of his leg. More men went down screaming, others shouted in frustrating anger, the Uthans forgotten as the confused Arturans tried to figure out from where this new attack was coming from.

Bronsen rolled off the general, a quick glance showed he was still unconscious but had not taken a hit. He grabbed the long end of the shaft protruding from the back of his leg and snapped it off close to the skin. The pain was excruciating with every movement of his leg but he forced himself to ignore it. There would be another flight of arrows soon enough and he had to get the general under some sort of cover. Just ahead of them, a small copse of thick brush and boulders offered a small bit of sanctuary—it was the best he could hope for.

"Help me with the general!" Bronsen shouted at an uninjured Arturan soldier who was standing dumbly looking at the carnage surrounding them. The man seemed to regain his senses when he heard Bronsen shouting at him and ran to help. They each grabbed the general by an arm and dragged him to the thicket where they pushed his limp body as far back against a big boulder as they could.

Bronsen was expecting a third shower of arrows when the unknown soldier pointed excitedly back towards the road where many of the Arturan soldiers were now trying to escape the deadly rain from the sky.

"Our calvary!" the man shouted and took off running. Bronsen could see long lines of horse-mounted troops thundering at full gallop towards them. Hurriedly he checked the general for vital signs. Thankfully the man was breathing and Bronsen could find no outward signs of anything being broken but there was a nasty contusion of his head. He would try to keep him out of harm's way until the mounted troops could arrive and regroup with the foot soldiers and find out what nasty business was at hand with the Torbekian archers. It couldn't have been a case of friendly fire. They had to know the Arturans would attack the flank of the Uthans. No, something else was up and to Bronsen it all pointed to treachery of the worst kind. He was checking the general again when a huge cry of alarm came from the troops who had retreated to the road.

One look answered many questions for Bronsen. The long lines of mounted horsemen had crashed directly into the milling Arturan foot soldiers now defending themselves from a new onslaught, for the mounted men were flying the falcon crest of General Ortair—the Arturans were being attacked by their former allies!

General Thoryl stirred and moaned but Bronsen could do little to help him, for out of the gap between the two ridges where they had previously been fleeing streamed the Uthans. They smashed into the disoriented groups of Arturans who had survived the rain of arrows only to find themselves fighting for their lives trapped between the Torbekian mounted troops and the Uthans. The fight was surging his way as small clumps of Arturans banded together in the desperate fighting.

"Bronsen!" A familiar gruff voice rang across the battlefield. A group of about twenty Arturans were running his way, with Oren Rand in their lead. Behind them streamed hundreds of fresh Uthan rebels.

"Where is Artemis?" the old veteran screamed as the group rushed up to the thicket. Bronsen pointed at the prostrate form of the general lying in the lee of the boulder.

"Alive, but unconscious," Bronsen shouted back. "It's too late to try and escape. We must form a defensive position and protect the general as best we can."

Oren Rand nodded solemnly, all too aware of the dire straits they now found themselves in. His trained eyes quickly took in the area around the thicket that was tucked in a slight hollow on the low ridge.

"Form a defensive wedge in front of this hollow!" He screamed out his orders. "Shields to the front! No one gets through!" Quickly the small knot of Arturans carried out his orders just before the first wave of Uthans slammed into them.

The wedge proved tough to crack as the large shields favored by the Arturans provided a formidable barrier upon which the Uthans could only throw their bodies against. Oren Rand's men fought with silent but deadly efficiency as the screaming Uthans died in heaps in front of the wedge. Some of them used the backs of the dead and the living alike to try to leap over the defensive line only to be met by the grim and bloodied sword of the old veteran himself and the darting and slashing blade of Bronsen. Bodies piled upon bodies and the ground became slick with blood and spilled guts.

But the overwhelming odds were slowly turning in favor of the rebels. Uthans using crossbows found gaps between the shields and picked apart the wedge. Wounded Uthans lying on the ground slashed at the exposed legs of the Arturans with the last of their strength before they died.

"We can't hold much longer," Bronsen shouted to Oren Rand as he slashed at a swarthy rebel who had just leaped across the wedge swinging a bloodied club, but the old warrior was too busy fighting two rebels of his own to answer. The rebel with the club swung it hard at Bronsen's head and he stepped backwards just in time to dodge the blow, but when he planted his weight on the leg with the arrow wound, it failed him and he went crashing to the ground on his back. The Uthan knew an opportunity when he saw one and the club came crashing down. Flat on his back Bronsen was able to get his sword up in an attempt to block the blow but the club struck his right forearm just behind his wrist—it broke in several places with a sickening crack. Bronsen grunted with pain as his sword clattered to the stony ground beside him, the Uthan grinned maniacally as he brought the club up for the finishing blow. Bronsen pawed frantically with his left hand for one of his hidden throwing knives but he had run out of time; down the club came again. Flinging his left arm up in a desperate attempt to ward off the blow, Bronsen tried to roll out of the way at the same time. The club glanced off his arm and came crashing down on his head. His movement had kept the blow from being a killing strike but the next one would be. Through the blood streaming out of the wound on his forehead, he watched as the Uthan prepared for the kill.

But instead of swinging the club, the Uthan threw it up to a blocking position in front of him with an astonished look on his face. Bronsen could only see a huge shadow blocking out the sun as a great sword came crashing down on the club, severing it in two in one massive stroke. The force of the blow drove the hapless Uthan to his knees and in the next instant, the man's head was rolling across the stony desert floor.

Bronsen faded in and out of consciousness. The last thing he heard was a labored voice shouting above the din and confusion of battle. He thought it was Oren Rand yelling at someone, but he couldn't tell for sure.

"It's about time ya quit lyin' 'round and come to the party, Artemis."

Chapter Thirty-Three

B RYAN PUSHED MEG AS HARD AS HE COULD but the old horse would not be forced any faster, and it was late evening before they came within sight of Brianna's knoll. Bryan pulled back on the reins and brought the tired animal to a stop.

"Will, look!" he shouted, pointing past the hill to the tree line. Tendrils of black smoke wormed in lazy fingers against the darkening sky. Bryan leaped off the horse and tore off down the trail at a frantic pace, leaving a distraught Willoughby on his own.

"Bryan, wait!" he yelled, but his friend had already disappeared around a bend in the trail. "Shit," Willoughby cursed as he slid off Meg's back. He wasn't about to ride the horse the rest of the way himself but she was happy the weight was off her back and followed compliantly as he took the reins and led her down the trail.

When Willoughby stepped out of the trees into the clearing next to Mattie's garden his heart nearly stopped; the scene in front of him unfolded like the climax of a war movie. The barn and Quint's smithy attached to it were nothing but a pile of charred and smoldering wood, and only a portion of the house was still upright. Bryan was standing amid what had been the kitchen, frantically pulling on pieces of splintered timbers that used to be roof rafters and yelling out for his grandmother and grandfather.

"Help me!" He turned sobbing towards where a stupefied Willoughby walked like a zombie into the yard in front of the wreckage. "I can't find them, Will! Help me!"

Willoughby dropped Meg's reins and shuffled slowly towards the house, or what was left of it. Free from his control, the horse whinnied her displeasure and backed away. Bryan's pleas for help might well have been a hundred miles away as Willoughby desperately tried to come to grips with what his eyes were seeing in the yard before him.

As he stood staring stupidly at the surreal scene, a frightful stink assailed his nose, roiling and churning his stomach. A dead horse lay directly in front of him, blocking his path to the house. The big animal's legs splayed out stiff, a man lay crushed halfway under it, something sticking grotesquely from both sides of his head. It took Willoughby a minute to figure out that it was an arrow. It had entered the man's left eye and stuck out the back nearly two feet. Thick gray matter flecked with blood oozed out around the wooden shaft at the back of the man's head, matting his dark hair. Flies buzzed in and out of the congealing mess. The stench of shit, both horse and human, hammered mercilessly at Willoughby's sensitive nose.

Another dead horse lay close by and two more dead men sprawled in the red dirt of the yard with arrows sticking out of them. Willoughby's eyes moved to the front of the house. At the bottom of what remained of the porch steps was another body—a man lay on his back, his head lolled at a crooked angle. Willoughby could see a gaping slash at the junction of the man's neck and shoulder, bone poking its way through. The blood, and there had been a lot of it, had turned into a thick, black mess. More bloated, black flies buzzed in and out of the crack. The man's mouth and eyes were open, frozen in a grotesque mask of death. Another body lay partially buried under the pile of wood that used to be the porch. The smell of blood, guts, and shit permeated the air with a thick, greasy stench. Finally, it overpowered Willoughby's senses. He dropped to his hands and knees and started emptying the contents of his stomach onto the ground.

He remained down, incapacitated, for quite some time, oblivious to everything except the horrible smells and his own discomfort. Every time he thought he had puked himself out, another powerful whiff would set his stomach into convulsions again. When

592

there was absolutely nothing left to bring up the dry heaves took over. His mind was numb and clear thought escaped his grasp as the gruesome reality around him blurred into an obscene mass. The only thing Willoughby could distinguish was his own puke mixing with the red dirt in front of his face.

"Will." Bryan's voice cut into his consciousness. Slowly Willoughby became aware that his friend was standing over him. "Will, are you all right?"

Willoughby rocked back onto his knees and wiped the slimy drool from his mouth and chin with his sleeve. His mind was still incapable of registering the surreal carnage surrounding him, and he stared stupidly up at his friend.

"What happened, Bryan? Where are Mattie and Quint?"

Bryan shook his head. His face was ghostly pale except for black sooty streaks. Willoughby could see that he had been crying and was instantly shamed that his weak stomach had caused him to temporarily abandoned his friend at such a crucial time.

"I can't find anything of them, Will," Bryan answered as he knelt down beside Willoughby and put his arm around the younger boy's shoulder.

"There are two more bodies over by what is left of the barn. One of them is another stranger and the other is burned so bad I cannot tell who it is but I know it is not Grandmother or Grandfather. I can't make any sense of this, Will. These men evidently attacked the house, but why? We have nothing bandits would want to steal."

Willoughby managed to get to his feet with Bryan's help. He took a few deep breaths, fighting to get control over his nausea. The smell was still overwhelming but he had to be strong, for his friend, if nothing else.

"If you can't find your grandparents, then maybe that means they're okay, Bryan. Maybe they went to the village for help."

"Something is wrong there too, Will." Bryan pointed in the direction of Lightwood. The sun was down below the horizon but Willoughby could see the smoke columns and haze from numerous fires smudging the twilight. "It looks like the whole village has burned."

The boys stood there in the decaying light, staring blankly towards the village. Neither spoke. For Willoughby, the situation was absolutely incomprehensible. The nightmare world he had found himself in after the plunge over the waterfall had begun to work its way back to some semblance of normalcy as he had become accustomed to life with Mattie, Quint, and Bryan. Thoughts of home and the agony and grief his family must have gone through had become less frequent as he had settled in and became absorbed in this new life. To see it smashed, burned, and broken was a shock his system was having great difficulty dealing with.

"We can't stay here, Will." Bryan's pained voice finally broke the silence. "It is getting dark and we don't know what the night will bring. Whoever did this may decide to return. We must hide in the woods and try to figure out what to do on the morrow. Fetch Meg for me while I see if I can find us some blankets. The night will come cold and we will not be able to have a fire that might give us away."

Willoughby found Meg at the back end of the pasture near the orchard. He led her back towards the house but she planted her feet and refused to budge when she got to the edge of the yard where she could smell the death. Willoughby didn't like it any more than she did so he didn't try to force her closer. They waited as the moonless night folded its black arms around them.

Bryan soon joined them with an arm full of thick wool blankets. "I was able to get in through the back of the house," he said. "Whatever happened, it didn't knock down the whole place."

Willoughby thought he knew. There just hadn't been an opportunity to explain it yet. "I think it was magic, Bryan."

"What?"

"It's kinda hard to explain but I can smell it and feel it. I think that's part of what made me sick. The residue is real strong in the yard in front of the house."

"Perhaps it was Grandmother, Will. That could be how they got away."

Willoughby shook his head. He wanted that to be the answer

but he didn't think so, and it wasn't a time for a lie, no matter how much easier it might make things.

"I wish it was, Bryan, but I don't believe it was her. I'm sorry I can't explain it any better but I guess you might say I can sense the good in her magic." Willoughby looked back towards what was left of the house. "Whoever had control over the power that did that was bad, Bryan. Really bad."

"All the more reason to hide ourselves and think on it tonight, Will. I know a place where we should be safe."

Willoughby wasn't as sure. "You don't think we should go to the village or maybe to Pel's? There's got to be somebody around that can help us or knows what the fuck happened here."

Bryan looked towards Lightwood where the glow of still-burning fires could now be seen against the dark of night. He shook his head.

"We can't be sure of what or who we might find. The village is burning, Will. Whatever happened here happened there, too."

Willoughby could see the logic in what his friend was saying. The fires could be seen clearly now that night had settled in and it looked like there were no less than a dozen still burning. If the village folk couldn't put out the fires there had to be a pretty convincing reason why. They could walk straight into a trap if they weren't careful.

"I guess you're right, Bryan," he shrugged helplessly. "But I just want to know what happened to Mattie and Quint. I need to know if they are all right."

"No more so than I, Will," Bryan answered firmly. Willoughby was surprised at how well his friend had managed to grab control over his emotions and was again embarrassed by how little control he had over his own.

"Grandfather taught me to plan for situations like this." Bryan gestured towards the smoldering piles that had been the barn and Quint's smithy and the gruesome carnage in the yard between them and the remains of the house.

"He said to work off what you can see, not what you hope. We need to look at the facts in front of us. Men came to the house and my grandparents fought with them. But we see only dead strangers, Will, not my grandparents. They must have gotten away somehow. There is a hidden escape tunnel that leads from Grandmother's kitchen to the woods beyond and maybe they were able to use it. We can't risk stumbling around in the dark and running into men who might be looking to kill us. If we hide tonight, we can check the tunnel tomorrow and then make our way to Pel's. I think that is the best we can do."

Willoughby nodded. He had to admit, Bryan's reasoning made sense. "I guess you're right Bryan. Where do we hide?"

The boys, with Meg in tow, followed the trail past Brianna's knoll, trying to keep as quiet as one could moving through the woods in the night, jumping nervously at every night noise, and wondering if they had been discovered. When they had gone what Bryan figured was a safe enough distance, they left the trail and plunged blindly into the thick cover. They stopped at a large fir with heavy branches that drooped nearly to the ground. After Bryan tied Meg near a small patch of grass that she could nibble if she got hungry, they crawled under the tree's branches into a secluded hideaway.

The floor under the tree was carpeted with layers upon layers of soft fir needles and after spreading their blankets, they found they were quite comfortable. But exhausted as they were, neither could sleep.

"When morning comes, Will, we must return and gather what we can. We don't know what we will find and must be prepared to be on our own. I should have picked up some weapons at the least."

Bryan's mention of weapons immediately caused Willoughby alarm. In the midst of the shock and carnage, he had forgotten Gael-ron's sword. Clutching at his neck, he was instantly relieved to find Fenrir's teeth secure on the leather collar. But while it comforted him some, the absence of the sword bothered him. He knew Mattie had Quint hide his belongings, but where? Were they destroyed in the carnage that brought most of the house down?

Willoughby tried to narrow his focus and bring an image of the sword into his mind like Mattie had taught him. But try as he might, he couldn't make it happen. Each time he concentrated, the horrible images of the death and destruction were the only things his mind would allow him to see. After a few exasperating minutes, he gave up.

Bryan sensed his troubled friend's frustration. "Things will be better in the morning, Will. There is nothing we can do until light comes. We must try and get some rest."

The two boys lay there, exhausted and silent, each lost in his own thoughts. For Willoughby, the images of what he had seen refused to leave his mind. Every time he closed his tired eyes, he saw dead men and dead horses. As much as he tried to fight against it, the visual aspect of the scene would force its way past his futile efforts to block it. He kept envisioning the wounds, the look of death frozen on the men's faces, the distorted posture of bodies stiffening as rigor mortis did its work. He had seen movies where the special effects were about as real as they could get but as much as it gave the desired shocking effect, there always was a little voice in the back of his head that kept saying, *it isn't real*, and it kept everything in perspective. But what he had seen and smelled was as real as it could get. Real blood and real guts spilled onto the ground. The smell of shit as men and horses had lost control over their muscles and vacated themselves. It had been real and it was a nightmare.

Willoughby tried to force sleep to come but every time, the horrific images pried his tired eyes awake. And each time he opened his eyes, he spied Bryan with a blank look, sitting and staring at nothing. He was covered with one of Mattie's wool blankets and rocking back and forth wordlessly. Willoughby knew he should say something to his friend, give him some sort of comfort, but words escaped him.

But eventually sleep prevailed. His mind, overloaded with the day's traumatic events that he was having a hard time coming to grips with, along with his body, overcome by fatigue, finally surrendered. But with sleep, came dreams…

Men were chasing him. Dead men with terrible wounds and arrows sticking grotesquely from their heads and bodies. Horses and wounded men screamed in Willoughby's dream. Never had he heard such a horrifying symphony, but he knew the reason behind the unearthly cries; it was the sound of people and animals dying. His legs were like lead bars as he tried to run, the dead men ever so close, reaching their dead hands out for him. Willoughby was searching for Mattie and Quint as he ran; he could sense Mattie's presence but there was something wrong with the way it all felt, and of Quint, there was nothing at all. On and on, he had to keep going, away from the dead men, away from the screams.

There was magic in Willoughby's dream; he had felt it before when he had been lying in bed, recovering from his wounds. The magic was close and it was evil. Reaching for him. Trying to snare him in its cold grip. Willoughby struggled to run on legs that refused to work for him. Now the dead men were gone but others had taken their places, the ones with the magic. The old witch Mogga, the one Bryan had kept from killing him in the forest. He couldn't turn and look but he knew she was behind him. Two strange, dark men; Willoughby knew immediately they were the ones responsible for the taint of magic he had felt in the yard. They were coming for him.

But there was one more. The one he had felt as he lay comatose, nestled deep in the arms of Mattie's powerful painkiller. This was the one who wanted him the most. His power was far stronger than any of the others; his formidable will driving the rest of them. Willoughby tried to force his leaden legs to move faster but they were bogged down in the betrayal of dream sleep. Closer the power of the evil one came, and with it, the terrifying premonition that if this man ever got his hands on him, Willoughby's life would be nothing but a never ending nightmare of agony and suffering.

But just as the dark horror was about to clamp its death grip around him, it vanished. Dream Willoughby stopped running. The evil was gone but for a long moment there was no sense of anything but oppressive darkness surrounding him, suffocating him. But suddenly, breaking through the black gloom, a tiny pinpoint of illumination beckoned to him from the dark horizon. Willoughby walked easily towards the light, the leaden nightmare legs gone. The closer he got, the more a sense of calm settled over him, pushing away the fear in his troubled mind. He had to hold his hands in front of his eyes, the brightness was so intense, but gradually it began to subside. Fuzzy at first, a shape started to take form in front of him.

"That is as close as you can come, Will Baxter," the old man said. "My power in this dream will not allow you to come any closer. Doing so will break the vision and I will fade."

Like a movie projected on a cloud, the vision was there, but viewed through a thick mist. The old man was standing on a rocky ledge above the ocean. Willoughby could hear the waves pounding heavily against the rocks, feel the wind whipping about, and see the white sea foam spraying around the man's feet. Behind the man, a granite cliff rose abruptly, a wall of gray and green stone glistening with the perpetual wetness and residue of the sea. Gulls whirled circles overhead adding a cacophony of bird cries to the thunder of the surf. The old man leaned heavily on a staff of dark wood, dressed in a slate gray robe, the same color as the stone surrounding him. A long bushy beard hung to his chest and swayed in the sea wind. Sitting atop the man's shoulder was a huge raven, a white patch splattered across its forehead. The raven cocked his head from side to side, black beady eyes staring intently at Willoughby. There was a hint of something vaguely familiar about the bird but the boy could not grasp what it was.

Willoughby wanted to get closer. This old man was important to him, of that there was no doubt, but try as he might, his legs, though they no longer felt like lead weights, would not move for him. "Who are you?" he pleaded instead.

"I am who I have always been." The words came clearly back to him, cutting through the thunder of the crashing waves and the howling of the wind. The gulls cried in chorus.

A name came into Willoughby's mind, a name he had heard somewhere. "Are you Theron?"

The old man chuckled. "Some have called me that. I have many other names. Some just call me dead."

Somewhere, deep inside Willoughby's troubled mind, was the intuition that this was a dream with a purpose. That intuition told him he needed to find out what that purpose was. "What am I supposed to do?"

The waves crashed, the wind shrieked, the gulls cried, and the raven cocked his head from side to side. The old man's words came through as clear as if he had been standing right next to him. "The question Will Baxter, is not so much what you are *supposed* to do, but what *will* you do? You seek answers, but before you lay many paths that may or may not lead you to those answers. Which path is the right one? Alas, I cannot tell you, for that is something you must seek for yourself. Let me say, and it is my hope you will find comfort in this, that the lives of you and young Bryan are linked. Inexplicably so, but linked all the same. The two of you will be sorely tested. Will you survive the test? Again, I cannot say."

At the mention of Bryan, another question popped into Willoughby's head that he had to ask, not so much for his sake, as that of his friend. "What about Mattie and Quint? Are they all right?"

The old gray man leaned forward on his staff. Willoughby wished he could see his face but the distance was too far and the mist obscured his features. "I wish I could tell you that young Will, for Mattie and Quint Ironhand were dear friends and were there for me at a time when I was sorely in need. But alas, dreams are fickle, and they pose questions more readily than they give answers. Would that I could, but I cannot see their fate."

For a time neither said anything. It might have been just for seconds, then again, it might have been hours. Willoughby didn't know. Was there time in a dream? In the end, it mattered not, for the old man finally spoke again. "The world turns in strange ways, Will Baxter, and with it the nuances of fate. Look where it has taken you already. Everything you knew before has been ripped asunder and is gone. Why have you found yourself here? Is there a purpose for this? I believe in fate, Will. For now your past is behind you and neither of us can know if you will ever find it again. Your destiny lies ahead. You must take the first step and go meet it."

Willoughby thought the whole path and fate thing sounded an awful lot like Jake. "Will I be able to find you?"

"Choose the right path, Will Baxter, and you will find me. Then mayhap I can help you. But as I said before, you will be sorely tested. Along the way you will find others who will be able to help but you will also cross paths with those who will seek to do you harm. Again, it is beyond my power to tell you who to trust and who not. But the one thing I will tell you is to trust in yourself. You are strong yet do not believe in your strength. Mattie showed you how to work on controlling the power within your talismans. Master it quickly for you will find yourself in desperate need of it. For now those who would cause you the most harm are blind; Mattie has shielded you from them. But this shield will fade and when the blindness lifts, they will come. You must be ready when they do, for the sake of both you and Bryan."

Willoughby had more questions but when he started to speak, the old man put up his hand. His form began to shimmer and fade.

"Your fates are entwined Will, and Bryan has a destiny of great importance to fulfill, the likes of which he cannot begin to imagine. Mayhap, somewhere in the midst of all this, you may find an answer to that which troubles you most. I will help you as I can but my power at such a distance is limited. The journey here will be long and troublesome my young friend. Good luck." Then he was gone and there was darkness.

Willoughby woke with a start. At first, he couldn't tell where he was, the drooping limbs of the old fir blocking his vision. But quickly it came back to him. A glance next to him showed an empty pile of blankets. Bryan was gone.

"Fuck," Willoughby cursed, forcing himself to a sitting position. Despite the layers of fir needles, his body ached from sleeping on the ground and he had to pee bad. Throwing his blanket off, he shivered and crawled out from the hiding place on his hands and knees. Another quick glance told him that Meg was gone, too.

A thick fog covered the wood, adding a damp chill to the air. Willoughby fumbled with cold fingers at the buttons of the hand-me-down trousers of Bryan's Mattie had taken up for him. A bad case of dick shrinkage made things even more difficult and he almost started peeing before he got himself free. A heavy sigh of relief escaped him as his bladder began emptying itself in a long, steaming arch.

Willoughby decided not to wait for Bryan to come back. There was only one place he would go and that was back to the house. Though revisiting that nasty mess was something he did not particularly find appealing, he was more uncomfortable being by himself. Plunging through the brush, he had just located the trail when he heard the sound of horses clopping towards him. His heart began to race—it sounded like more than one horse. But they were close and Willoughby was out of time. He did the only thing he could think of and dove into the thick brush behind a pair of boulders flanking the trail.

Burrowing himself into the dead leaves and dirt, branches poking at his face, and rocks digging into his body, he made himself as small as possible. But even with that, he could tell it was only going to be good if a man on horseback didn't ride close to the boulders and see his legs poking out. Willoughby held his breath and hoped for the best. The horses clopped closer.

As it turned out, it was effort wasted.

"I am going to have to teach you how to hide yourself a little better than that, Will," Bryan said as he brought Meg and another horse trailing behind to a stop. He slid down off her back as Willoughby disentangled himself from his poor choice of a hiding spot.

"Crap, Bryan!" he exclaimed as he brushed himself off. "You scared the shit outta me! Why didn't you wake me up?"

"I tried, Will," Bryan answered as he tied Meg and the other horse to a tree. "You just rolled over and mumbled something about finding somebody. I thought it better to just let you sleep."

As Willoughby came around the boulders, he noticed that the horses were fully loaded, and he was much relieved to see his sword

602

and shield tied to the second horse.

"Is that Bonnie?"

"It is. I found her this morning in the orchard eating apples." Bryan sat down on a flat rock. Willoughby could tell by the look on his face that his friend was deeply troubled.

"Sit, Will. You and I have much to discuss. Here, I brought you a bit of breakfast." He pulled a folded cloth from inside his shirt and handed it to Willoughby as he sat down on the rock beside him. Inside were two of Mattie's delicious biscuits with maple honey and butter. Even cold and a day old they were just what Willoughby needed. He hadn't eaten since lunch yesterday and had deposited all of that on the ground in front of the house last night. His stomach rumbled its pleasure as he tore into them.

"I thought I might find some answers down at the house this morning Will, but instead I am more puzzled than ever." Bryan talked as Willoughby ate and listened. "Finding Bonnie was the first surprise but when I saw that two of the dead men were killed with arrows made by Pel, it made a bit more sense. He must have been at the house when the attack came."

"Any idea of what might have happened?" Willoughby mumbled through a mouthful of biscuit.

"No." Bryan shook his head. "But I think Grandfather was able to kill at least four of the men who attacked the house. There were two killed by his arrows in the yard and there were the two dead men on the porch. But of Grandmother and he or Pel, I could find nothing."

"Do you think they could have made it to the village, Bryan?" Willoughby asked.

"I do not know, Will." He shrugged. "There was sign of many horses in the road, and for whatever reason there was also sign of horses going through the field. I just don't know what it all means."

Bryan stood up and went to where Meg was tied. "But I did find this, though it only begs for more answers." When he came back, he was holding a crossbow. He handed it to Willoughby but the weapon was heavier than he anticipated and he nearly dropped it.

"It has markings on the stock that identify it as being the type issued to the king's crossbowmen," said Bryan.

Willoughby examined the dark, well-oiled stock. Near the butt he found the symbols Bryan was talking about.

"Grandfather had one like it hanging on the wall in the smithy." Willoughby remembered it now.

"He preferred the longbow and had planned to make you one but was concerned you would not yet have the strength to draw it. He said the crossbow would be better to start you on. It looks like we will have to begin your training soon."

Willoughby liked the feel of it as he put it to his shoulder though the butt of the weapon wasn't nearly as comfortable as that of a rifle. He had tried drawing Bryan's longbow once and hadn't even been able to get the bowstring more than part of the way back. Once he figured out how to load and fire this thing though, he thought he might be able to get used to it.

"I found a good supply of quarrels to go with it," Bryan added.

"Some what?"

"Quarrels. Bolts." Willoughby was still confused. "Arrows, Will. They are also call quarrels or bolts."

Now he understood. "Does this mean it was king's men who attacked the house, Bryan?"

"That or bandits found a way to get their hands on some of the king's weapons. There was another in the yard that was also marked as coming from the king's armory."

"Why would the king send men out here to go after your family?"

Bryan shook his head. "I asked myself the same question and could come up with no answer. But I think Grandmother may have been able to explain at least part of it in this." He pulled a rolled up sheet of rough paper out of his shirt and held it out to Will.

Willoughby sat the crossbow down. "What is it?"

"Grandmother had time to write this before they were attacked. Evidently she knew something bad was coming. It was in the hidden crawlspace in the cold cellar stuck in the flap of Gaelron's pack. I found it when I was getting the supplies we need for our journey."

That got Willoughby's attention. "Our journey? You mean just you and me?"

"Read it and you will understand, Will."

Willoughby carefully unrolled it and started to read. The long elegant script of Mattie's hand flowed across the stiff paper.

Bryan and Will,

If you are reading this it means that something has happened to Quint and I. There is trouble in the village and I sense it will soon be here. My feeling tells me it has something to do with the two of you and I pray that if it comes you will not be here to be part of it. If you have found this note at least it means that for now, the danger has not found you.

Whatever the situation may be here at the house, the two of you must leave immediately. Follow the plan we talked about. Do not try to find us if we are not here, the danger will be too great.

Bryan-My dearest grandson. Know that your grandfather and I love you more than anything. We have tried our best to raise you as your mother would have and to that end you have grown into a fine young man. But there is a secret that your grandfather and I have not told you. It concerns your heritage. I will not try to explain it here in this letter, mayhap we should have told you a long time ago but we were afraid of what the consequences might have been. Please forgive us. Many years ago your grandfather and I entrusted our good friend Theron with this secret. I believe he is alive and is the only one who can help both you and Will. Follow the plan and seek him out.

We love you both,

M.

Willoughby looked from the letter to his friend; Bryan

was staring off into space. Contrary to what he said, the letter left Willoughby more confused than ever. "What's she talking about Bryan? What's this secret?"

Bryan shrugged. "If I knew that Will, it wouldn't be a secret. It doesn't make any sense. Grandmother says she thought the trouble coming had something to do with you and me. She warded your magic because she thought someone was searching for it. That may be part of it, but why me? I'm just a farm boy."

Willoughby thought Bryan was looking past the obvious. "Maybe you ain't just a farm boy, Bryan. The secret, the story about your mom and all that. There's got to be something more to all of this. Shit like what went down yesterday don't happen for no reason."

Neither boy spoke for a while. The sun was well up in the sky and patchy clouds promised a pleasant early fall day. Bonnie and Meg contentedly munched grass on the side of the trail and birds went about their daily business noisily in the undergrowth and the treetops.

"We need to go find that guy—Theron. We need to find him," Willoughby finally said. "I had a dream about him last night, Bryan. I think he knows we will be looking for him."

Bryan stared into the ground, lost in thought for a moment. "That is what Grandmother wanted us to do. She thinks he is the only one who can help."

"Do you know how to get there?"

Bryan walked over to Meg and fished around inside the large pack she was carrying. He took out a long hard leather tube with a cap on one end. Kneeling down, he pulled out a rolled up parchment and spread it on the ground."

"This is Grandfather's map. He used it to teach me about Artura—where things were, the roads, villages, cities, and other important places. It will help us get to Theron."

The map was detailed and full of tiny notations carefully printed in a fine hand. To Willoughby maps were things you got from a gas station or Dari-Mart for a couple of bucks, and then you only bought a map if you drove a cheap car without a GPS or didn't want to pay by the month to have an app on your cell phone. Quint's map was a piece of art.

Bryan pointed to a spot on the map. "This is Lightwood." Under the name of the village, Quint had written a single word—home. "We have to get to here." Bryan traced his finger out to the far left corner of the map. A piece of land jutted far out into the sea, wide where it left the mainland and then gradually narrowing. It made a long slow curve before petering out to a point. It looked like a tail and the fine lettering confirmed Willoughby's suspicions.

"The Tail of the Dragon?"

Bryan nodded, tracing his finger along the map. "This is the spine and this thin strip the tail. It sticks out into the North Sea and at the very end is where Theron's keep is said to be, or was."

Willoughby had no concept of the scale on Quint's map but his gut told him. "It looks like a long way."

"A long way even if we could travel by the good roads. If people are looking for us, Will, we must keep off the main routes; that will add time and difficulty to the journey. Once we reach Backwater Cove there will be no roads at all."

"Mattie said we had to find a guide to get us there. At a place called Barftown or something like that."

"Bargtown, here." Bryan pointed. "I think that is where we need to travel first. We can keep off the main roads and get to the river; it's the same one you were following when I found you. We follow the river to Bargtown."

It sounded far easier than Willoughby thought it would be. "Then what? I don't want to sound like I'm scared or nothin' Bryan, but you ain't never been there, have you? We don't know anybody. How can we tell who to trust? With Mattie and Quint it would have been different. I just ain't sure we can do this."

Bryan rolled the map up and put it back into the leather case. "I understand, Will. But as difficult as it may be, we have no choice. We can't stay here. Grandmother warned against that and she must have felt strongly about it. She thinks this is our only chance."

Willoughby knew that his friend was right. It just wasn't what he wanted to hear. "I just wish we knew what happened to Mattie and Quint."

"If I thought we wouldn't be putting ourselves in greater danger I would stay here and not undertake this journey, Will." He kicked at the dirt, his frustration visible. "My grandparents mean everything to me. Not knowing what has happened to them is tearing me up inside but I know Grandmother. She would not tell us to do this if she did not think we were in great danger. She wants us to find Theron, to see if he can help you, and evidently he knows something of my past. Grandmother thinks this secret is so important that she would risk us traveling to the far corner of Artura to find out. I am curious and yet afraid at the same time, Will. Do you understand?"

Willoughby did and it made him feel bad. He knew his friend was suffering terribly. There was no other choice. "Then we shouldn't waste any more time discussing it, Bryan. It's funny, I don't know how much to believe in dreams, but the one I had last night, I think it meant something. The guy, Theron. He said that our fates were intertwined; that you and I are connected. My friend Jake, he was a big believer in fate. I think he knew something was going to happen to me and in his own way, he tried to prepare me for it. Mattie was dead set on us going to find this Theron guy. If she felt that strong about it, then that is what we need to do."

Bryan smiled at him. "It is good to hear you say that, Will. It reminds me of something Grandmother told me while you were recovering from the wound Mogga gave you. She said there was something very special about you, and that it was fate that brought us together. I think she believed like this Jake fellow of yours—nothing happens simply by chance. You finding the same cave that was Gaelron's tomb and having the ability to access the magic in the sword; being able to slay Fenrir and him passing his power on to you; me finding you when I did. Grandmother says it is all connected."

Bryan stood up and held out his hand. Willoughby grasped it and pulled himself to his feet. They locked their hands around each other's forearms in the Arturan handshake. "I guess it is up to us to take it from here and find out what it all leads to."

"I think we need to make up a story Bryan, just in case people ask. We can't tell people we are looking for Theron. I think that would cause us trouble if we were to say that. Let's say that we are brothers, our parents got sick and died and we are trying to find our only relative, a long lost uncle."

Bryan smiled. "It is a good story, Will, and I am proud to have you as a brother. What is the name of this uncle?"

Willoughby grinned wide. "Jake. We're looking for our uncle, Jake."

THE END

Made in the USA
San Bernardino, CA
27 August 2018